Merrill Advanced Mathematical Concepts

Lee E. Yunker is chairman of the Mathematics Department at West Chicago Community High School, West Chicago, Illinois. Mr. Yunker obtained his B.S. from Elmhurst College and his M. Ed. in mathematics from the University of Illinois. Mr. Yunker is very active in professional mathematics organizations for which he frequently speaks or conducts workshops on a variety of topics. Currently, Mr. Yunker is on the editorial panel for the *Student Math Notes* for the National Council of Teachers of Mathematics and on the Board of Directors of the National Council of Supervisors of Mathematics.

Glen D. Vannatta was Supervisor of Mathematics for the Indianapolis Public Schools in Indianapolis, Indiana. Currently, Dr. Vannatta is a Mathematics Consultant for Special Projects for the Indianapolis Public Schools. Dr. Vannatta received his B.S., M.S., and Ed. D. from Indiana University. Dr. Vannatta has authored numerous mathematics textbooks on several levels. In addition, he has written articles for the Mathematics Teacher and has developed mathematics programs.

Valarie A. Elswick is a teacher of mathematics and computer science at Roy C. Ketcham High School, Wappingers Falls, New York. She obtained her B.S. in secondary mathematics education from State University of New York at New Paltz. Ms. Elswick has done graduate work at the University of San Francisco, Indiana University, and Vassar College. She has spoken extensively at the local, regional, and national levels on the application and use of computers in education. Ms. Elswick is President-Elect of the Association of Mathematics Teachers of New York State.

F. Joe Crosswhite is currently President of the National Council of Teachers of Mathematics. He is also Professor Emeritus in the Mathematics Department at Ohio State University. Dr. Crosswhite obtained his B.S. in education and M. Ed. from the Missouri University and his Ph. D. in mathematics education from the Ohio State University. Dr. Crosswhite has published widely in professional journals and has contributed to mathematics textbooks for over 20 years.

Merrill Publishing Co.
A Bell & Howell Company
Columbus, Ohio

Toronto • London • Sydney

Reviewers

Paul R. Abad
Mathematics Teacher
De La Salle High School
Concord, California

Sandra E. Brown
Mathematics Curriculum Associate
Cheltenham Township Schools
Elkins Park, Pennsylvania

James T. Cochran
Mathematics Department
Chairperson
Piedmont High School
Piedmont, California

Joseph Depa
Mathematics Teacher,
Department Chairperson
Acadiana High School
Lafayette, Louisana

Gene Gardenhire
Mathematics Department Chairperson
Albuquerque Academy
Albuquerque, New Mexico

Phil Huneke
Professor of Mathematics
Ohio State University
Columbus, Ohio

David Rasmussen
Mathematics Department
Chairperson
New Hampton Community
High School
New Hampton, Iowa

Laurie R. Rosborough
Mathematics Teacher
Fairport Central Schools
Fairport, New York

Marjorie Valentine
Mathematics Department
Coordinator
John Jay High School
San Antonio, Texas

Staff

Editorial

Project Editor: Cynthia Zengler; *Editor:* Deborah Maren Mahle;
Photo Editor: Kristy Schooler; *Production Editor:* Kimberly Munsie

Art

Project Artist: Dotte Turner Russell; *Book Designer:* Larry Collins;
Illustrators: Lorraine Woost, James Hubbard

Photo Credits

Cover Photo: Joseph A. DiChello, Jr.

2, *Photo Research International;* **30, 64,** *Sheryl S. McNee/Tom Stack & Assoc.;* **91,** *Steve Lissau;* **96,** *Eric Kroll/Taurus Photos;* **124,** *DAvid Frazier;* **158,** *Columbus Symphony Orchestra;* **158** *insert, Tom Stack/Tom Stack & Assoc.;* **186,** *Fairchild Aerial Surveys, Inc.;* **218,** *Rich Brommer;* **252,** *Ruth Dixon;* **282,** *Roger K. Burnard;* **318,** *Ruth Dixon;* **344,** *NASA;* **372,** *Battelle's Columbus Laboratories;* **388,** *Gary Milburn/Tom Stack & Assoc.;* **420,** *Eric Hoffhines;* **454,** *M.I.T. Historical Collection;* **496,** *Doug Martin*

ISBN 0-675-05920-8

Published by
MERRILL PUBLISHING CO.
A Bell & Howell Company
Columbus, Ohio 43216

Printed in the United States

Merrill Advanced Mathematical Concepts both encompasses and extends topics and concepts of intermediate algebra. The goals of the text are to develop proficiency with mathematical skills, to expand understanding of mathematical concepts, to improve logical thinking, and to promote success. To achieve these goals the following strategies are used.

Build upon a Solid Foundation Review is provided for those topics generally presented in first - and second-year algebra. Thus, the student's understanding is strengthened before the introduction of more difficult concepts.

Utilize Sound Pedagogy *Merrill Advanced Mathematical Concepts* covers all topics generally presented at this level in logical sequence. Concepts are introduced when they are needed. Each concept presented is then used both within that lesson and in later lessons.

Facilitate Learning A clear, concise format aids the student in understanding the mathematical concepts. Furthermore, many photographs, illustrations, graphs, and tables provide help for the student in visualizing the ideas presented. As a result, the student is able to read with increased understanding.

Use Relevant Real-Life Applications Applications provide motivation and help in understanding how concepts are used.

The text offers a variety of useful aids for the student studying advanced mathematics.

Student Annotations	Help students to identify important concepts as they study. They also help to remind students of mathematical reasoning.
Selected Answers	Allow students to check their progress as they work.
Chapter Summary	Provides students a compact listing of major concepts presented within each chapter.
Chapter Review	Permits students to reveiw each chapter by working sample problems from each section.
Chapter Test	Enables students to check their own progress.

The following special features, which appear periodically throughout the text, provide interesting and useful extra topics.

Using Mathematics	Illustrates how mathematics can be and is used in everyday life. Topics are varied and include glimpses into the development of mathematics.
For the Scholar	Provides students with the opportunity to develop and maintain problem-solving skills related to mathematical topics. These problems appear after each lesson and draw upon the background of the students.
Using Calculators	Relates how a calculator can aid in performing various computations. The use of several function keys are presented and practiced.
Appendix	Introduces students to the computer language of Pascal. Mathematical concepts are reinforced during the study of the computer language. Programming exercises are included for use with each chapter.
Glossary	Provides students with definitions of important words and terms.

Students will find the practical, straightforward approach of *Merrill Advanced Mathematical Concepts* both interesting and easy to understand. Teachers will find that the careful sequencing of topics and thorough treatment of essential ideas provide an effective course in high school mathematics.

Table of Contents

1 Linear Relations and Functions

2 Theory of Equations

3 Matrices and Vectors

4 The Circular Functions

5 The Trigonometric Functions

6 Graphs and Inverses of the Trigonometric Functions

7 Applications of Trigonometry

8 Sequences and Series

9 Polar Coordinates and Complex Numbers

10 Exponential and Logarithmic Functions

11 The Straight Line

12 Conics

13 Probability

14 Descriptive Statistics

15 Limits, Derivatives, and Integrals

Appendix: Pascal

CHAPTER 1

Linear Relations and Functions

Straight lines are used in art to create a pleasing design. In mathematics, graphs of lines are representations of relationships between two variables. These relationships, called linear relationships, can be used to define such concepts as profit, depreciation, and rate of change.

1-1 Relations and Functions

A pairing of elements of a set with elements of the same or a second set is called a mathematical **relation**. The following set is a relation.

$$\{(1, 3), (2, 4), (3, 5), (2, 7)\}$$

The set of abscissas {1, 2, 3} of the ordered pairs is called the **domain** of the relation. The set of ordinates {3, 4, 5, 7} is called the **range**. Notice that an element of the domain is paired with more than one element of the range in this relation.

The first coordinate of an ordered pair is the <u>abscissa</u>. The second coordinate is the <u>ordinate</u>.

A relation is a set of ordered pairs. The domain is the set of all abscissas of the ordered pairs. The range is the set of all ordinates of the ordered pairs.	*Definition of Relation, Domain, and Range*

Example

1 State the relation represented by the equation $y = 5x$, if x is a positive integer less than 6. Then, state the domain and range of the relation.

The relation is {(1, 5), (2, 10), (3, 15), (4, 20), (5, 25)}.
The domain is {1, 2, 3, 4, 5}.
The range is {5, 10, 15, 20, 25}.

The ordered pairs are written in the form (x, y).

The relation in the preceding example is a special type of relation, called a **function**. *All functions are relations, but not all relations are functions.*

A function is a relation in which each element of the domain is paired with exactly one element of the range.	*Definition of Function*

A relation or function can be represented as a graph, a table of values, a list of ordered pairs, or by any rule in words or symbols which determines pairs of values.

Example

2 Is $\left\{\left(2, \frac{1}{2}\right), \left(\frac{1}{4}, 3\right), \left(4, 0\right), \left(1, 5\right)\right\}$ a function?

Since each element of the domain is paired with exactly one element of the range, this relation is a function.

Examples

3 **Does $y > 2x$ represent a function?**

For each value of x, several values could be chosen for y. Therefore, $y > 2x$ does not represent a function. $y > 2x$ *is a relation.*

4 **State the relation represented by the graph. Is the relation a function?**

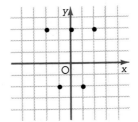

The graph represents the relation
    $\{(-2, 3), (-1, -2), (0, 3), (1, -2), (2, 3)\}$.

This relation is a function since each element of the domain is paired with exactly one element of the range.

A function can also be defined as a set of ordered pairs in which no two pairs have the same first element. This definition can be applied when a relation is represented by a graph. If every vertical line drawn on the graph of a relation passes through no more than one point of the graph, then the relation is a function.

This is called the vertical line test.

Example

5 **Use the vertical line test to determine if the relation graphed is a function.**

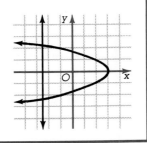

The vertical line passes through two points of the graph. Therefore, the graph does not represent a function.

A function is commonly denoted by f. The symbol $f(x)$ is read "f of x" and should be interpreted as the value of the function f at x. The expression $y = f(x)$ indicates that for each element which replaces x, the function assigns one and only one replacement for y. The ordered pairs of the function are written in the form (x, y) or $(x, f(x))$.

x is called the independent variable. y is called the dependent variable.

Examples

6 Find $f(3)$ if $f(x) = 2x^2 - 2x + 8$.

$$f(3) = 2(3)^2 - 2(3) + 8$$
$$= 20$$

7 Find $f(-1)$ if $f(x) = |3x - 2|$.   *The symbol '| |' represents absolute value.*

$$f(-1) = |3(-1) - 2|$$
$$= |-5|$$
$$= 5$$

Often the equation for a function is given but the domain is not specified. Then, the domain includes all the real numbers for which the corresponding values in the range are also real numbers.

Example

8 Name all values of x that are not in the domain of f, for $f(x) = \dfrac{3x}{x^2 - 5}$.

Since $\dfrac{3x}{0}$ is undefined, any value of x that makes the denominator equal zero must be excluded from the domain of f. By solving the equation $x^2 - 5 = 0$, these values can be obtained. Therefore, $x \neq \pm\sqrt{5}$. The values $+\sqrt{5}$ and $-\sqrt{5}$ are not in the domain of f.

The graph of a function sometimes approaches lines containing the values for which the function is undefined. These lines are called asymptotes. The asymptotes for $f(x) = \dfrac{3x}{x^2-5}$ are $x = \sqrt{5}$ and $x = -\sqrt{5}$.

Exploratory Exercises

State the domain and range of each relation.

1. $\{(0, 0)\}$

2. $\{(16, -4), (16, 4)\}$

3. $\{(5, 5), (6, 6)\}$

4. $\{(-3, 0), (4, -2), (2, -6)\}$

5. $\{(1, 2), (2, 4), (-3, -6), (0, 0)\}$

6. $\{(0, 3), (5, 3), (6, 3), (2, 3)\}$

7. $\{(-2, 9), (-2, 8), (-2, 7)\}$

8. $\{(1, 5), (2, 6), (3, 7), (4, 8)\}$

9. $\{(4, -2), (4, 2), (9, -3), (9, 3)\}$

10. $\{(8, -3), (7, 3), (6, -3)\}$

11-20. State whether each relation in problems **1-10** is a function. Write *yes* or *no*.

Written Exercises

State the relation represented by each of the following given that x is an integer.

1. $y = 3x - 3$ and $0 < x < 6$ **2.** $y = 11 - x$ and $-3 \le x \le 0$

3. $y = x^2$ and $-4 < x \le -2$ **4.** $y = 5$ and $1 \le x \le 9$

5. $|2y| = x$ and $x = 4$ **6.** $y = |x| - 1.5$ and $-2 \le x < 4$

7-12. State the domain and range of each relation in problems **1-6**.

13-18. State whether each relation in problems **1-6** is a function. Write *yes* or *no*.

State whether each graph represents a function. Write *yes* or *no*.

19. 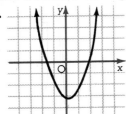   **20.** 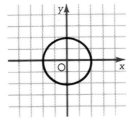   **21.**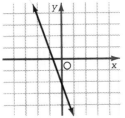

22. 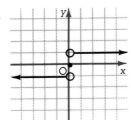   **23.** 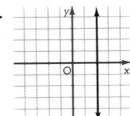   **24.**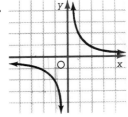

Given $f(x) = 7 - x^2$, find each value.

25. $f(0)$ **26.** $f(4)$ **27.** $f(-3)$ **28.** $f(11)$

29. $f\left(\frac{1}{2}\right)$ **30.** $f(3.7)$ **31.** $f(2a)$ **32.** $f(6 + n)$

Given $f(x) = 4 + 6x - x^3$, find each value.

33. $f(0)$ **34.** $f(-1)$ **35.** $f(3)$ **36.** $f(14)$

37. $f(9)$ **38.** $f\left(\frac{1}{2}\right)$ **39.** $f(2 + a)$ **40.** $f(3k)$

Given [x] means the greatest integer not greater than x and $f(x) = [x] + 4$, find each value.

41. $f(-4)$ **42.** $f(2.5)$ **43.** $f(-6.3)$ **44.** $f(\sqrt{2})$

45. $f(-\sqrt{3})$ **46.** $f(\pi)$ **47.** $f(-4 + t)$ **48.** $f(q + 1)$

Given $f(x) = |x^2 - 13|$, find each value.

49. $f(0)$ **50.** $f(-4)$ **51.** $f(-\sqrt{13})$ **52.** $f(2)$

53. $f(4.8)$ **54.** $f\left(1\frac{1}{2}\right)$ **55.** $f(n + 4)$ **56.** $f(5m)$

Name all values of x that are not in the domain of the given function.

57. $f(x) = \dfrac{3}{x - 1}$

58. $f(x) = \dfrac{3 - x}{5 + x}$

59. $f(x) = \dfrac{x^3 + 5x}{4x}$

60. $f(x) = \dfrac{x^2 - 18}{32 - x^2}$

61. $f(x) = \dfrac{15}{|2x| - 9}$

62. $f(x) = \dfrac{x}{x^2 - 6}$

For the Scholar

Describe the graph of $x^2 - 4y^2 = 0$ and then graph the relation to verify your conjecture.

1-2 Linear Functions

A **linear equation** in two variables, such as $3x - 2y = 6$, is an equation whose graph is a straight line. Each term in a linear equation is a constant or the product of a constant and a variable. Any linear equation can be written in **standard form**.

The standard form of a linear equation is $$Ax + By + C = 0$$ where A, B, and C are real numbers, and A and B are not both zero.	**Standard Form of a Linear Equation**

Each solution to a linear equation is an ordered pair. Each ordered pair corresponds to a point in the coordinate plane. Since two points determine a line, only two points are needed to graph a linear equation.

In checking your work, it is helpful to graph a third point.

Example

1 **Graph $3x - 2y = 6$.**

Isolate one variable.
$$-2y = -3x + 6$$
$$y = \frac{3}{2}x - 3$$

Next, find three ordered pairs that satisfy the equation.

Any real number can be substituted for x.

x	y	(x, y)
0	-3	$(0, -3)$
1	$-\dfrac{3}{2}$	$\left(1, -\dfrac{3}{2}\right)$
2	0	$(2, 0)$

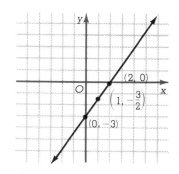

Then, graph the ordered pairs and connect them with a line.
This linear equation represents a function.

Example

2 **Graph 2x = 7.**

Since $x = \frac{7}{2}$ for all values of y,
the graph is a vertical line.

Does this linear equation represent a function?

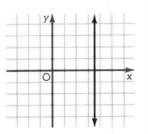

Not all linear equations represent functions, as shown by example 2. A **linear function** is defined as follows.

A linear function is defined by $f(x) = mx + b$ where m and b are real numbers.	*Linear Function*

Values of x for which $f(x) = 0$ are called **zeros** of the function. For a linear function, these values are found by solving the equation $mx + b = 0$. If $m \neq 0$, then $-\frac{b}{m}$ is the only zero of the function. The graph of the function crosses the x-axis at the point $\left(-\frac{b}{m}, 0\right)$.

$-\frac{b}{m}$ is called the x-intercept.

Example

3 **Find the zero of $f(x) = 3x - 1$. Then, graph the function.**

$3x - 1 = 0$
$x = \frac{1}{3}$ Thus, $\frac{1}{3}$ is a zero of the function.
Find the coordinates of a second point.
When $x = 1$, $y = 3(1) - 1$, or 2.

Graph $\left(\frac{1}{3}, 0\right)$ and $(1, 2)$ and connect the points with a line.

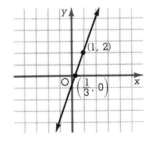

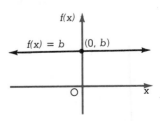

If $m = 0$, then $f(x) = b$. The graph is a horizontal line. This function is a **constant function**. A constant function either has *no* zeros ($b \neq 0$), or every value of x is a zero ($b = 0$).

More than one linear equation can be graphed on the same coordinate system. If the graphs intersect, the ordered pair for the point of intersection is the common solution to the equations.

Example

4 **Solve the system of equations.**

$$y = 5x - 2$$
$$y = -2x + 5$$

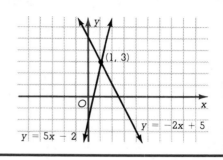

The solution of the system is $(1, 3)$.

Exploratory Exercises

Write each equation in standard form.

1. $y = 3x + 2$ **2.** $2x - 4y = 6$ **3.** $x = 3$

4. $5 = 9x - 7 + y$ **5.** $y = -4$ **6.** $x - 6 = 2y$

Name the zero of each function whose graph is shown.

7.

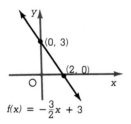

$f(x) = -\frac{3}{2}x + 3$

8.

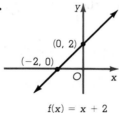

$f(x) = x + 2$

9.

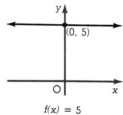

$f(x) = 5$

State whether each ordered pair is a solution to $y = 3x - 7$. Write *yes* or *no*.

10. $(0, 7)$ **11.** $(0, -7)$ **12.** $(15, 38)$ **13.** $(2, 1)$

14. $(k, 3k - 7)$ **15.** $(2d, 6d - 14)$ **16.** $(2r, 6r - 7)$ **17.** $(m-1, 3m-10)$

Written Exercises

Graph each equation.

1. $y = 3x - 2$ **2.** $3x = 2y$ **3.** $y - 7 = x$ **4.** $x + 2y = 5$

5. $x = -\frac{1}{2}y$ **6.** $7 - x = y$ **7.** $4y = 2 + 3x$ **8.** $y = \frac{1}{2}x - 1.5$

Find the zero of each function.

9. $f(x) = 0.5x + 6$ **10.** $f(x) = 14x$ **11.** $f(x) = 9x + 5$

12. $f(x) = 5x - 8$ **13.** $f(x) = 19$ **14.** $f(x) = 3x + 1$

Solve each system of equations by graphing.

15. $x = 0$
$y = 1$

16. $x = 0$
$4x + 5y = 20$

17. $x + 4y = 12$
$3x - 2y = -6$

18. $3x - 2y = -6$
$x + y = -2$

19. $x + y = -2$
$3x - y = 10$

20. $3x - y = 10$
$x + 4y = 12$

Challenge Exercise

21. Find the vertices of the triangle with sides determined by the following equations:
$4x + 3y + 1 = 0$, $4x - 3y - 17 = 0$, and $4x - 9y + 13 = 0$.

For the Scholar

In dividing a positive integer x by a positive integer y, the quotient is m with a remainder of p, where m and p are integers. Find the remainder when $x + 4my$ is divided by y.

1-3 Distance and Slope

The distance between two points on a number line can be found by using absolute value. Let A and B be two points on the line with coordinates a and b, respectively. The distance between A and B is $|a - b|$ or $|b - a|$.

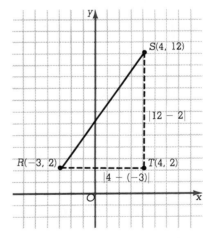

AB denotes the length of *AB*, the segment with endpoints *A* and *B*.

The distance can also be found between points in the coordinate plane. Consider points $R(-3, 2)$ and $S(4, 12)$. To find RS, first choose a point T such that $\overline{RT}$ is parallel to the x-axis and $\overline{ST}$ is parallel to the y-axis. T has coordinates $(4, 2)$. Since S has the same abscissa as T, ST is equal to the absolute value of the difference in the ordinates of S and T, $|12 - 2|$. Similarly, RT is equal to the absolute value of the difference in the abscissas of R and T, $|4 - (-3)|$.

Since $\triangle RST$ is a right triangle, RS can be found by using the Pythagorean theorem.

$$(RS)^2 = (RT)^2 + (ST)^2$$
$$RS = \sqrt{(RT)^2 + (ST)^2}$$
$$= \sqrt{|4 - (-3)|^2 + |12 - 2|^2}$$
$$= \sqrt{7^2 + 10^2}$$
$$= \sqrt{149} \text{ or } 12.2 \text{ units}$$

Assume (x_1, y_1) and (x_2, y_2) represent the coordinates of any two points in the plane. The figure at the right illustrates how the formula for finding the distance between (x_1, y_1) and (x_2, y_2) is derived.

$$d = \sqrt{|x_2 - x_1|^2 + |y_2 - y_1|^2}$$

Why does $|x_2 - x_1|^2 = (x_2 - x_1)^2$?

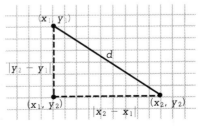

The distance, d, between two points (x_1, y_1) and (x_2, y_2) is given by the following formula.

$$d = \sqrt{(x_2 - x_1)^2 + (y_2 - y_1)^2}$$

Distance Formula for Two Points in the Plane

Example

1 **Find the distance between $(3, -5)$ and $(-1, 2)$.**

$$\begin{aligned}
d &= \sqrt{(x_2 - x_1)^2 + (y_2 - y_1)^2} \\
&= \sqrt{(-1 - 3)^2 + (2 - (-5))^2} \\
&= \sqrt{(-4)^2 + 7^2} \\
&= \sqrt{65} \quad \text{The distance is about 8.1 units.}
\end{aligned}$$

Let $(x_1, y_1) = (3, -5)$ and $(x_2, y_2) = (-1, 2)$.

Any two points determine a line. The **slope** of the line is the ratio of the change in the ordinates of the points to the corresponding change in the abscissas. The slope of a line is constant.

Slope is often defined as $\frac{rise}{run}$.

The slope of a line through (x_1, y_1) and (x_2, y_2) is given by the following equation, if $x_2 \neq x_1$.

$$\text{slope} = \frac{y_2 - y_1}{x_2 - x_1}$$

Definition of Slope

Why do we have the restriction $x_2 \neq x_1$?

Examples

2 **Find the slope of the line through $(-3, 2)$ and $(5, 7)$.**

$$\text{slope} = \frac{y_2 - y_1}{x_2 - x_1} = \frac{7 - 2}{5 - (-3)} = \frac{5}{8} \quad \textit{Either point can be } (x_1, y_1).$$

3 **Graph the line through $(4, 5)$ and $(4, -3)$. Then, find the slope of the line.**

$$\text{slope} = \frac{y_2 - y_1}{x_2 - x_1}, \text{ if } x_2 \neq x_1$$

Because the abscissas of the two points are the same, the slope is undefined. Any line parallel to the y-axis has undefined slope.

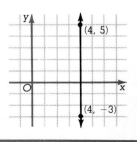

Exploratory Exercises

Find the distance between the given points.

1. $(4, 1), (7, 1)$ **2.** $(5, 1), (5, 11)$ **3.** $(-1, 3), (-1, -3)$

4. $(0, 0), (-4, -3)$ **5.** $(-1, 1), (4, 13)$ **6.** $(-2, 2), (0, 4)$

7-12. Find the slope of the line passing through each pair of points in problems **1-6**.

Written Exercises

Find the distance between the given points.

1. $(5, -3), (-1, -6)$ **2.** $(6, 0), (0, 6)$ **3.** $(5, 7), (0, 0)$

4. $(1, -5), (-7, 11)$ **5.** $(3, a), (8, a)$ **6.** $(b, 6 + a), (b, a + 3)$

7. $(2t, t), (5t, 5t)$ **8.** $(r, s), (r + 2, s - 1)$ **9.** $(n, 4n), (n + 1, n)$

10-18. Find the slope of the line passing through each pair of points in problems **1-9**.

Find the perimeter of the triangle with the given points as vertices.

19. $(2, 3), (14, 3), (14, 8)$ **20.** $(2, 2), (5, 2), (2, 6)$

21. $(1, -1), (1, 3), (-2, -1)$ **22.** $(3, 3), (3, -9), (-2, 3)$

Determine whether the figure with the given points as vertices is a parallelogram.

23. $(3, 4), (6, 2), (8, 7), (5, 9)$ **24.** $(4, 11), (8, 14), (4, 19), (0, 15)$

25. $(-2, 1), (-1, 5), (-5, 6), (-6, 2)$ **26.** $(2, -3), (-2, 3), (-3, -2), (3, 2)$

Challenge Exercises

Collinear points lie on the same line. Find the value of k for which each set of points is collinear. *Remember, the slope of a line is constant.*

27. $(4, 0), (k, 3), (4, -3)$ **28.** $(2, -5), (-4, -11), (k, 1)$ **29.** $(7, -2), (0, 5), (3, k)$

30. $(15, 1), (-3, -8), (3, k)$ **31.** $(9, 2), (k, 3), (-1, 4)$ **32.** $(3, 7), (4, k), (2, 7)$

For the Scholar

A wholesaler buys an article at "$32 less $12\frac{1}{2}\%$." She then sells the article at a gain of 25% of her cost after allowing a 20% discount on her marked price. What was her marked price for the article?

1-4 Forms of Linear Equations

The graph of $y = 3x + 7$ has slope 3 and y-intercept 7. When the equation is written in this form, the slope and y-intercept are easy to find. The equation is said to be in **slope-intercept form**.

Since the y-intercept is 7, $(0, 7)$ is a point on the graph.

> The slope-intercept form of the equation of a line is $y = mx + b$. The slope is m and the y-intercept is b.

Slope-Intercept Form

Example

1 Write the equation $2x + 5y - 10 = 0$ in slope-intercept form. Then, name the slope and y-intercept.

$$2x + 5y - 10 = 0 \qquad \textit{This equation is in standard form.}$$
$$5y = -2x + 10$$
$$y = -\frac{2}{5}x + 2$$

The slope is $-\frac{2}{5}$ and the y-intercept is 2.

If one point and the slope of a line are known, the slope-intercept form can be used to find the equation of the line.

Example

2 Write the equation for the line through (1, 5) that has a slope of -2.

Substitute the slope and coordinates of the point in the general slope-intercept form of a linear equation and solve for b.

$$y = mx + b$$
$$5 = -2(1) + b$$
$$7 = b$$

The slope-intercept form of the equation of the line is $y = -2x + 7$.

The slope formula can also be used to find the equation of a line when a point and the slope are known.

Example

3 Find an equation for the line through (1, 6) that has a slope of 2. Then, write the equation in slope-intercept form.

Suppose a second point on the line is (x, y). Substitute the values into the slope formula.

$$m = \frac{y_2 - y_1}{x_2 - x_1}$$
$$2 = \frac{y - 6}{x - 1}$$
$$2(x - 1) = y - 6 \qquad \textit{This equation is in point-slope form.}$$
$$2x - 2 = y - 6$$
$$2x + 4 = y$$

The slope-intercept form of the equation is $y = 2x + 4$.

The form of a linear equation derived from the slope formula is called the **point-slope form** of the equation.

If the point (x_1, y_1) lies on a line having slope m, the point-slope form of the equation of the line can be written as follows. $$y - y_1 = m(x - x_1)$$	**Point-Slope Form**

If two points on a line are known, the slope can be found. Then the equation for the line can be written using slope-intercept form or point-slope form.

Examples

4 **Find the slope-intercept form of the equation of the line through (1, 4) and (5, 7).**

First, find the slope. $m = \dfrac{7 - 4}{5 - 1} = \dfrac{3}{4}$

Then, substitute values into the general slope-intercept form and solve for b.

$y = mx + b$

$4 = \dfrac{3}{4}(1) + b$ *The coordinates of either point can be used.*

$3\dfrac{1}{4} = b$

The slope-intercept form of the equation is $y = \dfrac{3}{4}x + 3\dfrac{1}{4}$.

5 **Find the point-slope form of the equation of the line through (2, 5) and (6, 3). Then, write the equation in slope-intercept form.**

First, find the slope. $m = \dfrac{3 - 5}{6 - 2}$ or $-\dfrac{1}{2}$

Then, substitute values into the general point-slope form.

$y - y_1 = m(x - x_1)$ *The ordered pair for either point can be (x_1, y_1).*

$y - 5 = -\dfrac{1}{2}(x - 2)$ *This equation is in point-slope form.*

$y = -\dfrac{1}{2}x + 6$

The slope-intercept form of the equation is $y = -\dfrac{1}{2}x + 6$.

Exploratory Exercises

Write each equation in slope-intercept form. Then, name the slope and y-intercept.

1. $3x - 2y = 7$
2. $-3x + 4y = 0$
3. $5x + 11y = 2$
4. $15y - x = 1$
5. $x - 2y - 4 = 0$
6. $3x + y = 2$
7. $8x = 2y - 1$
8. $2x - 5y - 10 = 0$
9. $4x + 3y = 0$

Written Exercises

Write the slope-intercept form of the line through the given point with the given slope.

1. $(3, 2)$, 4

2. $(5, 7)$, 0

3. $(-3, -4)$, -6

4. $(-6, 2)$, 8

5. $(-5, -12)$, -5

6. $(3, 5)$, -3

7. $(-10, 4)$, $\frac{3}{4}$

8. $(-7, 3)$, $-\frac{1}{4}$

9. $(9, 11)$, $\frac{2}{3}$

Write the slope-intercept form of the line through the given points.

10. $(6, 6)$, $(-6, -6)$

11. $(-2, 0)$, $(1, -3)$

12. $(4, 2)$, $(7, 2)$

13. $(-1, 4)$, $(-1, 7)$

14. $(3, -5)$, $(2, -1)$

15. $(5, 2)$, $(7, 9)$

16. $(2, 5)$, $(7, 8)$

17. $(3, 1)$, $(-2, 4)$

18. $(-7, -1)$, $(4, -2)$

Answer each of the following.

19. Find the equation of a line parallel to $y = 7x - 10$ and passing through $(2, -4)$.

20. Find the equation of a line perpendicular to $y = \frac{2}{3}x + 8$ and passing through the origin.

21. Find the equation of a line perpendicular to $y = 3x - 6$ and passing through $(0, 3)$.

22. Find the equations of the lines that make a 45° angle with $y = x + 1$ and pass through $(1, 2)$.

Challenge Exercise

23. Write equations for the sides of the triangle that has vertices $A(2, -7)$, $B(5, 1)$, and $C(-3, 2)$.

For the Scholar

Find the product of two numbers with the ratio of $1:11:60$ between their difference, their sum, and their product.

1-5 Linear Inequalities in Two Variables

The graph of $y = -\frac{1}{2}x + 2$ is a line which separates the coordinate plane into two regions. The graph of $y > -\frac{1}{2}x + 2$ is the region above the line. The graph of $y < -\frac{1}{2}x + 2$ is the region below the line.

The line described by $y = -\frac{1}{2}x + 2$ is called the **boundary** of each region. If the boundary is part of a graph, it is drawn as a solid line. If the boundary is not part of a graph, it is drawn as a broken line.

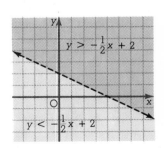

Examples

1 **Graph $5y + 2x \leq -10$.**

$$5y + 2x \leq -10$$
$$5y \leq -2x + -10$$
$$y \leq -\frac{2}{5}x - 2$$

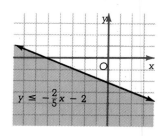

2 **Graph $8 - y > 3x$.**

$$8 - y > 3x$$
$$-y > 3x - 8$$
$$y < -3x + 8$$

Remember to reverse the direction of an inequality when you multiply by a negative number.

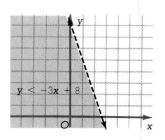

Relations such as $2 < x + y \leq 5$ also can be graphed. The graph of this relation is the intersection of the graph of $2 < x + y$ and the graph of $x + y \leq 5$. Notice that the boundary $x + y = 5$ is part of the graph but the boundary $2 = x + y$ is not part of the graph.

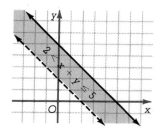

Example

3 **Graph $3 \leq 2x - y \leq 8$.**

$$-y \leq -2x + 3$$
$$y \geq 2x - 3$$

Notice both boundaries are included as part of the graph.

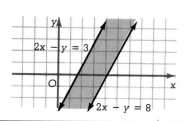

A system of two or more inequalities may be graphed on the same coordinate plane. The intersection of the graphs represents common solutions to the inequalities.

Examples

4 Solve the following system by graphing.

$x + 2y \geq 4$
$x - y \leq 3$

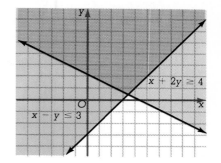

Points in the darkest region satisfy both inequalities.

5 Solve the following system by graphing.

$y > x + 5$
$y < x - 2$

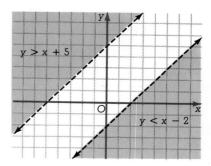

Because the graphs have no points in common, no ordered pairs satisfy both inequalities.

If a system of linear inequalities is graphed so that the intersection set is a convex polygon and its interior, the region is called a **polygonal convex set**.

Example

6 Solve the following system by graphing. Then, name the vertices of the polygonal convex set.

$x \geq 0$
$y \geq 0$
$x + y \leq 5$

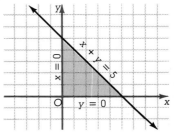

The vertices of the region are (0, 0), (5, 0), and (0, 5).

Exploratory Exercises

Describe the shaded region with an inequality.

1.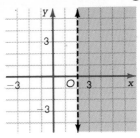

2.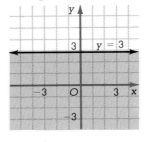

3.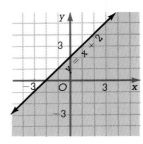

4.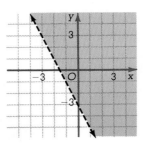

5.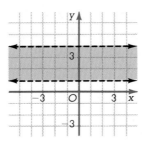

6.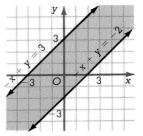

Name which points $(0, 0)$, $(3, 2)$, $(-4, 2)$, or $(-2, 4)$ satisfy each inequality.

7. $x + y \geq 3$

8. $x > 4y + 3$

9. $y < x + 2$

10. $x + y \leq 4$

11. $y \neq x - 5$

12. $3x - 4y \geq -5$

Written Exercises

Graph each inequality.

1. $x < 5$

2. $y \geq -2$

3. $y > -x$

4. $x - y < 5$

5. $y < -2x + 8$

6. $2y \leq x - 5$

7. $-y < 2x + 1$

8. $y \leq -\frac{1}{3}x + 2$

9. $y > \frac{2}{5}x + \frac{19}{5}$

10. $0 < x - y < 2$

11. $2 < 2x + y < 8$

12. $-6 \leq 3x - y \leq 12$

13. $-2 \leq x + 2y \leq 4$

14. $y > |x|$

15. $|x + 3| < y - 1$

Solve the following systems by graphing. Then, name the vertices of each polygonal convex set.

16. $x \geq 0$
    $y \geq 0$
    $2x + y \leq 4$

17. $x \leq 0$
    $y + 3 \geq 0$
    $y \leq x$

18. $x + y \leq 5$
    $y - x \leq 5$
    $y \geq -10$

19. $y \geq 0$
$\quad 0 \leq x \leq 5$
$\quad -x + y \leq 2$
$\quad x + y \leq 6$

20. $x \geq 1$
$\quad y \geq 2$
$\quad y \leq 8$
$\quad x + y \leq 10$
$\quad 2x + y \leq 14$

21. $x \leq 3$
$\quad y \leq 5$
$\quad x + y \geq 1$
$\quad x \geq 0$
$\quad y \geq 0$

Challenge Exercise

22. Write a system of inequalities that determines the polygonal convex set with vertices $(0, 0)$, $(5, 1)$, $(1, 6)$, and $(6, 4)$.

For the Scholar

State the negation of the following statement.

For all x, $x^3 - x > 0$.

1-6 Maximum or Minimum of a Polygonal Convex Set

Linear programming is a procedure for finding the maximum or the minimum value of a function in two variables, subject to given conditions, called **constraints**, on the variables. The constraints are often expressed as linear inequalities.

Suppose it is necessary to find the maximum or minimum value for the function $f(x, y) = 5x - 3y$. The values of x and y have the following constraints.

$$y \geq 0 \qquad\qquad 0 \leq x \leq 5$$
$$-x + y \leq 2 \qquad\qquad x + y \leq 6$$

By graphing each inequality and finding the intersection of the graphs, you can determine a polygonal convex set of points for which the function can be evaluated. The region shown is the polygonal convex set determined by the above inequalities.

The polygonal convex set has an infinite number of points. It would be impossible to evaluate the function for all points within the region. According to the Vertex Theorem, the function needs to be evaluated *only* for the vertices of the polygon.

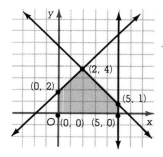

The maximum or minimum value of $f(x, y) = ax + by + c$, defined for a polygonal convex set, occurs at a vertex of the polygon.	*Vertex Theorem*

The value of $5x - 3y$ at each vertex can be found as follows.

$f(x, y) = 5x - 3y$ $\qquad$ $f(2, 4) = 5(2) - 3(4) = -2$
$f(0, 0) = 5(0) - 3(0) = 0$ $\qquad$ $f(5, 1) = 5(5) - 3(1) = 22$
$f(0, 2) = 5(0) - 3(2) = -6$ $\qquad$ $f(5, 0) = 5(5) - 3(0) = 25$

Thus, the maximum value is 25 and the minimum value is -6.

The following intuitive argument supports the results obtained by the Vertex Theorem.

When $5x - 3y$ is equal to some constant k, a line is determined by the equation. The figure at the right shows lines determined by $5x - 3y = k$, where each value of k is the value of $5x - 3y$ at a vertex. Notice that the distance from a line to the origin varies according to the value of k. Any value of k greater than 25 or less than -6 will determine a line that passes outside the polygon. Therefore, that the maximum value of $f(x, y) = 5x - 3y$ for the polygonal convex set is 25 and the minimum is -6.

If the value of a function is the same for two consecutive vertices of a polygon, any point on that side of the polygon represents a maximum or minimum as the case may be.   *Why?*

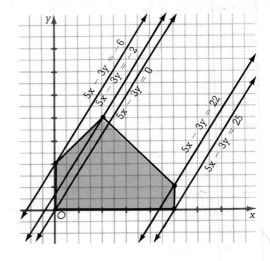

Example

1 **Find the maximum and minimum values of $f(x, y) = x + 2y + 1$ for the polygonal convex set determined by the following inequalities.**

$$x \geq 0 \qquad y \geq 0 \qquad 2x + y \leq 4 \qquad x + y \leq 3$$

First, graph the inequalities and find the coordinates of the vertices of the resulting polygon.

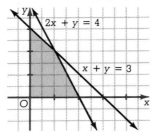

The coordinates of the vertices are (0, 0), (2, 0), (1, 2), and (0, 3).

Then, evaluate the function $f(x, y) = x + 2y + 1$ at each vertex.

$f(0, 0) = 0 + 2(0) + 1 = 1$ $f(1, 2) = 1 + 2(2) + 1 = 6$
$f(2, 0) = 2 + 2(0) + 1 = 3$ $f(0, 3) = 0 + 2(3) + 1 = 7$

The maximum value of the function is 7 and the minimum value is 1.

Exploratory Exercises

Given $f(x, y) = 3x + 2y + 1$, find each value.

1. $f(3, 2)$
2. $f(-2, 1)$
3. $f(2, 4)$
4. $f(-3, -4)$
5. $f(0, 0)$
6. $f\left(\frac{1}{3}, \frac{1}{2}\right)$
7. $f(0, 4)$
8. $f\left(-\frac{3}{2}, 4\right)$

Given $f(x, y) = 5x - 2y + 1$, find each value.

9. $f(0, 0)$ **10.** $f(-3, 2)$ **11.** $f(-3, -5)$ **12.** $f(7, -3)$

13. $f(4, 2)$ **14.** $f(-7, 4)$ **15.** $f(-7, -1)$ **16.** $f(4, -4)$

Find the maximum and minimum values of each function defined for the polygonal convex set having vertices $(0, 0)$, $(4, 0)$, $(3, 5)$, and $(0, 5)$.

17. $f(x, y) = x + y$ **18.** $f(x, y) = 8x + y$ **19.** $f(x, y) = 4y - 3x$

20. $f(x, y) = y - x$ **21.** $f(x, y) = x + 2y$ **22.** $f(x, y) = \frac{1}{2}x - \frac{1}{3}y$

Written Exercises

Solve the following systems by graphing. Then, name the vertices of each polygonal convex set.

1. $x \geq 0$
$y \geq 1$
$x + y \leq 4$

2. $x + 4y \leq 12$
$3x - 2y \geq -6$
$x + y \geq -2$
$3x - y \leq 10$

3. $y \geq x - 4$
$y \geq -3x$
$y \leq \frac{1}{2}x + \frac{7}{2}$
$x \leq 5$

4-6. Find the maximum and minimum values of $f(x, y) = 4x + 2y + 7$ for each polygonal convex set in problems **1-3**.

7-9. Find the maximum and minimum values of $f(x, y) = x - y + 2$ for each polygonal convex set in problems **1-3**.

10-12. Find the maximum and minimum values of $f(x, y) = y + 2x + 7$ for each polygonal convex set in problems **1-3**.

13-15. Find the maximum and minimum values of $f(x, y) = 2x + 8y + 10$ for each polygonal convex set in problems **1-3**.

Challenge Exercise

16. Graph the following system to form a polygonal convex set. Determine which lines intersect and solve pairs of equations to determine the coordinates of each vertex. Then, find the maximum and minimum values of $f(x, y) = 5x + 6y$ for the region defined.

$0 \leq 2y \leq 17$ $y \leq 3x + 1$ $y \geq 7 - 2x$
$y \geq 2x - 13$ $3y \geq -2x + 11$ $y \leq 16 - x$

For the Scholar

If P is a point in the interior of rectangle $MNOQ$ with $PM = 6$, $PQ = 8$, and $PO = 10$, find PN.

1-7 Linear Programming

Many practical problems can be solved by linear programming. These problems are of such a nature that certain constraints exist or are placed upon the variables, and some function of these variables must be maximized or minimized. Use the following method to solve linear programming problems.

1. **Define variables.**
2. **Write the constraints as a system of inequalities.**
3. **Graph the system. Find vertices of the polygon formed.**
4. **Write an expression to be maximized or minimized.**
5. **Substitute values from vertices into the expression.**
6. **Select the greatest or least result.**

Linear Programming Procedure

Example

1   A farmer has a choice of planting a combination of two different crops on 20 acres of land. For crop A, seed costs \$120 per acre, and for crop B, seed costs \$200 per acre. Government restrictions limit acreage of crop A to 15 acres but do not limit crop B. Crop A will take 15 hours of labor per acre at a cost of \$5.60 per hour, and crop B will require 10 hours of labor per acre at \$5.00 per hour. If the expected income from crop A is \$600 per acre and from crop B is \$520 per acre, how should the 20 acres be apportioned between the two crops to get maximum profit?

Define variables.

Let x equal the number of acres of crop A.
Let y equal the number of acres of crop B.

Write inequalities.

$x \geq 0, y \geq 0$ *The number of acres of crops cannot be less than 0.*
$x \leq 15$ *No more than 15 acres of crop A are permitted.*
$x + y \leq 20$ *No more than 20 acres can be planted in all.*

Graph the system.

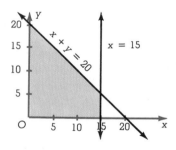

The vertices are
(0, 0), (15, 0), (15, 5), and (0, 20).

Write an expression to be maximized.

The profit from any crop equals the income less the costs. The profit from crop A equals $600x - 120x - 15(5.60)x$, or $396x$. The profit from crop B equals $520y - 200y - 10(5.00)y$, or $270y$. Thus, the profit function is $P(x, y) = 396x + 270y$.

Substitute values into the expression.

$P(0, 0) = 396(0) + 270(0) = 0$
$P(15, 0) = 396(15) + 270(0) = 5940$
$P(15, 5) = 396(15) + 270(5) = 7290$
$P(0, 20) = 396(0) + 270(20) = 5400$

Answer the problem.

The farmer should plant 15 acres of crop A and 5 acres of crop B to obtain the maximum profit of \$7290.

Exploratory Exercises

The Champion Lumber Company converts logs into lumber or plywood. In a given week, the total production cannot exceed 800 units, of which 200 units of lumber and 300 units of plywood are required by regular customers. The profit on a unit of lumber is $20 and the profit on a unit of plywood is $30. With this information, answer each of the following. Let x represent the units of lumber and y represent the units of plywood.

1. Write an inequality to represent the total production.

2. Write an inequality to represent the production of lumber.

3. Write an inequality to represent the production of plywood.

4. Write an equation to represent the total profit.

5. Graph the polygonal convex set determined by the inequalities.

6. Name the vertices of the polygon.

7. Find the number of units each of lumber and plywood that should be produced to maximize profit.

8. What is the maximum profit?

Written Exercises

Answer each of the following.

1. A manufacturer makes widgets and gadgets. At least 500 widgets and 700 gadgets are needed to meet minimum daily demands. The machinery can produce no more than 1200 widgets and 1400 gadgets per day. The combined number of widgets and gadgets that the packaging department can handle is 2300 per day. If the company sells widgets for 40 cents each and gadgets for 50 cents each, how many of each item should be produced for maximum daily income? What is the maximum daily income?

2. A company makes two models of light fixtures, A and B, each of which must be assembled and packed. The time required to assemble model A is 12 minutes, and model B takes 18 minutes. It takes 2 minutes to package model A and 1 minute to package model B. Each week there are available 240 hours of assembly time and 20 hours for packing. If model A sells for $1.50 and model B sells for $1.70, how many of each model should be made to obtain the maximum weekly income? What is the maximum weekly income?

3. In addition to the information given in problem 1, suppose the cost of producing a widget is 7 cents and the cost of producing a gadget is 18 cents. How many widgets and gadgets should be produced for maximum daily profit? What is the maximum daily profit?

4. In addition to the information given in problem 2, suppose the cost of producing model A is 75¢ and the cost of producing model B is 85¢. How many model A light fixtures and model B light fixtures should be produced for maximum weekly profit? What is the maximum weekly profit?

5. A manufacturer can show a profit on a bicycle of $6 and a profit on a tricycle of $4. Department A requires 3 hours to manufacture the parts for a bicycle and 4 hours to manufacture parts for a tricycle. Department B takes 5 hours to assemble a bicycle and 2 hours to assemble a tricycle. How many bicycles and tricycles should be produced to maximize the profit if the total time available in department A is 450 hours and in department B is 400 hours?

6. A diet is to include at least 140 mg of Vitamin A and at least 145 mg of Vitamin B. These requirements are to be obtained from two types of food. Type X contains 10 mg of Vitamin A and 20 mg of Vitamin B per pound. Type Y contains 30 mg of Vitamin A and 15 mg of Vitamin B per pound. If type X food costs $12 and type Y food costs $8 per pound, how many pounds of each type of food should be purchased to satisfy the requirements at the minimum cost?

7. A packer makes a kind of wurst using beef, pork, cereal, fat, water, and spices. The minimum cereal content is 12%, the minimum fat content is 15%, the minimum water content is 6.5%, and the spices are 0.5%. The remaining ingredients are beef and pork. There must be at least 30% beef for flavor and at least 20% pork for texture. The beef content must equal or exceed the pork content. The cost of all the content except beef and pork is $32 per 100 lb. Beef can be purchased for $140 per 100 lb and pork for $90 per 100 lb. Find the combination of beef and pork for the minimum cost. What is the minimum cost per 100 lb?

8. A company is planning to buy new fork hoists for material handling. There are two models that will serve their needs. The warehouse supervisor feels that a minimum of 3 Model M hoists and 5 Model R hoists will be needed. The supplier has 8 Model M hoists and 10 Model R hoists on hand for delivery. The company purchasing agent has decided that no more than 14 hoists can be purchased. Model M can handle 12,000 kg per hour and Model R can handle 10,000 kg per hour. What number of hoists of each model should be purchased for maximum weight handling capacity?

9. A chemical company uses two types of fuel for heating and processing. At least 3800 gallons of fuel are used each day. The burning of each gallon of #1 crude leaves a residue of 0.02 pounds of ash and 0.06 pounds of soot. Each gallon of #2 crude leaves a residue of 0.05 pounds of ash and 0.01 pounds of soot. The factory needs at least 120 pounds of ash and at least 136 pounds of soot each day. If #1 crude costs $1.50 per gallon and #2 crude costs $1.10 per gallon, then how many gallons of each type should be purchased in order to minimize the cost?

10. A pharmaceutical company manufactures two drugs. Each case of drug one requires 3 hours of processing time and 1 hour of curing time per week. Each case of drug two requires 5 hours of processing time and 5 hours of curing time per week. The schedule allows 55 hours of processing time and 45 hours of curing time weekly. The company must produce no more than 10 cases of drug one and no more than 9 cases of drug two. If the company makes a profit of $320 on each case of drug one and $500 on each case of drug two, how many cases of each drug should be produced in order to maximize profit?

For the Scholar

Find the difference of the roots of the following quadratic equation.

$$(3 + 2\sqrt{2})x^2 + (1 + \sqrt{2})x = 2$$

Using Mathematics

In producing and selling a product, the amount that must be sold in order to make a zero profit is the break-even point. To determine this point, either graph the equation for cost with the equation for profit or solve the system of equations algebraically. The point where the equations intersect is the break-even point.

Example   A manufacturer has a fixed cost of $2000 a week. If each item costs $5 per unit to produce and can be sold for $15 apiece. What is the break-even point?

First, determine the equations of the cost and the profit.

The cost equation would be $y = 2000 + 5x$.

The profit equation would be $y = 15x$.

Graph the system of equations.

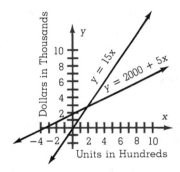

Check by solving the system algebraically.

$$2000 + 5x = 15x$$
$$2000 = 10x$$
$$200 = x$$

Therefore, the break-even point is 200 units per week.

Exercises   **Find the cost and profit equations. Then, graph the system to find the break-even point. Use algebra to check.**

1. The West Corporation has a weekly fixed cost of $5,000. It costs $16,000 to produce 400 units. The units can be sold for $60 a piece.

2. The City Corporation has a weekly fixed cost of $260,000. To produce 100 units of a product it costs $130,000. The selling price is $1,800 per unit.

Chapter Summary

1. **Definition of Relation, Domain, and Range:** A relation is a set of ordered pairs. The domain is the set of all abscissas of the ordered pairs. The range is the set of all ordinates of the ordered pairs. (3)

2. **Definition of Function:** A function is a relation in which each element of the domain is paired with exactly one element of the range. (3)

3. **Standard Form of a Linear Equation:** The standard form of a linear equation is $Ax + By + C = 0$, where A, B, and C are real numbers, and A and B are not both zero. (7)

4. **Linear Function:** A linear function can be defined by $f(x) = mx + b$ where m and b are real numbers. (8)

5. **Distance Formula for Two Points in the Plane:** The distance, d, between two points (x_1, y_1) and (x_2, y_2) is given by the formula

$$d = \sqrt{(x_2 - x_1)^2 + (y_2 - y_1)^2}. \quad (11)$$

6. **Slope:** The slope of a line through (x_1, y_1) and (x_2, y_2) is given by the following equation, if $x_2 \neq x_1$.

$$\text{slope} = \frac{y_2 - y_1}{x_2 - x_1} \qquad (11)$$

7. **Slope-Intercept Form:** The slope-intercept form of the equation of a line is $y = mx + b$. The slope is m and the y-intercept is b. (12)

8. **Point-Slope Form:** If the point (x_1, y_1) lies on a line having slope m, the point-slope form of the equation of the line can be written as follows.

$$y - y_1 = m(x - x_1) \qquad (14)$$

9. A system of two or more inequalities may be graphed on the same coordinate plane. The intersection of the graphs represents the common solutions to the inequalities. (16)

10. If a system of linear inequalities is graphed so that the intersection set is a convex polygon and its interior, the region is called a polygonal convex set. (17)

11. **Vertex Theorem:** The maximum or minimum value of $f(x, y) = ax + by + c$, defined for a polygonal convex set occurs at a vertex of the polygon. (19)

12. **Linear Programming Procedure:**
    1. Define variables.
    2. Write the constraints as a system of inequalities.
    3. Graph the system. Find vertices of the polygon formed.
    4. Write an expression to be maximized or minimized.
    5. Substitute values from the vertices into the expression.
    6. Select the greatest or least result. (22)

Chapter Review

State the domain and range of each relation. (1-1)

1. $\{(3, 5), (4, 5), (5, 5)\}$

2. $\{(0, 4), (0, 5)\}$

3. $\{(8, 4), (8, -4), (10, 5), (10, -5)\}$

4. $\{(-2, 1), (-1, 2), (0, 3)\}$

5. $\{(9, 81), (8, 64), (7, 49)\}$

6. $\{(5, 11), (11, 5), (6, 11), (11, 6)\}$

State the relation represented by each of the following, given that x is an integer. (1-1)

7. $y = 5x - 7$ and $0 \le x \le 3$

8. $y = 3x^3$ and $-2 < x < 3$

9. $|y| = x - 4$ and $5 \le x < 7$

10. $y = |4 + x|$ and $-8 \le x < -2$

11-20. State whether each relation in problems **1-10** is a function. Write *yes* or *no*.

Given $f(x) = |x - 6| + x^2$, find each value. (1-1)

21. $f(0)$ **22.** $f(3)$ **23.** $f(11)$ **24.** $f(5.9)$

Name all values of x that are not in the domain of the given function. (1-1)

25. $f(x) = \dfrac{5}{x}$

26. $f(x) = \dfrac{x^2}{x^2 - 3}$

27. $f(x) = \dfrac{2(x^2 - 9)}{x + 3}$

28. $f(x) = \dfrac{2x^3 - 5}{2|x| - 5}$

Write each equation in standard form. (1-2)

29. $y = \dfrac{1}{3}x + \dfrac{5}{3}$

30. $y = \dfrac{1}{2}x - 3$

31. $3x = 2y + x$

32. $y + 9 = 4x + 7$

33. $y = -8$

34. $7 = x$

35-40. Graph each equation in problems **29-34**.

Find the zero of each function. (1-2)

41. $f(x) = 3x - 8$ **42.** $f(x) = 19$ **43.** $f(x) = 0.25x - 5$

Solve each system of equations by graphing. (1-2)

44. $y = -2x$
$x + y = -2$

45. $x - y = 5$
$x = 6y$

46. $5y - 2x = 0$
$3y + x = -1$

Find the distance between the given points. (1-3)

47. $(0, 0), (5, 12)$

48. $(3, 8), (5, 11)$

49. $(a, b), (a + 3, b + 4)$

50. $(2k, 4k), (3k, 6k)$

51-54. Find the slope of the line passing through each pair of points in problems **47-50**.

Write the slope-intercept form of the line through the given point with the given slope. (1-4)

55. $(5, 5), 2$

56. $(-2, 3), -1$

57. $(0, 0), \dfrac{3}{5}$

58. $(1, 4), -\dfrac{4}{3}$

Write the slope-intercept form of the line through the given points. (1-4)

59. (3, 7), (6, 10)

60. (5, −2), (3, −8)

61. (9, 6), (−3, 3)

62. (−1, 0), (5, 9)

63. (4, 4), (2, −3)

64. (11, −6), (10, −9)

Graph each inequality. (1-5)

65. $x + y < 8$

66. $y < x - 5$

67. $3y \geq 2x + 6$

68. $-2 \leq x - 3y \leq 4$

69. $0 < y + x < 10$

70. $|x - 2| \leq 3y$

Solve the following systems by graphing. Then, name the vertices of each polygonal convex set. (1-5)

71. $x \geq 0$
$y \geq 0$
$4y + x \leq 10$

72. $x \geq 1$
$y \geq -2$
$y \leq 6 - x$
$y + 2x \leq 10$

73. $x \geq 0$
$y \geq 4$
$2y \leq 18 - x$
$x \leq 6$
$y \leq 11 - x$

Given $f(x, y) = 7x + 3y$, find each value. (1-6)

74. $f(0, 3)$

75. $f(4, 7)$

76. $f(6, 2)$

77. $f(-3, -2)$

78. $f(2, 1.5)$

79. $f(2.3, 5)$

80. $f(-4, 9)$

81. $f(0.5, 3.5)$

Find the maximum and minimum values of the given function, defined for the polygonal convex set having vertices (1, 4), (11, 4), (9, 6), (6, 8), and (1, 8). (1-6)

82. $f(x, y) = 4y + 3x$

83. $f(x, y) = 6x + y$

84-86. Find the maximum and minimum values of $f(x, y) = 3y + 2x - 4$ for each polygonal convex set in problems **71-73**.

Answer each of the following. (1-7)

87. Joe has a small carpentry shop in his basement to make bookcases. He makes two sizes, large and small. His profit on a large bookcase is $50 and his profit on a small bookcase is $20. It takes Joe 6 hours to make a large bookcase and 2 hours to make a small one. He can spend only 24 hours each week on his carpentry work. He must make at least two of each size each week. How many of each size should Joe make each week to obtain the maximum weekly profit? What is the maximum weekly profit?

88. A company manufactures two types of clocks, Model 82 and Model 47. There are three stations, A, B, and C, on the assembly line. The assembly of one Model 82 requires 30 minutes at station A, 20 minutes at station B, and 12 minutes at station C. Model 47 requires 15 minutes at station A, 30 minutes at station B, and 10 minutes at station C. Station A can be operated for no more than 4 hours a day, station B can be operated for no more than 6 hours, and station C can be operated for no more than 8 hours. If the profit on each Model 82 is $10 and on Model 47 is $6, how many of each model should be assembled each day to provide maximum profit? What is the maximum daily profit?

Chapter Test

State the relation represented by each of the following, given that x is an integer.

1. $y = 3x - 1$ and $-3 < x \leq 2$
2. $|y| = 2x + 5$ and $0 \leq x \leq 4$

3-4. State whether each relation in problems **1-2** is a function. Write *yes* or *no*.

Given $f(x) = x - 3x^2$, find each value.

5. $f(0)$
6. $f(4)$
7. $f(13)$
8. $f(7.1)$

Write each equation in standard form.

9. $2x = 5$
10. $y = 0.2x + 0.4$
11. $3x = x - 2y$

Find the zero of each function.

12. $f(x) = 5x + 8$
13. $f(x) = 25$
14. $f(x) = 0.3 + 2x$

Solve each system of equations by graphing.

15. $x - 4 = y$
    $y = 2x - 8$
16. $x + 5 = y$
    $3x = y - 1$
17. $y - 3x = 8$
    $x + y = 4$

Find the distance between the given points.

18. $(-1, 2), (3, 1)$
19. $(5, 11), (12, 12)$
20. $(3k, k + 1), (2h, k - 1)$

21-23. Find the slope of the line passing through each pair of points in problems **18-20**.

Write the slope-intercept form of the line through the given point with the given slope.

24. $(0, 0), \frac{3}{8}$
25. $(2, 7), -\frac{1}{2}$
26. $(-1, 3), \frac{5}{3}$

Write the slope-intercept form of the line through the given points.

27. $(5, 1), (8, 10)$
28. $(6, -4), (1, 2)$
29. $(0, 4), (8, -2)$

Solve the following systems by graphing. Then, name the vertices of each polygonal convex set.

30. $y \geq 0 \quad x + y \leq 6$
    $x \geq 1 \quad y + 3x \leq 12$
31. $y \leq 5 \quad x \leq 3$
    $y + 2x \geq 0 \quad y \geq x - 2$

Given $f(x, y) = 5x - 2y$, find each value.

32. $f(3, 0)$
33. $f(4, 2)$
34. $f(1.5, 4)$
35. $f(5, 3.2)$

36-37. Find the maximum and minimum values of $f(x, y) = 5y + 3x$ for each polygonal convex set in problems **30-31**.

38. A toy manufacturer produces two types of model space ships, the Voyager and the Explorer. Each of the toys requires the same three operations, plastic molding, machining, and bench assembly. Each Voyager requires 5 minutes for molding, 3 minutes for machining, and 5 minutes for assembly. Each Explorer requires 6 minutes for molding, 2 minutes for machining, and 18 minutes for assembly. The manufacturer can afford a daily schedule of not more than 4 hours for molding, 2 hours for machining, and 9 hours for assembly. If the profit is $2.40 on each Voyager and $5.00 on each Explorer, how many of each toy should be produced for maximum profit? What is the maximum daily profit?

CHAPTER 2

Theory of Equations

The graph of a polynomial equation is a smooth curve. The design of a roller coaster is based upon the application of many polynomial equations and their graphs.

2-1 Polynomial Equations

A **polynomial** in one variable, x, is an expression of the form $a_0x^n + a_1x^{n-1} + \cdots + a_{n-1}x + a_n$. The coefficients $a_0, a_1, \cdots, a_n$ are real numbers, and n is a nonnegative integer. The **degree** of a polynomial in one variable is n, the greatest exponent of its variable.

A **linear expression** such as $4x - 7$ is a first degree polynomial. A second degree polynomial, such as $5x^2 + 6x - 3$ is called a **quadratic expression.**

The terms of a polynomial are usually written in order of decreasing degree.

Third, fourth, and fifth degree expressions are called <u>cubic</u>, <u>quartic</u>, and <u>quintic</u>, respectively.

Example

1 **Which of the following expressions are polynomials in one variable?**

   a. $b^2 + 2a^2 + 2b$
   b. $y^3 - y + 4y^4 - 3y^3$
   c. $x^2 + \dfrac{3}{x} + 7$

   a. $b^2 + 2a^2 + 2b$ is not a polynomial in one variable.   *There are two variables.*
   b. $y^3 - y + 4y^4 - 3y^3$ is a polynomial in one variable.
   c. $x^2 + \dfrac{3}{x} + 7$ is not a polynomial in one variable. $\dfrac{3}{x}$ *cannot be written in the form* x^n, *where n is a nonnegative integer.*

If a polynomial is equal to zero, the equation is called a polynomial equation. Thus, if $P(x)$ represents a polynomial, $P(x) = 0$ is a **polynomial equation.** A **root** of the equation is a value of x for which the value of $P(x)$ is zero. Thus, 5 is a root of the equation $x^2 - 6x + 5 = 0$, since $(5)^2 - 6(5) + 5 = 0$. A root is also called a solution.

A root of P(x) = 0 is a <u>zero</u> of P(x).

Examples

2 **Is 6 a root of $x^3 - 5x^2 - 3x - 18 = 0$?**

$$P(6) = 6^3 - 5(6)^2 - 3(6) - 18$$
$$= 216 - 180 - 18 - 18$$
$$= 0$$

Thus, 6 is a root of the equation.

3 **Is -2 a root of $x^4 - 3x^2 - 2x + 4 = 0$?**

$$P(-2) = (-2)^4 - 3(-2)^2 - 2(-2) + 4$$
$$= 16 - 12 + 4 + 4$$
$$= 12$$
$$P(-2) \neq 0$$

Thus, -2 is not a root of the equation.

To solve an equation means to find the roots of the equation. Some polynomial equations can be solved by factoring. If the product of two or more factors is zero, at least one of the factors must be zero. For example, if $ab = 0$, either $a = 0$, $b = 0$, or both are zero.

Examples

4 **Solve $x^2 - 4x - 21 = 0$.**

$x^2 - 4x - 21 = 0$
$(x - 7)(x + 3) = 0$
$x - 7 = 0$ or $x + 3 = 0$
$\qquad x = 7$ or $x = -3$

Check.
$(7)^2 - 4(7) - 21 = 0$
The roots are 7 and -3. $\qquad (-3)^2 - 4(-3) - 21 = 0$

5 **Solve $(x - 4)(x + 9)(2x + 7) = 0$.**

$(x - 4)(x + 9)(2x + 7) = 0$
$x - 4 = 0$, $x + 9 = 0$, or $2x + 7 = 0$
$\qquad x = 4$, $x = -9$, or $x = -\dfrac{7}{2}$

Check.
$(4 - 4)(4 + 9)(2(4) + 7) = 0$
$(-9 - 4)(-9 + 9)(2(-9) + 7) = 0$
The roots are 4, -9, and $-\dfrac{7}{2}$. $\qquad \left(-\dfrac{7}{2} - 4\right)\left(-\dfrac{7}{2} + 9\right)\left(2\left(-\dfrac{7}{2}\right) + 7\right) = 0$

Exploratory Exercises

Which of the following expressions are polynomials in one variable?

1. $5x + xy + y$

2. $a^3 + 2a + \sqrt{3}$

3. $\dfrac{1}{c} + c^2$

4. $\dfrac{1}{x} = \dfrac{1}{2x}$

5. $2m^3 + 5m^2 + 9$

6. $5a + 4b + 2c$

7. $x^4 - 3x^3 + x - \sqrt{7}$

8. $y\sqrt{2} + y$

Which of the following are roots of $x^4 - 4x^3 - x^2 + 4x = 0$?

9. 2 $\qquad$ **10.** 0 $\qquad$ **11.** -1 $\qquad$ **12.** -2

13. 4 $\qquad$ **14.** -4 $\qquad$ **15.** 3 $\qquad$ **16.** 1

Written Exercises

Solve each equation.

1. $x - 2 = 0$

2. $2a + 4 = 0$

3. $x^2 - 4 = 0$

4. $t^2 - t = 0$

5. $z^2 - z - 2 = 0$

6. $(s - 2)(s - 5) = 0$

7. $(u + 2)(u^2 - 4) = 0$

8. $(2q - 3)(3q - 2) = 0$

9. $(x - 1)(x - 2)(x - 3)(x - 4) = 0$
10. $x^2 - x - 6 = 0$
11. $r^2 - 18r + 81 = 0$
12. $6c^2 - 3c - 45 = 0$
13. $y^2 - 9 = 0$
14. $6m^2 - 39m + 45 = 0$
15. $14y^2 + 19y - 3 = 0$
16. $6y^2 + y - 2 = 0$
17. $20x^2 - 73x + 63 = 0$
18. $2x^2 + x - 6 = 0$
19. $18x^2 + 3x - 1 = 0$
20. $n^3 - 9n = 0$
21. $12x^2 + 8x - 15 = 0$
22. $6m^2 + 7m - 3 = 0$
23. $16b^2 - 121 = 0$
24. $18x^3 - 34x^2 + 16x = 0$
25. $x^2 + ax + bx + ab = 0$
26. $y^2 - cy - dy + cd = 0$

For the Scholar

Find $f(x^2 + 2)$ if $f(x)$ is a polynomial function such that, for all real values of x, $f(x^2 + 1) = x^4 + 3x^2 + 3$.

2-2 Quadratic Equations and Imaginary Roots

Any **quadratic equation** can be written in the form $ax^2 + bx + c = 0$, when a, b, and c are real numbers and $a \neq 0$. Many quadratic equations can be solved by factoring. If the factors of a quadratic equation are difficult to determine, other methods can be used to solve the equation.

If an equation can be written as a perfect square equal to a constant, it can be solved by using square roots. For example, the equation $(x + 3)^2 = 5$ can be solved as follows.

$(x + 3)^2 = 5$ *The quadratic form of this equation is $x^2 + 6x + 4 = 0$.*

$x + 3 = \pm\sqrt{5}$ *Why is the symbol $\pm$ necessary?*

$x = -3 \pm \sqrt{5}$ *The roots are $-3 + \sqrt{5}$ and $-3 - \sqrt{5}$.*

A method called **completing the square** is based on this concept. For any real number b, the perfect square of a binomial $(x + b)$ has the form $x^2 + 2bx + b^2$. Notice the constant term is equal to the square of half the coefficient of the middle term. Therefore, the roots of a quadratic equation can be found by completing the square.

1 **Solve $3x^2 - 14x + 8 = 0$.**

$x^2 - \dfrac{14}{3}x + \dfrac{8}{3} = 0$ 　　　*Divide each side by 3 so that the leading coefficient is 1.*

$x^2 - \dfrac{14}{3}x = -\dfrac{8}{3}$ 　　　*Subtract $\frac{8}{3}$ from each side.*

$x^2 - \dfrac{14}{3}x + \dfrac{49}{9} = -\dfrac{8}{3} + \dfrac{49}{9}$ 　　　*Add $\left(-\frac{14}{3} \div 2\right)^2$ or $\frac{49}{9}$ to each side.*

$\left(x - \dfrac{7}{3}\right)^2 = \dfrac{25}{9}$ 　　　*Factor.*

$x - \dfrac{7}{3} = \pm\dfrac{5}{3}$ 　　　*Take the square root of each side.*

$x = 4$ or $\dfrac{2}{3}$ 　　　*Solve for x.*

The roots are 4 and $\dfrac{2}{3}$.

Completing the square can be used to develop a general formula for solving equations of the form $ax^2 + bx + c = 0$. The formula is called the **quadratic formula** and can be used to find the roots of any quadratic equation.

The roots of a quadratic equation of the form $ax^2 + bx + c = 0$ with $a \neq 0$ are given by the following formula. $$x = \frac{-b \pm \sqrt{b^2 - 4ac}}{2a}$$

Quadratic Formula

2 **Solve $6x^2 + 7x + 2 = 0$ using the quadratic formula.**

$x = \dfrac{-b \pm \sqrt{b^2 - 4ac}}{2a}$ 　　　$a = 6, b = 7, c = 2$

$x = \dfrac{-7 \pm \sqrt{7^2 - 4(6)(2)}}{2(6)}$

$x = \dfrac{-7 \pm \sqrt{1}}{12}$

$x = \dfrac{-7 \pm 1}{12}$ 　　　　　　$\dfrac{-7 + 1}{12} = -\dfrac{1}{2}$ and $\dfrac{-7 - 1}{12} = -\dfrac{2}{3}$

The roots are $-\dfrac{1}{2}$ and $-\dfrac{2}{3}$.

Many equations have roots that are not real numbers. The quadratic formula can be used to solve such equations.

Example

3 **Solve $x^2 - 6x + 13 = 0$.**

$$x = \frac{-b \pm \sqrt{b^2 - 4ac}}{2a} \qquad a = 1, b = -6, c = 13$$

$$x = \frac{6 \pm \sqrt{36 - 52}}{2}$$

$$x = \frac{6 \pm \sqrt{-16}}{2}$$

$$x = 3 \pm 2\sqrt{-1}$$

There is no real number whose square is -1.

The square root of a negative number is an **imaginary number.** Imaginary numbers can be represented by using the number i, which is called the **imaginary unit.** The imaginary unit i is defined by $i^2 = -1$. For example, the imaginary numbers $\sqrt{-11}$ and $\sqrt{-36}$ can be represented as $i\sqrt{11}$ and $6i$, respectively.

Numbers such as $3 + 2i$ and $4 - i\sqrt{3}$ are complex numbers. A **complex number** is any number that can be written in the form $a + bi$, where a and b are real numbers and i is the imaginary unit. A complex number is real when $b = 0$ and imaginary when $b \neq 0$.

The roots of the equation in example 3 are complex numbers, $3 + 2i$ and $3 - 2i$. Complex numbers of the form $a + bi$ and $a - bi$ are called **conjugates** of each other.

In general, the roots of a quadratic equation are imaginary if the value of $b^2 - 4ac$, the **discriminant,** is negative. Such roots always occur as conjugate pairs as an inspection of the formula $x = \frac{-b \pm \sqrt{b^2 - 4ac}}{2a}$ will show, providing a, b, and c are real numbers. Imaginary roots also occur in pairs for higher degree polynomial equations.

If $b^2 - 4ac \geq 0$, then the root x is real. If $b^2 - 4ac < 0$, then the root x is imaginary.

Suppose a and b are real numbers with $b \neq 0$. Then, if $a + bi$ is a root of a polynomial equation, $a - bi$ is also a root of the equation.

Complex Conjugates Theorem

Exploratory Exercises

Name the conjugate of each complex number.

1. i 2. $3 + i$ 3. $5 - 2i$ 4. $-2i$

5. $-\frac{1}{2} + \frac{1}{2}i$ 6. $-4 + 2i$ 7. $5 - i\sqrt{2}$ 8. $-7 - i\sqrt{5}$

Find the value of c that makes each trinomial a perfect square.

9. $x^2 + 4x + c$ 10. $x^2 - 8x + c$ 11. $p^2 - p + c$ 12. $y^2 + \frac{3}{2}y + c$

13. $z^2 + \frac{4}{3}z + c$ 14. $y^2 - 25y + c$ 15. $n^2 - 30n + c$ 16. $r^2 + 50r + c$

17. $x^2 - \frac{1}{4}x + c$ 18. $a^2 + 11a + c$ 19. $x^2 - \frac{4}{7}x + c$ 20. $m^2 - 3m + c$

Written Exercises

Solve each equation by completing the square.

1. $y^2 - 3y - 88 = 0$ 2. $z^2 - 2z = 24$ 3. $x^2 + 8x - 20 = 0$

4. $x^2 + 2x - 48 = 0$ 5. $x^2 - \frac{3}{4}x + \frac{1}{8} = 0$ 6. $6m^2 + 7m - 3 = 0$

7. $2y^2 + 11y - 21 = 0$ 8. $4x^2 + 19x - 5 = 0$ 9. $x^2 - 3x - 7 = 0$

10. $r^2 + 5r - 8 = 0$ 11. $3x^2 - 12x + 4 = 0$ 12. $6s^2 + 2s - 3 = 0$

Solve each equation using the quadratic formula. The roots may be real or complex.

13. $3x^2 - 7x - 20 = 0$ 14. $r^2 + 13r + 42 = 0$ 15. $4x^2 - 9x + 5 = 0$

16. $12x^2 - 7x - 12 = 0$ 17. $7n^2 + 20n - 32 = 0$ 18. $5m^2 + 7m + 3 = 0$

19. $6y^2 - 5y - 6 = 0$ 20. $2z^2 + 2z + 3 = 0$ 21. $2x^2 + 3x + 3 = 0$

22. $8r^2 + 6r + 1 = 0$ 23. $6y^2 + 8y + 5 = 0$ 24. $x^2 - 7x + 5 = 0$

25. $3x^2 + 7x + 4 = 0$ 26. $15a^2 - 10a + 1 = 0$ 27. $4b^2 + b - 6 = 0$

28. $r^2 - 4r + 10 = 0$ 29. $5x^2 - 2x + 8 = 0$ 30. $3k^2 + 3k + 2 = 0$

Challenge Exercise

31. Derive the quadratic formula.
    Hint: Solve the equation $ax^2 + bx + c = 0$ by completing the square.

For the Scholar

How many four-digit numbers, with all digits different, are there between 1,000 and 9,999 such that the difference between the first and last digits is ±3?

2-3 Synthetic Division

Synthetic division is a shortcut for dividing a polynomial by a binomial of the form $x - r$. This procedure is helpful when factoring polynomials. To divide $x^3 + 3x^2 - 2x - 8$ by $x + 2$, follow the steps given on the next page.

Step 1	Arrange the terms of the polynomial in descending order. Then, write the coefficients as shown.	$x^3 + 3x^2 - 2x - 8$ 1 3 −2 −8	*The coefficient of x^3 is 1.*

Step 1 Arrange the terms of the polynomial in descending order. Then, write the coefficients as shown.

$$x^3 + 3x^2 - 2x - 8$$

$$1 \quad 3 \quad -2 \quad -8$$

The coefficient of x^3 is 1.

Step 2 Write the constant r of the divisor $x - r$. For the divisor $x + 2$, r is -2.

$$-2 \,\rfloor\, 1 \quad 3 \quad -2 \quad -8$$

Step 3 Bring down the first coefficient.

$$-2 \,\rfloor\, 1 \quad 3 \quad -2 \quad -8$$
$$\overline{}$$
$$1$$

Step 4 Multiply the first coefficient by r. Then, write the product under the second coefficient. Add.

$$-2 \,\rfloor\, 1 \quad 3 \quad -2 \quad -8$$
$$\;\; -2$$
$$\overline{}$$
$$1 \quad 1$$

Step 5 Multiply the sum by r. Then, write the product under the next coefficient. Add.

$$-2 \,\rfloor\, 1 \quad 3 \quad -2 \quad -8$$
$$\;\; -2 \quad -2$$
$$\overline{}$$
$$1 \quad 1 \quad -4 \;\rceil$$

Step 6 Repeat step 5 until all coefficients in the dividend have been used.

$$-2 \,\rfloor\, 1 \quad 3 \quad -2 \quad -8$$
$$\;\; -2 \quad -2 \quad 8$$
$$\overline{}$$
$$1 \quad 1 \quad -4 \;\rceil 0$$

Step 7 Write the quotient and remainder. The last sum represents the remainder. The other sums are the coefficients of the quotient.

$$x^2 + x - 4$$

The remainder is zero.

Compare the long division process to the synthetic division process.

$$\begin{array}{r} x^2 + x - 4 \\ x + 2 \overline{)\, x^3 + 3x^2 - 2x - 8} \\ \underline{x^3 + 2x^2} \\ x^2 - 2x \\ \underline{x^2 + 2x} \\ -4x - 8 \\ \underline{-4x - 8} \\ 0 \end{array}$$

$$-2 \,\rfloor\, 1 \quad 3 \quad -2 \quad -8$$
$$\;\; -2 \quad -2 \quad 8$$
$$\overline{}$$
$$1 \quad 1 \quad -4 \;\rceil 0$$

A vertical bar separates the quotient from the remainder.

Because the remainder is zero, $x + 2$ is a factor of $x^3 + 3x^2 - 2x - 8$.

Example

1 **Use synthetic division to divide $x^3 - 2x - 18$ by $x - 3$.**

$$3 \,\rfloor\, 1 \quad 0 \quad -2 \quad -18$$
$$\;\; 3 \quad 9 \quad 21$$
$$\overline{}$$
$$1 \quad 3 \quad 7 \;\rceil 3$$

Notice that there is no x^2 term. Therefore, a zero is placed in the x^2 position.

The quotient is $x^2 + 3x + 7$ with a remainder of 3.

Example

2 Use synthetic division to divide $x^5 - 3x^2 - 20$ by $x - 2$.

$$\underline{2\,|}\ \begin{array}{rrrrrr} 1 & 0 & 0 & -3 & 0 & -20 \\ & 2 & 4 & 8 & 10 & 20 \\ \hline 1 & 2 & 4 & 5 & 10 & 0 \end{array}$$

What does each zero represent?

The quotient is $x^4 + 2x^3 + 4x^2 + 5x + 10$.

A combined and shortened form of synthetic division is shown below for binomial divisors of $x^3 - 4x^2 - 7x + 10$. The value of r in $x - r$ is at the left, and beside it is the last line of the synthetic division procedure. The last numeral in each row is the remainder. Notice how this procedure can be used to determine factors of a polynomial.

r	1	−4	−7	10	
1	1	−3	−10	0	*x − 1 is a factor*
2	1	−2	−11	−12	
3	1	−1	−10	−20	
4	1	0	−7	−18	
5	1	1	−2	0	*x − 5 is a factor*
−1	1	−5	−2	12	
−2	1	−6	5	0	*x − (−2) or x + 2 is a factor*

Example

3 Use synthetic division to determine the binomial factors of $x^3 + 2x^2 - 16x - 32$. Test all integral values of r from −4 to 4.

r	1	2	−16	−32	
−4	1	−2	−8	0	*x + 4 is a factor*
−3	1	−1	−13	7	
−2	1	0	−16	0	*x + 2 is a factor*
−1	1	1	−17	−15	
0	1	2	−16	−32	
1	1	3	−13	−45	
2	1	4	−8	−48	
3	1	5	−1	−35	
4	1	6	8	0	*x − 4 is a factor*

Thus, $x + 4$, $x + 2$, and $x - 4$ are binomial factors of $x^3 + 2x^2 - 16x - 32$.

Exploratory Exercises

For each synthetic division, state the divisor, dividend, quotient, and remainder.

1. $\underline{2}\,\rfloor$ 3   0 −5   10
          6 12 14
       3   6   7 $\rfloor$ 24

2. $\underline{-3}\,\rfloor$ 1   3 −4   1
          −3   0 12
       1   0 −4 $\rfloor$ 13

3. $\underline{-3}\,\rfloor$ 1   0 −11 10
          −3   9   6
       1 −3   2 $\rfloor$ 16

4. $\underline{2}\,\rfloor$ 1   6   3 −38
          2 16 38
       1   8 19 $\rfloor$ 0

5. $\underline{-1}\,\rfloor$ 2   0 −5   1
          −2   2   3
       2 −2 −3 $\rfloor$ 4

6. $\underline{5}\,\rfloor$ 1   2 −35   4
          5 35   0
       1   7   0 $\rfloor$ 4

7. $\frac{1}{2}\,\rfloor$ 1 $\frac{3}{2}$ 3 −2
          $\frac{1}{2}$ 1   2
       1   2   4 $\rfloor$ 0

8. $-\frac{3}{4}\,\rfloor$ 2 $\frac{1}{2}$ $\frac{1}{4}$ $-\frac{1}{4}$
          $-\frac{3}{2}$ $\frac{3}{4}$ $-\frac{3}{4}$
       2 −1   1 $\rfloor$ −1

9. $-\frac{1}{3}\,\rfloor$ 3   1 −6   3
          −1   0   2
       3   0 −6 $\rfloor$ 5

Written Exercises

Divide using synthetic division.

1. $(x^2 + 8x + 12) \div (x + 2)$

2. $(x^2 - x - 56) \div (x + 7)$

3. $(x^3 + 2x + 3) \div (x - 2)$

4. $(x^2 - x + 4) \div (x - 2)$

5. $(x^4 - 8x^2 + 16) \div (x + 2)$

6. $(x^3 + x^2 - 17x + 15) \div (x + 5)$

7. $(x^3 - x^2 + 2) \div (x + 1)$

8. $(x^4 + x^3 - 1) \div (x - 2)$

9. $(x^3 + 6x^2 + 12x + 12) \div (x + 2)$

10. $(x^3 - 9x^2 + 27x - 28) \div (x - 3)$

11. $(2x^3 - 2x - 3) \div (x - 1)$

12. $(x^2 + 20x + 91) \div (x + 7)$

13. $(8x^2 - 4x + 11) \div (x + 5)$

14. $(3x^4 - 2x^3 + 5x^2 - 4x - 2) \div (x + 1)$

Find the remainder for each of the following. Is the divisor a factor of the polynomial?

15. $(x^3 - 3x + 2) \div (x + 1)$

16. $(x^3 - 30x) \div (x + 5)$

17. $(x^4 - 2x^2 - 8) \div (x - 3)$

18. $(x^4 - 6x^2 + 8) \div (x - \sqrt{2})$

19. $(x^4 - 36) \div (x - \sqrt{6})$

20. $(5x^2 - 2x + 6) \div \left(x - \frac{2}{5}\right)$

21. $(12x^2 + 19x + 4) \div \left(x + \frac{4}{3}\right)$

22. $(x^5 + 32) \div (x + 2)$

23. $(x^5 - 6x^3 + 4x^2 - 3) \div (x - 2)$

24. $(3x^2 - 7x + 5) \div \left(x - \frac{7}{3}\right)$

Challenge Exercises

Divide using synthetic division. *Transform the problem so that the divisor has the form $x - r$.*

25. $(4y^4 - 5y^2 - 8y + 3) \div (2y - 3)$

26. $(6x^3 - 28x^2 + 19x + 3) \div (3x - 2)$

27. $(2b^3 - 3b^2 - 8b + 4) \div (2b + 1)$

28. $(3a^4 - 2a^3 + 5a^2 - 4a - 2) \div (3a + 1)$

29. $(4x^3 - 4x^2 - 17x - 3) \div (4x + 6)$

30. $(10x^3 + x^2 - 7x + 2) \div (5x - 2)$

For the Scholar

In the cube, the diagonal, $\overline{AB}$, has a length of d units. Find the total surface area of the cube in terms of d.

2-4 The Remainder and Factor Theorems

Assume $P(x)$ is any polynomial of degree n in x, and let $(x - r)$ be a divisor. The quotient, $Q(x)$, will be of degree $n - 1$, and the remainder, R, will be a real number since the divisor is of the first degree. The relationship between the dividend, divisor, quotient, and remainder can be expressed as follows.

$$P(x) = (x - r) \cdot Q(x) + R$$

Notice the result when r is substituted for x in the equation.

$$P(r) = (r - r) \cdot Q(x) + R$$
$$P(r) = R$$

The **Remainder Theorem** can be derived from this result.

> If a polynomial $P(x)$ is divided by $x - r$, the remainder is a constant, $P(r)$, and
> $$P(x) = (x - r) \cdot Q(x) + P(r)$$
> where $Q(x)$ is a polynomial with degree one less than the degree of $P(x)$.

The Remainder Theorem

Examples

1 Let $P(x) = x^3 - 7x - 4$. Show that $P(-1)$ is the remainder when $P(x)$ is divided by $x + 1$.

Divide using synthetic division.

$$
\begin{array}{r|rrrr}
-1 & 1 & 0 & -7 & -4 \\
 & & -1 & 1 & 6 \\
\hline
 & 1 & -1 & -6 & \,\vert\; 2
\end{array}
$$
The remainder is 2.

Evaluate $P(-1)$.
$$P(-1) = (-1)^3 - 7(-1) - 4$$
$$= 2 \quad \textit{The result is the same as the remainder.}$$

2 Use the Remainder Theorem to find the remainder when $x^3 + 8x + 1$ is divided by $x - 2$.

Let $f(x) = x^3 + 8x + 1$.
$$f(2) = 2^3 + (8)2 + 1$$
$$= 25$$

The remainder is 25. *Check this by synthetic division.*

If the remainder is zero when $P(x)$ is divided by $x - r$, then $x - r$ is a factor of $P(x)$. A corollary to the Remainder Theorem, the **Factor Theorem,** can be used to identify factors of a polynomial.

	The Factor Theorem
The binomial $x - r$ is a factor of the polynomial $P(x)$ if and only if $P(r) = 0$.	

Examples

3 **Is $x - 5$ a factor of $x^3 - 4x^2 - 7x + 10$?**

$P(5) = 5^3 - 4(5)^2 - 7(5) + 10$
$P(5) = 0$
Since $P(5) = 0$, $x - 5$ is a factor.

For some polynomials, factors can be tested more quickly by using synthetic division instead of substitution.

4 **Is $x + 1$ a factor of $x^3 - 4x^2 - 3x + 12$?**

$P(-1) = (-1)^3 - 4(-1)^2 - 3(-1) + 12$ or 10
Since $P(-1) = 10$, $x + 1$ is not a factor.

A calculator can be used to evaluate polynomials quickly.

Exploratory Exercises

Find the value of $P(3)$ for each of the following polynomials.

1. $P(x) = x^2 - 6x + 9$

2. $P(x) = x^2 + 2x - 15$

3. $P(x) = x^2 - 5x + 6$

4. $P(x) = x^4 + x^2 - 2$

5-8. State whether $x - 3$ is a factor of each polynomial in problems **1-4**. Write *yes* or *no*.

Written Exercises

Use the Remainder Theorem to find the remainder when the given polynomial is divided by the given binomial.

1. $(x^2 - 2) \div (x - 1)$

2. $(x^2 + 1) \div (x + 1)$

3. $(x^2 + x - 1) \div (x - 3)$

4. $(x^2 + 5x - 2) \div (x + 5)$

5. $(x^2 - 2x - 63) \div (x + 7)$

6. $(2x^2 - x + 3) \div (x - 3)$

7. $(x^3 - x + 6) \div (x - 2)$

8. $(2x^3 - 3x^2 + x) \div (x - 1)$

9. $(x^4 + x^2 + 2) \div (x - 3)$

10. $(2x^4 - x^3 + 1) \div (x + 3)$

11-20. State whether the given binomial is a factor of the polynomial for problems **1-10**.

Find values of k so that each remainder is zero.

Pg 63 - 5-12

21. $(x^2 + 8x + k) \div (x - 2)$

22. $(x^3 + 8x^2 + kx + 4) \div (x + 2)$

23. $(x^2 + kx + 3) \div (x - 1)$

24. $(x^3 + 4x^2 - kx + 1) \div (x + 1)$

Challenge Exercises

Find $P(x)$ for each of the following.

25. $P(x) = ax^2 + bx + c$ if $P(3 + 4i) = 0$ and $P(3 - 4i) = 0$

26. $P(x) = ax^3 + bx^2 + cx + d$ if $P(3) = 0$, $P(-2) = 0$, and $P(2) = 0$

For the Scholar

For what integral values of x is $(x + i)^4$ also an integer? (Remember, $i^2 = -1$.)

2-5 The Fundamental Theorem of Algebra

An important theorem concerning roots of polynomial equations is the **Fundamental Theorem of Algebra.**

Every polynomial equation with degree greater than zero has at least one root in the set of complex numbers.	*The Fundamental Theorem of Algebra*

Karl Friedrich Gauss (1777–1855) is credited with the first proof of the Fundamental Theorem.

The Fundamental Theorem of Algebra has an important corollary that can be derived using the Factor Theorem.

Every polynomial $P(x)$ of degree n can be transformed into the product of n linear factors. That is, $P(x)$ of degree n equals $k(x - r_1)(x - r_2)(x - r_3) \cdots (x - r_n)$. Thus a polynomial equation of the form $P(x) = 0$ of degree n has exactly n roots, namely, $r_1, r_2, r_3, \cdots, r_n$.	*Corollary*

For example, the equation $x^3 - 2x^2 - 7x - 4 = 0$ has three roots. Since it can be written as $(x - 4)(x + 1)(x + 1) = 0$, the roots are -1, -1, and 4. Notice in the corollary that r is a root of $P(x) = 0$ if and only if $x - r$ is a factor of $P(x)$.

Examples

1 **Find the roots of $x^3 - 2x^2 - 5x + 6 = 0$.**

First, write the polynomial as a product of linear factors.

Synthetic division can be used to find one or more factors.

$$\begin{array}{r|rrrr} r & 1 & -2 & -5 & 6 \\ \hline 1 & 1 & -1 & -6 & 0 \end{array} \quad \textit{x − 1 is a factor}$$

The product of the remaining factors is $x^2 - x - 6$, which is equal to $(x + 2)(x - 3)$. Thus, $x^3 - 2x^2 - 5x + 6 = (x - 1)(x + 2)(x - 3)$.

Since $(x - 1)(x + 2)(x - 3) = 0$, the roots are 1, -2, and 3.

2 **Find the roots of $2x^3 + 2x^2 + 8x + 8 = 0$.** (Hint: $x + 1$ is one factor of the polynomial.)

$2x^3 + 2x^2 + 8x + 8 = 0$
$2(x^3 + x^2 + 4x + 4) = 0$ *Each term has a factor of 2.*
$2(x + 1)(x^2 + 4) = 0$ *Factor $x + 1$ from the polynomial.*
$2(x + 1)(x - 2i)(x + 2i) = 0$ *The quadratic formula can be used to factor $x^2 + 4$.*

The roots of $2x^3 + 2x^2 + 8x + 8 = 0$ are -1, $2i$, and $-2i$.

The roots of an equation $P(x) = 0$ are not necessarily unique. If $x - r$ occurs as a factor of $P(x)$ more than once, r is a **multiple root** of $P(x) = 0$.

A root which is not a multiple root is called a <u>simple root</u>.

Example

3 The equation $x^5 - 15x^3 - 10x^2 + 60x + 72 = 0$ has multiple roots -2 and 3. Determine how many times each root occurs.

Use synthetic division to write the equation as a product of linear factors.

r	1	0	-15	-10	60	72
3	1	3	-6	-28	-24	0
3	1	6	12	8	0	
-2	1	4	4	0		
-2	1	2	0			
-2	1	0				

Notice the arrangement of successive synthetic divisions.

The equation $x^5 - 15x^3 - 10x^2 + 60x + 72 = 0$ can be written as follows.
$(x - 3)(x - 3)(x + 2)(x + 2)(x + 2) = 0$

Thus, 3 is a double root and -2 is a triple root.

If all the roots of a polynomial equation are known, the simplest form of the equation can be written.

Examples

4 Write the simplest equation with 2 as a simple root and $3i$ as another root. Express the answer as a polynomial equation with integral coefficients.

Since imaginary roots occur in pairs, $-3i$ is also a root. Therefore, $x - 2$, $x - 3i$, and $x + 3i$ are the linear factors of the polynomial. Find the product of the linear factors.

$$(x - 3i)(x + 3i)(x - 2) = (x^2 - 9i^2)(x - 2)$$
$$= (x^2 + 9)(x - 2) \qquad \textit{Remember that } i^2 = -1.$$
$$= x^3 - 2x^2 + 9x - 18$$

Thus, the simplest equation with roots 2, $3i$, and $-3i$ is $x^3 - 2x^2 + 9x - 18 = 0$.

5 Write the simplest equation with roots -4, 2, and i.

The linear factors are $x + 4$, $x - 2$, $x - i$, and $x + i$.
$(x + 4)(x - 2)(x - i)(x + i) = 0$
$(x^2 + 2x - 8)(x^2 + 1) = 0$
$(x^4 + 2x^3 - 7x^2 + 2x - 8) = 0$

The simplest equation with roots -4, 2, and i is $x^4 + 2x^3 - 7x^2 + 2x - 8 = 0$.

Exploratory Exercises

State the number of roots of each equation.

1. $2x^2 - x = 0$

2. $x^2 + 3x + 2 = 0$

3. $2x^2 + 3x - 20 = 0$

4. $5x^2 - 14x + 8 = 0$

5. $6x^2 + 7x - 3 = 0$

6. $x^3 - 3x^2 + x + 1 = 0$

7. $2x^3 - 3x^2 - 11x + 6 = 0$

8. $x^4 - 10x^2 + 9 = 0$

9. $6x^3 + 37x^2 + 32x - 15 = 0$

10. $x^3 - 6x^2 + 11x - 6 = 0$

11. $x^3 + x^2 - 4x - 4 = 0$

12. $x^3 + 2x^2 - x - 2 = 0$

13. $2x^3 - 11x^2 + 12x + 9 = 0$

14. $x^3 - 3x^2 - 53x - 9 = 0$

Written Exercises

Solve each of the following.

1-14. Find the roots of each equation in the exploratory exercises.

Determine how many times 2 is a root of each equation.

15. $x^4 - 5x^2 + 4 = 0$

16. $x^2 + 8x - 20 = 0$

17. $x^4 - 8x^2 + 16 = 0$

18. $x^6 - 9x^4 + 24x^2 - 16 = 0$

Determine how many times -1 is a root of each equation. Then, find all other roots of each equation.

19. $x^4 + 8x^3 + 22x^2 + 24x + 9 = 0$

20. $x^4 - 5x^3 + 9x^2 - 7x + 2 = 0$

21. $x^3 - x^2 - 5x - 3 = 0$

22. $x^3 + 2x^2 - x - 2 = 0$

Write the simplest equation that has the given roots. Express the answer as a polynomial equation with integral coefficients.

23. $2, 1 + i, 1 - i$

24. $1, -1, 1 + i, 1 - i$

25. $1, \dfrac{-1 \pm i\sqrt{3}}{2}$

26. $-2 + i, 1 - 3i$

27. $3, 3, 2i$

28. $2, 2 + 3i, -1 + i$

For the Scholar

In the figure, the area of the small circle is A_1 square units. The area of the shaded region is $(A_2 - A_1)$ square units. As a result, the area of the larger circle is A_2 square units. If A_1, $(A_2 - A_1)$, and A_2 are consecutive terms in an arithmetic sequence, and the radius of the larger circle is 6, find the radius of the smaller circle.

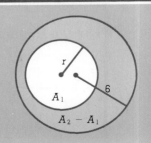

2-6 The Rational Root Theorem

The **Rational Root Theorem** can be used to identify possible roots of polynomial equations which have integral coefficients.

Let $a_0x^n + a_1x^{n-1} + \cdots + a_{n-1}x + a_n = 0$ represent a polynomial equation of degree n with integral coefficients. If a rational number $\frac{p}{q}$, where p and q have no common factors, is a root of the equation, then p is a factor of a_n and q is a factor of a_0.	**Rational Root Theorem**

Example

1 **Find all rational roots of $2x^5 + 3x^4 - 6x^3 + 6x^2 - 8x + 3 = 0$.**

According to the Rational Root Theorem, if $\frac{p}{q}$ is a root of the equation, then p is a factor of 3 and q is a factor of 2.

p is ±1 or ±3
q is ±1 or ±2

The possible rational roots are ±1, ±3, $\pm\frac{1}{2}$, and $\pm\frac{3}{2}$. Each possible root can be tested using substitution or synthetic division.

r	2	3	-6	6	-8	3	
1	2	5	-1	5	-3	0	*1 is a root.*
-1	2	1	-7	13	-21	24	
3	2	9	21	69	199	600	
-3	2	-3	3	-3	1	0	*-3 is a root.*
$\frac{1}{2}$	2	4	-4	4	-6	0	*$\frac{1}{2}$ is a root.*
$-\frac{1}{2}$	2	2	-7	$9\frac{1}{2}$	$-12\frac{3}{4}$	$9\frac{3}{8}$	
$\frac{3}{2}$	2	6	3	$10\frac{1}{2}$	$7\frac{3}{4}$	$14\frac{1}{8}$	
$-\frac{3}{2}$	2	0	3	$1\frac{1}{2}$	$-10\frac{1}{4}$	$18\frac{3}{8}$	

The rational roots of $2x^5 + 3x^4 - 6x^3 + 6x^2 - 8x + 3 = 0$ are 1, -3, and $\frac{1}{2}$.

The Rational Root Theorem can be proven as follows.

First, replace x by the known root $\frac{p}{q}$ where $\frac{p}{q}$ is in simplest form.

p and q are said to be in simplest form if they have no common factors other than 1.

$$a_0\frac{p^n}{q^n} + a_1\frac{p^{n-1}}{q^{n-1}} + \cdots + a_{n-1}\frac{p}{q} + a_n = 0$$

Then, multiply both sides by q^n.

$$a_0 p^n + a_1 p^{n-1}q + \cdots + a_{n-1}pq^{n-1} + a_n q^n = 0$$

Next factor p from the first n terms and subtract $a_n q^n$ from both sides.

$$p(a_0 p^{n-1} + a_1 p^{n-2}q + \cdots + a_{n-1}q^{n-1}) = -a_n q^n$$

Since p is a factor of the left side, it is also a factor of the right side. But p and q have no common factors, so p is a factor of a_n rather than q^n. To prove that q is a factor of a_0, use a similar approach, except factor q from the last n terms. Therefore, p is a factor of a_n and q is a factor of a_0.

The Rational Root Theorem has an important corollary that pertains to integral roots of polynomial equations.

Let $x^n + a_1x^{n-1} + \cdots + a_{n-1}x + a_n = 0$ represent a polynomial equation which has leading coefficient 1, integral coefficients, and $a_n \neq 0$. Then any rational roots of the equation must be integral factors of a_n.

Integral Root Theorem

Example

2 **Find all rational roots of $x^3 - x^2 - x - 2 = 0$.**

The possible rational roots are ± 1 and ± 2.
Test each possible root by substitution or synthetic division.

r	1	-1	-1	-2
1	1	0	-1	-3
-1	1	-2	1	-3
2	1	1	1	0
-2	1	-3	5	-12

The only rational root is 2.

It may not be necessary to test all possible roots. Once a root is found, the polynomial can be factored. In example 2, a root of $x^3 - x^2 - x - 2 = 0$ was found to be 2. Therefore, $x - 2$ is a factor of $x^3 - x^2 - x - 2$ and the quotient is $x^2 + x + 1$. All other roots of $x^3 - x^2 - x - 2 = 0$ must also be roots of $x^2 + x + 1 = 0$. Possible rational roots of $x^2 + x + 1 = 0$ are 1 and -1, which were already tested. Thus, -2 does not need to be tested, and 2 is the only rational root.

Exploratory Exercises

Find all possible rational roots of each equation.

1. $x^3 - 4x^2 + x + 2 = 0$
2. $x^3 + 2x^2 - 5x - 6 = 0$
3. $x^4 + 5x^3 + 5x^2 - 5x - 6 = 0$
4. $x^3 - 5x^2 - 4x + 20 = 0$
5. $x^3 + 2x^2 + x + 18 = 0$
6. $x^4 - 5x^3 + 9x^2 - 7x + 2 = 0$
7. $2x^3 + 3x^2 - 8x + 3 = 0$
8. $6x^3 - 11x^2 - 24x + 9 = 0$
9. $4x^3 + 5x^2 + 2x - 6 = 0$
10. $2x^4 - x^3 - 6x + 3 = 0$
11. $x^3 - x^2 - 40x + 12 = 0$
12. $6x^3 + 4x^2 - 14x + 4 = 0$

Written Exercises

Solve each of the following.

1-12. Find all rational roots of the equations in problems **1-12** in the exploratory exercises.

Find all rational roots of each equation.

13. $x^4 + x^2 - 2 = 0$
14. $3x^4 - 5x^2 + 4 = 0$
15. $x^3 + 5x^2 - 3 = 0$
16. $3x^4 - 2x^2 + 18 = 0$
17. $2x^3 + x^2 + 5x - 3 = 0$
18. $2x^3 - 5x^2 - 28x + 15 = 0$
19. $6x^4 + 35x^3 - x^2 - 7x - 1 = 0$
20. $x^3 - 3x^2 + x - 3 = 0$

For the Scholar

In $\triangle PQR$, $m\angle PQR = 160°$, and $PS = ST = TQ = QR$. Find the measure of $\angle QPR$.

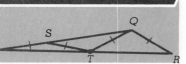

2-7 Locating Zeros of Functions

A **zero** of a function is a value of x for which $f(x) = 0$. A theorem first proved by the French mathematician René Descartes provides information about the existence of zeros of a polynomial function.

A zero of a function $y = f(x)$ is a root of the equation $f(x) = 0$.

Suppose $P(x)$ is a polynomial whose terms are arranged in descending powers of the variable. The number of positive real zeros of $y = P(x)$ is the same as the number of changes in sign of the coefficients of the terms, or is less than this by an even number. The number of negative real zeros is the same as the number of changes in sign of $P(-x)$, or is less than this by an even number.

Descartes' Rule of Signs

Zero coefficients are ignored.

Example

1 State the number of possible positive and negative real zeros for
$P(x) = x^4 - 3x^3 - 2x^2 + 3x + 8.$

There is a sign change from the first to the second term and another from the third to the fourth term. Thus, there must be 2 or 0 positive real zeros.

To determine the number of negative zeros, write an expression for $P(-x)$.
$P(-x) = x^4 + 3x^3 - 2x^2 - 3x + 8$ *Notice that the terms with odd powers change signs.*

There are two sign changes so there must be 2 or 0 negative real zeros.

The graph of a polynomial function $y = f(x)$ is a continuous curve. Thus, if $f(x)$ is positive for some values of x and negative for other values of x, the graph of $y = f(x)$ must cross the x-axis. The point at which the graph crosses the x-axis represents a zero of the function. The figure illustrates the **location principle**.

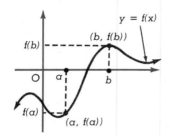

Suppose $y = f(x)$ represents a polynomial function. If a and b are two numbers with $f(a)$ negative and $f(b)$ positive, the function has at least one real zero between a and b.	*The Location Principle*

If $f(a) > 0$ and $f(b) < 0$, then the function also has at least one real zero between a and b.

Example

2 Locate between successive integers the real zeros of $f(x) = x^3 + 2x^2 - 3x - 5.$

Use synthetic division or substitution to evaluate the function for successive integral values of x.

r	1	2	-3	-5
-4	1	-2	5	-25
-3	1	-1	0	-5
-2	1	0	-3	1
-1	1	1	-4	-1
0	1	2	-3	-5
1	1	3	0	-5
2	1	4	5	5

Since -5 and 1 have opposite signs, a zero is located between -3 and -2.

← *What does this indicate?*

← *What does this indicate?*

Changes in sign indicate that zeros are located between -3 and -2, between -2 and -1, and between 1 and 2.

3 Approximate to the nearest tenth the positive real zeros of the function $f(x) = x^4 - 3x^3 - 2x^2 + 3x + 8$. *Use a calculator for easier evaluation.*

By Descartes Rule of Signs, there must be 2 or 0 positive real zeros. Use synthetic division or substitution to evaluate the function for several positive values of x.

r	1	−3	−2	3	8
1	1	−2	−4	−1	7
2	1	−1	−4	−5	−2
3	1	0	−2	−3	−1
4	1	1	2	11	52

By the Location Principle, there is a zero between 1 and 2, and a zero between 3 and 4.

Locate the zero between 1 and 2. Locate the zero between 3 and 4.

x	$f(x)$
2.0	−2
1.9	−1.06
1.8	−0.08
1.7	0.93

The zero is "closer" to 1.8.

$\longleftarrow f(1.75) \approx 0.43$

x	$f(x)$
3.0	−1
3.1	1.06
3.2	3.67

$\longleftarrow f(3.05) \approx 0.04$
The zero is "closer" to 3.0.

The positive real zeros are approximately 1.8 and 3.0.

The function $f(x) = x^3 - 2x^2 + x - 3$ has 3 or 1 positive real zeros. Synthetic division can be used to find several values of $f(x)$, as shown in the table. Notice the table indicates that a zero exists between 2 and 3.

r	1	−2	1	−3
1	1	−1	0	−3
2	1	0	1	−1
3	1	1	4	9
4	1	2	9	33

Instead of testing higher values of x to determine if more positive zeros exist, apply the theorem below to the results shown in the table. The theorem can be used to determine an **upper bound** of the zeros of a function.

Coefficients of zero in the quotient are not considered sign changes.

Suppose c is a positive number and $P(x)$ is divided by $x - c$ (using synthetic division). If the resulting quotient and remainder have no changes in sign, then $P(x)$ has no real zeros greater than c. Thus, c is an upper bound of the zeros of $P(x)$.	**Upper Bound Theorem**

The synthetic divisions shown indicate that 3 and 4 are upper bounds of the zeros of $f(x) = x^3 - 2x^2 + x - 3$. Notice there can be more than one upper bound. Therefore, it is helpful to find the least integral upper bound of the zeros of a function. The least positive integral upper bound of the zeros of $f(x) = x^3 - 2x^2 + x - 3$ is 3.

A least upper bound of the zeros of a function, using the Upper Bound Theorem, is not necessarily the absolute least integral upper bound of the zeros.

Example

4 Using the Upper Bound Theorem, find the least positive integral upper bound of the zeros of the function $f(x) = x^4 - 3x^3 - 2x^2 + 3x - 5$.

r	1	-3	-2	3	-5
1	1	-2	-4	-1	-6
2	1	-1	-4	-5	-15
3	1	0	-2	-3	-14
4	1	1	2	11	39

This row has no changes in sign.

Any value greater than 4 is also an upper bound.

Thus, 4 is the least positive integral upper bound.

A **lower bound** of the zeros of $P(x)$ can be found by determining an upper bound for the zeros of $P(-x)$. Therefore, if c is an upper bound of $P(-x)$, then $-c$ is a lower bound of $P(x)$.

Example

5 Using the Upper Bound Theorem, find the greatest negative integer that is a lower bound of the function $f(x) = x^4 - 3x^3 - 2x^2 + 3x - 5$.

$f(-x) = x^4 + 3x^3 - 2x^2 - 3x - 5$

r	1	3	-2	-3	-5
1	1	4	2	-1	-6
2	1	5	8	13	21

Since this row has no changes in sign, 2 is the least positive integral upper bound of $f(-x)$.

Since 2 is an upper bound of $f(-x)$, -2 is the greatest negative integral lower bound of $f(x)$.

Exploratory Exercises

State the number of possible positive real zeros of each function.

1. $f(x) = x^3 - 4x^2 + x + 2$

2. $f(x) = x^3 + 2x^2 - 5x - 6$

3. $f(x) = x^4 + 5x^3 + 5x^2 - 5x - 6$

4. $f(x) = 2x^3 + 3x^2 - 8x + 3$

5. $f(x) = x^3 - 5x^2 - 4x - 20$

6. $f(x) = 6x^3 - 11x^2 - 24x + 9$

7. $f(x) = x^3 + 2x^2 + x + 18$

8. $f(x) = 4x^3 + 5x^2 + 2x - 6$

9. $f(x) = x^4 - 5x^3 + 9x^2 - 7x + 2$

10. $f(x) = 2x^4 - x^3 - 6x + 3$

11-20. For each function in problems **1-10**, state the number of possible negative real zeros.

Written Exercises

Locate between successive integers the real zeros of each function.

1. $f(x) = x^2 + 3x + 1$

2. $f(x) = x^2 - x - 1$

3. $f(x) = x^2 - 4x - 2$

4. $f(x) = 2x^2 - 5x + 1$

5. $f(x) = x^3 - 2$

6. $f(x) = x^3 - 3x + 1$

7. $f(x) = x^4 - 2x^3 + x - 2$

8. $f(x) = 2x^4 + x^2 - 3x + 5$

Approximate to the nearest tenth the real zeros of each function.

9. $f(x) = x^2 - x - 5$

10. $f(x) = 2x^2 + x - 1$

11. $f(x) = x^2 + 3x + 2$

12. $f(x) = 2x^3 - 4x^2 - 3$

13. $f(x) = x^3 - 4x + 6$

14. $f(x) = 3x^4 + x^2 - 1$

15. $f(x) = 2x^4 - x^3 + x - 2$

16. $f(x) = -x^3 + x^2 - x + 1$

Using the Upper Bound Theorem, find the least positive integral upper bound of the zeros of each function.

17. $f(x) = x^3 + 3x^2 - 5x - 10$

18. $f(x) = x^4 - 8x + 2$

19. $f(x) = 3x^3 - 2x^2 + 5x - 1$

20. $f(x) = x^5 + 5x^4 - 3x^3 + 20x^2 - 15$

21-24. Using the Upper Bound Theorem, find the greatest negative integral lower bound of the zeros of each function in problems **17-20.**

For the Scholar

The numbers 584, 695, and 880 all have something in common. When they are all divided by the same integer greater than 1, they have the same remainder. Find the difference between the common divisor and the remainder.

2-8 Tangent to a Curve

A **tangent** is a straight line that touches a curve at exactly one point on the curve. The drawing shows two tangents to the graph of $f(x) = x^2$. The slope of a tangent to a curve at a point on the curve can be found.

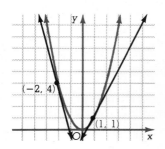

Suppose the graph of an equation $y = f(x)$ has been drawn in the coordinate plane. Let A and B be two points near each other on the continuous curve, and let the coordinates of A be $(x, f(x))$. Suppose the abscissa of B differs from the abscissa of A by a small amount, h. Then, the coordinates of B are $(x + h, f(x + h))$.

Points near each other are said to be in the same neighborhood.

A straight line that passes through A and B is called a **secant line** to the curve. Its slope is $\dfrac{f(x + h) - f(x)}{h}$. *Why?*

Suppose that A remains fixed while B moves along the curve toward A. Then, the value of h will become smaller, approaching zero. Thus, h can be considered as a variable that approaches zero as B approaches A. If B is made to coincide with A, then the secant line becomes a tangent to the curve at point A.

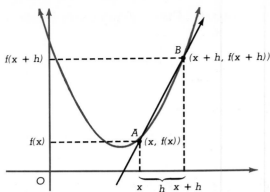

Notice $\dfrac{f(x + h) - f(x)}{h}$ is undefined for $h = 0$. Therefore, in order to evaluate the slope of the tangent, the slope must be defined in a special way. The slope can be defined by examining a function to which it is equal.

Consider the slope of the tangent to the graph of $y = 2x^2 - 3x + 1$ at the point $(2, 3)$ on the curve. The slope of the secant through two general points $A(x, f(x))$ and $B(x + h, f(x + h))$ is equal to $\dfrac{f(x + h) - f(x)}{h}$. An expression for the slope of the secant to the graph of $y = 2x^2 - 3x + 1$ can be found as follows.

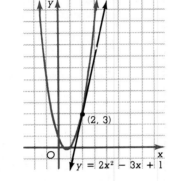

$$f(x + h) = 2(x + h)^2 - 3(x + h) + 1$$
or
$$
\begin{array}{rcl}
f(x + h) &=& 2x^2 + 4xh + 2h^2 - 3x - 3h + 1 \\
f(x) &=& 2x^2 \qquad\qquad\quad\; - 3x \qquad\;\; + 1 \\
\hline
f(x + h) - f(x) &=& \qquad\; 4xh + 2h^2 \qquad\; - 3h
\end{array}
$$

$$\frac{f(x + h) - f(x)}{h} = \frac{4xh + 2h^2 - 3h}{h} = 4x + 2h - 3$$

An expression for the slope of the secant is $4x + 2h - 3$. The slope of the secant through specific points can be found by substituting values for x and h.

When $x = 2$ and $h = 1$, the slope of the secant is $4(2) + 2(1) - 3 = 7$.

When $x = 2$ and $h = \dfrac{1}{2}$, the slope of the secant is $4(2) + 2\left(\dfrac{1}{2}\right) - 3 = 6$.

When $x = 2$ and $h = \dfrac{1}{4}$, the slope of the secant is $4(2) + 2\left(\dfrac{1}{4}\right) - 3 = 5\dfrac{1}{2}$.

As h approaches zero, the slope of the secant becomes very close to the slope of the tangent. The middle term of $4x + 2h - 3$ vanishes as h approaches zero. Thus, an expression for the slope of the tangent is $4x - 3$.

The slope of the tangent to $y = 2x^2 - 3x + 1$ at point $(2, 3)$ can be found by replacing x by 2 in the expression $4x - 3$. Thus, the slope of the tangent at the point $(2, 3)$ is equal to $4(2) - 3$, or 5.

The symbol $f'(x)$ is often used to denote the slope of the tangent. It is defined as follows.

$$f'(x) = \lim_{h \to 0} \frac{f(x + h) - f(x)}{h} \qquad \text{\textit{$f'(x)$ is read "f prime of x."}}$$

The symbol $\lim_{h \to 0}$ means the limiting value of the function as the value of h approaches zero. The function $f'(x)$ is called the **derivative** of $f(x)$.

Example

1 **Find the slope of the tangent to the graph of $y = 5x^3 - 2x^2 + x - 1$ at the point on the curve where the abscissa is -1.**

Let $(x, f(x))$ and $(x + h, f(x + h))$ be two points on the curve.

First, write an expression for $f(x + h) - f(x)$.

$$f(x + h) = 5(x + h)^3 - 2(x + h)^2 + (x + h) - 1$$

or

$$f(x + h) = 5x^3 + 15x^2h + 15xh^2 + 5h^3 - 2x^2 - 4xh - 2h^2 + x + h - 1$$
$$\underline{f(x) = 5x^3 \qquad\qquad\qquad\qquad - 2x^2 \qquad\qquad\qquad + x \qquad - 1}$$
$$f(x + h) - f(x) = \qquad 15x^2h + 15xh^2 + 5h^3 \qquad -4xh - 2h^2 \qquad + h$$

Next, divide the expression by h to obtain an expression for the slope of the secant.

$$\frac{f(x + h) - f(x)}{h} = 15x^2 + 15xh + 5h^2 - 4x - 2h + 1$$

Then, write an expression for the slope when $h = 0$.

$$\lim_{h \to 0} \frac{f(x + h) - f(x)}{h} = 15x^2 - 4x + 1$$

$$f'(x) = 15x^2 - 4x + 1$$

Finally, substitute -1 for x in the equation for $f'(x)$.
$$f'(-1) = 15(-1)^2 - 4(-1) + 1 = 20$$

The slope of the tangent at the point $(-1, -9)$ is 20. \qquad *$f(-1) = -9$*

If coordinates of one point on a curve are known, and the slope of the tangent to the curve at the point is known, the equation for the tangent can be written in point-slope form.

Example

2 Find the equation of the tangent to the graph of $y = 2x^3 - x^2 + 3x - 1$ at the point $(-2, -27)$.

First, write an expression for the slope of the tangent.

$$f(x + h) = 2(x + h)^3 - (x + h)^2 + 3(x + h) - 1$$

or

$$f(x + h) = 2x^3 + 6x^2h + 6xh^2 + 2h^3 - x^2 - 2xh - h^2 + 3x + 3h - 1$$
$$\underline{f(x) = 2x^3 \qquad\qquad\qquad\qquad - x^2 \qquad\qquad\quad + 3x \qquad\quad - 1}$$
$$f(x + h) - f(x) = \qquad\quad 6x^2h + 6xh^2 + 2h^3 \quad\; - 2xh - h^2 \qquad + 3h$$

$$\frac{f(x + h) - f(x)}{h} = 6x^2 + 6xh + 2h^2 - 2x - h + 3$$

$$f'(x) = \lim_{h \to 0} \frac{f(x + h) - f(x)}{h} = 6x^2 - 2x + 3$$

Next, evaluate $f'(-2)$.
$$f'(-2) = 6(-2)^2 - 2(-2) + 3 = 31$$

Then, write an equation in point-slope form for the line through $(-2, -27)$ which has slope 31.

$$y - (-27) = 31(x - (-2)) \qquad \textit{The point-slope form is } y - y_1 = m(x - x_1).$$

In slope-intercept form, the equation is $y = 31x + 35$.

Exploratory Exercises

For each given function, write an expression for $\dfrac{f(x + h) - f(x)}{h}$.

1. $f(x) = x^2$
2. $f(x) = x^2 + 1$
3. $f(x) = 2x^2$
4. $f(x) = \frac{1}{2}x^2$
5. $f(x) = -2x^2 + 3x + 1$
6. $f(x) = 0.5x^2 - 0.4x - 0.3$

7-12. For each function in problems **1-6**, write an expression for $f'(x)$.

Written Exercises

Find the slope of the tangent to the graph of the given function at the indicated point.

1. $y = x^2$, $(1, 1)$
2. $y = x^2$, $(0, 0)$
3. $y = x^2 + 1$, $(2, 5)$
4. $y = x^2 + 1$, $(0, 1)$
5. $y = 2x^2$, $(2, 8)$
6. $y = 2x^2$, $(-1, 2)$
7. $y = \frac{1}{2}x^2$, $(2, 2)$
8. $y = \frac{1}{2}x^2$, $\left(-3, 4\frac{1}{2}\right)$
9. $y = -2x^2 + 3x + 1$, $(0, 1)$
10. $y = -2x^2 + 3x + 1$, $(1, 2)$

11. $y = 0.5x^2 - 0.4x - 0.3, (1, -0.2)$

12. $y = 0.5x^2 - 0.4x - 0.3, (-1, 0.6)$

13. $y = x^2 + \frac{1}{6}x - \frac{1}{3}, \left(\frac{1}{2}, 0\right)$

14. $y = \frac{x^3 - 1}{8}, \left(2, \frac{7}{8}\right)$

15. $y = 2x^2 - 3x - 4$ at the point with abscissa -2.

16. $y = \frac{1}{2}x^2 + \frac{1}{4}x + \frac{1}{8}$ at the point with abscissa $\frac{1}{2}$.

Find the equation of the tangent to the graph of the given function at the indicated point.

17. $y = x^2, (2, 4)$

18. $y = x^2 - 3, (3, 6)$

19. $y = 2x^2 - 3x, (-1, 5)$

20. $y = x^2 - 3x + 2, (1, 0)$

21. $y = x^2 - 5x + 6, \left(2\frac{1}{2}, -\frac{1}{4}\right)$

22. $y = -x^2 - x + 2, \left(\frac{1}{2}, 1\frac{1}{4}\right)$

23. $y = -3x^2 + 5, (-2, -7)$

24. $y = \frac{1}{2}x^2 + x - 1, (-4, 3)$

For the Scholar

What is the ratio of the area of square *DGFH* to the area of the square *ABCD*?

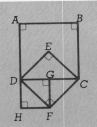

2-9 Critical Points

When $f'(x) = 0$, the tangent to the curve at (x, y) is parallel to the x-axis. There are three possible forms a curve may have around a point for which $f'(x) = 0$. Points for which the derivative equals zero are called **critical points**. In the figures, P represents a **maximum point**, Q represents a **minimum point,** and R represents a **point of inflection.**

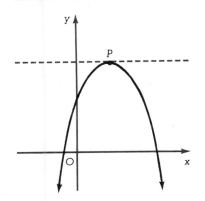

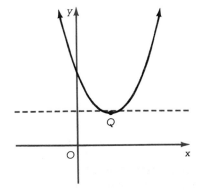

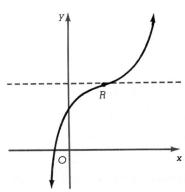

Sometimes a function has a **relative maximum** or a **relative minimum.** Point A represents a relative maximum. The ordinate of A is *not* the greatest value of the function, although it represents a maximum for a small interval. Likewise, point B represents a relative minimum.

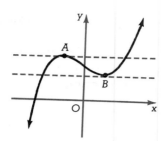

Example

1 **The derivative of the function $f(x) = 3x^3 - 9x + 5$ is given by $f'(x) = 9x^2 - 9$. Find the critical points of the graph of $f(x)$.**

First, set $f'(x) = 0$ and solve for x.
$$9x^2 - 9 = 0$$
$$9(x^2 - 1) = 0$$
$$9(x - 1)(x + 1) = 0$$
$$x = 1 \text{ or } -1$$

Next, evaluate $f(x)$ for $x = 1$ or -1.
$$f(1) = 3(1)^3 - 9(1) + 5 = -1$$
$$f(-1) = 3(-1)^3 - 9(-1) + 5 = 11$$

The critical points are $(1, -1)$ and $(-1, 11)$.

Suppose $(a, f(a))$ is a critical point. It is possible to determine if the critical point represents a maximum, a minimum, or a point of inflection by evaluating $f(a + h)$ and $f(a - h)$ for small values of h. The critical point represents a maximum if $f(a + h)$ and $f(a - h)$ are both less than $f(a)$, for small values of h. The critical point represents a minimum if $f(a + h)$ and $f(a - h)$ are both greater than $f(a)$. If one is greater than $f(a)$ and the other is less than $f(a)$, the critical point represents a point of inflection.

For a maximum or minimum, the slope of the tangent is positive on one side of the critical point and negative on the other side.

For a point of inflection, the slopes are either both positive or both negative on either side of the critical point.

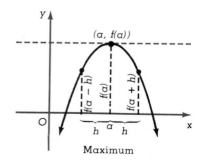

Maximum

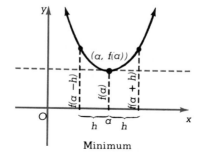

Minimum

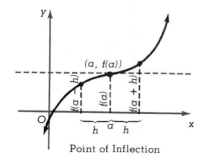

Point of Inflection

2 **The point (0, 1) is a critical point of the function $f(x) = x^3 - x^2 + 1$. Determine whether the point (0, 1) represents a maximum, a minimum, or a point of inflection.**

$f(0) = 1$

$f(0.1) = (0.1)^3 - (0.1)^2 + 1 = 0.991$ *Use a calculator for easier evaluation.*

$f(-0.1) = (-0.1)^3 - (-0.1)^2 + 1 = 0.989$

Since $f(0.1)$ and $f(-0.1)$ are both less than $f(0)$, the point (0, 1) represents a maximum value for the function.   *This is a relative maximum.*

3 **Find the critical points of the graph of $f(x) = x^2 + 4x - 12$. Then, determine whether each point represents a maximum, a minimum, or a point of inflection.**

First, find $f'(x)$.

$f(x + h) - f(x) = (x + h)^2 + 4(x + h) - 12 - (x^2 + 4x - 12)$

$\qquad\qquad\qquad = 2xh + h^2 + 4h$

$\dfrac{f(x + h) - f(x)}{h} = 2x + h + 4$

$f'(x) = 2x + 4$

Then set $f'(x) = 0$ to find the abscissas of the critical points.

$2x + 4 = 0$

$\qquad x = -2$

Find values of $f(x)$ at and near the critical point.

$f(-1.9) = -15.99$

$f(-2) = -16$ *The point (-2, -16) is a critical point.*

$f(-2.1) = -15.99$

Since $f(-1.9)$ and $f(-2.1)$ are both greater than $f(-2)$, the point (-2, -16) represents a minimum for the function.

Critical points can be used when graphing equations. If the zeros and the critical points of a polynomial function are graphed, the general shape of the graph can usually be determined.

Example

4 **The zeros of the function $f(x) = x^3 + x^2 - 6x$ occur at 2, -3, and 0. The critical points are approximately (-1.8, 8.2) and (1.1, -4.1). Graph the function.**
Graph the zeros on the x-axis.
Then graph the critical points.
Connect the points with a smooth curve.

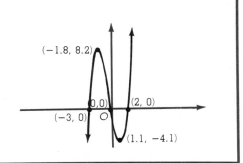

Exploratory Exercises

Find the critical points of each function. The derivative of each function is given.

1. $f(x) = 3x^2 - 6x - 1, f'(x) = 6x - 6$

2. $f(x) = x^2 - 8x + 10, f'(x) = 2x - 8$

3. $f(x) = 2x^2 + 6x - 5, f'(x) = 4x + 6$

4. $f(x) = x - x^2, f'(x) = 1 - 2x$

5. $f(x) = \frac{1}{3}x^3 - 9x - 1, f'(x) = x^2 - 9$

6. $f(x) = 3x^3 - \frac{9}{2}x^2 - 4, f'(x) = 9x^2 - 9x$

Written Exercises

Find the critical points of the graph of each function. Then, determine whether each point represents a maximum, a minimum, or a point of inflection.

1. $y = x^2 - x - 6$

2. $y = 8 - 2x - x^2$

3. $y = x^2 + 2x - 15$

4. $y = 2x^2 - 3x + 1$

5. $y = x^3 - x^2 + 3$

6. $y = x^4 - 8x^2 + 16$

7. $y = x^3$

8. $y = x^5 - 27$

9-16. Locate the zeros of each function in problems **1-8**. Then, graph each function.

Graph each function.

17. $y = x^3 - 2x^2 - 5x + 6$

18. $y = x^3 + x$

19. $y = x^4 - 2x^2 - 8$

20. $y = x^3 - 7x - 6$

21. $y = x^4 + x^2$

22. $y = \sqrt{2}x^2 - 1$

Answer each of the following.

23. A company manufactures an open fruit bin. If the bin must be 6 feet high and have a volume of 294 cubic units, what are the dimensions of a rectangular base that will minimize the total surface area of each bin?

24. An open fruit bin has a height of 6 feet and a volume of 192 cubic feet. The material for the front and back costs $5 per square foot, the material for the sides costs $10 per square foot, and the material for the bottom costs $20 per square foot. What are the dimensions of a rectangular base that will minimize the total cost?

25. The director of a zoo needs to enclose a rectangular area of 20,000 square feet into three cages of equal size. Find the dimensions of rectangular cages that will minimize the length of the fence used.

26. A rectangular field of 125,000 square feet needs to be enclosed. If the fence along the sides costs $10 per foot and the fence along the front and back costs $20 per foot, what are the dimensions of the field that minimize the fence cost?

27. If Mrs. Huffman harvests her apple crop now, she will pick on the average 120 pounds per tree and will get $0.48 per pound for the apples. However, she knows if she waits her yield will increase by about 10 pounds a week and her price will decrease by $0.03 per pound. How many weeks should Mrs. Huffman wait in order to maximize her profit? What is the maximum profit?

For the Scholar

What is the smallest prime number dividing the sum $7^{11} + 11^{13}$?

Suppose it is necessary to write an equation with roots which are 2 less than those of $x^2 - 8x + 15 = 0$. One method is to find the roots of the given equation, subtract 2 from each root, and then form the new equation by multiplying the appropriate linear factors together. For example, the roots of $x^2 - 8x + 15 = 0$ are 3 and 5. The roots of the desired equation are 1 and 3. By multiplying $x - 1$ by $x - 3$, the desired equation, $x^2 - 4x + 3 = 0$, is obtained.

Another method is sometimes used, especially when the roots of an equation are difficult to identify. Suppose each root of $P(x) = 0$ is to be decreased by a constant, h. By successively dividing $P(x)$ and the resulting quotients by $x - h$, the coefficients of the desired equation can be obtained. Study the following example.

Example **Write the equation which has roots that are 2 less than those of $2x^3 - x^2 - 13x - 6 = 0$.**

Divide $2x^3 - x^2 - 13x - 6$ by $x - 2$.

Then divide the quotient by $x - 2$.

Divide until the quotient is a constant.

$$
\begin{array}{r|rrrr}
 & 2 & -1 & -13 & -6 \\
\hline
2 & 2 & 3 & -7 & (-20) \\
2 & 2 & 7 & (7) & \\
2 & 2 & (11) & & \\
\end{array}
$$

$$2x^3 + 11x^2 + 7x - 20$$

The final quotient and the remainders in parentheses are the coefficients of the desired equation.

The equation is $2x^3 + 11x^2 + 7x - 20 = 0$.

Verify that the roots of the given equation are 3, -2, and $-\dfrac{1}{2}$, and the roots of the derived equation are 1, -4, and $-2\dfrac{1}{2}$.

Exercises   Solve each problem.

1. Write an equation with real roots that are one less than the roots of
$$x^3 - 4x^2 + x - 2 = 0.$$

2. Write an equation with real roots that are two less than the roots of
$$x^3 + 2x^2 - 5x - 6 = 0.$$

3. Write an equation with real roots that are one more than the roots of
$$x^4 - 5x^3 + 9x^2 - 7x + 2 = 0.$$

4. Write an equation with real roots that are two more than the roots of
$$3x^4 - 7x^3 - 23x^2 + 7x + 20 = 0.$$

5. Write an equation with real roots that are two less than the roots of
$$x^4 + 5x^3 - 25x^2 - 5x + 24 = 0.$$

6. Write an equation with real roots that are one more than the roots of
$$14x^3 + 5x^2 - 71x + 10 = 0.$$

1. The degree of a polynomial in one variable is the greatest exponent of its variable. (31)

2. If $P(x)$ represents a polynomial, then $P(x) = 0$ is a polynomial equation. A root of the equation is a value of x for which the value of $P(x)$ is zero. (31)

3. To solve an equation means to find the roots of the equation. (32)

4. Any quadratic equation can be written in the form $ax^2 + bx + c = 0$, where a, b, and c are real numbers and $a \neq 0$. (33)

5. Quadratic Formula: The roots of a quadratic equation of the form $ax^2 + bx + c = 0$ with $a \neq 0$ are given by the following formula.

$$x = \frac{-b \pm \sqrt{b^2 - 4ac}}{2a} \qquad (34)$$

6. Complex Conjugates Theorem: Suppose a and b are real numbers with $b \neq 0$. Then, if $a + bi$ is a root of a polynomial equation, $a - bi$ is also a root of the equation. (35)

7. The Remainder Theorem: If a polynomial $P(x)$ is divided by $x - r$, the remainder is a constant, $P(r)$, and $P(x) = (x - r) \cdot Q(x) + P(r)$, where $Q(x)$ is a polynomial with degree one less than the degree of $P(x)$. (40)

8. The Factor Theorem: The binomial $x - r$ is a factor of the polynomial $P(x)$ if and only if $P(r) = 0$. (41)

9. The Fundamental Theorem of Algebra: Every polynomial with degree greater than zero has at least one root in the set of complex numbers. (42)

10. Corollary: Every polynomial $P(x)$ of degree n can be transformed into the product of n linear factors. That is, $P(x)$ of degree n equals $k(x - r_1)(x - r_2)(x - r_3) \cdots (x - r_n)$. Thus a polynomial equation of the form $P(x) = 0$ of degree n has exactly n roots, namely, $r_1, r_2, r_3, \cdots, r_n$. (42)

11. Rational Root Theorem: Let $a_0 x^n + a_1 x^{n-1} + \cdots + a_{n-1} x + a_n = 0$ represent a polynomial equation of degree n with integral coefficients. If a rational number $\frac{p}{q}$, where p and q have no common factors, is a root of the equation, then p is a factor of a_n and q is a factor of a_0. (45)

12. Integral Root Theorem: Let $x^n + a_1 x^{n-1} + \cdots + a_{n-1} x + a_n = 0$ represent a polynomial equation which has leading coefficient 1, integral coefficients, and $a_n \neq 0$. Then any rational roots of the equation must be integral factors of a_n. (46)

13. Descartes Rule of Signs: Suppose $P(x)$ is a polynomial whose terms are arranged in descending powers of the variable. The number of positive real zeros of $y = P(x)$ is the same as the number of changes in sign of the coefficients of the terms, or is less than this by an even number. The number of negative real zeros is the same as the number of changes in sign of $P(-x)$, or is less than this by an even number.   (47)

14. The Location Principle: Suppose $y = f(x)$ represents a polynomial function. If a and b are two numbers with $f(a)$ negative and $f(b)$ positive, the function has at least one real zero between a and b.   (48)

15. Upper Bound Theorem: Suppose c is a positive number and $P(x)$ is divided by $x - c$ (using synthetic division). If the resulting quotient and remainder have no changes in sign, then $P(x)$ has no real zeros greater than c. Thus, c is an upper bound of the zeros of $P(x)$.   (49)

16. The derivative of $f(x)$ is defined as follows.

$$f'(x) = \lim_{h \to 0} \frac{f(x + h) - f(x)}{h} \qquad (53)$$

17. Points for which the derivative equals zero are called critical points. A critical point $(a, f(a))$ represents a maximum if $f(a + h)$ and $f(a - h)$ are both less than $f(a)$, for small values of h. The critical point is a minimum if $f(a + h)$ and $f(a - h)$ are both greater than $f(a)$. If one is greater and the other is less, the critical point is a point of inflection.   (56)

Chapter Review

Solve each equation.   (2-1)

1. $(3x - 2)(x - 4)(x - 6) = 0$

2. $x^2 - 40x + 400 = 0$

Solve each equation by completing the square.   (2-2)

3. $2x^2 + 7x - 4 = 0$

4. $x^2 - 7x - 1 = 0$

Solve each equation by using the quadratic formula.   (2-2)

5. $3x^2 + 5x - 3 = 0$

6. $4x^2 + 5x - 6 = 0$

Divide using synthetic division. Write the quotient and remainder.   (2-3)

7. $(5x^3 - 4x^2 - 8x + 2) \div (x - 2)$

8. $(x^4 + 5x^3 - 18x - 8) \div (x + 4)$

Use the Remainder Theorem to find the remainder when the given polynomial is divided by the given binomial. (2-4)

9. $(x^3 - 5x + 8) \div (x + 3)$

10. $(3x^3 - 5x^2 + 4) \div (x - 1)$

Find all roots of the following equations. (2-5)

11. $x^3 + 4x^2 - 3x - 18 = 0$

12. $x^4 - 2x^3 + 13x^2 - 32x - 48 = 0$

Find all rational roots of each equation. (2-6)

13. $8x^2 - 6x + 1 = 0$

14. $x^4 + x^3 - 11x^2 + x - 12 = 0$

State the number of possible positive real zeros of each function. (2-7)

15. $y = 4x^2 - 3x + 2$

16. $y = x^5 + 3x^4 - x^3 - 2x - 5$

17-18. For each function in problems **15-16,** state the number of possible negative real zeros.

Using the Upper Bound Theorem, find the least positive integral upper bound of the zeros of each function. (2-7)

19. $f(x) = x^4 + x^2 - 6$

20. $f(x) = x^4 - x^3 - 4x^2 + 8x - 4$

21-22. Using the Upper Bound Theorem, find the greatest negative integral lower bound of the zeros of each function in problems **19-20.**

23-24. Approximate to the nearest tenth the real zeros of each function in problems **19-20.**

Find the slope of the tangent to the graph of the given function at the indicated point. (2-8)

25. $y = 3x^2 + 4x - 2$, $(1, 5)$

26. $y = 2x^2 - 9x + 5$, $(2, -3)$

27-28. For each function and point given in problems **25-26,** find the equation of the tangent to the graph of the given function at the indicated point.

Find the critical points of each function. Then, determine whether each point represents a maximum, a minimum, or a point of inflection. (2-9)

29. $f(x) = 4 + x - x^2$

30. $f(x) = x^3 - 6x^2 + 9x$

31-32. Find the zeros of each function in problems **29-30.** Round values to the nearest tenth. Then, graph each function.

Chapter Test

Solve each equation.

1. $x^2 - 5x + 4 = 0$
2. $(3x - 5)(x - 3)(2x + 5) = 0$
3. $3x^2 + 4x - 15 = 0$
4. $6x^2 + 7x - 3 = 0$
5. $6m^2 - 2m + 1 = 0$
6. $2x^2 - 5x + 4 = 0$

Divide using synthetic division. Write the quotient and remainder.

7. $(2x^3 - x^2 - 10x + 8) \div (x - 2)$
8. $(x^4 + x^2 - 5) \div (x + 3)$

Use the Remainder Theorem to find the remainder when the given polynomial is divided by the given binomial.

9. $(x^3 - 5x + 1) \div (x + 1)$
10. $(2x^3 - 3x^2 - 8x + 4) \div (x + 2)$

Find all roots of each equation.

11. $x^3 - 2x^2 - 2x - 3 = 0$
12. $x^3 + 2x^2 - 1 = 0$

Find all rational roots of each equation.

13. $x^3 - 2x^2 - 13x - 10 = 0$
14. $x^4 - 13x^2 + 36 = 0$
15. $2x^2 - 7x + 3 = 0$
16. $x^4 - 6x^2 + 8 = 0$

State the number of possible positive real zeros of each function.

17. $y = x^7 - x^3 + 2x - 1$
18. $y = 4x^4 - 3x^3 + 2x^2 - x + 1$

19-20. For each function in problems **17-18**, state the number of possible negative real zeros.

Using the Upper Bound Theorem, find the least positive integral upper bound and the greatest negative integral lower bound of the zeros of each function.

21. $f(x) = x^3 + 3x^2 - 5x - 10$
22. $f(x) = x^4 - 8x + 2$
23. $f(x) = x^3 - 4x + 6$
24. $f(x) = x^5 + 5x^4 - 3x^3 + 20x^2 - 15$

Approximate to the nearest tenth the real zeros of each function.

25. $y = x^2 - 3x - 3$
26. $y = x^3 - x + 1$

For each given function, write an expression for $f'(x)$.

27. $f(x) = 3x - 4$
28. $f(x) = 2x^2 + 3x - 1$
29. $f(x) = 2x^3 - x$
30. $f(x) = x^4 + 7$

Find the slope of the tangent to the graph of the given function at the indicated point.

31. $y = x^2 - 4x + 1$, $(1, -2)$
32. $y = 3x^2 - 2x + 1$, $(2, 9)$

33-34. For each function and point given in problems **31-32**, find the equation of the tangent to the graph of the given function at the indicated point.

Find the critical points of each function. Then, determine whether each point represents a maximum, a minimum, or a point of inflection.

35. $y = x^2 - 8x + 4$
36. $y = 3 - 2x - x^2$

37-38. Find the zeros of each function in problems **35-36**. Round the values to the nearest tenth, then graph each function.

CHAPTER 3

Matrices and Vectors

Matrices and vectors have many scientific and business applications. Matrices are useful in the airline industry to organize and store the vast amounts of flight data available. Vectors can be used to determine the velocity and direction of an airplane.

3-1 Matrices and Determinants

A **matrix** is any rectangular array of terms called **elements.** The elements of a matrix are arranged in rows and columns and are usually enclosed by brackets. A matrix with m rows and n columns is an **$m \times n$ matrix** (read "m by n"). The **dimensions** of the matrix are m and n.

$$\begin{bmatrix} 5 & -7 \\ 10 & 2 \end{bmatrix} \qquad \begin{bmatrix} 3 & \frac{1}{2} & 5 & 25 \\ -8 & 2 & 14 & -4 \end{bmatrix} \qquad \begin{bmatrix} 1 & -4 \\ 0 & 8 \\ 9 & 6 \end{bmatrix}$$

Large parentheses are sometimes used instead of brackets.

2 × 2 Matrix   **2 × 4 Matrix**   **3 × 2 Matrix**

A **square matrix** has the same number of rows as columns. A matrix of **nth order** has n rows and n columns.

Each square matrix has a **determinant.** The determinant of $\begin{bmatrix} 8 & 7 \\ 4 & 5 \end{bmatrix}$ is denoted by $\begin{vmatrix} 8 & 7 \\ 4 & 5 \end{vmatrix}$ or $\det \begin{bmatrix} 8 & 7 \\ 4 & 5 \end{bmatrix}$. The value of a second order determinant is defined as follows.

The term determinant is often used to mean the value of the determinant.

The value of $\det \begin{bmatrix} a_1 & b_1 \\ a_2 & b_2 \end{bmatrix}$ or $\begin{vmatrix} a_1 & b_1 \\ a_2 & b_2 \end{vmatrix} = a_1 b_2 - a_2 b_1.$

The Value of a Second Order Determinant

Example

1 Find the value of $\begin{vmatrix} 7 & 9 \\ 3 & 6 \end{vmatrix}$.

$$\begin{vmatrix} 7 & 9 \\ 3 & 6 \end{vmatrix} = 7(6) - 3(9)$$
$$= 42 - 27$$
$$= 15$$

The minor of an element of an nth order matrix is a determinant of $(n - 1)$th order. This minor can be found by deleting the row and column containing the element.

$$\begin{vmatrix} a_1 & b_1 & c_1 \\ a_2 & b_2 & c_2 \\ a_3 & b_3 & c_3 \end{vmatrix} \qquad \textit{The minor of } a_1 \textit{ is } \begin{vmatrix} b_2 & c_2 \\ b_3 & c_3 \end{vmatrix}.$$

To evaluate a determinant of the nth order, expand the determinant by minors, using the elements in the first row. Find the determinants of the minors, then add. The signs of the terms alternate, with the first term being positive.

$$\begin{vmatrix} a_1 & b_1 & c_1 \\ a_2 & b_2 & c_2 \\ a_3 & b_3 & c_3 \end{vmatrix} = a_1 \begin{vmatrix} b_2 & c_2 \\ b_3 & c_3 \end{vmatrix} - b_1 \begin{vmatrix} a_2 & c_2 \\ a_3 & c_3 \end{vmatrix} + c_1 \begin{vmatrix} a_2 & b_2 \\ a_3 & b_3 \end{vmatrix}$$

Expansion of a Third Order Determinant

Example

2 Find the value of $\begin{vmatrix} 8 & 9 & 3 \\ 3 & 5 & 7 \\ -1 & 2 & 4 \end{vmatrix}$.

$$\begin{vmatrix} 8 & 9 & 3 \\ 3 & 5 & 7 \\ -1 & 2 & 4 \end{vmatrix} = 8 \begin{vmatrix} 5 & 7 \\ 2 & 4 \end{vmatrix} - 9 \begin{vmatrix} 3 & 7 \\ -1 & 4 \end{vmatrix} + 3 \begin{vmatrix} 3 & 5 \\ -1 & 2 \end{vmatrix}$$

$$= \quad 8(6) \quad - \quad 9(19) \quad + \quad 3(11)$$

$$= -90$$

Determinants can be used to solve systems of linear equations. If a system of two equations in two variables is given, the solution set, if it exists as a single ordered pair, can be found by using Cramer's rule.

The solution to $\begin{matrix} a_1 x + b_1 y = c_1 \\ a_2 x + b_2 y = c_2 \end{matrix}$ is (x, y) where

$$x = \frac{\begin{vmatrix} c_1 & b_1 \\ c_2 & b_2 \end{vmatrix}}{\begin{vmatrix} a_1 & b_1 \\ a_2 & b_2 \end{vmatrix}} \text{ and } y = \frac{\begin{vmatrix} a_1 & c_1 \\ a_2 & c_2 \end{vmatrix}}{\begin{vmatrix} a_1 & b_1 \\ a_2 & b_2 \end{vmatrix}} \text{ and } \begin{vmatrix} a_1 & b_1 \\ a_2 & b_2 \end{vmatrix} \neq 0.$$

Cramer's Rule
Notice the positions of the constants, c_1 and c_2, in the top determinants.

Example

3 Use Cramer's rule to solve the following system of equations.

$$2x - 3y = 12$$
$$5x + 9y = 63$$

$$x = \frac{\begin{vmatrix} 12 & -3 \\ 63 & 9 \end{vmatrix}}{\begin{vmatrix} 2 & -3 \\ 5 & 9 \end{vmatrix}} \qquad y = \frac{\begin{vmatrix} 2 & 12 \\ 5 & 63 \end{vmatrix}}{\begin{vmatrix} 2 & -3 \\ 5 & 9 \end{vmatrix}}$$

$$= \frac{297}{33} \qquad\qquad = \frac{66}{33}$$

$$= 9 \qquad\qquad = 2$$

The solution is $(9, 2)$.

Cramer's rule can be extended to solve a system of n linear equations in n variables. The determinant in each denominator contains the coefficients of the variables arranged in order and is called the **determinant of the system.** If the determinant of the system is equal to zero, there is no unique common solution. *Why?*

A matrix which has a non-zero determinant is called a non-singular matrix.

Exploratory Exercises

Find the value of each determinant.

1. $\begin{vmatrix} 3 & -5 \\ 7 & 9 \end{vmatrix}$

2. $\begin{vmatrix} 7 & 16 \\ 3 & 8 \end{vmatrix}$

3. $\begin{vmatrix} -4 & 8 \\ 0 & 2 \end{vmatrix}$

4. $\begin{vmatrix} 10 & 50 \\ -5 & 25 \end{vmatrix}$

5. $\begin{vmatrix} 14 & 21 \\ 26 & 39 \end{vmatrix}$

6. $\begin{vmatrix} 16 & 17 \\ 15 & 16 \end{vmatrix}$

Name the determinants you would use to solve each system by Cramer's rule.

7. $3x + 2y = 5$
$\ 4x - 3y = 1$

8. $2x - 3y = 7$
$\ 3x + y = 16$

9. $2x + y = 6$
$\ 6x - y = 2$

10. $5x - 3y = 7$
$\ 2x + y = 27$

11. $4x + y = 6$
$\ x - 2y = -12$

12. $8x + 12y = 6$
$\ 4x - 3y = 0$

Written Exercises

Find the value of each determinant using expansion by minors.

1. $\begin{vmatrix} 7 & 1 & 6 \\ 3 & -1 & 4 \\ -2 & 3 & 0 \end{vmatrix}$

2. $\begin{vmatrix} 2 & 3 & 4 \\ 5 & 6 & 7 \\ 8 & 9 & 10 \end{vmatrix}$

3. $\begin{vmatrix} 6 & 7 & 4 \\ -2 & -4 & 3 \\ 1 & 1 & 1 \end{vmatrix}$

4. $\begin{vmatrix} 2 & 4 & 6 \\ 1 & 2 & 3 \\ 3 & -1 & 4 \end{vmatrix}$

5. $\begin{vmatrix} 3 & 0 & 2 \\ 0 & -1 & 5 \\ 6 & 7 & 0 \end{vmatrix}$

6. $\begin{vmatrix} 4 & 2 & -3 \\ 5 & 1 & 0 \\ -2 & 1 & 11 \end{vmatrix}$

7-12. Solve each system of equations in exploratory exercises **7-12** using Cramer's rule.

Solve each system of equations using Cramer's rule.

13. $5x - y = 16$
$\ 2x + 3y = 3$

14. $-7x + y = 19$
$\ 2x - y = -9$

15. $2x + 5y = 23$
$\ 3x - 2y = 6$

16. $2x + y = 13$
$\ x - 5y = 1$

17. $x - y = 8$
$\ 3x + 2y = 4$

18. $7x + 8y = -5$
$\ 4x + 9y = 6$

19. $x + 6y = 6$
$\ 3x - 2y = 8$

20. $3x - y = 3$
$\ 6x + 5y = -1$

21. $5x + y = 0$
$\ 10x - 3y = -15$

Challenge Exercises

Find the value of each determinant using expansion by minors.

22. $\begin{vmatrix} 1 & 2 & 3 & 1 \\ 4 & 3 & -1 & 0 \\ 2 & -5 & 4 & 4 \\ 1 & -2 & 0 & 2 \end{vmatrix}$

23. $\begin{vmatrix} 7 & 0 & 9 & 5 \\ 8 & 2 & -1 & 2 \\ -5 & 3 & 7 & 9 \\ 0 & -1 & -4 & -6 \end{vmatrix}$

24. $\begin{vmatrix} 3 & 0 & 0 & 4 & 0 \\ 6 & -3 & 2 & 0 & 7 \\ 0 & 4 & 3 & 0 & 5 \\ 0 & 2 & 1 & 3 & -4 \\ 6 & 0 & -2 & -3 & 0 \end{vmatrix}$

Solve each system of equations using Cramer's rule.

25. $4x + 3y + z = -10$
$x - 12y + 2z = -5$
$x + 18y + z = 4$

26. $x + y + z = -1$
$2x + 4y + z = 1$
$3x - y - z = -15$

For the Scholar

Given that polygon $ABCD$ is a square with each side 10 units long and with $DE = 3$. If $\overline{FH}$ is the perpendicular bisector of $\overline{CE}$, find the ratio of FG to GH.

3-2 Addition of Matrices

Many of the properties and operations of real numbers also apply to matrices. For example, two matrices are equal if and only if they have the same dimensions and are identical, element by element.

This is the definition of equal matrices.

Example

1 Find the values of x and y for which the following equation is true.

$$\begin{bmatrix} y - 3 \\ y \end{bmatrix} = \begin{bmatrix} x \\ 2x \end{bmatrix}$$

Since corresponding elements are equal, the following equations are true.

$y - 3 = x$
$y = 2x$

Solve the system of equations.

$2x - 3 = x$ *Substitute 2x for y.*
$x = 3$ *Solve for x.*
$y = 2(3)$ or 6 *Substitute 3 for x to find y.*

The matrices are equal if $x = 3$ and $y = 6$.

The elements of an $m \times n$ matrix can be represented using double subscript notation.

$$\begin{bmatrix} a_{11} & a_{12} & a_{13} & \cdots & a_{1n} \\ a_{21} & a_{22} & a_{23} & \cdots & a_{2n} \\ \cdots & \cdots & \cdots & \cdots & \cdots \\ a_{m1} & a_{m2} & a_{m3} & \cdots & a_{mn} \end{bmatrix}$$

a_{ij} would be the element in the ith row and the jth column.

Matrices with the same dimensions can be added. The ijth element of the sum of matrices A and B is $a_{ij} + b_{ij}$.

Addition is not defined for matrices with different dimensions.

> **The sum of two $m \times n$ matrices is an $m \times n$ matrix in which the elements are the sum of the corresponding elements of the given matrices.**

Definition of Addition of Matrices

Example

2 Find the sum of A and B if $A = \begin{bmatrix} 3 & 4 & -7 \\ -2 & 0 & 4 \end{bmatrix}$ and $B = \begin{bmatrix} -2 & 7 & 3 \\ 5 & -9 & 1 \end{bmatrix}$.

$$A + B = \begin{bmatrix} 3 + -2 & 4 + 7 & -7 + 3 \\ -2 + 5 & 0 + -9 & 4 + 1 \end{bmatrix}$$

$$= \begin{bmatrix} 1 & 11 & -4 \\ 3 & -9 & 5 \end{bmatrix}$$

Matrices, like real numbers, have identity elements. For every matrix A, another matrix can be found such that their sum is A. For example, if $A = \begin{bmatrix} a_{11} & a_{12} \\ a_{21} & a_{22} \end{bmatrix}$, then $\begin{bmatrix} a_{11} & a_{12} \\ a_{21} & a_{22} \end{bmatrix} + \begin{bmatrix} 0 & 0 \\ 0 & 0 \end{bmatrix} = \begin{bmatrix} a_{11} & a_{12} \\ a_{21} & a_{22} \end{bmatrix}$.

The matrix $\begin{bmatrix} 0 & 0 \\ 0 & 0 \end{bmatrix}$ is called a **zero matrix.** Thus, the **identity matrix under addition** for any $m \times n$ matrix is an $m \times n$ zero matrix.

Zero is the additive identity element for the real numbers.

A zero matrix is often denoted by 0.

Matrices also have additive inverses. If $A = \begin{bmatrix} a_{11} & a_{12} \\ a_{21} & a_{22} \end{bmatrix}$, the matrix which must be added to A in order to obtain a zero matrix is $\begin{bmatrix} -a_{11} & -a_{12} \\ -a_{21} & -a_{22} \end{bmatrix}$ or $-A$. Therefore, $-A$ is the additive inverse of A.

$A + (-A) = 0$

The additive inverse of any real number a is $-a$.

Example

3 Write the additive inverse of each matrix.

a. $\begin{bmatrix} 4 & -7 \\ -9 & 3 \end{bmatrix}$ **b.** $\begin{bmatrix} c^2 & -t \\ 3x & -r^3 \end{bmatrix}$

a. $\begin{bmatrix} -4 & 7 \\ 9 & -3 \end{bmatrix}$ **b.** $\begin{bmatrix} -c^2 & t \\ -3x & r^3 \end{bmatrix}$

The additive inverse of a matrix is determined by finding the additive inverse of each element.

The additive inverse is used when subtracting matrices.

The difference $A - B$ of two $m \times n$ matrices is equal to the sum $A + (-B)$, where $-B$ represents the additive inverse of B.	Definition of Subtraction of Matrices

Example

4 Find $A - B$ if $A = \begin{bmatrix} 3 & 8 \\ -2 & 4 \end{bmatrix}$ and $B = \begin{bmatrix} 1 & 5 \\ -2 & 8 \end{bmatrix}$.

$$A - B = A + -B$$

$$= \begin{bmatrix} 3 & 8 \\ -2 & 4 \end{bmatrix} + \begin{bmatrix} -1 & -5 \\ 2 & -8 \end{bmatrix}$$

$$= \begin{bmatrix} 3 + -1 & 8 + -5 \\ -2 + 2 & 4 + -8 \end{bmatrix}$$

$$= \begin{bmatrix} 2 & 3 \\ 0 & -4 \end{bmatrix}$$

Exploratory Exercises

Using double subscript notation, write the general matrix which has the given dimensions.

1. 3×3 **2.** 2×5 **3.** 6×4 **4.** 1×6

Find the additive inverse of each matrix.

5. $\begin{bmatrix} 6 & 5 \\ 8 & 4 \end{bmatrix}$ **6.** $\begin{bmatrix} -3 & -2 \\ -5 & -9 \end{bmatrix}$ **7.** $\begin{bmatrix} -2 & 1 \\ 0 & -3 \end{bmatrix}$ **8.** $\begin{bmatrix} 8 & -3 \\ 4 & -5 \end{bmatrix}$

Written Exercises

Use matrices A, B, and C to find each sum or difference.

$$A = \begin{bmatrix} -1 & -5 & -7 \\ -5 & -2 & +6 \\ -3 & -0 & +2 \end{bmatrix} \quad B = \begin{bmatrix} +3 & -6 & +9 \\ -4 & +3 & -0 \\ -8 & +2 & -3 \end{bmatrix} \quad C = \begin{bmatrix} -6 & -9 & +4 \\ +11 & -13 & -8 \\ -20 & -4 & -2 \end{bmatrix}$$

1. $A + B$ **2.** $A + C$ **3.** $B + C$ **4.** $(A + B) + C$

5. $B + (-A)$ **6.** $C - B$ **7.** $B - C$ **8.** $C - A$

Find the values of x and y for which each matrix equation is true.

9. $[x \quad 2y] = [y + 5 \quad x - 3]$

10. $[5 \quad 4x] = [2x \quad 5y]$

11. $\begin{bmatrix} 2x \\ 0 \\ 16 \end{bmatrix} = \begin{bmatrix} 8 - y \\ y \\ 4x \end{bmatrix}$

12. $\begin{bmatrix} y \\ 8x \end{bmatrix} = \begin{bmatrix} 15 + x \\ 2y \end{bmatrix}$

Prove each statement.

13. Addition of second order matrices is commutative.

14. Addition of second order matrices is associative.

For the Scholar

In square WXYZ, $\widehat{WPY}$ is a quarter circle with center Z and $\widehat{XPZ}$ is a quarter circle with center W. If $\overline{PQ}$ is perpendicular to $\overline{XY}$ and WX = 12, then find PQ.

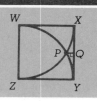

3-3 Multiplication of Matrices

A matrix can be multiplied by a constant called a **scalar.** The product of a scalar k and a matrix A is defined as follows.

> The product of an $m \times n$ matrix A and a scalar k is an $m \times n$ matrix kA. Each element of kA is equal to k times the corresponding element of A.

Scalar Product
$k[a_{ij}] = [ka_{ij}]$

Example

1 Multiply the matrix $\begin{bmatrix} 4 & 3 & -2 \\ -2 & 7 & -9 \end{bmatrix}$ **by 6.**

$$6\begin{bmatrix} 4 & 3 & -2 \\ -2 & 7 & -9 \end{bmatrix} = \begin{bmatrix} 6(4) & 6(3) & 6(-2) \\ 6(-2) & 6(7) & 6(-9) \end{bmatrix} = \begin{bmatrix} 24 & 18 & -12 \\ -12 & 42 & -54 \end{bmatrix}$$

A matrix can also be multiplied by another matrix, provided that the first matrix has the same number of columns as the second matrix has rows. The product of the two matrices is found by multiplying rows and columns. The product of a row $[a\ b\ c]$ and a column $\begin{bmatrix} x \\ y \\ z \end{bmatrix}$ is the real number $ax + by + cz$. The row and column must have the same number of elements.

Suppose $A = \begin{bmatrix} a_1 & b_1 \\ a_2 & b_2 \end{bmatrix}$ and $X = \begin{bmatrix} x_1 & y_1 \\ x_2 & y_2 \end{bmatrix}$. Each element of matrix AX is the product of one row of matrix A and one column of matrix X.

$$AX = \begin{bmatrix} a_1 & b_1 \\ a_2 & b_2 \end{bmatrix}\begin{bmatrix} x_1 & y_1 \\ x_2 & y_2 \end{bmatrix} = \begin{bmatrix} a_1x_1 + b_1x_2 & a_1y_1 + b_1y_2 \\ a_2x_1 + b_2x_2 & a_2y_1 + b_2y_2 \end{bmatrix}$$

In general, the product of two matrices is defined as follows.

> **The product of an $m \times n$ matrix A and an $n \times r$ matrix B is an $m \times r$ matrix AB. The ijth element of AB is the product of the ith row of A and the jth column of B.**
>
> **Product of Two Matrices**

Examples

2 Find the product of A and B if $A = \begin{bmatrix} 4 & 3 \\ 7 & 2 \end{bmatrix}$ and $B = \begin{bmatrix} 8 & 5 \\ 9 & 6 \end{bmatrix}$.

$$AB = \begin{bmatrix} 4(8) + 3(9) & 4(5) + 3(6) \\ 7(8) + 2(9) & 7(5) + 2(6) \end{bmatrix}$$

$$= \begin{bmatrix} 59 & 38 \\ 74 & 47 \end{bmatrix}$$

3 Find the product of C and D if $C = \begin{bmatrix} 3 & 0 & -4 & -1 \\ -6 & 9 & 8 & -2 \end{bmatrix}$ and $D = \begin{bmatrix} 3 \\ 7 \\ -1 \\ 5 \end{bmatrix}$.

$$CD = \begin{bmatrix} 3(3) + 0(7) + (-4)(-1) + (-1)(5) \\ (-6)(3) + 9(7) + 8(-1) + (-2)(5) \end{bmatrix}$$

$$= \begin{bmatrix} 9 + 0 + 4 + (-5) \\ (-18) + 63 + (-8) + (-10) \end{bmatrix}$$

$$= \begin{bmatrix} 8 \\ 27 \end{bmatrix}$$

The product has as many rows as the first matrix and as many columns as the second matrix.

Exploratory Exercises

Find each product.

1. $3[6 \quad 10]$

2. $-5[7 \quad 8 \quad -\sqrt{2}]$

3. $6[\sqrt{5} \quad -1 \quad 4]$

4. $8\begin{bmatrix} -3 \\ 5 \end{bmatrix}$

5. $\frac{1}{2}\begin{bmatrix} 9 & -3 \\ -6 & 6 \end{bmatrix}$

6. $\frac{3}{4}\begin{bmatrix} 8 & -7 \\ -4 & 0 \end{bmatrix}$

Name the dimensions of matrix C for each of the following. The dimensions of A and B are written as subscripts.

7. $A_{2\times3} \cdot B_{3\times6} = C$

8. $A_{5\times2} \cdot B_{2\times1} = C$

9. $A_{6\times4} \cdot C = B_{6\times3}$

10. $A_{4\times5} \cdot C = B_{4\times3}$

11. $C \cdot B_{1\times3} = A_{3\times3}$

12. $C \cdot B_{2\times4} = A_{4\times4}$

Written Exercises

Use matrices A, B, and C to find each product.

$$A = \begin{bmatrix} 7 & 0 \\ 5 & 3 \end{bmatrix} \qquad B = \begin{bmatrix} 2 & 4 \\ 8 & -4 \\ -2 & 6 \end{bmatrix} \qquad C = \begin{bmatrix} 3 & -3 & 6 \\ 5 & 4 & -2 \end{bmatrix}$$

1. $3A$
2. $4B$
3. $2C$
4. $-5A$
5. BA
6. BC
7. CB
8. AC
9. AA
10. $(CB)A$
11. $B(AC)$
12. $-4BC$

13. Find $2A - 3B$ if $A = \begin{bmatrix} 1 & -7 \\ 3 & 2 \end{bmatrix}$ and $B = \begin{bmatrix} -4 & 5 \\ 1 & -1 \end{bmatrix}$.

Answer each of the following.

14. Write the following equation as a system of 3 equations in 3 variables.

$$\begin{bmatrix} a_1 & b_1 & c_1 \\ a_2 & b_2 & c_2 \\ a_3 & b_3 & c_3 \end{bmatrix} \begin{bmatrix} x \\ y \\ z \end{bmatrix} = \begin{bmatrix} d_1 \\ d_2 \\ d_3 \end{bmatrix}$$

15. Let $A = \begin{bmatrix} a_{11} & a_{12} \\ a_{21} & a_{22} \end{bmatrix}$, $X = \begin{bmatrix} x \\ y \end{bmatrix}$, $Z = \begin{bmatrix} 0 \\ 0 \end{bmatrix}$, and $B = \begin{bmatrix} b_1 \\ b_2 \end{bmatrix}$. Write $AX + B = Z$ as a system of linear equations.

16. Prove or disprove that the product of two general second order matrices is commutative.

17. Prove or disprove that the product of three general second order matrices is associative.

18. Find two square matrices A and B for which $(A + B)^2$ does not equal $A^2 + 2AB + B^2$.

For the Scholar

If B and C are the real roots of $x^2 + Bx + C = 0$, where $B \neq 0$ and $C \neq 0$, find the product of the roots, $B \cdot C$.

3-4 Inverses of Matrices

The identity matrix under multiplication for any matrix A is the matrix I, such that $IA = A$ and $AI = A$. A second order matrix can be represented by $\begin{bmatrix} a_1 & b_1 \\ a_2 & b_2 \end{bmatrix}$. Since $\begin{bmatrix} a_1 & b_1 \\ a_2 & b_2 \end{bmatrix} \begin{bmatrix} 1 & 0 \\ 0 & 1 \end{bmatrix} = \begin{bmatrix} a_1 & b_1 \\ a_2 & b_2 \end{bmatrix}$, the matrix $\begin{bmatrix} 1 & 0 \\ 0 & 1 \end{bmatrix}$ is the identity matrix under multiplication for any second order matrix.

The multiplicative identity element for the real numbers is 1.

For any $m \times m$ matrix the identity matrix, I, must be $m \times m$.

> The identity matrix of nth order, I_n, is the square matrix whose elements in the main diagonal, from upper left to lower right, are 1's, while all other elements are 0's.

Identity Matrix under Multiplication

1 **Write the identity matrix under multiplication for a fifth order matrix.**

$$I_5 = \begin{bmatrix} 1 & 0 & 0 & 0 & 0 \\ 0 & 1 & 0 & 0 & 0 \\ 0 & 0 & 1 & 0 & 0 \\ 0 & 0 & 0 & 1 & 0 \\ 0 & 0 & 0 & 0 & 1 \end{bmatrix}$$

Multiplicative inverses exist for some matrices. Suppose A is equal to $\begin{bmatrix} a_1 & b_1 \\ a_2 & b_2 \end{bmatrix}$, a non-zero matrix of second order. The inverse matrix, A^{-1}, can be designated as $\begin{bmatrix} x_1 & y_1 \\ x_2 & y_2 \end{bmatrix}$. The product of a matrix A and its inverse matrix A^{-1} must equal the identity matrix, I, for multiplication.

The multiplicative inverse of a non-zero real number x is $\frac{1}{x}$.

$$\begin{bmatrix} a_1 & b_1 \\ a_2 & b_2 \end{bmatrix} \begin{bmatrix} x_1 & y_1 \\ x_2 & y_2 \end{bmatrix} = \begin{bmatrix} 1 & 0 \\ 0 & 1 \end{bmatrix}$$

$$\begin{bmatrix} a_1x_1 + b_1x_2 & a_1y_1 + b_1y_2 \\ a_2x_1 + b_2x_2 & a_2y_1 + b_2y_2 \end{bmatrix} = \begin{bmatrix} 1 & 0 \\ 0 & 1 \end{bmatrix}$$

From the previous matrix equation, two systems of linear equations can be written as follows.

$$a_1x_1 + b_1x_2 = 1 \qquad a_1y_1 + b_1y_2 = 0$$
$$a_2x_1 + b_2x_2 = 0 \qquad a_2y_1 + b_2y_2 = 1$$

By solving each pair of equations simultaneously, values for x_1, x_2, y_1, and y_2 can be obtained.

$$x_1 = \frac{b_2}{a_1b_2 - a_2b_1} \qquad y_1 = \frac{-b_1}{a_1b_2 - a_2b_1}$$

$$x_2 = \frac{-a_2}{a_1b_2 - a_2b_1} \qquad y_2 = \frac{a_1}{a_1b_2 - a_2b_1}$$

The denominator $a_1b_2 - a_2b_1$ is equal to the determinant of A. If the determinant of $A \neq 0$, the inverse exists and can be defined as follows.

In order for A to have an inverse, A must be non-singular.

If $A = \begin{bmatrix} a_1 & b_1 \\ a_2 & b_2 \end{bmatrix}$ and $\begin{vmatrix} a_1 & b_1 \\ a_2 & b_2 \end{vmatrix} \neq 0$, then

$$A^{-1} = \frac{1}{\begin{vmatrix} a_1 & b_1 \\ a_2 & b_2 \end{vmatrix}} \begin{bmatrix} b_2 & -b_1 \\ -a_2 & a_1 \end{bmatrix}$$

Inverse of a Second Order Matrix

Example

2 Find the inverse under multiplication of the matrix $\begin{bmatrix} 3 & -1 \\ 4 & 2 \end{bmatrix}$.

$\begin{vmatrix} 3 & -1 \\ 4 & 2 \end{vmatrix} = 3(2) - 4(-1) = 10$

The inverse is $\dfrac{1}{10}\begin{bmatrix} 2 & 1 \\ -4 & 3 \end{bmatrix}$ or $\begin{bmatrix} \dfrac{1}{5} & \dfrac{1}{10} \\ -\dfrac{2}{5} & \dfrac{3}{10} \end{bmatrix}$.

Check to see if $A \cdot A^{-1} = I$.

The inverse exists only when the determinant is not zero. Why?

Matrix equations can be solved using inverse matrices.

Example

3 Find matrix M if $\begin{bmatrix} 2 & 1 \\ -3 & 2 \end{bmatrix} M = \begin{bmatrix} 8 & -9 \\ 5 & -3 \end{bmatrix}$.

$\dfrac{1}{\begin{vmatrix} 2 & 1 \\ -3 & 2 \end{vmatrix}} \begin{bmatrix} 2 & -1 \\ 3 & 2 \end{bmatrix} \begin{bmatrix} 2 & 1 \\ -3 & 2 \end{bmatrix} M = \dfrac{1}{\begin{vmatrix} 2 & 1 \\ -3 & 2 \end{vmatrix}} \begin{bmatrix} 2 & -1 \\ 3 & 2 \end{bmatrix} \begin{bmatrix} 8 & -9 \\ 5 & -3 \end{bmatrix}$

Notice that the inverse is written at the left of both sides of the equation. This is necessary since multiplication of matrices is not commutative.

$\dfrac{1}{7}\begin{bmatrix} 7 & 0 \\ 0 & 7 \end{bmatrix} M = \dfrac{1}{7}\begin{bmatrix} 11 & -15 \\ 34 & -33 \end{bmatrix}$

$\begin{bmatrix} 1 & 0 \\ 0 & 1 \end{bmatrix} M = \begin{bmatrix} \dfrac{11}{7} & \dfrac{-15}{7} \\ \dfrac{34}{7} & \dfrac{-33}{7} \end{bmatrix}$

$M = \begin{bmatrix} \dfrac{11}{7} & \dfrac{-15}{7} \\ \dfrac{34}{7} & \dfrac{-33}{7} \end{bmatrix}$

Exploratory Exercises

Find the determinant of each matrix.

1. $\begin{bmatrix} 1 & 3 \\ 2 & 5 \end{bmatrix}$
2. $\begin{bmatrix} -1 & -2 \\ 3 & -6 \end{bmatrix}$
3. $\begin{bmatrix} 4 & 3 \\ 8 & 6 \end{bmatrix}$
4. $\begin{bmatrix} 7 & 40 \\ 2 & 12 \end{bmatrix}$
5. $\begin{bmatrix} 10 & 4 \\ -4 & 1 \end{bmatrix}$

6. $\begin{bmatrix} 5 & 9 \\ 7 & -3 \end{bmatrix}$
7. $\begin{bmatrix} 4 & 1 \\ -6 & 2 \end{bmatrix}$
8. $\begin{bmatrix} -9 & 3 \\ 14 & -3 \end{bmatrix}$
9. $\begin{bmatrix} 29 & -32 \\ 16 & -12 \end{bmatrix}$
10. $\begin{bmatrix} -15 & 5 \\ -9 & 3 \end{bmatrix}$

11-20. State whether an inverse exists for each matrix in problems **1-10.**

Written Exercises

Answer each of the following.

1-10. Find the inverse of each matrix in the exploratory exercises, if it exists.

Find matrix X for each of the following.

11. $\begin{bmatrix} 2 & -1 \\ 3 & 5 \end{bmatrix} X = \begin{bmatrix} 4 & 3 \\ 1 & -2 \end{bmatrix}$

12. $\begin{bmatrix} 5 & 1 \\ -2 & 2 \end{bmatrix} X + \begin{bmatrix} 3 & -2 \\ 4 & 6 \end{bmatrix} = \begin{bmatrix} 4 & 3 \\ 10 & 2 \end{bmatrix}$

13. $\begin{bmatrix} 1 & 2 \\ 3 & 6 \end{bmatrix} \begin{bmatrix} 2 & 2 \\ -1 & -1 \end{bmatrix} = X$

14. $\begin{bmatrix} 1 & 1 \\ 1 & 1 \end{bmatrix} \begin{bmatrix} 3 & 5 \\ -3 & -5 \end{bmatrix} = X$

15. $\begin{bmatrix} 3 & 7 \\ 8 & 9 \end{bmatrix} X - \begin{bmatrix} 2 & 7 \\ 6 & 9 \end{bmatrix} = \begin{bmatrix} 3 & 6 \\ 9 & 6 \end{bmatrix}$

16. $\begin{bmatrix} 3 & 1 \\ -2 & 0 \end{bmatrix} - \begin{bmatrix} 3 & 7 \\ 5 & -8 \end{bmatrix} X = \begin{bmatrix} -2 & 8 \\ 7 & 4 \end{bmatrix}$

Prove each statement.

17. $AI = IA = A$ for second order matrices.

18. $AA^{-1} = A^{-1}A = I$ for second order matrices.

19. If $AB = C$, where A, B, and C are second order matrices, prove that the product of the determinants of A and B is the determinant of C.

For the Scholar

If the perimeter of a rectangular region is 100 feet, find the least possible length for one of its diagonals.

3-5 Augmented Matrix Solutions

Matrices can be used to solve systems of linear equations. The coefficients and constants of the system of equations shown below can be written in the form of a 3×4 **augmented matrix**.

System of Equations	**Augmented Matrix**
$x - 2y + z = 7$	
$3x + y - z = 2$	$\begin{bmatrix} 1 & -2 & 1 & 7 \\ 3 & 1 & -1 & 2 \\ 2 & 3 & 2 & 7 \end{bmatrix}$
$2x + 3y + 2z = 7$	

An augmented matrix is an array of the coefficients and constants of a system of equations.

This matrix can be modified by transforming rows since each row represents an equation. Each change of the matrix represents a corresponding change of the system. Any operation which results in an equivalent system of equations is permitted for the matrix. The objective is to get as many zeros in the matrix as possible. This method is also known as the Gauss-Jordan method of solving linear systems. In general, any of the following row operations can be used to transform an augmented matrix.

1. Interchange any two rows.
2. Replace any row with a non-zero multiple of that row.
3. Replace any row with the sum of that row and a multiple of another row.

Row Operations on Matrices

Why are these operations permitted?

Example

1 Solve the system of equations by using row operations.

$$x - 2y + z = 7$$
$$3x + y - z = 2$$
$$2x + 3y + 2z = 7$$

First, write the augmented matrix.

$$\begin{bmatrix} 1 & -2 & 1 & 7 \\ 3 & 1 & -1 & 2 \\ 2 & 3 & 2 & 7 \end{bmatrix}$$

The objective is to get as many zeros in the matrix as possible.

Multiply row one by -3 and add the result to row two.

$$\begin{bmatrix} 1 & -2 & 1 & 7 \\ 0 & 7 & -4 & -19 \\ 2 & 3 & 2 & 7 \end{bmatrix}$$

A zero is obtained in the a_{21} position.

Multiply row one by -2 and add the result to row three.

$$\begin{bmatrix} 1 & -2 & 1 & 7 \\ 0 & 7 & -4 & -19 \\ 0 & 7 & 0 & -7 \end{bmatrix}$$

A zero is obtained in the a_{31} position.

Multiply row two by -1 and add the result to row three.

$$\begin{bmatrix} 1 & -2 & 1 & 7 \\ 0 & 7 & -4 & -19 \\ 0 & 0 & 4 & 12 \end{bmatrix}$$

Add row three to row two.

$$\begin{bmatrix} 1 & -2 & 1 & 7 \\ 0 & 7 & 0 & -7 \\ 0 & 0 & 4 & 12 \end{bmatrix}$$

Multiply row two by $\frac{1}{7}$.

$$\begin{bmatrix} 1 & -2 & 1 & 7 \\ 0 & 1 & 0 & -1 \\ 0 & 0 & 4 & 12 \end{bmatrix}$$

Multiply row three by $\frac{1}{4}$.

$$\begin{bmatrix} 1 & -2 & 1 & 7 \\ 0 & 1 & 0 & -1 \\ 0 & 0 & 1 & 3 \end{bmatrix}$$

The system of equations which this matrix represents could be easily solved by substitution.
$$x - 2y + z = 7$$
$$y = -1$$
$$z = 3$$

Multiply row two by 2 and add the result to row one.

$$\begin{bmatrix} 1 & 0 & 1 & 5 \\ 0 & 1 & 0 & -1 \\ 0 & 0 & 1 & 3 \end{bmatrix}$$

Multiply row three by -1 and add the result to row one.

$$\begin{bmatrix} 1 & 0 & 0 & 2 \\ 0 & 1 & 0 & -1 \\ 0 & 0 & 1 & 3 \end{bmatrix}$$

Notice the positions of the 1's and 0's.

Thus, $x = 2$, $y = -1$, and $z = 3$.

The augmented matrix can be used to solve a variety of problems.

Example

2 Find the equation of a parabola that contains the points $(1, 9)$, $(4, 6)$, and $(6, 14)$.

The general form of the equation of a parabola is $y = ax^2 + bx + c$.
Since each of the points satisfy the general equation, the following
can be generated.

$$a(1)^2 + b(1) + c = 9 \qquad \text{Use } (1, 9).$$
$$a(4)^2 + b(4) + c = 6 \qquad \text{Use } (4, 6).$$
$$a(6)^2 + b(6) + c = 14 \qquad \text{Use } (6, 14).$$

Simplify.

$$a + b + c = 9$$
$$16a + 4b + c = 6$$
$$36a + 6b + c = 14$$

Use an augmented matrix and row operations to solve.

Thus, $\begin{bmatrix} 1 & 1 & 1 & 9 \\ 16 & 4 & 1 & 6 \\ 36 & 6 & 1 & 14 \end{bmatrix}$ becomes $\begin{bmatrix} 1 & 0 & 0 & 1 \\ 0 & 1 & 0 & -6 \\ 0 & 0 & 1 & 14 \end{bmatrix}$.

So, $a = 1$, $b = -6$, and $c = 14$.

Therefore, the equation of the parabola is $y = x^2 - 6x + 14$.

Exploratory Exercises

State the row operations you would use to locate a zero in the second column of row one.

1. $\begin{bmatrix} 3 & 5 & 7 \\ 6 & -1 & -8 \end{bmatrix}$

2. $\begin{bmatrix} 4 & -7 & -2 \\ 1 & 2 & 7 \end{bmatrix}$

3. $\begin{bmatrix} 3 & 3 & -9 \\ -2 & 1 & -4 \end{bmatrix}$

4. $\begin{bmatrix} 2 & 4 & 3 \\ -2 & -3 & 1 \end{bmatrix}$

5. $\begin{bmatrix} -6 & -2 & -3 \\ 4 & 3 & 1 \end{bmatrix}$

6. $\begin{bmatrix} 5 & -3 & 0 \\ 3 & 6 & -6 \end{bmatrix}$

7-12. State the row operations you would use to locate a zero in the first column of row two for the matrices in problems **1-6**.

Written Exercises

Solve each system of equations using augmented matrices.

1. $3x + 5y = 7$
$6x - y = -8$

2. $4x - 7y = -2$
$x + 2y = 7$

3. $3x + 3y = -9$
$-2x + y = -4$

4. $x - y + z = 3$
$2y - z = 1$
$2y - x + 1 = 0$

5. $x + y + z = -2$
$2x - 3y + z = -11$
$-x + 2y - z = 8$

6. $2x + 6y + 8z = 5$
$-2x + 9y - 12z = -1$
$4x + 6y - 4z = 3$

Write each equation in standard form. Then solve each system of equations using matrices.

7. $5x = 3y - 50$
$2y = 1 - 3x$

8. $2x + y - 2z - 7 = 0$
$x - 2y - 5z + 1 = 0$
$4x + y + z + 1 = 0$

9. $x + y + z - 6 = 0$
$2x - 3y + 4z - 3 = 0$
$4x - 8y + 4z - 12 = 0$

10. $x + 2y = 5$
$3x + 4z = 2$
$2y + 3w = -2$
$3z - 2w = 1$

11. $w + x + y + z = 0$
$2w + x - y - z = -4$
$-w - x + y + z = 2$
$2x + y = 1$

12. $4x + 2y + 3z = 6$
$2x + 7y = 3z$
$-3x - 9y + 13 = -2z$

Find the equation of a parabola that contains the points given.

13. $(1, 4)$, $(5, 40)$, and $(3, 14)$.

14. $(2, 3)$, $(3, 6)$, and $(-2, 31)$

For the Scholar

If the numeral 14 in base A represents a two-digit number and the numeral 41 in base A also represents a two-digit number, then find the value of A if 41 (Base A) is three times that of 14 (Base A).

3-6 Geometrical Vectors

A **vector** is a quantity which possesses both magnitude and direction. For example, velocity and voltage may be represented as vectors. Geometrically, a vector is represented as a directed line segment.

A directed line segment with an initial point at O and terminal point at P is shown. It can be designated $\vec{v}$ or $\overrightarrow{OP}$. The direction of the arrowhead indicates the direction of the vector, and the length of the line segment indicates its **magnitude**. The magnitude of $\vec{v}$ is denoted by $|\vec{v}|$.

A vector in **standard position** has its initial point at the origin. The **amplitude** of the vector is the directed angle between the positive x-axis and the vector. The amplitude of $\vec{u}$ is 65°.

A scalar possesses only magnitude. Real numbers are scalars.

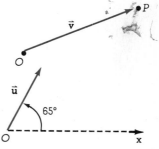

Example

1 Measure the magnitude (in centimeters) and amplitude of $\vec{a}$.

  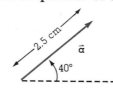

The magnitude is 2.5 cm.
The amplitude is 40°.

Two **vectors are equal** if and only if they have the same direction and the same magnitude. Five vectors are shown at the right. Vectors $\vec{a}$ and $\vec{b}$ are equal, since $|\vec{a}| = |\vec{b}|$ and they have the same direction. Since $|\vec{c}| \neq |\vec{d}|$, $\vec{c} \neq \vec{d}$. Since $\vec{c}$ and $\vec{e}$ have different directions, $\vec{c} \neq \vec{e}$, although $|\vec{c}| = |\vec{e}|$.

Addition of vectors involves both direction and magnitude. The sum of two or more vectors is called the resultant of the vectors. The resultant of vectors can be found by using either the triangle method or the parallelogram method. These methods are illustrated by the following examples.

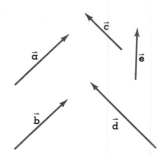

Examples

2 **Find the sum of $\vec{p}$ and $\vec{q}$.**

Copy $\vec{p}$. Then copy $\vec{q}$, placing the initial point of $\vec{q}$ at the initial point of $\vec{p}$.
Form a parallelogram which has $\vec{p}$ and $\vec{q}$ as two of its sides. Draw broken lines to represent the other two sides.

> *This is called the parallelogram method.*

The resultant is the vector from the initial point of $\vec{p}$ and $\vec{q}$ to the opposite corner of the parallelogram.

3 **Find the sum of $\vec{r}$ and $\vec{s}$.**

Copy $\vec{r}$. Then copy $\vec{s}$, placing the initial point of $\vec{s}$ at the terminal point of $\vec{r}$.

> *This is called the triangle method.*

The resultant is the vector from the initial point of $\vec{r}$ to the terminal point of $\vec{s}$.

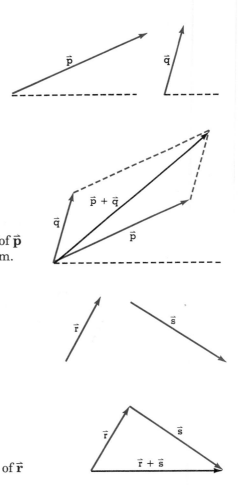

The product of a scalar k and a vector $\vec{a}$ is a vector with the same direction as $\vec{a}$. The magnitude of $k\vec{a}$ is equal to $k|\vec{a}|$. In the figure, $\vec{d}$ is equal to $3\vec{c}$.

A vector having direction opposite to that of a vector $\vec{v}$ and having the same magnitude is represented by $-\vec{v}$. In subtracting with numbers, $a - b = a + (-b)$. Similarly, vectors can be subtracted using $\vec{u} - \vec{v} = \vec{u} + (-\vec{v})$.

Example

4 **Subtract $\vec{s}$ from $2\vec{r}$.**

$$2\vec{r} - \vec{s} = 2\vec{r} + -\vec{s}$$

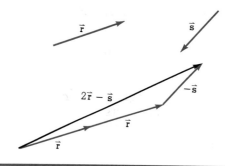

Two or more vectors whose sum is a given vector are called components of this vector. Components of a vector can be found in any direction. In the figure at the right, $\vec{y}$ and $\vec{x}$ are respectively the vertical and horizontal components of $\vec{a}$.

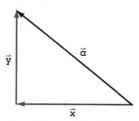

Example

5 **Graph a vector which has a magnitude of 3 cm and an amplitude of 53°. Then, graph its vertical and horizontal components. Find the magnitude of each component.**

Graph the vector. Then, draw a horizontal vector through the initial point and a vertical vector through the terminal point. The vectors will form a right triangle. Measure the sides of the triangle to determine their magnitudes. The magnitude of the vertical component is about 2.4 cm. The magnitude of the horizontal component is about 1.8 cm.

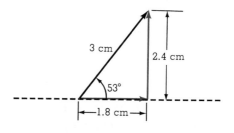

Exploratory Exercises

Draw a vector with the given magnitude and amplitude. Use a metric ruler and a protractor.

1. 5 cm; 40°   2. 10 cm; 50°   3. 4 cm; 180°

4. 3 cm; 120°   5. 7.5 cm; 270°   6. 6 cm; 65°

Answer each of the following.

7. Is vector addition commutative?   8. Is vector addition associative?

Written Exercises

Use vectors $\vec{a}$, $\vec{b}$, $\vec{c}$, and $\vec{d}$, a metric ruler, and a protractor to find each vector sum or difference.

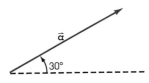   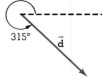   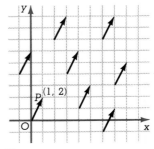

1. $\vec{a} + \vec{b}$ 2. $\vec{a} + \vec{c}$ 3. $\vec{c} + \vec{d}$
4. $\vec{b} + \vec{d}$ 5. $\vec{a} + \vec{d}$ 6. $\vec{b} + \vec{c}$
7. $\vec{a} + \vec{b} + \vec{c}$ 8. $2\vec{a} + \vec{b}$ 9. $3\vec{c} + 2\vec{d}$
10. $\vec{a} + (-\vec{b})$ 11. $\vec{b} - \vec{c}$ 12. $2\vec{b} - \vec{d}$

13-24. Measure to find the magnitude and amplitude of each resultant in problems 1-12.

Find the magnitude of the vertical and horizontal components of each vector.

25. $\vec{a}$ 26. $\vec{b}$ 27. $\vec{c}$ 28. $\vec{d}$

For the Scholar

How many significant digits are in the number represented by $4^{18}5^{32}$ when it is expanded into its usual base 10 form?

3-7 Algebraic Vectors

Vectors can be represented algebraically, using ordered pairs of real numbers. The ordered pair (x, y) represents the vector $\overrightarrow{OP}$ from the origin O to the point P with coordinates (x, y). For example, the ordered pair $(1, 2)$ represents the vector from the origin to the point $(1, 2)$.

Since vectors having the same magnitude and direction are equal, many vectors can be represented by the same ordered pair. Each vector on the graph can be represented by the ordered pair $(1, 2)$.

The initial point of a vector can be anywhere in the plane i.e. vectors are moveable.

Suppose P_1 and P_2 are any two points in the plane. The diagram at the right shows a right triangle with $\overrightarrow{P_1P_2}$ as its hypotenuse. A single ordered pair can be found to represent $\overrightarrow{P_1P_2}$.

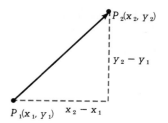

Suppose $P_1(x_1, y_1)$ is the initial point of a vector, and $P_2(x_2, y_2)$ is the terminal point. The ordered pair of numbers which represents $\overrightarrow{P_1P_2}$ is $(x_2 - x_1, y_2 - y_1)$. Its magnitude $\|\overrightarrow{P_1P_2}\| = \sqrt{(x_2 - x_1)^2 + (y_2 - y_1)^2}$.	*Representation of a Vector as an Ordered Pair*

The order of the coordinates of P_1 and P_2 is important. For example, $\overrightarrow{P_2P_1}$ is represented by $(x_1 - x_2, y_1 - y_2)$.

Examples

1 **Find the ordered pair which represents the vector from $A(4, 9)$ to $B(8, 3)$.**

$\overrightarrow{AB} = (8 - 4, 3 - 9) = (4, -6)$

2 **Find the magnitude of the vector from $C(5, 7)$ to $D(-3, 8)$.**

$\begin{aligned}
\|\overrightarrow{CD}\| &= \sqrt{(-3 - 5)^2 + (8 - 7)^2} \\
&= \sqrt{(-8)^2 + 1^2} \\
&= \sqrt{65}
\end{aligned}$

Vectors, when represented as ordered pairs, can be added or subtracted algebraically. A vector can also be multiplied by a scalar. The rules for operations on vectors are similar to those for matrices.

The following operations are defined for $\bar{a} = (a_1, a_2)$, $\bar{b} = (b_1, b_2)$, and any real number k. **Addition** $\bar{a} + \bar{b} = (a_1, a_2) + (b_1, b_2) = (a_1 + b_1, a_2 + b_2)$ **Subtraction** $\bar{a} - \bar{b} = (a_1, a_2) + (-b_1, -b_2)$ $= (a_1 - b_1, a_2 - b_2)$ **Scalar Multiplication** $k\bar{a} = k(a_1, a_2) = (ka_1, ka_2)$	*Vector Operations*

Example

3 If $\vec{r} = (4, 5)$, and $\vec{s} = (-2, 7)$, find each of the following.

a. $\vec{r} + \vec{s}$ **b.** $\vec{r} - \vec{s}$ **c.** $6\vec{s}$

a. $\vec{r} + \vec{s} = (4, 5) + (-2, 7)$
$\qquad = (2, 12)$

b. $\vec{r} - \vec{s} = (4, 5) - (-2, 7)$
$\qquad = (6, -2)$

c. $6\vec{s} = 6(-2, 7)$
$\qquad = (-12, 42)$

A vector of unit length in the direction of the positive x-axis is represented by the symbol $\vec{i}$ (not to be confused with the imaginary unit i). Also $\vec{j}$ is a vector of unit length in the positive direction of the y-axis. Therefore, $\vec{i} = (1, 0)$ and $\vec{j} = (0, 1)$. These vectors are called **unit vectors.**

A vector of unit length has a magnitude of 1.

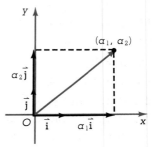

Vector $\vec{a}$, (a_1, a_2), can be expressed as $a_1\vec{i} + a_2\vec{j}$.

$$a_1\vec{i} + a_2\vec{j} = a_1(1, 0) + a_2(0, 1)$$
$$\qquad\qquad = (a_1, 0) + (0, a_2) \qquad \textit{Scalar Product}$$
$$\qquad\qquad = (a_1 + 0, 0 + a_2) \qquad \textit{Addition of Vectors}$$
$$\qquad\qquad = (a_1, a_2) \qquad \textit{Zero is the additive identity element.}$$

But $(a_1, a_2) = \vec{a}$, so $\vec{a} = a_1\vec{i} + a_2\vec{j}$.
Thus, any vector which is represented by an ordered pair can also be written as the sum of unit vectors.

Examples

4 Write $\vec{r}$, $(-4, 6)$, as the sum of unit vectors.

$\vec{r} = -4\vec{i} + 6\vec{j}$

5 Write $\overrightarrow{ST}$ as the sum of unit vectors, for points $S(-1, 3)$ and $T(3, 8)$.

First, write $\overrightarrow{ST}$ as an ordered pair.
$\overrightarrow{ST} = (3 - (-1), 8 - 3) = (4, 5)$
Then, write $\overrightarrow{ST}$ as the sum of unit vectors.
$\overrightarrow{ST} = 4\vec{i} + 5\vec{j}$

Exploratory Exercises

Find the magnitude of each vector.

1. $(4, 3)$ **2.** $(6, 7)$ **3.** $(5, 8)$ **4.** $(-2, -3)$

5. $(5, -9)$ **6.** $(24, 7)$ **7.** $(-16, 11)$ **8.** $(-5, 15)$

9-16. Write each vector in problems **1-8** as the sum of unit vectors.

Find the sum of the given vectors algebraically.

17. $(3, 5) + (-1, 2)$

18. $(-5, 2) + (1, -8)$

19. $(-1, 6) + (-8, -5)$

20. $(-2, -3) + (2, 4)$

21. $\vec{i} + \vec{j}$

22. $2\vec{i} + -\vec{j}$

23. $3\vec{i} + 4\vec{j}$

24. $5\vec{i} + -3\vec{j}$

25. $-7\vec{i} + 5\vec{j}$

Answer each of the following.

26. If two vectors have the same magnitude, is it true that the ordered pairs representing them are necessarily identical?

27. If two vectors have the same amplitude, is it true that the ordered pairs representing them are necessarily identical?

Written Exercises

For each pair of points A and B, find an ordered pair which represents $\overrightarrow{AB}$.

1. $A(1, 3); B(-2, 5)$

2. $A(7, 7); B(-2, -2)$

3. $A(5, 0); B(7, 6)$

4. $A(0, 5); B(-5, 0)$

5. $A(5, -6); B(6, -5)$

6. $A(-4, -3); B(-9, 2)$

7-12. Find the magnitude of $\overrightarrow{AB}$ for problems 1-6.

Find an ordered pair to represent $\vec{u}$ in each equation below, if $\vec{v} = (3, -5)$ and $\vec{w} = (-4, 2)$.

13. $\vec{u} = \vec{v} + \vec{w}$

14. $\vec{u} = \vec{v} - \vec{w}$

15. $\vec{u} = 5\vec{w}$

16. $\vec{u} = 3\vec{v}$

17. $\vec{u} = \vec{w} - 2\vec{v}$

18. $\vec{u} = \vec{v} - 3\vec{w}$

19. $\vec{u} = 4\vec{v} + 3\vec{w}$

20. $\vec{u} = 5\vec{w} - 3\vec{v}$

21. $\vec{u} = 6\vec{w} - 2\vec{v}$

22. Prove that $\vec{a} + \vec{b} = \vec{b} + \vec{a}$.

23. Find the zero vector in two dimensions. By definition this is the vector which does not alter any vector upon addition.

For the Scholar

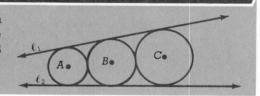

Given $\odot A$, $\odot B$, and $\odot C$ tangent to each other and to lines, ℓ_1 and ℓ_2. What is the radius of the $\odot B$ if the radius of $\odot A$ is 6 and the radius of $\odot C$ is 24?

3-8 Vectors in Space

Imagine three real number lines intersecting at the zero point of each in a manner such that each line is perpendicular to the plane determined by the other two. To show this arrangement on paper, a figure is used which conveys the feeling of depth. The axes are named the x-axis, y-axis, and z-axis.

Each point in space corresponds to an ordered triple of real numbers. To locate a point P which has the coordinates (x_1, y_1, z_1), first find x_1 on the x-axis, y_1 on the y-axis, and z_1 on the z-axis. Then construct (in your imagination) a plane perpendicular to the x-axis at x_1, and construct planes in a similar manner to the y-axis and z-axis at y_1 and z_1, respectively. The three planes intersect at the point P, the only point in space with the coordinates (x_1, y_1, z_1).

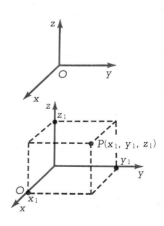

Example

1 **Locate the point (3, 5, 4).**

First, locate 3 on the x-axis, 5 on the
y-axis, and 4 on the z-axis.

Then, draw broken lines, forming paral-
lelograms to represent planes.

The planes intersect at the point (3, 5, 4).

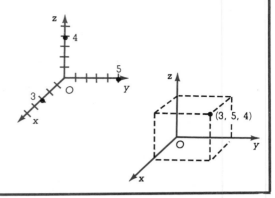

A vector in space can be represented as an ordered triple. The
geometric interpretation is basically the same as that for a vector in
the plane. A directed line segment from the origin O to $P(x, y, z)$ is
called the vector $\overrightarrow{OP}$ corresponding to vector (x, y, z).

*All vectors have both
magnitude and direction,
except the zero vector.*

The distance between two points in space is found by a formula
which is an extension of that used in the plane. The distance from
the origin to point (x, y, z) is $\sqrt{x^2 + y^2 + z^2}$. Therefore, the magnitude of a vector (x, y, z) is $\sqrt{x^2 + y^2 + z^2}$.

**A vector from $P_1(x_1, y_1, z_1)$ to $P_2(x_2, y_2, z_2)$ in space can be
represented by an ordered triple as follows.**

$$\overrightarrow{P_1P_2} = (x_2 - x_1, y_2 - y_1, z_2 - z_1)$$

Its magnitude $|\overrightarrow{P_1P_2}| = \sqrt{(x_2 - x_1)^2 + (y_2 - y_1)^2 + (z_2 - z_1)^2}$

**Representation of a
Vector as an
Ordered Triple**

How can it be proven that $|\overrightarrow{P_1P_2}| = \sqrt{(x_2 - x_1)^2 + (y_2 - y_1)^2 + (z_2 - z_1)^2}$?

Examples

2 **Find the ordered triple which represents the vector from $Q(9, 8, 7)$ to $R(10, 6, 4)$.**

$$\overrightarrow{QR} = (10 - 9, 6 - 8, 4 - 7) = (1, -2, -3)$$

3 **Find the magnitude of $\overrightarrow{QR}$.**

$$|\overrightarrow{QR}| = \sqrt{1^2 + (-2)^2 + (-3)^2} = \sqrt{14}$$

It is possible to add or subtract vectors which are represented by
ordered triples. They can also be multiplied by scalars.

Example

4 Find an ordered triple which represents $2\vec{u} - \vec{w}$, if $\vec{u} = (3, -2, 7)$ and $\vec{w} = (4, 7, -5)$.

$$2\vec{u} - \vec{w} = 2(3, -2, 7) - (4, 7, -5)$$
$$= (6, -4, 14) - (4, 7, -5)$$
$$= (2, -11, 19)$$

Three unit vectors, called $\vec{i}, \vec{j}$, and $\vec{k}$ are required for a three dimensional coordinate system. The unit vector on the x-axis is $\vec{i}, \vec{j}$ is the unit vector on the y-axis, and $\vec{k}$ is the unit vector on the z-axis. Therefore $\vec{i} = (1, 0, 0)$, $\vec{j} = (0, 1, 0)$, and $\vec{k} = (0, 0, 1)$. These unit vectors are shown at the right with a representation of vector $\vec{a}(a_1, a_2, a_3)$. The component vectors of $\vec{a}$ along the three axes are $a_1\vec{i}, a_2\vec{j}$, and $a_3\vec{k}$. Vector $\vec{a}$ can be written in the form $\vec{a} = a_1\vec{i} + a_2\vec{j} + a_3\vec{k}$.

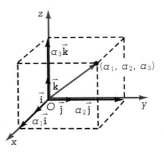

Examples

5 Write $\vec{v}, (4, -8, 1)$, as the sum of unit vectors.

$\vec{v} = 4\vec{i} + -8\vec{j} + \vec{k}$

6 Write $\overrightarrow{PQ}$ as the sum of unit vectors, for points $P(2, 5, 5)$ and $Q(3, -1, 4)$.

$\overrightarrow{PQ} = (3 - 2, -1 - 5, 4 - 5)$
$\overrightarrow{PQ} = (1, -6, -1)$
$\overrightarrow{PQ} = \vec{i} + -6\vec{j} + -\vec{k}$ or $\vec{i} - 6\vec{j} - \vec{k}$

Exploratory Exercises

Locate points having the given coordinates.

1. $(2, 1, 3)$ **2.** $(3, 4, 9)$ **3.** $(1, 0, 3)$ **4.** $(-2, 1, 3)$ **5.** $(-1, 0, 4)$

6. $(5, 2, 6)$ **7.** $(4, 1, -3)$ **8.** $(6, -2, 4)$ **9.** $(7, 2, 4)$ **10.** $(-1, -1, 5)$

11-20. Find the magnitude of a vector from the origin to the given point for problems **1-10**.

21-30. Write each vector in problems **1-10** as the sum of unit vectors.

Written Exercises

For each pair of points A and B, find an ordered triple which represents $\overrightarrow{AB}$.

1. $A(3, 3, -1); B(5, 3, 2)$ **2.** $A(8, 1, 1); B(4, 0, 1)$ **3.** $A(-2, 5, 8); B(3, 9, -3)$

4. $A(-2, 4, 7); B(-3, 5, 2)$ **5.** $A(32, 6, 9); B(20, 11, 10)$ **6.** $A(23, 17, 56); B(20, 21, 44)$

7-12. Find the magnitude of $\overrightarrow{AB}$ for problems **1-6.**

13-18. Write $\overrightarrow{AB}$ as the sum of unit vectors for problems **1-6.**

Find an ordered triple to represent $\vec{u}$ in each equation below, if $\vec{v} = (2, -5, -3)$ and $\vec{w} = (-3, 4, -7)$.

19. $\vec{u} = \vec{v} + \vec{w}$ **20.** $\vec{u} = \vec{w} - \vec{v}$ **21.** $\vec{u} = 3\vec{v} - \vec{w}$

22. $\vec{u} = \vec{v} - 3\vec{w}$ **23.** $\vec{u} = 5\vec{v} - 3\vec{w}$ **24.** $\vec{u} = 2\vec{w} - 4\vec{v}$

25-30. Write $\vec{u}$ as the sum of unit vectors for problems **19-24.**

31. Show that $|\overrightarrow{P_1P_2}| = |\overrightarrow{P_2P_1}|$.

32. If $\vec{a} = (a_1, a_2, a_3)$, then $-\vec{a}$ is defined to be $(-a_1, -a_2, -a_3)$. Show that $|-\vec{a}| = |\vec{a}|$.

For the Scholar

If a triangle has vertices $(0, 0)$, $(-1, 4)$, and $(-9, 4)$, find the equation of a vertical line that divides the triangular region into two regions of equal area.

3-9 Perpendicular Vectors

The vectors $\vec{a}$, $\vec{b}$, and $\overrightarrow{BA}$ are shown in the figure. If $\vec{a}$ is perpendicular to $\vec{b}$, their magnitudes satisfy the Pythagorean theorem.

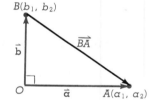

$$|\overrightarrow{BA}|^2 = |\vec{a}|^2 + |\vec{b}|^2$$

The equation can be rewritten as follows.

$$
\begin{aligned}
|\overrightarrow{BA}|^2 &= \left(\sqrt{(a_1 - b_1)^2 + (a_2 - b_2)^2}\right)^2 \\
&= (a_1 - b_1)^2 + (a_2 - b_2)^2 \\
&= a_1^2 - 2a_1b_1 + b_1^2 + a_2^2 - 2a_2b_2 + b_2^2 \\
&= (a_1^2 + a_2^2) + (b_1^2 + b_2^2) - 2(a_1b_1 + a_2b_2) \\
|\overrightarrow{BA}|^2 &= |\vec{a}|^2 + |\vec{b}|^2 - 2(a_1b_1 + a_2b_2)
\end{aligned}
$$

Compare this equation with the original one.

Thus, $|\overrightarrow{BA}|^2 = |\vec{a}|^2 + |\vec{b}|^2$ if and only if $a_1b_1 + a_2b_2 = 0$.

The expression $a_1b_1 + a_2b_2$ is often used in studying vectors. It has a special name, the **inner product** of $\vec{a}$ and $\vec{b}$.

> If $\vec{a}$ and $\vec{b}$ are two vectors, (a_1, a_2) and (b_1, b_2), the inner product of $\vec{a}$ and $\vec{b}$ is defined as follows.
>
> $$\vec{a} \cdot \vec{b} = a_1b_1 + a_2b_2$$
>
> $\vec{a} \cdot \vec{b}$ is read "$\vec{a}$ dot $\vec{b}$" and is often called the <u>dot product</u>.

Inner Product of Vectors in the Plane

Two vectors are perpendicular if and only if their inner product is zero.

The inner product of two vectors is a scalar.

Examples

1 **Find the inner product of $\vec{a}$ and $\vec{b}$ if $\vec{a} = (3, 5)$ and $\vec{b} = (8, -3)$.**

$$\vec{a} \cdot \vec{b} = 3(8) + 5(-3)$$
$$= 9 \qquad \textit{The vectors are \underline{not} perpendicular.}$$

2 **Find the inner product of $\vec{p}$ and $\vec{q}$, if $\vec{p} = (7, -2)$ and $\vec{q} = (4, 14)$.**

$$\vec{p} \cdot \vec{q} = 7(4) + -2(14)$$
$$= 0 \qquad \textit{The vectors are perpendicular.}$$

The inner product of vectors in space can also be found.

If $\vec{a} = (a_1, a_2, a_3)$ and $\vec{b} = (b_1, b_2, b_3)$, then $\vec{a} \cdot \vec{b} = a_1 b_1 + a_2 b_2 + a_3 b_3$.	***Inner Product of Vectors in Space***

Example

3 **Find the inner product of $\vec{u}$ and $\vec{v}$ if $\vec{u} = (2, -1, 3)$ and $\vec{v} = (5, 3, 0)$.**

$$\vec{u} \cdot \vec{v} = 2(5) + (-1)(3) + 3(0)$$
$$= 10 + -3 + 0$$
$$= 7 \qquad \textit{The vectors are \underline{not} perpendicular.}$$

Another important product of vectors in space is called the **cross product.** The cross product of two vectors is a vector which does not lie in the plane of the given vectors but is perpendicular to each. Thus, it is perpendicular to the plane containing the two vectors.

The cross product of $\vec{a}$ and $\vec{b}$ if $\vec{a} = (a_1, a_2, a_3)$ and $\vec{b} = (b_1, b_2, b_3)$ is defined as follows. $$\vec{a} \times \vec{b} = \begin{vmatrix} a_2 & a_3 \\ b_2 & b_3 \end{vmatrix} \vec{i} - \begin{vmatrix} a_1 & a_3 \\ b_1 & b_3 \end{vmatrix} \vec{j} + \begin{vmatrix} a_1 & a_2 \\ b_1 & b_2 \end{vmatrix} \vec{k}$$	***Cross Product***

An easy way to remember the coefficients of $\vec{i}, \vec{j},$ and $\vec{k}$ is to set up a determinant as shown and expand by minors using the first row.

$$\begin{vmatrix} \vec{i} & \vec{j} & \vec{k} \\ a_1 & a_2 & a_3 \\ b_1 & b_2 & b_3 \end{vmatrix}$$

Example

4 Find the cross product of $\vec{a}$ and $\vec{b}$ if $\vec{a} = (2, 4, -3)$ and $\vec{b} = (-1, 5, 2)$. Then, verify that the resulting vector is perpendicular to $\vec{a}$ and $\vec{b}$.

$$\vec{a} \times \vec{b} = \begin{vmatrix} \vec{i} & \vec{j} & \vec{k} \\ 2 & 4 & -3 \\ -1 & 5 & 2 \end{vmatrix}$$

$$= \begin{vmatrix} 4 & -3 \\ 5 & 2 \end{vmatrix} \vec{i} - \begin{vmatrix} 2 & -3 \\ -1 & 2 \end{vmatrix} \vec{j} + \begin{vmatrix} 2 & 4 \\ -1 & 5 \end{vmatrix} \vec{k}$$

$$= 23\vec{i} - 1\vec{j} + 14\vec{k} \text{ or } (23, -1, 14)$$

Check the inner product of $(23, -1, 14)$ and $(2, 4, -3)$.
$23(2) + (-1)(4) + 14(-3) = 0$ *The vectors are perpendicular.*
Check the inner product of $(23, -1, 14)$ and $(-1, 5, 2)$.
$23(-1) + (-1)(5) + 14(2) = 0$ *The vectors are perpendicular.*

Exploratory Exercises

Find each inner product and state whether or not the vectors are perpendicular.

1. $(4, -2) \cdot (3, 5)$ **2.** $(-3, 6) \cdot (4, 2)$ **3.** $(2, 4) \cdot (8, 4)$ **4.** $(1, 3) \cdot (3, -2)$ **5.** $(5, -1) \cdot (2, 3)$
6. $\vec{i} \cdot \vec{j}$ **7.** $\vec{j} \cdot \vec{j}$ **8.** $\vec{j} \cdot \vec{i}$ **9.** $(-6,1) \cdot (-1,2)$ **10.** $(2, 5) \cdot (0, -1)$

Use determinants to set up the cross product of the following vectors. Do not evaluate.

11. $(2, 3, -4), (-2, -3, 1)$ **12.** $(5, 2, 3), (-2, 5, 0)$ **13.** $(7, 2, 1), (2, 5, 3)$
14. $(7, -2, 4), (3, 8, 1)$ **15.** $(1, -3, 2), (5, 1, -2)$ **16.** $(-1, 0, 4), (5, 2, -1)$
17. $(-6, 2, 10), (4, 1, 9)$ **18.** $(-4, 9, -8), (3, 2, -2)$ **19.** $(3, -2, 4), (1, -4, 0)$

Written Exercises

Answer each of the following.

1-9. Find the inner product of each pair of vectors in exploratory exercises **11-19**.

10-18. State if the vectors given in exploratory exercises **11-19** are perpendicular.

19-27. Find the cross product of each pair of vectors in exploratory exercises **11-19**. Verify the cross products obtained are perpendicular to each vector used.

28. Prove $\vec{a} \cdot \vec{b} = \vec{b} \cdot \vec{a}$ for two-dimensional vectors.

29. Prove $\vec{a} \cdot \vec{b} = \vec{b} \cdot \vec{a}$ for three-dimensional vectors.

30. Show that $\vec{a} \times \vec{b} = -(\vec{b} \times \vec{a})$ for three-dimensional vectors.

31. Prove that $\vec{i} \cdot \vec{i} = 1, \vec{j} \cdot \vec{j} = 1$, and $\vec{k} \cdot \vec{k} = 1$.

Find a vector perpendicular to a plane containing the given points.

32. $(1, 2, 3), (-4, 2, -1)$, and $(5, -3, 0)$ **33.** $(-1, -1, -1), (-2, 2, 4)$, and $(0, 1, 2)$

For the Scholar

Given $\triangle ABC$ is an equilateral triangle and *BCDEF* and *AGHIC* are regular pentagons, find the measure of $\angle GCE$.

To solve problems involving forces, velocity, and displacements, vector diagrams can be used. A sharp pencil, a metric ruler, and a protractor are needed.

Example   A plane flying due east at 100 m/s is blown due south at 40 m/s by a strong wind. Find the plane's resultant velocity (speed and direction).

First, choose an appropriate scale. Let 1 cm = 20 m/s.

Next, draw the two component vectors to scale. Place the initial point of the second vector at the terminal point of the first vector.

Finally, draw the resultant and measure its direction and length. Multiply the length of the resultant by the scale to find the magnitude.

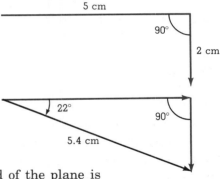

The direction is 22° south of east. The speed of the plane is 5.4 × 20 m/s, or 108 m/s.

Exercises   Use vector diagrams to solve each of the following.

1. An airplane flies due west at 240 km/h. At the same time, the wind blows it due south at 70 km/h. What is the plane's resultant velocity?

2. A hiker leaves camp and walks 15 km due north. The hiker then walks 15 km due east. What is the hiker's direction and displacement from the starting point?

3. Two soccer players kick the ball at the same time. One player's foot exerts a force of 70 newtons west. The other's foot exerts a force of 50 newtons north. What is the magnitude and direction of the resultant force on the ball?

4. An airplane flies at 150 km/h and heads 30° south of east. A 40 km/h wind blows it in the direction 30° west of south. What is the plane's resultant velocity?

Chapter Summary

1. **The Value of a Second Order Determinant:** The value of

$$\det \begin{bmatrix} a_1 & b_1 \\ a_2 & b_2 \end{bmatrix} \text{ or } \begin{vmatrix} a_1 & b_1 \\ a_2 & b_2 \end{vmatrix} = a_1 b_2 - a_2 b_1. \quad (65)$$

2. **Expansion of a Third Order Determinant:**

$$\begin{vmatrix} a_1 & b_1 & c_1 \\ a_2 & b_2 & c_2 \\ a_3 & b_3 & c_3 \end{vmatrix} = a_1 \begin{vmatrix} b_2 & c_2 \\ b_3 & c_3 \end{vmatrix} - b_1 \begin{vmatrix} a_2 & c_2 \\ a_3 & c_3 \end{vmatrix} + c_1 \begin{vmatrix} a_2 & b_2 \\ a_3 & b_3 \end{vmatrix} \quad (66)$$

3. **Cramer's Rule:** The solution to the system $\begin{array}{l} a_1 x + b_1 y = c_1 \\ a_2 x + b_2 y = c_2 \end{array}$ is

$$(x, y) \text{ where } x = \frac{\begin{vmatrix} c_1 & b_1 \\ c_2 & b_2 \end{vmatrix}}{\begin{vmatrix} a_1 & b_1 \\ a_2 & b_2 \end{vmatrix}} \text{ and } y = \frac{\begin{vmatrix} a_1 & c_1 \\ a_2 & c_2 \end{vmatrix}}{\begin{vmatrix} a_1 & b_1 \\ a_2 & b_2 \end{vmatrix}} \text{ and } \begin{vmatrix} a_1 & b_1 \\ a_2 & b_2 \end{vmatrix} \neq 0. \quad (66)$$

4. **Addition of Matrices:** The sum of two $m \times n$ matrices is an $m \times n$ matrix in which the elements are the sum of the corresponding elements of the given matrices. (69)

5. **Subtraction of Matrices:** The difference $A - B$ of two $m \times n$ matrices is equal to the sum $A + (-B)$, where $-B$ is the additive inverse of B. (70)

6. **Scalar Product:** The product of an $m \times n$ matrix A and a scalar k is an $m \times n$ matrix kA. Each element of kA is equal to k times the corresponding element of A. (71)

7. **Product of Two Matrices:** The product of an $m \times n$ matrix A and an $n \times r$ matrix B is an $m \times r$ matrix AB. The ijth element of AB is the product of the ith row of A and the jth column of B. (72)

8. **Identity Matrix under Multiplication:** The identity matrix of nth order, I_n, is the square matrix whose elements in the main diagonal, from upper left to lower right, are 1's, while all other elements are 0's. (73)

9. **Inverse of a Second Order Matrix:** If $A = \begin{bmatrix} a_1 & b_1 \\ a_2 & b_2 \end{bmatrix}$ and $\begin{vmatrix} a_1 & b_1 \\ a_2 & b_2 \end{vmatrix} \neq 0$, then $A^{-1} = \dfrac{1}{\begin{vmatrix} a_1 & b_1 \\ a_2 & b_2 \end{vmatrix}} \begin{bmatrix} b_2 & -b_1 \\ -a_2 & a_1 \end{bmatrix}. \quad (74)$

10. **Row Operations on Matrices:**
    1. Interchange any two rows.
    2. Replace any row with a non-zero multiple of that row.
    3. Replace any row with the sum of that row and a multiple of another row. (76)

11. A vector is a quantity which possesses both magnitude and direction. (79)

12. Representation of a Vector as an Ordered Pair: Suppose P_1 is the initial point of a vector, and P_2 is the terminal point. The ordered pair of numbers which represents $\overrightarrow{P_1P_2}$ is $(x_2 - x_1, y_2 - y_1)$. Its magnitude $|\overrightarrow{P_1P_2}| = \sqrt{(x_2 - x_1)^2 + (y_2 - y_1)^2}$.   (83)

13. The following operations are defined for $\vec{a} = (a_1, a_2)$, $\vec{b} = (b_1, b_2)$, and any real number k.

   Addition: $\vec{a} + \vec{b} = (a_1, a_2) + (b_1, b_2) = (a_1 + b_1, a_2 + b_2)$

   Subtraction: $\vec{a} - \vec{b} = (a_1, a_2) + (-b_1, -b_2) = (a_1 - b_1, a_2 - b_2)$

   Scalar Multiplication: $k\vec{a} = k(a_1, a_2) = (ka_1, ka_2)$ (83)

14. Representation of a Vector as an Ordered Triple: A vector from $P_1(x_1, y_1, z_1)$ to $P_2(x_2, y_2, z_2)$ in space can be represented by an ordered triple as follows; $\overrightarrow{P_1P_2} = (x_2 - x_1, y_2 - y_1, z_2 - z_1)$. Its magnitude $|\overrightarrow{P_1P_2}| = \sqrt{(x_2 - x_1)^2 + (y_2 - y_1)^2 + (z_2 - z_1)^2}$.   (86)

15. Inner Product of Vectors in the Plane: If $\vec{a}$ and $\vec{b}$ are two vectors, (a_1, a_2) and (b_1, b_2), the inner product of $\vec{a}$ and $\vec{b}$ is defined as $\vec{a} \cdot \vec{b} = a_1b_1 + a_2b_2$.   (88)

16. Inner Product of Vectors in Space: If $\vec{a} = (a_1, a_2, a_3)$ and $\vec{b} = (b_1, b_2, b_3)$, then $\vec{a} \cdot \vec{b} = a_1b_1 + a_2b_2 + a_3b_3$.   (89)

17. Cross Product: The cross product of $\vec{a}$ and $\vec{b}$ for $\vec{a} = (a_1, a_2, a_3)$ and $\vec{b} = (b_1, b_2, b_3)$ is defined as follows.

$$\vec{a} \times \vec{b} = \begin{vmatrix} a_2 & a_3 \\ b_2 & b_3 \end{vmatrix} \vec{i} - \begin{vmatrix} a_1 & a_3 \\ b_1 & b_3 \end{vmatrix} \vec{j} + \begin{vmatrix} a_1 & a_2 \\ b_1 & b_2 \end{vmatrix} \vec{k} \quad (89)$$

Chapter Review

Find the value of each determinant.   (3-1)

1. $\begin{vmatrix} 7 & -4 \\ 5 & -3 \end{vmatrix}$

2. $\begin{vmatrix} 8 & -4 \\ -6 & 3 \end{vmatrix}$

3. $\begin{vmatrix} 5 & 0 & 4 \\ 7 & 3 & -1 \\ 2 & -2 & 6 \end{vmatrix}$

4. $\begin{vmatrix} 3 & -1 & 4 \\ 5 & -2 & 6 \\ 7 & 3 & -4 \end{vmatrix}$

Solve each system of equations using Cramer's rule.   (3-1)

5. $3x + 2y = -2$
   $6x - y = 6$

6. $x + 4y = -9$
   $3x - 2y = 8$

Use matrices A, B, and C to find each matrix sum or difference.   (3-2)

$$A = \begin{bmatrix} 3 & 0 & 4 \\ 1 & 2 & -3 \\ 2 & -5 & 1 \end{bmatrix} \quad B = \begin{bmatrix} 6 & -1 & 5 \\ 2 & 1 & 3 \\ -4 & -3 & 3 \end{bmatrix} \quad C = \begin{bmatrix} 3 & 0 & -1 \\ -4 & 5 & 2 \\ 9 & -3 & 1 \end{bmatrix}$$

7. $A + B$

8. $A + C$

9. $B - C$

10. $C - B$

Use matrices R, S, and T to find each product.   (3-3)

$$R = \begin{bmatrix} 2 & 1 \\ -3 & 4 \end{bmatrix} \quad S = \begin{bmatrix} 5 & -1 & -3 \\ 7 & 2 & 5 \end{bmatrix} \quad T = [5 \quad -7]$$

11. $3R$

12. $4S$

13. TR

14. RS

Find the inverse of each matrix. (3-4)

15. $\begin{bmatrix} 3 & 2 \\ 1 & -5 \end{bmatrix}$
16. $\begin{bmatrix} -3 & 5 \\ -2 & 4 \end{bmatrix}$
17. $\begin{bmatrix} 5 & -4 \\ -4 & 3 \end{bmatrix}$
18. $\begin{bmatrix} 7 & 5 \\ 9 & 8 \end{bmatrix}$

Find matrix X for each of the following. (3-4)

19. $X \begin{bmatrix} 2 & 5 \\ -1 & -3 \end{bmatrix} = \begin{bmatrix} 1 & -3 \\ 2 & -1 \end{bmatrix}$
20. $\begin{bmatrix} 3 & 2 \\ -6 & 4 \end{bmatrix} X = \begin{bmatrix} -3 & 5 \\ 6 & 10 \end{bmatrix}$

Solve each system of equations using augmented matrices. (3-5)

21. $x - 2y - 3z = 2$
$x - 4y + 3z = 14$
$-3x + 5y + 4z = 0$

22. $2x + 3y - 4z = 5$
$x + y + 2z = 3$
$-x + 2y - 6z = 4$

Given vectors $\vec{a}$, $\vec{b}$, $\vec{c}$, and $\vec{d}$, find each vector sum or difference. (3-6)

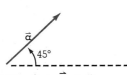
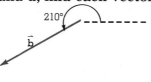

23. $\vec{a} + \vec{b} + \vec{c}$
24. $2\vec{c} - \vec{d}$
25. $2\vec{a} - 3\vec{b}$
26. $4\vec{d} - \vec{c}$

27-30. Find the magnitude and amplitude of each resultant in exercises **23-26.**

Find the magnitude of the vertical and horizontal components of each vector shown above. (3-6)

31. $\vec{a}$
32. $\vec{b}$
33. $\vec{c}$
34. $\vec{d}$

Find an ordered pair which represents $\overrightarrow{AB}$ for points A and B with the given coordinates. (3-7)

35. $A(2, 3); B(7, 15)$
36. $A(-2, 8); B(4, 12)$

37-38. Find the magnitude of $\overrightarrow{AB}$ for problems **35-36.**

Find an ordered pair to represent $\vec{u}$ in each equation below, if $\vec{v} = (2, -5)$ and $\vec{w} = (3, -1)$. (3-7)

39. $\vec{u} = \vec{v} + \vec{w}$
40. $\vec{u} = \vec{w} - \vec{v}$
41. $\vec{u} = 3\vec{v} + 2\vec{w}$
42. $\vec{u} = 3\vec{v} - 2\vec{w}$

For each pair of points A and B, find an ordered triple which represents $\overrightarrow{AB}$ for points A and B with the given coordinates. (3-8)

43. $A(2, -1, 4); B(6, -2, 1)$
44. $A(9, 8, 5); B(-1, 5, 11)$

45-46. Find the magnitude of $\overrightarrow{AB}$ for problems **43-44.**

Find an ordered triple to represent $\vec{u}$ in each equation below, if $\vec{v} = (4, 1, -2)$ and $\vec{w} = (-7, 3, 6)$. (3-8)

47. $\vec{u} = 2\vec{v} + \vec{w}$
48. $\vec{u} = \vec{v} - 3\vec{w}$
49. $\vec{u} = 3\vec{v} + 2\vec{w}$
50. $\vec{u} = 5\vec{w} - 3\vec{v}$

51-54. Write $\vec{u}$ as the sum of unit vectors for problems **47-50.**

Find each inner product or cross product. (3-9)

55. $(5, -1) \cdot (-2, 6)$
56. $(6, -5) \cdot (5, 6)$
57. $(4, 1, -2) \cdot (3, -4, 4)$
58. $(3, 8, 2) \cdot (7, -3, 1)$
59. $(2, -1, 4) \times (6, -2, 1)$
60. $(5, 2, -1) \times (2, -4, -4)$

Chapter Test

Find the value of each determinant.

1. $\begin{vmatrix} 8 & 5 \\ -3 & -2 \end{vmatrix}$

2. $\begin{vmatrix} 2 & 1 & -1 \\ 6 & 4 & -3 \\ 0 & 2 & -2 \end{vmatrix}$

Solve each system of equations using Cramer's rule.

3. $2x - y = 5$
  $5x - 4y = -1$

4. $3x + y = 2$
  $6x + 3y = 11$

Use matrices A, B, C, and D to find each sum, difference, or product.

$A = \begin{bmatrix} 5 & 4 \\ -1 & -2 \end{bmatrix}$ $\qquad B = \begin{bmatrix} -1 & -2 \\ 5 & 4 \end{bmatrix}$ $\qquad C = \begin{bmatrix} -2 & 4 & 6 \\ 5 & -7 & -1 \end{bmatrix}$ $\qquad D = \begin{bmatrix} 1 & -2 \\ 0 & 4 \\ -3 & 4 \end{bmatrix}$

5. $2A + B$ $\qquad\qquad$ **6.** $2B - A$ $\qquad\qquad$ **7.** CD $\qquad\qquad$ **8.** $AB + CD$

9. Find matrix X if $AX = B$.

10. Solve the following system of equations using augmented matrices.

$x + 2y + z = 3$
$2x - 3y + 2z = -1$
$x - 3y + 2z = 1$

Use vectors $\vec{a}$ and $\vec{b}$ to solve each problem.

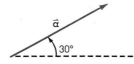

11. Find the magnitude and amplitude of $\vec{a} + \vec{b}$.

12. Find the magnitude and amplitude of $2\vec{a} - 3\vec{b}$.

13. Find the vertical and horizontal components of $\vec{a}$.

14. Find the vertical and horizontal components of $\vec{b}$.

For each pair of points A and B, find an ordered pair or ordered triple which represents $\overrightarrow{AB}$, for points A and B with the given coordinates.

15. $A(3, 6)$; $B(-1, 9)$

16. $A(-2, 7)$; $B(3, 10)$

17. $A(2, -4, 5)$; $B(9, -3, 7)$

18. $A(-4, -8, -2)$; $B(-8, -10, 2)$

Solve each of the following, for $\vec{u} = (-3, 7)$ and $\vec{v} = (4, 2)$.

19. Find $\vec{u} + \vec{v}$.

20. Find $4\vec{u} - 3\vec{v}$.

21. Find $|\vec{u}|$.

22. Find $|\vec{v}|$.

23. Write $\vec{u}$ as the sum of unit vectors.

24. Write $\vec{v}$ as the sum of unit vectors.

25. Find $\vec{u} \cdot \vec{v}$.

26. Is $\vec{u}$ perpendicular to $\vec{v}$?

Solve each of the following, for $\vec{r} = (-1, 3, 4)$ and $\vec{s} = (4, 3, -6)$.

27. Find $\vec{r} - \vec{s}$. $\qquad$ **28.** Find $3\vec{s} - 2\vec{r}$. $\qquad$ **29.** Find $|\vec{r}|$. $\qquad$ **30.** Find $|\vec{s}|$.

31. Write $\vec{r}$ as the sum of unit vectors.

32. Write $\vec{s}$ as the sum of unit vectors.

33. Find $\vec{r} \cdot \vec{s}$.

34. Find $\vec{r} \times \vec{s}$.

CHAPTER 4

The Circular Functions

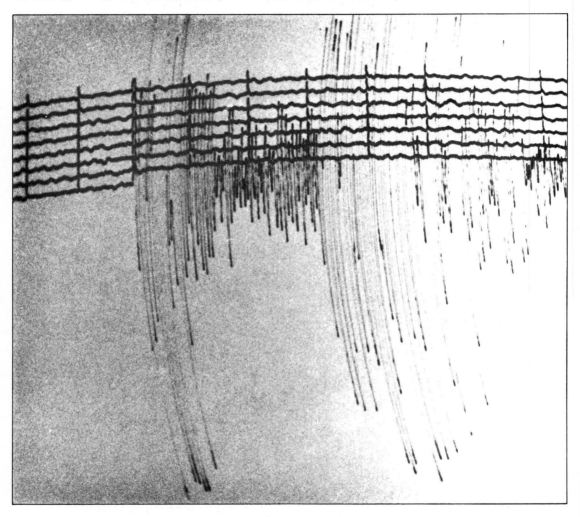

Scientists study waves to interpret earth tremors, vibrations, and particle counts. These waves have a repetitive pattern. The circular functions also have the property of repetitiveness that can be used as a reference in these interpretations.

4-1 The Wrapping Function

The set of real numbers is sometimes associated with points on a circle to form a function. Under this function each real number corresponds to *exactly one* point on the unit circle. A **unit circle** is a circle on the coordinate plane with its center at the origin and with radius 1 unit.

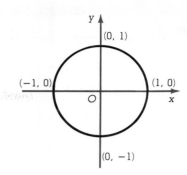

The set of real numbers has a one-to-one correspondence with the points of a number line as shown below. Let the measure of one unit of the number line be equal to the measure of the radius of the unit circle.

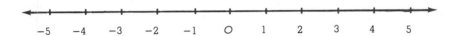

Next, orient the number line so that it is tangent to the unit circle at the point $(1, 0)$. The zero point on the number line is the point of tangency.

Imagine that the number line is a string which is *wrapped* around the unit circle in both directions from the point of tangency. Each point on the number line would coincide with a point on the circle. For example, the point π on the number line would lie on the point on the unit circle that has coordinates $(-1, 0)$ since the circumference of the unit circle is 2π. This wrapping procedure describes a function whose domain is the set of real numbers and whose range is the set of points on the unit circle. The inverse relation is *not* a function since each point on the circle can be associated with many real numbers.

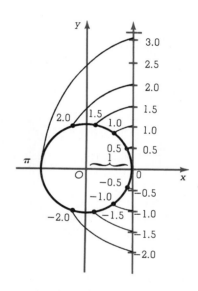

Consider an arc from the point $A(1, 0)$ to the point $P(x, y)$ on the unit circle. The real number $|s|$ represents the measure of the arc length in the same units as the number line. Define **function C** such that for each real number s, there corresponds exactly one ordered pair of real numbers, $C(s) = (x, y)$, which are coordinates of a point on the unit circle. If $s > 0$, the arc is measured counterclockwise along the circle from the point $(1, 0)$. If $s < 0$, the arc is measured clockwise along the circle from the point $(1, 0)$.

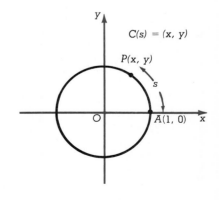

Example

1 Complete the following tables, given $C(s)$ and the unit circle.

Function C

s	0	$\dfrac{\pi}{2}$	π	$\dfrac{-\pi}{2}$	$\dfrac{\pi}{4}$
$C(s)$	a.	b.	c.	d.	e.

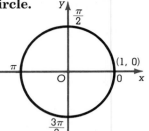

a. $C(0) = (1, 0)$

b. $C\left(\dfrac{\pi}{2}\right) = (0, 1)$

Use the fact that the circumference of a unit circle is 2π.

c. $C(\pi) = (-1, 0)$

d. $C\left(-\dfrac{\pi}{2}\right) = (0, -1)$

e. Let $P(x, y)$ represent $C\left(\dfrac{\pi}{4}\right)$. The length of the arc from (x, y) to $(0, 1)$ is equal to the length of the arc from (x, y) to $(1, 0)$. Thus, (x, y) is equidistant from $(0, 1)$ and $(1, 0)$.

Use the distance formula.

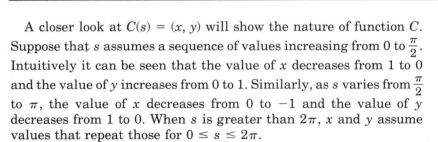

$$\sqrt{(x - 0)^2 + (y - 1)^2} = \sqrt{(x - 1)^2 + (y - 0)^2}$$
$$y = x \qquad \text{\textit{Solve for x.}}$$
$$x^2 + y^2 = 1 \qquad \text{\textit{Use the Pythagorean Theorem.}}$$
$$x^2 + x^2 = 1 \qquad \text{\textit{Substitute x for y.}}$$
$$x = \dfrac{\sqrt{2}}{2} \text{ and } y = \dfrac{\sqrt{2}}{2}$$

Thus, $C\left(\dfrac{\pi}{4}\right) = \left(\dfrac{\sqrt{2}}{2}, \dfrac{\sqrt{2}}{2}\right)$.

A closer look at $C(s) = (x, y)$ will show the nature of function C. Suppose that s assumes a sequence of values increasing from 0 to $\dfrac{\pi}{2}$. Intuitively it can be seen that the value of x decreases from 1 to 0 and the value of y increases from 0 to 1. Similarly, as s varies from $\dfrac{\pi}{2}$ to π, the value of x decreases from 0 to -1 and the value of y decreases from 1 to 0. When s is greater than 2π, x and y assume values that repeat those for $0 \leq s \leq 2\pi$.

How do x and y change as s increases from π to 2π?

Since the values of function C are the same for $C(s)$ and $C(s + 2\pi)$, function C is called a **periodic function** with a **period** of 2π.

A function is periodic if, for some real number α, $f(x + \alpha) = f(x)$ for each x in the domain of f. The least positive value of α for which $f(x) = f(x + \alpha)$ is the period of the function.

Periodic Function and Period

Example

2 **For each value of s, find the quadrant in which $C(s)$ is located.**

a. $\dfrac{7\pi}{4}$ b. $-\dfrac{3\pi}{4}$ c. $\dfrac{14\pi}{3}$ d. 10

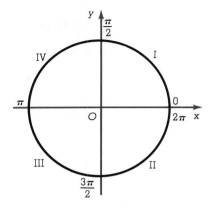

a. $s = \dfrac{7\pi}{4}$

$\dfrac{3\pi}{2} < \dfrac{7\pi}{4} < 2\pi$

Thus, $C\left(\dfrac{7\pi}{4}\right)$ is in Quadrant IV.

b. $s = -\dfrac{3\pi}{4}$

$-\pi < -\dfrac{3\pi}{4} < -\dfrac{\pi}{2}$

Thus, $C\left(-\dfrac{3\pi}{4}\right)$ is in Quadrant III.

c. $s = \dfrac{14\pi}{3}$

$= 4\pi + \dfrac{2\pi}{3}$

$= 2(2\pi) + \dfrac{2\pi}{3}$

$C\left(\dfrac{14\pi}{3}\right) = C\left(2(2\pi) + \dfrac{2\pi}{3}\right)$ or $C\left(\dfrac{2\pi}{3}\right)$ *Why?*

$\dfrac{\pi}{2} < \dfrac{2\pi}{3} < \pi$

Thus, $C\left(\dfrac{14\pi}{3}\right)$ is in Quadrant II.

d. $s = 10 = 6.28 + 3.72$ or $2\pi + 3.72$
$C(10) = C(2\pi + 3.72)$ or $C(3.72)$ *Use 3.14 for π.*

$\pi < 3.72 < \dfrac{3\pi}{2}$

Thus, $C(10)$ is in Quadrant III.

Exploratory Exercises

For each value of s, find the quadrant in which $C(s)$ is located.

1. $\dfrac{6\pi}{5}$

2. $\dfrac{16\pi}{3}$

3. 2

4. $-\dfrac{8\pi}{5}$

5. -5

6. $-\dfrac{\pi}{4}$

7. $\dfrac{5\pi}{6}$

8. $-\dfrac{48\pi}{7}$

9. 7.5

Suppose $C\left(\frac{7\pi}{8}\right) = (p, q)$. Solve each of the following.

10. Find a positive real number, a, other than $\frac{7\pi}{8}$, such that $C(a) = (p, q)$.

11. Find a negative real number, b, such that $C(b) = (p, q)$.

Suppose $C(4) = (s, t)$. Solve each of the following.

12. Write an expression that names all the other positive real numbers with coordinates (s, t) under function C.

13. Write an expression that names all the negative real numbers with coordinates (s, t) under function C.

Written Exercises

For each real number s, find the coordinates (x, y) determined by $C(s) = (x, y)$. Make a sketch of the unit circle if necessary.

1. $s = -\pi$
2. $s = \frac{5\pi}{4}$
3. $s = 4\pi$
4. $s = -\frac{19\pi}{4}$

5. $s = \frac{3\pi}{4}$
6. $s = 15\pi$
7. $s = -\frac{13\pi}{2}$
8. $s = -\frac{23\pi}{2}$

Make a sketch of the unit circle, separating it into 6 congruent arcs starting at (1, 0).

9-14. Find the shortest positive arc lengths in terms of π from (1, 0) to each point of division.

15-20. Use geometric relationships to find the coordinates (x, y) of each point of division.

For each real number s, find the coordinates (x, y) determined by $C(s) = (x, y)$. Use the results of problems 9-20.

21. $-\frac{\pi}{3}$
22. $6\pi - \frac{5\pi}{3}$
23. $\frac{79\pi}{3}$
24. $-\frac{5\pi}{3} + \pi$

Suppose $C(s) = \left(\frac{5}{13}, \frac{12}{13}\right)$. Find each of the following.

25. $C(-s)$
26. $C(s + 2\pi)$
27. $C(s + \pi)$
28. $C(\pi - s)$

Estimate the least positive value of s if $C(s) = (x, y)$. Use $\pi = 3.14$.

29. $(x, y) = (0, 1)$
30. $(x, y) = (-1, 0)$
31. $(x, y) = (0.97, 0.25)$
32. $(x, y) = (0.45, -0.89)$

33-36. Estimate the negative value of s which has the least absolute value for problems 29-32.

37-40. Estimate a positive value of s such that $s > 2\pi$ for problems 29-32.

Challenge Exercise

41. If $C(s) = (x, y)$, show that $C(-s) = (x, -y)$.

For the Scholar

A group of newscasters and weather reporters have an average age of 40 years. What is the ratio of newscasters to weather reporters, if the average age of the newscasters is 54 years and of the weather reporters is 32 years?

Using Calculators

Calculators have become very useful in finding the values for trigonometric functions. Before attempting to find these values, it is necessary to make sure the proper unit for the angle is being used. On most scientific calculators there is a key that will allow the unit of measure for an angle to be chosen from among degrees, radians, and grades. Most calculators are in the degree mode when turned on.

The following examples show how calculators can be used to find the values for trigonometric functions.

1 Find the value of sin 75°.

> Enter: 75 $\boxed{\text{sin}}$ *Calculator should be in degree mode.*
>
> Display: 0.965925826
>
> Thus, sin 75° ≈ 0.965295826.

Some calculators have a combination of keys that will allow the user to round to a particular place value without the user rounding.

2 Find the value of cos 42° to the nearest thousandth.

> Enter: $\boxed{\text{2ndF}}$ $\overset{\text{TAB}}{\boxed{\text{F↔E}}}$ 3   42 $\boxed{\text{cos}}$
>
> Display: 0.000   42   0.743
>
> Thus, cos 42° = 0.743 to the nearest thousandth.

3 Find the value of tan $\frac{\pi}{3}$ to the nearest hundredth.

> *changes degrees to radians   sets decimal*
>
> $\overset{\text{DRG}}{}$ $\overset{\text{TAB}}{}$ $\overset{\pi}{}$
>
> Enter: $\boxed{\text{2ndF}}$ $\boxed{\cdot}$ $\boxed{\text{2ndF}}$ $\boxed{\text{F↔E}}$ 2 $\boxed{\text{2ndF}}$ $\boxed{\text{EXP}}$ ÷ 3 $\boxed{=}$ $\boxed{\text{tan}}$
>
> Display: 0.00   3.14   3 1.05 1.73
>
> Thus, tan $\frac{\pi}{3}$ = 1.73 to the nearest hundredth.

To find the angle measurement given a value for the trigonometric function, use $\boxed{\text{2ndF}}$ and the trigonometric function key.

4 Find the radian measure of an angle with a tangent of 1.735.

> $\overset{\text{DRG}}{}$ $\overset{\text{tan}^{-1}}{}$
>
> Enter: $\boxed{\text{2ndF}}$ $\boxed{\cdot}$ 1.735 $\boxed{\text{2ndF}}$ $\boxed{\text{tan}}$
>
> Display: 1.735   1.047933909
>
> Thus, 1.047933909 is the radian measure of an angle whose tangent is 1.735.
>
> *All the inverse function values given are the principal values of those functions.*

Exercise Find the values for each of the following to the indicated place value.

1. cos 45°; thousandths **2.** sin $\frac{\pi}{4}$; tenths **3.** tan $\frac{3\pi}{4}$; hundredths **4.** tan 105°; hundredths

5. cos $\frac{\pi}{12}$; thousandths **6.** sin 60°; tenths **7.** cos 75°; hundredths **8.** tan 23°; thousandths

4-2 The Circular Functions

Using function C, each real number s now can be associated with a certain point on the unit circle having coordinates (x, y).

Two new functions may be formed from function C. The **cosine function** maps each real number s onto the value of the x-coordinate of $C(s)$. The **sine** function maps each real number s onto the value of the y-coordinate of $C(s)$.

> **For any real number s, where $C(s) = (x, y)$ such that $x^2 + y^2 = 1$, the cosine of $s = x$ and the sine of $s = y$. In abbreviated form, cos $s = x$ and sin $s = y$.**

Cosine and Sine Functions

The cosine function assigns a real number x to each real number s such that $-1 \le x \le 1$. The sine function assigns a real number y to each real number s such that $-1 \le y \le 1$. The domain of each of these circular functions is the set of all real numbers, and the range of each consists of the set of real numbers between -1 and $+1$, inclusive.

If (x, y) are the coordinates of any point $C(s)$ on the unit circle, then $x^2 + y^2 = 1$. But since $x = \cos s$ and $y = \sin s$ for any real number s, the following equation can be defined.

$$\cos^2 s + \sin^2 s = 1 \qquad cos^2 \ s \ means \ (cos \ s)^2.$$

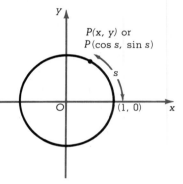

$P(x, y)$ or $P(\cos s, \sin s)$

Example

1 Find sin s when cos $s = \frac{3}{4}$ and $C(s)$ is in Quadrant I.

$$\sin^2 s + \cos^2 s = 1$$
$$\sin^2 s + \left(\frac{3}{4}\right)^2 = 1 \qquad \textit{Substitute } \frac{3}{4} \textit{ for cos s.}$$
$$\sin^2 s = 1 - \frac{9}{16}$$
$$\sin s = \pm\sqrt{\frac{7}{16}}$$

Since $C(s)$ is in Quadrant I, $\sin s = +\sqrt{\frac{7}{16}}$ or $\frac{\sqrt{7}}{4}$.

The ratios $\dfrac{\sin s}{\cos s}$ and $\dfrac{\cos s}{\sin s}$ and the reciprocals of the cosine and sine functions also determine circular functions. They are the **tangent** (tan), **cotangent** (cot), **secant** (sec), and **cosecant** (csc) functions.

Let s represent any real number. The tangent, cotangent, secant, and cosecant functions are defined as follows.

$$\tan s = \frac{\sin s}{\cos s} \qquad (\cos s \neq 0)$$

$$\cot s = \frac{\cos s}{\sin s} \qquad (\sin s \neq 0)$$

$$\sec s = \frac{1}{\cos s} \qquad (\cos s \neq 0)$$

$$\csc s = \frac{1}{\sin s} \qquad (\sin s \neq 0)$$

Tangent, Cotangent, Secant, and Cosecant Functions

Example

2 Find the values of the six circular functions of s if $s = \frac{3\pi}{4}$.

Using the definitions of the circular functions, each value can be found from $C\left(\frac{3\pi}{4}\right)$.
Recall that $C\left(\frac{3\pi}{4}\right) = \left(-\frac{\sqrt{2}}{2}, \frac{\sqrt{2}}{2}\right)$.

$$\cos \frac{3\pi}{4} = -\frac{\sqrt{2}}{2} \qquad\qquad \sec \frac{3\pi}{4} = \frac{1}{-\frac{\sqrt{2}}{2}} \text{ or } -\sqrt{2}$$

$$\sin \frac{3\pi}{4} = \frac{\sqrt{2}}{2} \qquad\qquad \csc \frac{3\pi}{4} = \frac{1}{\frac{\sqrt{2}}{2}} \text{ or } \sqrt{2}$$

$$\tan \frac{3\pi}{4} = \frac{\frac{\sqrt{2}}{2}}{-\frac{\sqrt{2}}{2}} \text{ or } -1 \qquad\qquad \cot \frac{3\pi}{4} = \frac{-\frac{\sqrt{2}}{2}}{\frac{\sqrt{2}}{2}} \text{ or } -1$$

Exploratory Exercises

State whether the value of each of the following is positive or negative.

1. $\sin \frac{\pi}{3}$

2. $\cos \frac{7\pi}{3}$

3. $\sec \frac{6\pi}{5}$

4. $\tan \frac{12\pi}{7}$

5. $\csc \frac{5\pi}{6}$

6. $\sin \left(-\frac{3\pi}{4}\right)$

7. $\cot \frac{9\pi}{4}$

8. $\cos \left(-\frac{5\pi}{4}\right)$

Determine the quadrant of the point $C(s)$ on the unit circle for each of the following conditions. Let n be some whole number.

9. $0 < (s \pm 2\pi n) < \dfrac{\pi}{2}$

10. $\dfrac{3\pi}{2} < (s \pm 2\pi n) < 2\pi$

11. $\pi < (s \pm 2\pi n) < \dfrac{3\pi}{2}$

12. $\dfrac{\pi}{2} < (s \pm 2\pi n) < \pi$

Suppose $C(s) = (0.6, 0.8)$. Find each of the following.

13. $\cos s$ **14.** $\csc s$ **15.** $\sin s$ **16.** $\cot s$

Suppose $C(s) = \left(\dfrac{\sqrt{2}}{2}, \dfrac{\sqrt{2}}{2}\right)$. Find each of the following.

17. $\tan s$ **18.** $\sec s$ **19.** $\cot s$ **20.** $\cos s$

Written Exercises

Copy and complete the following table using geometric relationships and the definitions of the six circular functions.

1.

s	$\cos s$	$\sin s$	$\tan s$	$\sec s$	$\csc s$	$\cot s$
0						
$\dfrac{\pi}{6}$						
$\dfrac{\pi}{4}$						
$\dfrac{\pi}{3}$						
$\dfrac{\pi}{2}$						

Find the value of each of the following.

2. $\sin \pi$

3. $\cos (-4\pi)$

4. $\sin 15\pi$

5. $\cos \dfrac{3\pi}{4}$

6. $\tan 2\pi$

7. $\sin \dfrac{15\pi}{2}$

8. $\cos \left(-\dfrac{5\pi}{6}\right)$

9. $\cot \dfrac{11\pi}{3}$

10. $\cos \dfrac{7\pi}{4}$

11. $\csc \dfrac{3\pi}{2}$

12. $\sec \dfrac{5\pi}{2}$

13. $\sin \left(-\dfrac{5\pi}{3}\right)$

Suppose $\cos r = \frac{3}{4}$ and $C(r)$ is in the first quadrant. Find the value of each of the following.

14. $\sec r$ **15.** $\tan r$ **16.** $\cot r$ **17.** $\csc r$

Suppose $\sin r = \frac{1}{2}$ and $C(r)$ is in the second quadrant. Find the value of each of the following.

18. $\cos r$ **19.** $\tan r$ **20.** $\csc r$ **21.** $\sec r$

Suppose $\cos r = \frac{8}{17}$ and $C(r)$ is in the fourth quadrant. Find the value of each of the following.

22. $\tan r$ **23.** $\sec r$ **24.** $\cot r$ **25.** $\csc r$

Copy and complete the following table which gives the signs of the circular functions in each quadrant.

26.

Function	I	II	III	IV
Cosine	+			+
Sine		+		−
Tangent	+		+	
Secant			−	
Cosecant		+		−
Cotangent	+			

Consider cos $(s + \alpha)$ and sin $(s + \alpha)$ where α is any real number.

27. Find three different values of α such that $\cos (s + \alpha) = \cos s$.

28. Find three different values of α such that $\sin (s + \alpha) = \sin s$.

29. What is the period of the cosine function?

30. What is the period of the sine function?

For the Scholar

Given rectangle *PQRS* with *PT* = *TU* = *UV* = *VR*, *PQ* = 15 and *QR* = 9. Find the area of $\triangle QUT$.

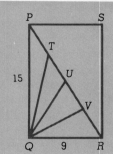

4-3 Finding Values of Circular Functions

Tables of values of circular functions usually are given only for s when $0 \le s \le \frac{\pi}{2}$. Therefore, relationships must be developed that permit use of the tables when s is either a negative number or a positive number greater than $\frac{\pi}{2}$.

It is possible to find an arc of measure s', where $0 < s' < \frac{\pi}{2}$, which is related to values of s outside the interval from 0 to $\frac{\pi}{2}$.

Multiples of $\frac{\pi}{2}$ are excluded in this development.

When the arc measured by s terminates in Quadrant I, every circular function $f(s)$ is equal to $f(s')$ where $s' = s - 2\pi n$, n is an integer, and $0 < s' < \frac{\pi}{2}$.	**Values of the Circular Functions in Quadrant I**

When the arc of measure s terminates in Quadrant II, the terminal point of the related arc with measure s' has the same ordinate of $C(s)$, y, and the additive inverse of the abscissa of $C(s)$, $-x$. This is equivalent to finding the image of $P(x, y)$ reflected on the y-axis.

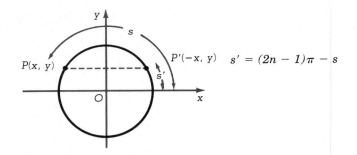

$s' = (2n - 1)\pi - s$

The following equations hold for any real number s when $C(s)$ is in Quadrant II where $s' = (2n - 1)\pi - s$, n is an integer, and $0 < s' < \dfrac{\pi}{2}$.

$\sin s = \sin s'$	$\cot s = -\cot s'$
$\cos s = -\cos s'$	$\sec s = -\sec s'$
$\tan s = -\tan s'$	$\csc s = \csc s'$

Values of Circular Functions in Quadrant II

Suppose $\pi < s < \dfrac{3\pi}{2}$. A double reflection, one on the x-axis and one on the y-axis, produces point $P'(-x, -y)$ which is the image of $P(x, y)$. Thus, when the arc of measure s terminates in Quadrant III, $P'(-x, -y)$ determines s', the measure of the related arc of s.

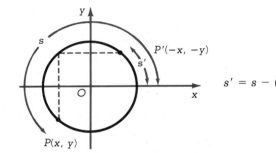

$s' = s - (2n - 1)\pi$

The following equations hold for any real number s when $C(s)$ is in Quadrant III where $s' = s - (2n - 1)\pi$, n is an integer, and $0 < s' < \dfrac{\pi}{2}$.

$\sin s = -\sin s'$	$\csc s = -\csc s'$
$\cos s = -\cos s'$	$\sec s = -\sec s'$
$\tan s = \tan s'$	$\cot s = \cot s'$

Values of Circular Functions in Quadrant III

For $\dfrac{3\pi}{2} < s < 2\pi$, the image of $P(x, y)$ under a reflection on the x-axis is $P'(x, -y)$. Thus, when the arc of measure s terminates in Quadrant IV, the terminal point of the related arc with measure s' has the same abscissa, x, and an ordinate which is the additive inverse of y.

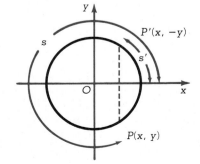

$s' = 2\pi n - s$

The following equations hold for any real number s when $C(s)$ is in Quadrant IV where $s' = 2\pi n - s$, n is an integer, and $0 < s' < \frac{\pi}{2}$.

$\sin s = -\sin s'$	$\csc s = -\csc s'$
$\cos s = \cos s'$	$\sec s = \sec s'$
$\tan s = -\tan s'$	$\cot s = -\cot s'$

Values of Circular Functions in Quadrant IV

Examples

1 **Find the value of $\cos \frac{7\pi}{6}$.**

$s = \frac{7\pi}{6}$. The arc of measure s terminates in Quadrant III and $s' = \frac{7\pi}{6} - \pi$.

$$\cos \frac{7\pi}{6} = -\cos \left(\frac{7\pi}{6} - \pi \right)$$

$$= -\cos \frac{\pi}{6} \text{ or } -\frac{\sqrt{3}}{2}$$

2 **Find the value of $\sin \frac{29\pi}{3}$.**

$s = \frac{29\pi}{3}$ or $9\pi + \frac{2\pi}{3}$. The arc of measure s terminates in Quadrant IV and $s' = 10\pi - s$.

$$\sin \frac{29\pi}{3} = -\sin \left(10\pi - \left(9\pi + \frac{2\pi}{3} \right) \right)$$

$$= -\sin \frac{\pi}{3} \text{ or } -\frac{\sqrt{3}}{2}$$

The values of the circular functions of any real number s may be found in the table on page 531 or by using a scientific calculator. A portion of the table of values is found on page 108.

Using **TAB** **F↔E** *4 will be the same 4 decimal places as the table.*

The real number s is represented by **radians** in the table. On a unit circle, an arc 1 unit in length is intercepted by the sides of a central angle whose measurement is one radian. Therefore, the measure of an intercepted arc on a unit circle, or s, is equal to the measure in radians of its central angle.

Angle	Radians	Sin	Cos	Tan	Cot	Sec	Csc		
18°00′	0.3142	0.3090	0.9511	0.3249	3.078	1.051	3.236	1.2566	72°00′
10′	0.3171	0.3118	0.9502	0.3281	3.047	1.052	3.207	1.2537	50′
20′	0.3200	0.3145	0.9492	0.3314	3.018	1.053	3.179	1.2508	40′
30′	0.3229	0.3173	0.9483	0.3346	2.989	1.054	3.152	1.2479	30′
40′	0.3258	0.3201	0.9474	0.3378	2.960	1.056	3.124	1.2450	20′
50′	0.3287	0.3228	0.9465	0.3411	2.932	1.057	3.098	1.2421	10′
19°00′	0.3316	0.3256	0.9455	0.3443	2.904	1.058	3.072	1.2392	71°00′
10′	0.3345	0.3283	0.9446	0.3476	2.877	1.059	3.046	1.2363	50′
30′	0.4625	0.4462	0.8949	0.4986	2.006	1.117	2.241	1.1083	30′
40′	0.4654	0.4488	0.8936	0.5022	1.991	1.119	2.228	1.1054	20′
50′	0.4683	0.4514	0.8923	0.5059	1.977	1.121	2.215	1.1025	10′
27°00′	0.4712	0.4540	0.8910	0.5095	1.963	1.122	2.203	1.0996	63°00′
		Cos	Sin	Cot	Tan	Csc	Sec	Radians	Angle

Angle and radian measures are listed on both sides of the table. Use the radian column heading at the top and read down the left-hand side to find the circular functions of s for $0 \le s \le 0.7854$. For example, tan $0.3229 = 0.3346$. Use the radian column heading at the bottom and read up the right-hand side to find the circular functions of s for $0.7854 \le s \le 1.5708$. For example, cot $1.2479 = 0.3346$.

$0.7854 \approx \frac{\pi}{4}$ and $1.5708 \approx \frac{\pi}{2}$.

Examples

3 Find the approximate value of cot (-1.86) using the table on page 531 or a calculator.

$s = -1.86$. The arc terminates in Quadrant III and $s' = s - (0 - 1)\pi$.
cot $(-1.86) =$ cot $(-1.86 + 3.14)$ *$\pi \approx 3.14$*
              $=$ cot (1.28) or 0.2994

4 Find the approximate value of csc 12.04 using the table on page 531 or a calculator.

$s = 12.04$. The arc terminates in Quadrant IV and $s' = 2\pi \cdot 2 - s$.
csc $12.04 = -$csc $(4(3.14) - 12.04)$
              $= -$csc (0.52) or -2.010

Using Calculators

Find the value of sec (-4.02) to three decimal places.

		TAB				DRG				
Enter:	2ndF	F↔E	3	2ndF	.	4.02	⁻⁄₊	cos	1/x	
Display:			0.000			4.02	−4.02	−0.638	−1.566	

Thus, sec $(-4.02) = -1.566$.

5 Find the approximate value of sin s = 0.9869 using the table on page 531 or a calculator.

sin s = 0.9869

The nearest sine value to 0.9869 is 0.9868. The value of s when sin s = 0.9868 is 1.4079. Thus, $s \approx 1.4079$.

6 Find the approximate value of cot s = 2.494 using the table on page 531 or a calculator.

cot s = 2.494

The nearest cotangent value to 2.494 is 2.496. The value of s when cot s = 2.496 is 0.3811. Thus, $s \approx 0.3811$.

Exploratory Exercises

Name the quadrant(s) which is described by each set of conditions.

1. sin s < 0, tan s < 0
2. sin s > 0, cot s < 0
3. cos s > 0, csc s < 0
4. cos s < 0, sin s < 0
5. tan s < 0, cos s < 0
6. sec s > 0, cos s > 0
7. cos s < 0, csc s < 0
8. sin s > 0, cot s > 0
9. sec s < 0, csc s > 0
10. sec s > 0, tan s < 0

Written Exercises

Find the approximate value of each of the following using the table on page 531 and π = 3.14 or a scientific calculator.

1. sin 0.175
2. cos $\frac{1}{3}$
3. tan $(\pi + 1)$
4. cos $\frac{2\pi}{5}$

5. tan $\left(-\frac{\pi}{10}\right)$
6. csc 4
7. sec 32
8. cot 6

9. sin (-13.25)
10. sec $(3\pi - 2)$
11. cot (-3π)
12. csc $\left(\frac{5\pi}{12} + 1.46\right)$

13. cos $(4\pi + 2)$
14. tan $\frac{\pi}{7}$
15. sin 100
16. sec $(5\pi - 1)$

Find the approximate value of s using the table on page 531 or a scientific calculator.

17. sin s = 0.1451
18. csc s = 1.053
19. tan s = 0.9000

20. csc s = 4.396
21. cos s = 0.9908
22. sec s = 1.305

23. cot s = 1.799
24. sin s = 0.8708
25. cot s = 0.2517

26. cos s = 0.5449
27. sec s = 6.291
28. tan s = 2.460

Answer each of the following.

29. Make a table of ordered pairs for $(x, \sin x)$ where x is an element of $\{0, 0.2, 0.4, 0.6, \ldots, 6.4\}$.

30. Make a table of ordered pairs for $(x, \cos x)$ where x is an element of $\{0, 0.2, 0.4, 0.6, \ldots, 6.4\}$.

31. Plot the points whose coordinates are given in the table in problem **29.**

32. Plot the points whose coordinates are given in the table in problem **30.**

For the Scholar

The points $(3, -4)$, $(1, 4)$, and $(0, 12)$ lie on the graph of $y = ax^2 + bx + c$. Find the value of $a + b + c$.

4-4 Graphs of the Circular Functions

The sine function generates ordered pairs of numbers of the form $(s, \sin s)$. If s is any real number, then $\sin s$ is a number such that $-1 \le \sin s \le 1$. The ordered pairs for values of s between 0 and $\frac{\pi}{2}$ can be read directly from the table or be determined on a calculator. For values of s outside the interval from 0 to $\frac{\pi}{2}$, ordered pairs can be determined by finding s' such that $0 \le s' \le \frac{\pi}{2}$ and then using the table or a calculator.

To graph the sine function, use the horizontal axis for values of s. Use the vertical axis for $\sin s$. The following charts provide the information necessary for plotting points.

	s	0	$\frac{\pi}{6}$	$\frac{\pi}{4}$	$\frac{\pi}{3}$	$\frac{\pi}{2}$	$\frac{2\pi}{3}$	$\frac{3\pi}{4}$	$\frac{5\pi}{6}$	π	$\frac{7\pi}{6}$	$\frac{5\pi}{4}$	$\frac{4\pi}{3}$	$\frac{3\pi}{2}$	$\frac{5\pi}{3}$	$\frac{7\pi}{4}$	$\frac{11\pi}{6}$	2π
$\sin s$	exact	0	$\frac{1}{2}$	$\frac{\sqrt{2}}{2}$	$\frac{\sqrt{3}}{2}$	1	$\frac{\sqrt{3}}{2}$	$\frac{\sqrt{2}}{2}$	$\frac{1}{2}$	0	$-\frac{1}{2}$	$-\frac{\sqrt{2}}{2}$	$-\frac{\sqrt{3}}{2}$	-1	$-\frac{\sqrt{3}}{2}$	$-\frac{\sqrt{2}}{2}$	$-\frac{1}{2}$	0
	nearest tenth	0.0	0.5	0.7	0.9	1.0	0.9	0.7	0.5	0.0	-0.5	-0.7	-0.9	-1.0	-0.9	-0.7	-0.5	0.0

After plotting points, complete the graph by connecting the plotted points with a smooth continuous curve.

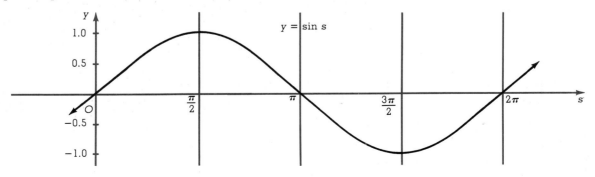

The graph of the cosine function is done in a similar manner.

Recall that both the sine and cosine function have a period of 2π.

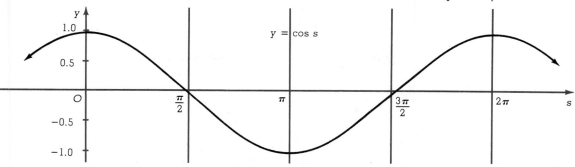

Example

1 **Find the quadrants in which both the sine and cosine functions are increasing.**

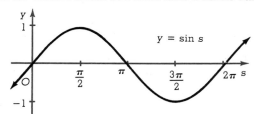

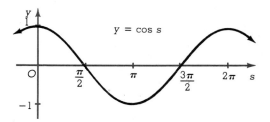

Look at the graphs of each function to find where each function is increasing. The sine function is increasing from 0 to $\frac{\pi}{2}$ and from $\frac{3\pi}{2}$ to 2π. The cosine function is increasing from π to $\frac{3\pi}{2}$ and from $\frac{3\pi}{2}$ to 2π. Thus, both functions are increasing from $\frac{3\pi}{2}$ to 2π or in the fourth quadrant.

From the graph of the ordered pairs $(s, \tan s)$ it is obvious that the tangent function is not defined for $\frac{\pi}{2}$ or $\frac{3\pi}{2}$. The graph is separated at these points by vertical asymptotes, indicated by broken lines. The graph of $\tan s$ approaches the asymptotes as s approaches $\frac{\pi}{2}$ and $\frac{3\pi}{2}$ from either side. The period of the tangent function is π.

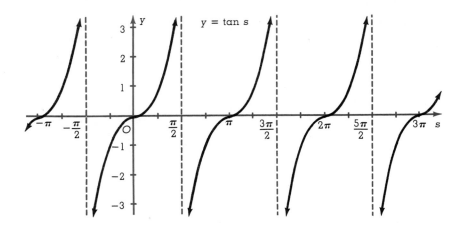

Notice how the following graphs of the secant, cosecant, and cotangent functions are related to the graphs of the cosine, sine, and tangent functions indicated by the broken curves.

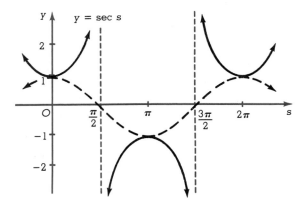

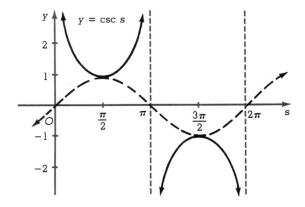

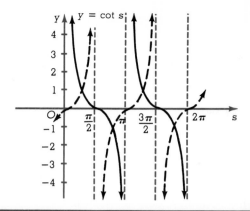

Example

2 State which circular functions of s are decreasing as values of s are increasing from 0 to $\frac{\pi}{2}$.

This information can be taken directly from the graphs of the circular functions. The cosine, cosecant, and cotangent functions are decreasing in the interval 0 to $\frac{\pi}{2}$.

Exploratory Exercises

State whether values of the following functions are increasing or decreasing as values of s increase from $\frac{\pi}{2}$ to π.

1. $y = \sin s$ **2.** $y = \cos s$ **3.** $y = \tan s$

4. $y = \cot s$ **5.** $y = \sec s$ **6.** $y = \csc s$

7-12. State whether values of the functions in problems **1-6** are increasing or decreasing as values of s increase from π to $\frac{3\pi}{2}$.

Written Exercises

State the values of s between and including 0 and 2π for which each expression is *not* defined.

1. $\sin s$ **2.** $\cos s$ **3.** $\tan s$

4. $\cot s$ **5.** $\sec s$ **6.** $\csc s$

Make a table of values for each of the following functions consisting of at least ten points for $0 \leq s \leq 2\pi$.

7. $y = \cos s$ **8.** $y = \tan s$ **9.** $y = \sec s$ **10.** $y = \cot s$

11-14. Graph each function in problems **7-10** using the tables from problems **7-10**.

Graph each of the following for values of s from -2π to 2π.

15. $y = \sin s$ **16.** $y = \cos s$

17-18. Find the negative value of s at which the functions in problems **15-16** are at a minimum.

19-20. Find the negative value of s at which the functions in problems **15-16** are at a maximum.

Find the quadrant(s) in which each pair of functions is decreasing.

21. $y = \sin s,\ y = \sec s$

22. $y = \cot s,\ y = \cos s$

23. $y = \sec s,\ y = \csc s$

24. $y = \csc s,\ y = \cot s$

Graph the sine and cosine functions on the same coordinate axes for $0 \le s \le 2\pi$. Use the graph to find values for s for which the equation or inequality is true.

25. $\sin s = \cos s$

26. $\sin s > \cos s$

27. $\sin s + \cos s = 2$

28. $|\sin s + \cos s| = 1$

29. $\cos s - \sin s = 1$

30. $\sin s \cdot \cos s = 0$

Challenge Exercise

31. Graph the six circular functions on the same coordinate axes for values of **s** from 0 to 2π. Use a different color for each function to distinguish curves.

For the Scholar

Triangle *DEF* is equilateral. $DF = 20$, $\overline{DP} \perp \overline{EF}$, and *K* is the midpoint of $\overline{DP}$. Find the length of $\overline{KE}$.

4-5 Addition Formulas

It is sometimes necessary to find the circular function of the sum or difference of two real numbers. A formula can be developed to find the cosine of the sum or difference of two real numbers.

Consider the unit circle on the right. The points P_1, P_2, and P_3 have coordinates as indicated. The measure of $\widehat{AP_1}$ is s_1. The measure of $\widehat{P_1P_2}$ and $\widehat{AP_3}$ is s_2. Thus $\widehat{AP_2}$ is congruent to $\widehat{P_1P_3}$ since each is measured by the sum, $s_1 + s_2$. From geometry, congruent arcs in the same circle have congruent chords. Therefore, $AP_2 = P_1P_3$.

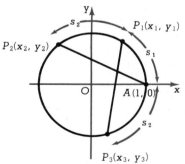

Remember $\widehat{P_1P_3}$ is the minor arc from P_1 to P_3.

$$AP_2 = P_1P_3$$

$$\sqrt{(x_2 - 1)^2 + (y_2 - 0)^2} = \sqrt{(x_1 - x_3)^2 + (y_1 - y_3)^2} \qquad \text{\textit{Use the distance formula}}$$

$$x_2{}^2 - 2x_2 + 1 + y_2{}^2 = x_1{}^2 - 2x_1x_3 + x_3{}^2 + y_1{}^2 - 2y_1y_3 + y_3{}^2$$

$$(x_2{}^2 + y_2{}^2) - 2x_2 + 1 = (x_1{}^2 + y_1{}^2) + (x_3{}^2 + y_3{}^2) - 2x_1x_3 - 2y_1y_3$$

$$1 - 2x_2 + 1 = \quad 1 \quad + \quad 1 \quad - 2x_1x_3 - 2y_1y_3 \qquad \text{\textit{Substitute, using the fact}}\ x^2 + y^2 = 1.$$

$$x_2 = x_1x_3 + y_1y_3$$

The following formula is obtained by substituting the appropriate function of s in the above equation. For example, $x_3 = \cos(-s_2)$.

Recall that $\cos(-s) = \cos s$ and $\sin(-s) = -\sin s$.

$$\cos(s_1 + s_2) = \cos s_1 \cos(-s_2) + \sin s_1 \sin(-s_2)$$

$$\mathbf{\cos(s_1 + s_2) = \cos s_1 \cos s_2 - \sin s_1 \sin s_2}$$

To find a formula for $\cos (s_1 - s_2)$, write $\cos (s_1 - s_2)$ as $\cos [s_1 + (-s_2)]$.

Then, use the formula above.

$$\cos [s_1 + (-s_2)] = \cos s_1 \cos (-s_2) - \sin s_1 \sin (-s_2)$$

$$\mathbf{\cos (s_1 - s_2) = \cos s_1 \cos s_2 + \sin s_1 \sin s_2}$$

The development of several other equations will lead to the formula for the sine of the sum or difference of two real numbers.

If s_1 is replaced with $\frac{\pi}{2}$ and s_2 with s in the formulas for $\cos (s_1 \pm s_2)$, the following equations are the result.

$$\cos \left(\frac{\pi}{2} + s\right) = -\sin s$$

$$\cos \left(\frac{\pi}{2} - s\right) = \sin s$$

Replace s with $\frac{\pi}{2} + s$ in the previous equation to obtain the following equation.

$$\cos s = \sin \left(\frac{\pi}{2} + s\right)$$

Replace s with $\frac{\pi}{2} - s$ in the equation for $\cos \left(\frac{\pi}{2} - s\right)$ to obtain the following equation.

$$\cos s = \sin \left(\frac{\pi}{2} - s\right)$$

In the equation for $\cos \left(\frac{\pi}{2} - s\right)$ replace s with $s_1 + s_2$.

$$\cos \left[\frac{\pi}{2} - (s_1 + s_2)\right] = \sin (s_1 + s_2)$$

$$\cos \left[\left(\frac{\pi}{2} - s_1\right) - s_2\right] = \sin (s_1 + s_2)$$

$$\cos \left(\frac{\pi}{2} - s_1\right) \cos s_2 + \sin \left(\frac{\pi}{2} - s_1\right) \sin s_2 = \sin (s_1 + s_2) \qquad \textit{Use formula for } \cos (s_1 - s_2).$$

$$\mathbf{\sin (s_1 + s_2) = \sin s_1 \cos s_2 + \cos s_1 \sin s_2} \qquad \textit{Substitute using previous equations.}$$

To obtain $\sin (s_1 - s_2)$ replace s_2 with $(-s_2)$ in the above formula.

$$\sin [s_1 + (-s_2)] = \sin s_1 \cos (-s_2) + \cos s_1 \sin (-s_2)$$

$$\mathbf{\sin (s_1 - s_2) = \sin s_1 \cos s_2 - \cos s_1 \sin s_2}$$

The following formulas hold for any real numbers s_1 and s_2.

$$\mathbf{\cos (s_1 \pm s_2) = \cos s_1 \cos s_2 \mp \sin s_1 \sin s_2}$$

$$\mathbf{\sin (s_1 \pm s_2) = \sin s_1 \cos s_2 \pm \cos s_1 \sin s_2}$$

Notice how the operation symbols in each equation are related.

Addition Formulas of Sine and Cosine Functions

1 **Find the cosine and sine of $\frac{7\pi}{12}$ using addition formulas for cosine and sine.**

$$\frac{7\pi}{12} = \frac{\pi}{4} + \frac{\pi}{3}$$ *Express as the sum of two real numbers.*

$$\cos \frac{7\pi}{12} = \cos \left(\frac{\pi}{4} + \frac{\pi}{3} \right)$$

$$= \cos \frac{\pi}{4} \cos \frac{\pi}{3} - \sin \frac{\pi}{4} \sin \frac{\pi}{3}$$ *Use formula for $\cos (s_1 + s_2)$.*

$$= \frac{\sqrt{2}}{2} \cdot \frac{1}{2} - \frac{\sqrt{2}}{2} \cdot \frac{\sqrt{3}}{2}$$

$$= \frac{\sqrt{2} - \sqrt{6}}{4}$$

$$\sin \frac{7\pi}{12} = \sin \left(\frac{\pi}{4} + \frac{\pi}{3} \right)$$

$$= \sin \frac{\pi}{4} \cos \frac{\pi}{3} + \cos \frac{\pi}{4} \sin \frac{\pi}{3}$$ *Use formula for $\sin (s_1 + s_2)$.*

$$= \frac{\sqrt{2}}{2} \cdot \frac{1}{2} + \frac{\sqrt{2}}{2} \cdot \frac{\sqrt{3}}{2}$$

$$= \frac{\sqrt{2} + \sqrt{6}}{4}$$

The cosine and sine of $\frac{7\pi}{12}$ are $\dfrac{\sqrt{2} - \sqrt{6}}{4}$ and $\dfrac{\sqrt{2} + \sqrt{6}}{4}$, respectively.

Using Calculators

Find the cosine and sine of $\frac{4\pi}{7}$ to four decimal places.

Enter:	2ndF	F↔E	4	2ndF	·	4	×	2ndF	EXP
Display:		0.0000				4	4.000		3.1416

Enter:	÷	7	=	M+	COS	CE	RM	sin
Display:	12.5664	7	1.7952		−0.2225	0.0000	1.7952	0.9749

Therefore, the cosine and sine of $\frac{4\pi}{7}$ are -0.2225 and 0.9749, respectively.

Exploratory Exercises

Write each value in terms of sums or differences of $\frac{\pi}{6}$, $\frac{\pi}{4}$, $\frac{\pi}{3}$, and $\frac{\pi}{2}$ or their multiples.

1. $\dfrac{5\pi}{6}$

2. $-\dfrac{\pi}{12}$

3. $-\dfrac{11\pi}{12}$

4. $\dfrac{11\pi}{12}$

5. $\dfrac{5\pi}{12}$

6. $-\dfrac{5\pi}{12}$

7. $\dfrac{19\pi}{12}$

8. $\dfrac{17\pi}{12}$

Written Exercises

Let $s_1 = \dfrac{\pi}{2}$ and $s_2 = \dfrac{\pi}{2}$. Verify the formulas for each of the following.

1. $\cos(s_1 + s_2)$

2. $\cos(s_1 - s_2)$

3. $\sin(s_1 + s_2)$

Let $s_1 = 0$ and $s_2 = \dfrac{\pi}{3}$. Verify the formulas for each of the following.

4. $\sin(s_1 - s_2)$

5. $\cos(s_1 - s_2)$

6. $\sin(s_1 + s_2)$

Evaluate each expression using the addition formulas.

7. $\sin\dfrac{5\pi}{12}$

8. $\sin\dfrac{11\pi}{12}$

9. $\sin\left(-\dfrac{19\pi}{12}\right)$

10. $\cos\dfrac{5\pi}{12}$

11. $\cos\dfrac{13\pi}{12}$

12. $\cos\dfrac{17\pi}{12}$

13. $\cos\left(-\dfrac{\pi}{12}\right)$

14. $\sin\dfrac{5\pi}{6}$

15. $\cos\left(-\dfrac{11\pi}{12}\right)$

Develop a formula for each of the following sums or differences.

16. $\sin(\pi + s)$

17. $\sin(\pi - s)$

18. $\cos(\pi - s)$

19. $\cos(\pi + s)$

20. $\sin(2\pi + s)$

21. $\sin(2\pi - s)$

22. $\cos(2\pi - s)$

23. $\cos(2\pi + s)$

24. $\tan(s_1 + s_2)$

25. $\tan(s_1 - s_2)$

26. $\cot(s_1 + s_2)$

27. $\cot(s_1 - s_2)$

Verify each of the following equations.

28. $\cos\left(\dfrac{\pi}{6} + s\right) + \sin\left(\dfrac{\pi}{3} + s\right) = \sqrt{3}\cos s$

29. $\sin\left(\dfrac{3\pi}{2} + s\right) - \cos\left(\dfrac{\pi}{2} - s\right) = -(\cos s + \sin s)$

30. $\tan(\pi + s)\cos s = -\cos\left(\dfrac{3\pi}{2} - s\right)$

31. $\cos\left(\dfrac{\pi}{3} - s_1\right)\cos\left(\dfrac{5\pi}{3} + s_2\right) - \sin\left(\dfrac{\pi}{3} - s_1\right)\sin\left(\dfrac{5\pi}{3} + s_2\right) = \cos(s_2 - s_1)$

For the Scholar

A merchant bought 336 sweaters for her shop. She sold the first 300 sweaters for the same price she paid for the original 336. What was her percent of gain when the remaining 36 sweaters sold for the same amount as each of the other 300 sweaters?

4-6 Double and Half Number Formulas

The formula for $\sin(s_1 + s_2)$ can be used to find a formula for $\sin 2s$.

$$\sin 2s = \sin(s + s)$$
$$= \sin s \cos s + \cos s \sin s$$
$$= 2 \sin s \cos s$$

Likewise, a formula for $\cos 2s$ can be developed.

$$\cos 2s = \cos(s + s)$$
$$= \cos s \cos s - \sin s \sin s$$
$$= \cos^2 s - \sin^2 s$$

Substituting $1 - \cos^2 s$ for $\sin^2 s$ and $1 - \sin^2 s$ for $\cos^2 s$ respectively in the formula above yields alternate forms of $\cos 2s$.

Since $\sin^2 s + \cos^2 s = 1$, $\sin^2 s = 1 - \cos^2 s$ and $\cos^2 s = 1 - \sin^2 s$.

$$\cos 2s = 2 \cos^2 s - 1$$
$$\cos 2s = 1 - 2 \sin^2 s$$

The following formulas hold for any real number s.

$$\mathbf{\sin 2s = 2 \sin s \cos s} \qquad \mathbf{\cos 2s = \cos^2 s - \sin^2 s}$$
$$\mathbf{= 2 \cos^2 s - 1}$$
$$\mathbf{= 1 - 2 \sin^2 s}$$

Double Number Formulas

Example

1 **Suppose $C(s)$ is in Quadrant I and $\sin s = \frac{4}{5}$. Find $\sin 2s$.**

Since $\sin 2s = 2 \sin s \cos s$, find $\cos s$ first. Use $\cos^2 s + \sin^2 s = 1$.

$$\cos^2 s + \left(\frac{4}{5}\right)^2 = 1 \qquad\qquad \text{Substitute } \tfrac{4}{5} \text{ for } \sin s.$$

$$\cos^2 s = 1 - \left(\frac{4}{5}\right)^2$$

$$\cos s = \pm\sqrt{\frac{9}{25}} \text{ or } \pm\frac{3}{5}$$

Since $C(s)$ is in Quadrant I, $\cos s$ must be positive.

$$\sin 2s = 2 \sin s \cos s$$
$$= 2\left(\frac{4}{5}\right)\left(\frac{3}{5}\right) \text{ or } \frac{24}{25}$$

The two alternate forms of the formula for $\cos 2s$ may be solved for $\cos s$ and $\sin s$, respectively.

$$\cos s = \pm\sqrt{\frac{1 + \cos 2s}{2}}$$

$$\sin s = \pm\sqrt{\frac{1 - \cos 2s}{2}}$$

The sign is chosen according to the quadrant in which the point determined by $C(s)$ is located.

Since s is a real number, $2s$ may be replaced with r and thus s with $\frac{r}{2}$ to derive the formulas for half of any real number r.

The following formulas hold for any real number r.	**Half Number Formulas**
$$\cos\frac{r}{2} = \pm\sqrt{\frac{1 + \cos r}{2}} \qquad \sin\frac{r}{2} = \pm\sqrt{\frac{1 - \cos r}{2}}$$	

Examples

2 **Find $\sin\frac{\pi}{8}$.**

$$\sin\frac{\pi}{8} = \sin\frac{\frac{\pi}{4}}{2}$$

Restate $\frac{\pi}{8}$ as half of a number

$$= \pm\sqrt{\frac{1 - \cos\frac{\pi}{4}}{2}}$$

$\frac{1}{2}$ of $\frac{\pi}{4}$ or $\frac{\frac{\pi}{4}}{2}$, then use the formula for $\sin\frac{r}{2}$.

$$= \pm\sqrt{\frac{1 - \frac{\sqrt{2}}{2}}{2}} \text{ or } \pm\sqrt{\frac{2 - \sqrt{2}}{4}} \qquad \cos\frac{\pi}{4} = \frac{\sqrt{2}}{2}$$

Since $C\left(\frac{\pi}{8}\right)$ is in Quadrant I, the value of $\sin\frac{\pi}{8}$ is positive.

The solution is $\dfrac{\sqrt{2 - \sqrt{2}}}{2}$.

3 **Find $\cos\frac{5\pi}{12}$.**

$$\cos\frac{5\pi}{12} = \cos\frac{\frac{5\pi}{6}}{2}$$

$$= \pm\sqrt{\frac{1 + \cos\frac{5\pi}{6}}{2}} \qquad \cos\frac{5\pi}{6} = -\frac{\sqrt{3}}{2}$$

$$= \pm\sqrt{\frac{1 + -\frac{\sqrt{3}}{2}}{2}} \text{ or } \pm\sqrt{\frac{2 - \sqrt{3}}{4}}$$

Since $C\left(\frac{5\pi}{12}\right)$ is in Quadrant I, the value of $\cos\frac{5\pi}{12}$ is positive.

The solution is $\sqrt{\dfrac{2 - \sqrt{3}}{4}}$.

Exploratory Exercises

Find the value of each of the following using the half number formulas.

1. $\sin \dfrac{\pi}{12}$

2. $\sin \dfrac{3\pi}{8}$

3. $\sin \dfrac{3\pi}{16}$

4. $\cos \dfrac{7\pi}{12}$

5. $\cos \dfrac{3\pi}{8}$

6. $\sin \dfrac{11\pi}{12}$

7. $\cos \dfrac{3\pi}{16}$

8. $\cos \dfrac{11\pi}{12}$

9. $\cos \dfrac{7\pi}{8}$

Written Exercises

Find $\sin 2s$ for each of the following.

1. $\sin s = \dfrac{1}{2}$, $C(s)$ is in Quadrant I

2. $\cos s = \dfrac{3}{5}$, $C(s)$ is in Quadrant I

3. $\cos s = -\dfrac{2}{3}$, $C(s)$ is in Quadrant III

4. $\sin s = \dfrac{4}{5}$, $C(s)$ is in Quadrant II

5. $\sin s = \dfrac{5}{13}$, $C(s)$ is in Quadrant II

6. $\cos s = \dfrac{1}{5}$, $C(s)$ is in Quadrant IV

7. $\sin s = -\dfrac{3}{4}$, $C(s)$ is in Quadrant IV

8. $\cos s = -\dfrac{1}{3}$, $C(s)$ is in Quadrant III

9-16. Find $\cos \dfrac{s}{2}$ for problems **1-8.**

17-24. Find $\sin \dfrac{s}{2}$ for problems **1-8.**

25-32. Find $\cos 2s$ for problems **1-8.**

Solve each of the following.

33. Develop a formula for $\tan 2s$ in terms of $\tan s$.

34. Develop a formula for $\tan \dfrac{r}{2}$ in terms of $\cos r$.

35. Develop a formula for $\sin 3s$ in terms of $\sin s$.

36. Develop a formula for $\cos 3s$ in terms of $\cos s$.

For the Scholar

In $\odot O$, chords $\overline{MN}$ and $\overline{KL}$ are perpendicular at point P. Find the length of the radius of $\odot O$ when $MP = 4$, $PN = 12$, and $PL = 3$.

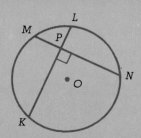

Chapter Summary

1. Function C is defined such that for each real number s, there corresponds exactly one ordered pair of real numbers (x, y) which are coordinates of a point on the unit circle. (97)

2. **Periodic Function and Period:** A function is periodic if, for some real number α, $f(x + \alpha) = f(x)$ for each x in the domain of f. The least positive value of α for which $f(x) = f(x + \alpha)$ is the period of the function. (98)

3. **Cosine and Sine Functions:** For any real number s, where $C(s) = (x, y)$ such that $x^2 + y^2 = 1$, the cosine of $s = x$ and the sine of $s = y$. In abbreviated form, $\cos s = x$ and $\sin s = y$. (102)

4. **Tangent, Cotangent, Secant, and Cosecant Functions:** Let s represent any real number. The tangent, cotangent, secant, and cosecant functions are defined as follows. (103)

$$\tan s = \frac{\sin s}{\cos s} \qquad (\cos s \neq 0)$$

$$\cot s = \frac{\cos s}{\sin s} \qquad (\sin s \neq 0)$$

$$\sec s = \frac{1}{\cos s} \qquad (\cos s \neq 0)$$

$$\csc s = \frac{1}{\sin s} \qquad (\sin s \neq 0)$$

5. **Values of the Circular Functions in Quadrants:** (105, 106, 107)

Quadrant s'	I $s' = s - 2\pi n$	II $s' = (2n-1)\pi - s$	III $s' = s - (2n-1)\pi$	IV $s' = 2\pi n - s$
Function				
$\sin s$	$\sin s'$	$\sin s'$	$-\sin s'$	$-\sin s'$
$\cos s$	$\cos s'$	$-\cos s'$	$-\cos s'$	$\cos s'$
$\tan s$	$\tan s'$	$-\tan s'$	$\tan s'$	$-\tan s'$
$\csc s$	$\csc s'$	$\csc s'$	$-\csc s'$	$-\csc s'$
$\sec s$	$\sec s'$	$-\sec s'$	$-\sec s'$	$\sec s'$
$\cot s$	$\cot s'$	$-\cot s'$	$\cot s'$	$-\cot s'$

6. **Addition Formulas of Sine and Cosine Functions:** The following formulas hold for any real numbers s_1 and s_2. (116)

$$\cos (s_1 \pm s_2) = \cos s_1 \cos s_2 \mp \sin s_1 \sin s_2$$
$$\sin (s_1 \pm s_2) = \sin s_1 \cos s_2 \pm \cos s_1 \sin s_2$$

7. **Double Number Formulas:** The following formulas hold for any real number s. (118)

$$\sin 2s = 2 \sin s \cos s \qquad \cos 2s = \cos^2 s - \sin^2 s$$
$$= 2 \cos^2 s - 1$$
$$= 1 - 2 \sin^2 s$$

8. **Half Number Formulas:** The following formulas hold for any real number r. (119)

$$\cos \frac{r}{2} = \pm \sqrt{\frac{1 + \cos r}{2}} \qquad \sin \frac{r}{2} = \pm \sqrt{\frac{1 - \cos r}{2}}$$

Chapter Review

For each real number s, find the coordinates (x, y) determined by $C(s) = (x, y)$. (4-1)

1. $\frac{5\pi}{4}$

2. $-\frac{13\pi}{2}$

3. 15π

4. $-\frac{\pi}{4}$

5. -4π

6. $6\pi - \frac{5\pi}{3}$

7. $-\frac{4\pi}{3} + \pi$

8. $-\frac{41\pi}{3}$

Suppose $C(s) = \left(\frac{3}{5}, \frac{4}{5}\right)$. Find each of the following. (4-2)

9. $\sin s$

10. $\cos s$

11. $\tan s$

12. $\csc s$

Find the value of each of the following. (4-2)

13. $\cos 0$

14. $\sin \frac{\pi}{6}$

15. $\cot \frac{\pi}{6}$

16. $\sec \frac{\pi}{4}$

17. $\csc \frac{\pi}{3}$

18. $\tan \frac{\pi}{2}$

19. $\cos (-3\pi)$

20. $\cot \frac{11\pi}{4}$

21. $\sin \left(-\frac{5\pi}{3}\right)$

22. $\sec \frac{3\pi}{2}$

23. $\tan \pi$

24. $\csc \left(-\frac{5\pi}{6}\right)$

Find the approximate value of each of the following using the table on page 531 and $\pi = 3.14$, or a scientific calculator. (4-3)

25. $\sin \frac{1}{3}$

26. $\tan \frac{3\pi}{8}$

27. $\cos (-6)$

28. $\csc \frac{2\pi}{7}$

29. $\sec (-12.35)$

30. $\sin 15$

31. $\sec 1.776$

32. $\cot (\pi + 0.5)$

Find the approximate value of s using the table on page 531 or a scientific calculator. (4-3)

33. $\sin s = 0.9939$

34. $\tan s = 0.6164$

35. $\cos s = 0.3121$

36. $\cot s = 3.275$

37. $\sec s = 1.427$

38. $\csc s = 48.79$

Graph each of the following for values of s from 0 to 4π. (4-4)

39. $y = \cos s$

40. $y = \sin s$

41. $y = \tan s$

Evaluate each expression using the sum or difference formulas. (4-5)

42. $\sin \frac{\pi}{12}$

43. $\cos \left(-\frac{5\pi}{12}\right)$

44. $\cos \frac{5\pi}{6}$

45. $\sin \left(-\frac{19\pi}{12}\right)$

Find each of the following. (4-6)

46. If $\sin s = -\frac{3}{5}$ and $C(s)$ is in the third quadrant, find $\sin 2s$.

47. If $\sin s = \frac{1}{4}$ and $C(s)$ is in the first quadrant, find $\cos 2s$.

48. If $\cos s = \frac{17}{25}$ and $C(s)$ is in the fourth quadrant, find $\cos \frac{s}{2}$.

Chapter Test

For each real number s, find the coordinates (x, y) determined by $C(s) = (x, y)$.

1. $\dfrac{3\pi}{2}$

2. $-\dfrac{5\pi}{4}$

3. $\dfrac{16\pi}{3}$

4. 32π

5. $-7\pi + \dfrac{4\pi}{3}$

6. $\dfrac{7\pi}{4}$

7. -5π

8. $\dfrac{5\pi}{3} - 9\pi$

Find the value of each of the following.

9. $\sin \dfrac{11\pi}{3}$

10. $\tan 0$

11. $\cos \left(-\dfrac{4\pi}{3}\right)$

12. $\sec \dfrac{3\pi}{4}$

13. $\cot \dfrac{\pi}{3}$

14. $\csc \dfrac{\pi}{2}$

15. $\sin \left(-\dfrac{\pi}{6}\right)$

16. $\cos 7\pi$

Suppose $\sin r = \dfrac{\sqrt{2}}{2}$ and r is in the second quadrant. Evaluate each of the following.

17. $\cos r$

18. $\tan r$

19. $\cot r$

20. $\sec r$

Find the approximate value of each of the following using the table on page 531 and $\pi = 3.14$, or using a scientific calculator.

21. $\sin 4$

22. $\cos \dfrac{4\pi}{5}$

23. $\tan (-6.1)$

24. $\csc \dfrac{15\pi}{8}$

Find the approximate value of s using the table on page 531 or using a scientific calculator.

25. $\cos s = 0.3805$

26. $\tan s = 0.0260$

27. $\sec s = 4.400$

28. $\sin s = 0.5830$

Graph each of the following for values of s from 0 to 2π.

29. $y = \sin s$

30. $y = \tan s$

Evaluate each expression using the sum or difference formulas.

31. $\sin \dfrac{17\pi}{12}$

32. $\cos \dfrac{5\pi}{12}$

33. $\sin \left(-\dfrac{\pi}{12}\right)$

34. If $C(s)$ is in the first quadrant and $\cos s = \dfrac{3}{4}$, find $\sin \dfrac{s}{2}$.

35. If $C(s)$ is in the third quadrant and $\sin s = -\dfrac{4}{5}$, find $\cos 2s$.

CHAPTER 5

The Trigonometric Functions

Angles and their relationships are used in building roads and bridges. One area of mathematics which deals with the functions of angles is called trigonometry.

5-1 Trigonometric Functions of an Angle

In the circular functions, the coordinates of the points on a unit circle are the basis for the definitions of the sine and cosine functions with the real numbers as the domain. An area of mathematics called **trigonometry** also involves the sine and cosine functions. In trigonometry the domain of each function is also the set of real numbers. However, each real number is the measure of an angle rather than the measure of an arc.

An **angle** is the union of two rays that have a common endpoint. An angle may be generated by the rotation of a ray with a fixed endpoint. The starting position of the ray is called the **initial side** and the final position is called the **terminal side.** If the rotation is counterclockwise, the measure of the angle is positive. If the rotation is clockwise, the measure of the angle is negative.

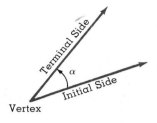

Let the positive x-axis of the coordinate system be the initial side of an angle with measure α, and let $P(x, y)$ be a point on the terminal side of an angle with measure α. The distance from the origin is given by r and is defined to be positive. By the Pythagorean Theorem, $r = \sqrt{x^2 + y^2}$.

An angle with its vertex at the origin and its initial side along the positive x-axis is in standard position.

The three numbers represented by x, y, and r can be arranged into six ratios. The values of these ratios depend upon the measure α of $\angle POM$. These ratios are called the **trigonometric functions** of α.

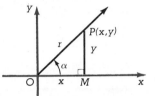

For any angle with measure α, point $P(x, y)$ on its terminal side, and $r = \sqrt{x^2 + y^2}$, the trigonometric functions of α are as follows.

$$\sin \alpha = \frac{y}{r} \qquad \cos \alpha = \frac{x}{r} \qquad \tan \alpha = \frac{y}{x}$$

$$\csc \alpha = \frac{r}{y} \qquad \sec \alpha = \frac{r}{x} \qquad \cot \alpha = \frac{x}{y}$$

Trigonometric Functions of an Angle in Standard Position

Example

1 **Find the values of the six trigonometric functions of an angle in standard position with measure α if the point (4, 3) lies on its terminal side.**

First find the value of r.
$$\begin{aligned} r &= \sqrt{x^2 + y^2} \\ &= \sqrt{16 + 9} \\ &= 5 \end{aligned}$$

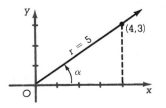

$$\sin \alpha = \frac{y}{r} \text{ or } \frac{3}{5} \qquad \cos \alpha = \frac{x}{r} \text{ or } \frac{4}{5} \qquad \tan \alpha = \frac{y}{x} \text{ or } \frac{3}{4}$$

$$\csc \alpha = \frac{r}{y} \text{ or } \frac{5}{3} \qquad \sec \alpha = \frac{r}{x} \text{ or } \frac{5}{4} \qquad \cot \alpha = \frac{x}{y} \text{ or } \frac{4}{3}$$

Right triangles are also used to define trigonometric functions. Let A, B, and C designate the vertices of a right triangle and the angles at those vertices. The lengths of the opposite sides are designated by a, b, and c, respectively. Possible ratios of the sides are $\frac{b}{a}$, $\frac{a}{b}$, $\frac{a}{c}$, $\frac{c}{a}$, $\frac{b}{c}$, and $\frac{c}{b}$.

All right triangles having acute angles congruent to angles A and B are similar. Thus, the ratios of corresponding sides are equal. These ratios are determined by the measures of the acute angles. Therefore, any two congruent angles of different right triangles will have the same ratios associated with them.

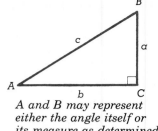

A and B may represent either the angle itself or its measure as determined by the context.

For an acute angle A in right triangle ABC, the trigonometric functions are as follows.

$$\sin A = \frac{\text{side opposite}}{\text{hypotenuse}} = \frac{a}{c} \qquad \cos A = \frac{\text{side adjacent}}{\text{hypotenuse}} = \frac{b}{c}$$

$$\tan A = \frac{\text{side opposite}}{\text{side adjacent}} = \frac{a}{b} \qquad \cot A = \frac{\text{side adjacent}}{\text{side opposite}} = \frac{b}{a}$$

$$\sec A = \frac{\text{hypotenuse}}{\text{side adjacent}} = \frac{c}{b} \qquad \csc A = \frac{\text{hypotenuse}}{\text{side opposite}} = \frac{c}{a}$$

Trigonometric Functions in A Right Triangle

What are the trigonometric functions of angle B in right triangle ABC?

Example

2 A right triangle has sides whose lengths are 7 cm, 24 cm, and 25 cm. Find the values of the six trigonometric functions of the angle opposite the shorter leg.

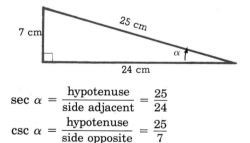

$$\sin \alpha = \frac{\text{side opposite}}{\text{hypotenuse}} = \frac{7}{25}$$

$$\tan \alpha = \frac{\text{side opposite}}{\text{side adjacent}} = \frac{7}{24}$$

$$\cos \alpha = \frac{\text{side adjacent}}{\text{hypotenuse}} = \frac{24}{25} \qquad \sec \alpha = \frac{\text{hypotenuse}}{\text{side adjacent}} = \frac{25}{24}$$

$$\cot \alpha = \frac{\text{side adjacent}}{\text{side opposite}} = \frac{24}{7} \qquad \csc \alpha = \frac{\text{hypotenuse}}{\text{side opposite}} = \frac{25}{7}$$

The trigonometric functions of certain angles may be derived from geometric relationships.

Recall that the hypotenuse of a 30°-60° right triangle is twice the length of the shorter leg. If A is 30° and C is the right angle, let the measurement of c be 2 units and the measurement of a be 1 unit. The measurement of b is $\sqrt{3}$ units found by using the Pythagorean Theorem. Now the values of the trigonometric functions can be written directly from the values of a, b, and c.

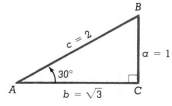

Example

3 Find the trigonometric functions of a 45° angle of a right triangle.

Recall that the legs of a 45°-45° right triangle are equal. If A and B are the 45° angles, let the measure of a and b equal 1. Thus, $c = \sqrt{(1)^2 + (1)^2}$ or $\sqrt{2}$.

$$\sin A = \frac{1}{\sqrt{2}} \text{ or } \frac{\sqrt{2}}{2} \qquad \cos A = \frac{1}{\sqrt{2}} \text{ or } \frac{\sqrt{2}}{2}$$

$$\tan A = \frac{1}{1} \text{ or } 1 \qquad \cot A = \frac{1}{1} \text{ or } 1$$

$$\sec A = \frac{\sqrt{2}}{1} \text{ or } \sqrt{2} \qquad \csc A = \frac{\sqrt{2}}{1} \text{ or } \sqrt{2}$$

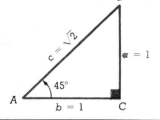

The coordinate graph is used to verify the trigonometric functions of 0° and 90°. An angle of 0° in standard position has point $P(1, 0)$ on its terminal side. Since $r = \sqrt{x^2 + y^2}$, $r = 1$. By referring to the definitions in terms of the graph, values of the six trigonometric functions may be found directly.

The values of the functions of 90° may be determined in a similar manner using the fact the point $P'(0, 1)$ lies on the terminal side of a 90° angle in standard position.

The table summarizes the values of the trigonometric functions of 0°, 30°, 45°, 60°, and 90°. These values are used often and should be recalled either from memory or by making a quick sketch.

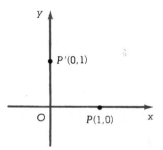

A	$\sin A$	$\cos A$	$\tan A$	$\cot A$	$\sec A$	$\csc A$
0°	0	1	0	—	1	—
30°	$\frac{1}{2}$	$\frac{\sqrt{3}}{2}$	$\frac{\sqrt{3}}{3}$	$\sqrt{3}$	$\frac{2\sqrt{3}}{3}$	2
45°	$\frac{\sqrt{2}}{2}$	$\frac{\sqrt{2}}{2}$	1	1	$\sqrt{2}$	$\sqrt{2}$
60°	$\frac{\sqrt{3}}{2}$	$\frac{1}{2}$	$\sqrt{3}$	$\frac{\sqrt{3}}{3}$	2	$\frac{2\sqrt{3}}{3}$
90°	1	0	—	0	—	1

A dash "—" means that the function is undefined for this angle.

Exploratory Exercises

Write an expression for each value in terms of a, b, c, h, x, and y.

1. $\cos B$
2. $\cot \angle DCB$
3. $\sin A$
4. $\sec \angle ACD$
5. $\sin B$
6. $\tan B$
7. $\tan A$
8. $\sec \angle DCB$
9. $\cos A$
10. $\csc \angle DCB$
11. $\cot \angle CDA$
12. $\csc \angle ACD$

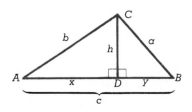

Find the value of each expression.

13. $\sin 30°$ **14.** $\cos 45°$ **15.** $\sec 30°$ **16.** $\cot 45°$

17. $\tan 60°$ **18.** $\sin 90°$ **19.** $\csc 90°$ **20.** $\cos 60°$

Written Exercises

Find the values of the six trigonometric functions of an angle in standard position if each of the following points lies on its terminal side.

1. $(5, 12)$ **2.** $(15, 8)$ **3.** $(3, 4)$ **4.** $(1, -8)$

5. $(-3, 0)$ **6.** $(-\sqrt{2}, \sqrt{2})$ **7.** $(5, -3)$ **8.** $(0, 2)$

Find the value of each expression.

9. $\sin 30° + \cos 30°$ **10.** $\sin 45° + \cos 45°$ **11.** $\sin 45° + \cos 60°$

12. $\sin 60° - \cos 60°$ **13.** $\sin 45° - \sin 90°$ **14.** $2 \sin 45° - \cos 30°$

15. $\sin 60° + \cos 30° - \tan 45°$ **16.** $\sin 45° \cos 60° - \tan 30° \sin 90°$

17. $2 \cos 30°$ **18.** $-\sin 60°$ **19.** $2 \sin 60° \cos 60°$

20. $\cos^2 30° - \sin^2 30°$ **21.** $\sec 60° + \cot 30°$ **22.** $\csc 45° - \sec 30°$

Find each value to four decimal places.

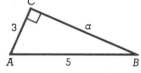 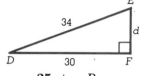 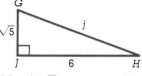

23. $\cos A$ **24.** $\sin B$ **25.** $\tan B$ **26.** $\sin E$ **27.** $\cos D$

28. $\tan E$ **29.** $\cos G$ **30.** $\tan G$ **31.** $\sin G$ **32.** $\tan H$

33. $\cot B$ **34.** $\sec D$ **35.** $\csc H$ **36.** $\csc A$ **37.** $\sec E$

Show that each of the following statements is true.

38. $1 - 2 \sin^2 30° = \cos 60°$ **39.** $1 = \cos^2 90° + \sin^2 90°$

40. $2 \sin 90° \cos 60° = 1$ **41.** $1 - \sin^2 45° = \cos^2 45°$

42. $\sec^2 30° - \cot^2 60° = 1$ **43.** $\sin^2 30° + \cos^2 30° = 1$

44. $\csc^2 45° - 1 = \cot^2 45°$ **45.** $\cos 60° = \cos^2 30° - \sin^2 30°$

Solve each problem.

46. The altitude to the hypotenuse of a right triangle is 6 inches long. If the hypotenuse is divided into segments 4 inches and 9 inches long by the altitude, find the values of the six trigonometric functions of the acute angles of the right triangle.

47. The longer base of an isosceles trapezoid is 10 m long. The legs of the trapezoid are 5 m long each. The base angles of the trapezoid are 60° each. Find the length of the shorter base of the trapezoid.

For the Scholar

Find the value of k when
$$m\angle U + m\angle V + m\angle W + m\angle X + m\angle Y + m\angle Z = 45k.$$

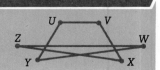

Decimal approximations for values of trigonometric functions can be determined by using a scientific calculator. Values for the six functions of angle measurement can be determined accurate to eight or nine decimal places. However, usually the values are rounded to three or four places for the final answer.

1 Find the value of cos 19°30′.
First convert the angle measurement to its equivalent decimal form.

    ENTER: 19.30   →DEG   **cos**   *Calculator should be in degree mode.*

    DISPLAY: 19.5   0.942641491   *Rounded to the ten-thousandth place.*

        Thus, cos 19°30′ ≈ 0.9426.

2 Find the value of tan 72°12′.

    ENTER: 72.12   →DEG   **tan**

    DISPLAY: 72.2   3.114635316

        Thus, tan 72°12′ ≈ 3.1146.

3 Find the value of cot 56°12′38″.

    ENTER: 56.1238   →DEG   **tan**   **1/x**   *Remember* $\cot x = \dfrac{1}{\tan x}$.

    DISPLAY: 56.21055555   1.49377645   0.669174892

        Thus, cot 56°12′38″ ≈ 0.6692.

The **2ndF** key can be used to determine the measure for a trigonometric function whose value is known.

4 If cos x = 0.8151, find the value of x to the nearest minute.

                               $\cos^{-1}$ →D.MS

    ENTER: 0.8151   **2ndF**   **cos**   **2ndF**   →DEG

    DISPLAY: 35.40274914   35.24098968

        The angle is approximately 35°24′.

Exercises   Use a calculator to find each trigonometric value given in the exploratory exercises on page 131.

5-2 Using Trigonometric Tables

Decimal approximations for values of trigonometric functions are given in the table on page 531. Values of all six functions of angle measurements from 0° to 90° in intervals of 10 minutes are given, accurate to four decimal places.

This table was also used to find values of circular functions.

The table is arranged so that angle measurements from 0° to 45° are read *down*, in the left-hand column. The headings at the top of the table are used for these measurements. The angle measurements from 45° to 90° are read *up* in the right-hand column. The headings at the bottom of the table are used for these measurements.

Degrees are separated into minutes. Sixty minutes are equivalent to one degree.

Examples

1 **Find the value of cos 19°30′.**

In the left-hand column of the table find 19°30′. Under the heading **cos,** find the value which corresponds to 19°30′.
cos 19°30′ = 0.9426

2 **Find the value of tan 72°12′.**

Since the values in the table are given for the nearest ten minutes, interpolation must be used. Use the table to find tan 72°10′ and tan 72°20′.

$$10'\left[\; 2'\left[\begin{array}{l} \text{tan } 72°20' = 3.1397 \\ \text{tan } 72°12' = \text{unknown} \\ \text{tan } 72°10' = 3.1084 \end{array}\right]d\right]0.0313$$

d represents the difference between 3.1084 and the unknown value.

Set up a proportion and solve for d.

$$\frac{2}{10} = \frac{d}{0.0313}$$

$$10d = 2(0.0313)$$
$$d = 0.0063$$

Round the value of d to four decimal places.

Add 0.0063 to the value of tan 72°10′.
tan 72°12′ ≈ 3.1084 + 0.0063 or 3.1147

3 **If cos x = 0.8151, find the value of x to the nearest minute.**

$$10'\left[\begin{array}{l} d\left[\begin{array}{l} \text{cos } 35°20' = 0.8158 \\ \text{cos } x \quad\;\; = 0.8151 \end{array}\right]0.0007 \\ \text{cos } 35°30' = 0.8141 \end{array}\right]0.0017$$

The value of x must be between 35°20′ and 35°30′.

$$\frac{d}{10} = \frac{0.0007}{0.0017}$$

$$0.0017d = 0.0070$$
$$d \approx 4$$

Round to the nearest whole number.

$$x \approx 35°20' + 4' \text{ or } 35°24'$$

Exploratory Exercises

Use the table to find each trigonometric value.

1. sin 16°10′
2. cos 38°
3. tan 66°20′
4. sin 55°40
5. cot 41°
6. csc 5°20′
7. cos 83°50′
8. sec 29°30

Find the value of x.

9. tan x = 0.9217
10. sec x = 5.487
11. sin x = 0.5373
12. csc x = 1.058
13. cos x = 0.9899
14. cot x = 0.3939

Written Exercises

Approximate each trigonometric value. Use interpolation when necessary.

1. sin 26°
2. csc 33°33′
3. sec 47°10′
4. cos 17°30′
5. sin 86°27′
6. cot 68°13′
7. tan 39°
8. csc 11°14′
9. cos 74°14′
10. cot 11°40′
11. sec 77°19′
12. tan 85°16′
13. sin 56°25′
14. tan 88°39′
15. sin 4°1′
16. cos 72°53′

Find x to the nearest minute.

17. sin x = 0.0872
18. csc x = 1.4129
19. tan x = 0.3153
20. sec x = 1.319
21. cos x = 0.8601
22. tan x = 0.2222
23. cot x = 2.300
24. csc x = 1.319
25. sin x = 0.9219
26. sin x = 0.5132
27. cos x = 0.0562
28. cos x = 0.7193
29. cot x = 1.2555
30. tan x = 0.9493
31. sin x = 0.7224

For the Scholar

Find the simplest possible form for the value of p, if

$$p = \frac{1}{\sqrt{6} - \sqrt{5}} + \frac{1}{2 - \sqrt{3}} - \frac{1}{\sqrt{7} - \sqrt{6}} + \frac{1}{\sqrt{7} + \sqrt{3}} - \frac{1}{\sqrt{5} - 2}.$$

5-3 Basic Trigonometric Identities

Equations that are true for all values of the variables for which they are defined are called **identities**. Various relationships exist between the trigonometric functions that are identities. Such relationships are often called **trigonometric identities**.

The six trigonometric functions can be paired so that a function is associated with a **cofunction**. The sine and cosine are cofunctions, as are the tangent and cotangent, and the secant and cosecant.

From right triangle ABC, the following relationships can be stated.

$$\sin A = \cos B = \frac{a}{c}$$

$$\tan A = \cot B = \frac{a}{b}$$

$$\sec A = \csc B = \frac{c}{b}$$

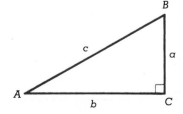

In the previous figure, angle A is the complement of angle B. Thus the trigonometric function of an acute angle is equal to the cofunction of the complement of the angle.

The following trigonometric identities hold for all values of A when $0° \le A \le 90°$.	Cofunction Identities
$\sin A = \cos (90° - A)$ $\qquad$ $\cos A = \sin (90° - A)$ $\tan A = \cot (90° - A)$ $\qquad$ $\cot A = \tan (90° - A)$ $\sec A = \csc (90° - A)$ $\qquad$ $\csc A = \sec (90° - A)$	

Example

1 If $\cos 11° = 0.9816$, find $\sin 79°$.

Use a cofunction identity.
$$\sin A = \cos (90° - A)$$
$$\sin 79° = \cos (90° - 79°)$$
$$= \cos 11°$$
$$= 0.9816$$

The definitions of the trigonometric functions are used to derive the following reciprocal relations.

The following trigonometric identities hold for all values of A except those for which any function is undefined.	Reciprocal Identities
$\sin A = \dfrac{1}{\csc A}$ $\qquad$ $\csc A = \dfrac{1}{\sin A}$ $\cos A = \dfrac{1}{\sec A}$ $\qquad$ $\sec A = \dfrac{1}{\cos A}$ $\tan A = \dfrac{1}{\cot A}$ $\qquad$ $\cot A = \dfrac{1}{\tan A}$	

Example

2 If $\cos B = 1.7$, find $\sec B$.

Use a reciprocal identity.
$$\sec B = \frac{1}{\cos B}$$
$$= \frac{1}{1.7}$$
$$\approx 0.5882$$

By definition, $\sin A = \frac{a}{c}$ and $\cos A = \frac{b}{c}$. Thus, the quotient $\frac{\sin A}{\cos A}$

is equal to $\dfrac{\frac{a}{c}}{\frac{b}{c}}$ or $\frac{a}{b}$. But $\tan A = \frac{a}{b}$. Thus, $\frac{\sin A}{\cos A} = \tan A$.

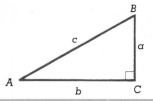

The following trigonometric identities hold for all values of A, except those for which any function is undefined.	
$\dfrac{\sin A}{\cos A} = \tan A \qquad \sin A = \cos A \tan A$ $\dfrac{\cos A}{\sin A} = \cot A \qquad \cos A = \sin A \cot A$	*Quotient Identities*

Using the right triangle ABC, the Pythagorean Theorem can be stated $a^2 + b^2 = c^2$. If each member is divided by c^2, the following equation results.

$$\frac{a^2}{c^2} + \frac{b^2}{c^2} = 1 \text{ or } \left(\frac{a}{c}\right)^2 + \left(\frac{b}{c}\right)^2 = 1$$

If the ratios are replaced with the proper trigonometric functions, the following identity results.

$$\sin^2 A + \cos^2 A = 1$$

Similarly, the following identities result when each member of $a^2 + b^2 = c^2$ is divided by b^2 and a^2, respectively.

$$\tan^2 A + 1 = \sec^2 A$$
$$1 + \cot^2 A = \csc^2 A$$

Note $\sin^2 A$ and $(\sin A)^2$ are the same but $\sin A^2$ is not.

The following trigonometric identities hold for all values of A, except those for which any function is undefined.	
$\sin^2 A + \cos^2 A = 1$ $\tan^2 A + 1 = \sec^2 A$ $1 + \cot^2 A = \csc^2 A$	*Pythagorean Identities*

Example

3 **If $\sin A = 0.5$, find $\tan A$.**

To find $\tan A$, first find $\cos A$.

Use a Pythagorean identity.
$$\sin^2 A + \cos^2 A = 1$$
$$(0.5)^2 + \cos^2 A = 1$$
$$\cos A = \sqrt{1 - 0.25}$$
$$\cos A \approx \pm 0.87$$

Use a quotient identity.
$$\tan A = \frac{\sin A}{\cos A}$$
$$\approx \pm\frac{0.5}{0.87} \text{ or about } \pm 0.57$$

Exploratory Exercises

Using $\triangle ABC$, find each of the following.

1. If $\sin A = \dfrac{\sqrt{3}}{3}$, find $\cos B$.
2. If $\tan B = 1.7$, find $\cot A$.
3. If $\cos A = 0.109$, find $\sin (90° - A)$.
4. If $\csc A = 2.736$, find $\sec B$.

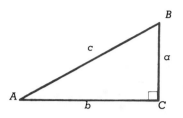

Solve each of the following.

5. If $\tan 30° = \dfrac{\sqrt{3}}{3}$, find $\cot 60°$.
6. If $\sin 45° = \dfrac{\sqrt{2}}{2}$, find $\cos 45°$.
7. If $\cos 4° = 0.9976$, find $\sin 86°$.
8. If $\tan 69° = 2.605$, find $\cot 21°$.
9. If $\tan 84° = 9.514$, find $\cot 6°$.
10. If $\sec 12° = 1.022$, find $\csc 78°$.
11. If $\sin 35°40' = 0.5831$, find $\cos 54°20'$.
12. If $\csc 52°28' = 1.2610$, find $\sec 37°32'$.

Written Exercises

Solve each of the following for values of θ between 0° and 90°.

1. If $\sin \theta = \dfrac{3}{4}$, find $\sec \theta$.
2. If $\cos \theta = \dfrac{3}{5}$, find $\sin \theta$.
3. If $\csc \theta = 3$, find $\sin \theta$.
4. If $\cot \theta = 2$, find $\tan \theta$.
5. If $\cos \theta = \dfrac{\sqrt{2}}{3}$, find $\sin \theta$.
6. If $\tan \theta = \dfrac{\sqrt{11}}{2}$, find $\sec \theta$.
7. If $\cos \theta = \dfrac{2}{3}$, find $\csc \theta$.
8. If $\tan \theta = \dfrac{\sqrt{3}}{2}$, find $\sec \theta$.
9. If $\sec \theta = 1.3$, find $\cos \theta$.
10. If $\cos \theta = 0.032$, find $\sec \theta$.
11. If $\sin \theta = \dfrac{4}{5}$, find $\cos \theta$.
12. If $\tan \theta = \dfrac{\sqrt{2}}{5}$, find $\cot \theta$.
13. If $\sec \theta = \dfrac{5}{3}$, find $\tan \theta$.
14. If $\cos \theta = \dfrac{2}{3}$, find $\sin \theta$.
15. If $\sec \theta = 1.7$, find $\cos \theta$.
16. If $\cos \theta = 0.32$, find $\sin \theta$.
17. If $\tan \theta = 4$, find $\sin \theta$.
18. If $\cot \theta = 0.8$, find $\csc \theta$.
19. If $\tan \theta = 1$, find $\cot \theta$.
20. If $\cos \theta = 0.32$, find $\tan \theta$.
21. If $\sin \theta = \dfrac{1}{2}$, find $\cos \theta$.
22. If $\sin \theta = \dfrac{1}{2}$, find $\csc \theta$.
23. If $\cos \theta = \dfrac{4}{5}$, find $\tan \theta$.
24. If $\tan \theta = \dfrac{7}{2}$, find $\sec \theta$.

Simplify each of the following.

25. $\tan \theta \cos \theta$
26. $\sec^2 \theta - 1$
27. $\sin x + \cos x \tan x$
28. $\csc \theta \cos \theta \tan \theta$
29. $2(\csc^2 \theta - \cot^2 \theta)$
30. $\dfrac{\tan^2 \theta - \sin^2 \theta}{\tan^2 \theta \sin^2 \theta}$

Write a formula for each of the following in terms of the given relation.

31. $\tan \theta$ in terms of $\sin \theta$ **32.** $\sec \theta$ in terms of $\cot \theta$ **33.** $\sin \theta$ in terms of $\sec \theta$

34. $\cos \theta$ in terms of $\tan \theta$ **35.** $\cot \theta$ in terms of $\csc \theta$ **36.** $\csc \theta$ in terms of $\cos \theta$

For the Scholar

A dish of mixed nuts contains cashews and peanuts. Then, 2 oz of peanuts are added to the dish making the new mixture 20% cashews. Sarah likes cashews, so she added 2 oz of them to the dish. The mixture in the dish is now $33\frac{1}{3}\%$ cashews. What was the percent of cashews in the original mixture of nuts?

5-4   Verifying Trigonometric Identities

Verifying trigonometric identities involves transforming one side of the equation into the same form as the other side by using the basic trigonometric identities and the principles of algebra. Either side may be transformed into the form of the other side, or both sides may be transformed separately into other forms that are the same.

1. **Transform the more complicated side of the equation into the form of the simpler side.** 2. **Substitute one or more basic trigonometric identities to simplify the expression.** 3. **Factor or multiply to simplify the expression.** 4. **Multiply both numerator and denominator by the same trigonometric expression.**	*Suggestions for Verifying Identities*

Example

1   **Verify that $\dfrac{\cos A}{\cot^2 A} = \sin A \tan A$ is an identity.**

$$\frac{\cos A}{\cot^2 A} \overset{?}{=} \sin A \tan A \qquad \textit{Arrange the work so that there is a vertical sequence of steps in the transformation of a side.}$$

$$\frac{\cos A}{\dfrac{\cos^2 A}{\sin^2 A}} \overset{?}{=} \sin A \tan A \qquad \cot^2 A = \frac{\cos^2 A}{\sin^2 A}$$

$$\frac{\sin^2 A}{\cos A} \overset{?}{=} \sin A \tan A \qquad \textit{Simplify.}$$

$$\sin A \left(\frac{\sin A}{\cos A}\right) \overset{?}{=} \sin A \tan A \qquad \textit{Factor.}$$

$$\sin A \tan A = \sin A \tan A \qquad \frac{\sin A}{\cos A} = \tan A$$

The transformation of the left side has produced an expression that is the same as the right side. Thus, the identity has been verified.

Examples

2 Verify that $\dfrac{\tan A - \sin A}{\tan A + \sin A} = \dfrac{\sec A - 1}{\sec A + 1}$ is an identity.

$$\frac{\tan A - \sin A}{\tan A + \sin A} = \frac{\sec A - 1}{\sec A + 1}$$

$$\frac{\dfrac{\sin A}{\cos A} - \sin A}{\dfrac{\sin A}{\cos A} + \sin A} = \frac{\sec A - 1}{\sec A + 1} \qquad \tan A = \frac{\sin A}{\cos A}$$

$$\frac{\sin A \left(\dfrac{1}{\cos A} - 1 \right)}{\sin A \left(\dfrac{1}{\cos A} + 1 \right)} = \frac{\sec A - 1}{\sec A + 1} \qquad \textit{Factor.}$$

$$\frac{\dfrac{1}{\cos A} - 1}{\dfrac{1}{\cos A} + 1} = \frac{\sec A - 1}{\sec A + 1} \qquad \textit{Simplify.}$$

$$\frac{\sec A - 1}{\sec A + 1} = \frac{\sec A - 1}{\sec A + 1} \qquad \frac{1}{\cos A} = \sec A$$

Thus, the identity has been verified by a transformation of the left side of the equation.

3 Find a numerical value of one trigonometric function of S if $\tan S \cos S = \frac{1}{2}$.

$$\tan S \cos S = \frac{1}{2}$$

$$\frac{\sin S}{\cos S} \cdot \cos S = \frac{1}{2}$$

$$\sin S = \frac{1}{2}$$

A numerical value of one trigonometric function of S is given by $\sin S = \frac{1}{2}$.

Exploratory Exercises

State an identity that could be used to verify each of the following.

1. $\csc^2 \alpha - \cot^2 \alpha = 1$

2. $\tan \theta \cot \theta = 1$

3. $\tan x \csc x = \sec x$

4. $\cos \alpha \csc \alpha = \cot \alpha$

5. $\sin \theta \cot \theta = \cos \theta$

6. $\cos^2 \theta = 1 - \sin^2 \theta$

7. $\dfrac{\tan x}{\sin x} = \sec x$

8. $\dfrac{\sin^2 \theta + \cos^2 \theta}{\sin^2 \theta} = \csc^2 \theta$

9. $\sec^2 \theta - 1 = \tan^2 \theta$

10. $\csc \theta \cos \theta \tan \theta = 1$

11-20. Verify each identity in problems **1-10.**

Written Exercises

Verify each identity.

1. $\sin^2 A \cot^2 A = (1 - \sin A)(1 + \sin A)$

2. $\cos^2 x + \tan^2 x \cos^2 x = 1$

3. $\tan B = \dfrac{\cos B}{\sin B \cot^2 B}$

4. $\dfrac{\tan \theta \cos \theta}{\sin \theta} = 1$

5. $\dfrac{1}{\sec^2 x} + \dfrac{1}{\csc^2 x} - 1 = 0$

6. $\dfrac{\sec x - 1}{\sec x + 1} + \dfrac{\cos x - 1}{\cos x + 1} = 0$

7. $\sin \theta \, (1 + \cot^2 \theta) = \csc \theta$

8. $\sin^4 A + \cos^2 A = \cos^4 A + \sin^2 A$

9. $\dfrac{\sin (90° - w)}{\cos (90° - w)} = \cot w$

10. $\sec (90° - z) = \dfrac{1}{\sin z}$

11. $1 + \tan^2 (90° - x) = \dfrac{1}{\cos^2 (90° - x)}$

12. $\dfrac{\sin A}{\csc A} + \dfrac{\cos A}{\sec A} = 1$

13. $\dfrac{\sec B}{\cos B} - \dfrac{\tan B}{\cot B} = 1$

14. $\dfrac{1}{\csc^2 \theta} + \sec^2 \theta + \dfrac{1}{\sec^2 \theta} = 2 + \dfrac{\sec^2 \theta}{\csc^2 \theta}$

15. $\sec^4 \alpha - \sec^2 \alpha = \dfrac{1}{\cot^4 \alpha} + \dfrac{1}{\cot^2 \alpha}$

16. $\dfrac{\cos x}{1 + \sin x} + \dfrac{\cos x}{1 - \sin x} = 2 \sec x$

17. $\dfrac{1 + \tan^2 A}{\csc^2 A} = \tan^2 A$

18. $\dfrac{1 - 2 \cos^2 \theta}{\sin \theta \cos \theta} = \tan \theta - \cot \theta$

Find a numerical value of one trigonometric function of each x.

19. $\sin x \sec x = 1$

20. $\sin x = \tan x$

21. $\sin x = 2 \cos x$

22. $2 \tan x = \cot x$

23. $2 \sin^2 x = 3 \cos^2 x$

24. $1 - \sin^2 x = \dfrac{1}{9}$

25. $\dfrac{\tan x}{\sin x} = \sqrt{2}$

26. $1 + \tan^2 x = \sin^2 x + \dfrac{1}{\sec^2 x}$

Solve each problem.

27. If $\sin \alpha = \dfrac{1}{3}$, find $\dfrac{\cos \alpha \tan \alpha}{\csc \alpha}$.

28. If $\tan \beta = \dfrac{3}{4}$, find $\dfrac{\sin \beta \sec \beta}{\cot \beta}$.

29. Show that $\sin x + \cos x \geq 1$ if $0° \leq x \leq 90°$.

30. Show that $\tan x + \cot x \geq 2$ if $0° \leq x \leq 90°$.

For the Scholar

Find the difference between the sum of the first 50 odd whole numbers and the sum of the first 50 even natural numbers.

5-5 Radians and Arc Length

A **radian** is the measure of a central angle whose sides intercept an arc which is the same length as the radius of the circle. If a central angle is measured in radians, the number of linear units in the intercepted arc on a unit circle is equal to the number of radians. Circular functions are functions of the measure of the intercepted arc while trigonometric functions are functions of the measure of the central angle.

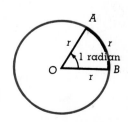

Since the circumference of a unit circle is 2π, an angle representing one complete revolution of the circle is 2π radians or $360°$. Thus the proportion relating radians to degrees is as follows.

Let R represent a number of radians. Let D represent a number of degrees. $$\frac{R}{\pi} = \frac{D}{180°}$$	*The Degree/Radian Proportion*

If either R or D is known, the proportion can be solved for the other. Often, angles expressed in radians are given in terms of π.

1 radian $\approx 57°18'$

Examples

1 **Change 60° to radian measure in terms of π.**

$$\frac{R}{\pi} = \frac{60°}{180°}$$

$$R = \frac{\pi}{3}$$

2 **Change $\frac{5\pi}{6}$ radians to degrees.**

$$\frac{\frac{5\pi}{6}}{\pi} = \frac{D}{180°}$$

$$D = 180°\left(\frac{5}{6}\right) \text{ or } 150°$$

Using Calculators

1 **Change 75° to radian measure.**

ENTER: 75 | sin | | 2ndF | • | 2ndF | sin | (DRG over the • ... sin⁻¹ over last sin)

DISPLAY: 75   0.965925826   1.3089

Thus, $75° \approx 1.3089$ radians.

Make sure the calculator is in the degree mode initially.

2 **Change $\frac{3\pi}{8}$ radians to degree measure to the nearest second.**

Make sure the calculator is in the radian mode initially.

ENTER: 3 | × | 2ndF | EXP | ÷ | 8 | = |

DISPLAY: 3   3.141592654 9.42777961 8 1.178097245

ENTER: | sin | 2ndF | • | 2ndF | • | 2ndF | sin | 2ndF | →DEG |

DISPLAY: 0.923879532   67.5   67.29599999

Thus, $\frac{3\pi}{8} \approx 67°30'00''$.

If two central angles in different circles are congruent, the ratio of the lengths of their intercepted arcs is equal to the ratio of their radii. For example, given $\odot O$ and $\odot Q$, if $\angle O \cong \angle Q$, then $\dfrac{m\widehat{AB}}{m\widehat{CD}} = \dfrac{OA}{QC}$.

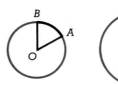

Now let O be the center of two concentric circles. Let r be the radius of the larger circle, and let the smaller circle be a unit circle. If a central angle of θ radians is drawn in the two circles it will intercept $\widehat{RT}$ on the unit circle and $\widehat{SW}$ on the other circle. Suppose $\widehat{SW}$ is s units long. $\widehat{RT}$ is θ units since it is an arc of a unit circle intercepted by a central angle of θ radians. The following proportion can be written.

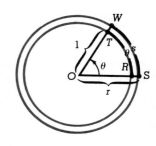

$$\frac{s}{\theta} = \frac{r}{1} \text{ or } s = r\theta$$

The length of any circular arc, s, is equal to the product of the radius of the circle, r, and the radian measure of the central angle it subtends, θ. $$s = r\theta$$	**Length of an Arc**

Example

3 **Find the length of an arc that subtends a central angle of 32° in a circle of radius 11 cm.**

$\dfrac{R}{\pi} = \dfrac{32}{180}$ *Find the radian measure of the central angle.*

$R = \dfrac{8\pi}{45}$

$s = (11)\left(\dfrac{8\pi}{45}\right)$ $s = r\theta$

≈ 6.14 cm

Exploratory Exercises

Change each of the following to radian measure.

1. 18°   **2.** 30°   **3.** 240°   **4.** 1°

Change each of the following to degree measure.

5. π **6.** $\dfrac{\pi}{4}$ **7.** $\dfrac{3\pi}{4}$ **8.** $\dfrac{\pi}{6}$

Written Exercises

Change each of the following to radian measure.

1. $270°$
2. $135°$
3. $210°$
4. $300°$
5. $75°$
6. $15°$
7. $225°$
8. $360°$

Change each of the following to degree measure.

9. $\dfrac{5\pi}{4}$
10. $\dfrac{7\pi}{8}$
11. $\dfrac{11\pi}{6}$
12. $\dfrac{3\pi}{5}$
13. 4π
14. 2
15. 0.75
16. 3.14

Given the radian measure of a central angle, find the measure of its intercepted arc in a circle of radius 10 cm.

17. $\dfrac{\pi}{4}$
18. $\dfrac{2\pi}{3}$
19. $\dfrac{5\pi}{6}$
20. $\dfrac{2\pi}{5}$

Given the measurement of a central angle, find the measure of its intercepted arc in a circle of diameter 30 in.

21. $30°$
22. $5°$
23. $77°$
24. $57°18'$

Given the measurement of an arc, find the degree measure of the central angle it subtends in a circle of radius 8 cm.

25. 5 cm
26. 14 cm
27. 24 cm
28. 12.5 cm

Solve each of the following.

29. An arc is 6.5 cm long and it subtends a central angle of $45°$. Find the length of the radius of the circle.

30. An arc is 70.7 m long and it subtends a central angle of $\dfrac{2\pi}{7}$. Find the length of the diameter of the circle.

For the Scholar

In the figure, $\overline{OP}$ is a diameter of $\odot A$. $\odot B$ is tangent internally to circle A and also tangent to $\overline{OP}$ at A. $\odot C$ is tangent externally to $\odot B$ and tangent internally to $\odot A$, and also tangent to $\overline{OP}$. Find the ratio of the diameter of $\odot C$ to $\odot A$.

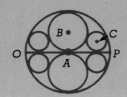

5-6 Functions of Angles

The definitions of trigonometric functions provide a basis for finding functions of angles in any quadrant, positive or negative. In the figure on the next page, let $P_1(x_1,\ y_1)$ be a point in the first quadrant on the terminal side of angle A_1; let $P_2(x_2,\ y_2)$ be a point in the second quadrant on the terminal side of angle A_2; let $P_3(x_3,\ y_3)$ be a point in the third quadrant on the terminal side of angle A_3; and let $P_4(x_4,\ y_4)$ be a point in the fourth quadrant on the terminal side of angle A_4.

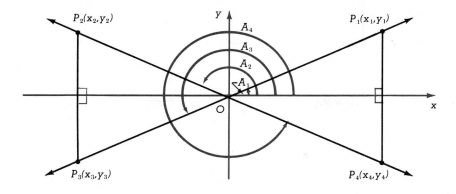

With each angle in standard position, recall the following ratios.

$$\sin A = \frac{y}{r} \qquad \csc A = \frac{r}{y} \qquad\qquad r = \sqrt{x^2 + y^2}$$

$$\cos A = \frac{x}{r} \qquad \sec A = \frac{r}{x}$$

$$\tan A = \frac{y}{x} \qquad \cot A = \frac{x}{y}$$

These definitions apply regardless of the quadrant in which the terminal side lies, or if it lies on either of the axes. Since r is defined to be positive, the signs of the functions in each quadrant will be determined by the signs of the coordinates x and y. The following table shows the signs of the six functions in each quadrant. Each sign can be verified by considering the signs of the coordinates of a point in each quadrant.

Function	Quadrant			
	First	Second	Third	Fourth
$\sin A$	+	+	−	−
$\cos A$	+	−	−	+
$\tan A$	+	−	+	−
$\csc A$	+	+	−	−
$\sec A$	+	−	−	+
$\cot A$	+	−	+	−

You should memorize the functions that are positive in each quadrant.

Note that the signs of reciprocally related functions are the same.

If a line is drawn from each of the points P_1, P_2, P_3, and P_4 perpendicular to the x-axis, right triangles are formed. For each right triangle the acute angle with its vertex at the origin is called the **reference angle** α. For each angle A, there is an angle α. In the first quadrant, $\alpha_1 = A_1$. In the second quadrant, $\alpha_2 = 180° - A_2$ or $\pi - A_2$. In the third quadrant, $\alpha_3 = A_3 - 180°$ or $A_3 - \pi$. In the fourth quadrant, $\alpha_4 = 360° - A_4$ or $2\pi - A_4$.

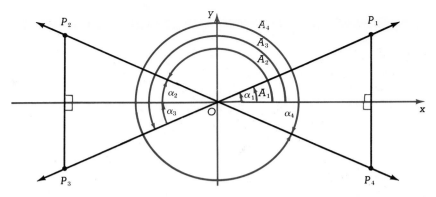

Since α is a positive angle less than 90°, the function of an angle of any size may be reduced to a function of an acute angle and the value found in the table on page 531. The proper sign for the given function can be selected from the table on page 141 or can be determined by the signs of the coordinates in the quadrant in which the terminal side lies.

Examples

1 **Find sin 120° in terms of the sine of an acute angle.**

The terminal side of 120° is in the second quadrant.
Find the reference angle.

$\alpha = 180° - 120°$
$= 60°$

Thus, sin 120° = sin 60°.   *The sine function is positive in the second quadrant.*

2 **Find tan 307°.**

The terminal side of 307° is in the fourth quadrant.
Find the reference angle.

$\alpha = 360° - 307°$
$= 53°$

tan 307° = −tan 53°   *The tangent function is negative in the fourth quadrant.*
$= -1.3270$

Thus, tan 307° = −1.3270.

Using Calculators

Find the value of cos 425°.

ENTER: 425
                                                    Make sure the calculator
DISPLAY: 425   0.422618261   *is in degree mode.*

The reference angles are determined by the calculator. Thus, cos 425° ≈ 0.4226.

Example

3 Find cos 575°.

An angle with measurement 575° is equivalent to an angle with measurement 215° since 575° = 360° + 215°. The terminal side of 215° is in the third quadrant.

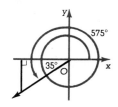

$\alpha = 215° - 180°$ *Find the reference angle.*
  $= 35°$

cos 575° = −cos 35° or about −0.8192   *The cosine function is negative in the third quadrant.*
Thus, cos 575° = −0.8192.

The cosine function has the property such that cos (−x) = cos x. A function with this property is called an **even function**. The sine function has the property such that sin (−x) = −sin x. A function with this property is called an **odd function**.

Exploratory Exercises

Find the reference angle for each of the following angles.

1. 206°   2. 111°   3. −16°   4. 424°
5. −127°   6. 248°   7. 358°   8. −102°

Express each of the following in terms of the same function of a positive acute angle.

9. sin 135°   10. cos 210°   11. tan 320°   12. cot 260°
13. sin 340°   14. cos 175°   15. tan 204°   16. sec 142°

Written Exercises

Express each of the following in terms of the same function of a positive acute angle. 90°

1. sin (−30°)   2. sin (−50°)   3. cot (−80°)   4. sin (−100°)
5. cos (−150°)   6. tan (−200°)   7. sec (−135°)   8. sin (−300°)

Express each of the following in terms of a function of a positive angle less than 45°.

9. cot 310°   10. cos 100°   11. tan 210°   12. sec (−125°)
13. sin 305°   14. cos 355°   15. tan (−262°)   16. csc 73°
17. sec (−213°)   18. sin (−128°)   19. csc 287°   20. cot 96°

21-28. Find the value of each expression in problems **9-16** of the Exploratory Exercises.

29-48. Find the value of each expression in problems **1-20** of the Written Exercises.

State whether each function is odd or even.

49. $y = \tan x$ 50. $y = \cot x$ 51. $y = \csc x$ 52. $y = \sec x$

For the Scholar

Find the sum of the coefficients of the binomial expansion of $(4x - 1)^{16}$.

$= \dfrac{}{0}$ or undefined $= \dfrac{}{-1}$ or 0

The following table gives the values of the trigonometric functions of common quadrantal angles.

Angle	Function					
	sin	cos	tan	csc	sec	cot
0	0	1	0	—	1	—
90° or $\frac{\pi}{2}$	1	0	—	1	—	0
180° or π	0	−1	0	—	−1	—
270° or $\frac{3\pi}{2}$	−1	0	—	−1	—	0
360° or 2π	0	1	0	—	1	—

Exploratory Exercises

Copy and complete the following table of quadrantal values of sin x and cos x.

1.

x	radians	0	$\frac{\pi}{2}$	π	$\frac{3\pi}{2}$	2π	$-\frac{\pi}{2}$	$-\pi$	$\frac{-3\pi}{2}$	-2π
	degrees	0°	90°	180°	270°	360°	−90°	−180°	−270°	−360°
sin x		0								
cos x		1								

Find two values of x which make each statement true.

2. $\cos x = 1$
3. $\sin x = 1$
4. $\cos x = 0$
5. $\sin x = 0$
6. $\cos x = -1$
7. $\sin x = -1$

Written Exercises

Find the value of each of the following without using tables.

1. $\cos \pi$
2. $\sin 360°$
3. $\cos 450°$
4. $\tan 2\pi$
5. $\csc \frac{3\pi}{2}$
6. $\sin 450°$
7. $\sec 270°$
8. $\cos 90°$
9. $\csc 180°$
10. $\sin \left(-\frac{\pi}{2}\right)$
11. $\tan 90°$
12. $\sec (-90°)$

Find the values of k for each of the following.

13. $\tan (k90°) = 0$
14. $\tan (k90°)$ is undefined
15. $\sin (k90°) = 1$
16. $\cos (k90°) = 1$
17. $\sin (k90°) = \csc (k90°)$
18. $\tan (k90°) = \cot (k90°)$

Challenge Exercises

Show each of the following.

19. $\sin (k90°) = 0$ if k is any even integer
20. $\cos (k90°) = 0$ if k is any odd integer

For the Scholar

Name the polygonal region formed by the set of all points (x, y) that satisfy all of the following conditions when n is a positive number: $n \le 2y \le 4n$; $2n \le x + y \le 5n$; $x + n \ge y$; $y + n \ge x$; $n \le 2x \le 4n$.

5-8 Functions of ($\alpha + \beta$)

Circular functions and trigonometric functions are related by the radian and degree measures of an angle. Thus, every formula or identity that was proved for circular functions is also true for trigonometric functions whether the variable represents degree or radian measure of an angle.

The sine and cosine of the sum or difference of the measurement of two angles are given by the following identities.

If α and β represent the measures of two angles, then the following identities hold for all values of α and β. $$\sin(\alpha \pm \beta) = \sin\alpha\cos\beta \pm \cos\alpha\sin\beta$$ $$\cos(\alpha \pm \beta) = \cos\alpha\cos\beta \mp \sin\alpha\sin\beta$$	*Sum and Difference Identities for Sine and Cosine Function*

Example

1 **Find sin 75° and cos 75° from the functions of 30° and 45° to four decimal places.**

$$\sin 75° = \sin(45° + 30°)$$
$$= \sin 45° \cos 30° + \cos 45° \sin 30°$$
$$= \frac{\sqrt{2}}{2} \cdot \frac{\sqrt{3}}{2} + \frac{\sqrt{2}}{2} \cdot \frac{1}{2}$$
$$= \frac{\sqrt{6} + \sqrt{2}}{4} \text{ or about } 0.9659$$

$$\cos 75° = \cos(45° + 30°)$$
$$= \cos 45° \cos 30° - \sin 45° \sin 30°$$
$$= \frac{\sqrt{2}}{2} \cdot \frac{\sqrt{3}}{2} - \frac{\sqrt{2}}{2} \cdot \frac{1}{2}$$
$$= \frac{\sqrt{6} - \sqrt{2}}{4} \text{ or about } 0.2588$$

The sin 75° is 0.9659 and the cos 75° is 0.2588.

Since $\tan x = \dfrac{\sin x}{\cos x}$, identities for $\tan(\alpha \pm \beta)$ can be developed.

$$\tan(\alpha + \beta) = \frac{\sin(\alpha + \beta)}{\cos(\alpha + \beta)}$$

$$\tan(\alpha + \beta) = \frac{\sin\alpha\cos\beta + \cos\alpha\sin\beta}{\cos\alpha\cos\beta - \sin\alpha\sin\beta}$$

$$\tan(\alpha + \beta) = \frac{\dfrac{\sin\alpha\cos\beta}{\cos\alpha\cos\beta} + \dfrac{\cos\alpha\sin\beta}{\cos\alpha\cos\beta}}{\dfrac{\cos\alpha\cos\beta}{\cos\alpha\cos\beta} - \dfrac{\sin\alpha\sin\beta}{\cos\alpha\cos\beta}}$$

Divide both numerator and denominator by $\cos\alpha\cos\beta$. Assume $\cos\alpha \neq 0$ and $\cos\beta \neq 0$.

$$\tan(\alpha + \beta) = \frac{\tan\alpha + \tan\beta}{1 - \tan\alpha\tan\beta}$$

Replace β by $-\beta$ to find $\tan (\alpha - \beta)$.

$$\tan (\alpha - \beta) = \frac{\tan \alpha - \tan \beta}{1 + \tan \alpha \tan \beta}$$

If α and β represent the measures of two angles, then the following identities hold for all values of α and β. $$\tan (\alpha \pm \beta) = \frac{\tan \alpha \pm \tan \beta}{1 \mp \tan \alpha \tan \beta}$$	***Sum and Difference Identities for the Tangent Functions***

Example

2 **Find $\tan 105°$ from functions of $60°$ and $45°$.**

$\tan 105° = \tan (60° + 45°)$

$\qquad = \dfrac{\tan 60° + \tan 45°}{1 - \tan 60° \tan 45°}$

$\qquad = \dfrac{\sqrt{3} + 1}{1 - \sqrt{3} \cdot 1}$ $\qquad$ *Multiply by $\dfrac{1 + \sqrt{3}}{1 + \sqrt{3}}$ to simplify.*

$\qquad = -2 - \sqrt{3}$

$\tan 105° \approx -3.7321$

The sum and difference identities may be used to verify other identities.

Example

3 **Verify that $\dfrac{\sqrt{2}}{2}(\sin x + \cos x) = \sin \left(x + \dfrac{\pi}{4} \right)$ is an identity.**

$\dfrac{\sqrt{2}}{2}(\sin x + \cos x) = \sin \left(x + \dfrac{\pi}{4} \right)$

$\dfrac{\sqrt{2}}{2}(\sin x + \cos x) = \sin x \cos \dfrac{\pi}{4} + \cos x \sin \dfrac{\pi}{4}$ $\qquad$ *Use $\sin (\alpha + \beta)$.*

$\dfrac{\sqrt{2}}{2}(\sin x + \cos x) = \sin x \left(\dfrac{\sqrt{2}}{2} \right) + \cos x \left(\dfrac{\sqrt{2}}{2} \right)$ $\qquad$ $\cos \dfrac{\pi}{4} = \dfrac{\sqrt{2}}{2}$ *and* $\sin \dfrac{\pi}{4} = \dfrac{\sqrt{2}}{2}$

$\dfrac{\sqrt{2}}{2}(\sin x + \cos x) = \dfrac{\sqrt{2}}{2}(\sin x + \cos x)$

Exploratory Exercises

Use the sum and difference identities to solve each of the following.

1. Find $\sin 105°$ from functions of $60°$ and $45°$. 2. Find $\cos 105°$ from functions of $60°$ and $45°$.

3. Find $\tan 75°$ from functions of $45°$ and $30°$. 4. Find $\sin 15°$ from functions of $45°$ and $30°$.

5. Find $\cos 15°$ from functions of $45°$ and $30°$. 6. Find $\cos 15°$ from functions of $45°$ and $60°$.

7. Find tan 15° from functions of 45° and 60°.

8. Find sin 150° from functions of 120° and 30°.

9. Find cos 150° from functions of 180° and 30°.

10. Find tan 150° from functions of 180° and 30°.

Write each of the following as a function of x.

11. $\sin\left(\dfrac{\pi}{2} - x\right)$

12. $\cos\left(\dfrac{3\pi}{2} + x\right)$

13. $\tan(2\pi - x)$

Find the value of each function for $0 < x < 90°$, $0 < y < 90°$, $\sin x = \dfrac{4}{5}$, and $\cos y = \dfrac{3}{5}$.

14. $\sin(x + y)$

15. $\cos(x - y)$

16. $\tan(x + y)$

Written Exercises

Use the sum and difference identities to evaluate each of the following.

1. $\sin 75°$
2. $\tan(-105°)$
3. $\sin 195°$
4. $\cos 255°$

5. $\cos 195°$
6. $\tan 30°$
7. $\tan(-195°)$
8. $\tan 255°$

9. $\sin 255°$
10. $\cos(-15°)$
11. $\sin 30°$
12. $\tan(-75°)$

If α and β are the measures of two first quadrant angles, find $\cos(\alpha + \beta)$.

13. $\sin\alpha = \dfrac{5}{13}$, $\cos\beta = \dfrac{4}{5}$ $\quad$ tan = $5/12$, $3/4$ $\quad$ 14. $\tan\alpha = \dfrac{4}{3}$, $\cot\beta = \dfrac{5}{12}$

15. $\cos\alpha = \dfrac{5}{13}$, $\cos\beta = \dfrac{35}{37}$ $\quad$ tan = $12/5$, $35/12$ $\quad$ 16. $\sin\alpha = \dfrac{8}{17}$, $\tan\beta = \dfrac{7}{24}$

17-20. If α and β are the measures of two first quadrant angles, find $\sin(\alpha - \beta)$ for problems 13-16.

21-24. If α and β are the measures of two first quadrant angles, find $\tan(\alpha + \beta)$ for problems 13-16.

Verify each identity.

25. $\sin(180° - \theta) = \sin\theta$

26. $\tan(270° - x) = \cot x$

27. $\cos\left(\dfrac{3\pi}{2} + \theta\right) = \sin\theta$

28. $\sin(270° + x) = -\cos x$

29. $\tan(90° + \theta) = -\cot\theta$

30. $\cos(360° - \theta) = \cos\theta$

31. $\tan(\pi - \theta) = -\tan\theta$

32. $\sin\left(\dfrac{\pi}{2} + x\right) = \cos x$

33. $-\sin\theta = \cos\left(\dfrac{\pi}{2} + \theta\right)$

34. $\cot x = \tan\left(\dfrac{\pi}{2} - x\right)$

35. $-\cos\theta = \cos(\pi + \theta)$

36. $-\cos\theta = \cos(180° - \theta)$

37. $\cos(30° - x) + \cos(30° + x) = \sqrt{3}\cos x$

38. $\sin^2\alpha - \sin^2\beta = \sin(\alpha + \beta)\sin(\alpha - \beta)$

39. $\cos(\alpha + \beta) + \cos(\alpha - \beta) = 2\cos\alpha\cos\beta$

40. $\dfrac{\sin(\beta - \alpha)}{\sin\alpha\sin\beta} = \cot\alpha - \cot\beta$

Challenge Exercises

Solve each of the following.

41. Derive a formula for $\cot(\alpha + \beta)$ in terms of $\cot\alpha$ and $\cot\beta$.

42. Derive a formula for $\sin(\alpha + \beta + \gamma)$ in terms of the functions of α, β, and γ.

For the Scholar

If $4a$ is a perfect square, what is the next greater perfect square?

5-9   Functions of Double Angles and Half Angles

The formulas that were used to find the sine or cosine of a double number may also be used to find the sine or cosine of a double angle. The variable may represent either the radian or degree measure of an angle.

The tangent of a double angle may be found by substituting θ for both α and β in $\tan(\alpha + \beta)$.

$$\tan(\alpha + \beta) = \frac{\tan \alpha + \tan \beta}{1 - \tan \alpha \tan \beta}$$

$$\tan(\theta + \theta) = \frac{\tan \theta + \tan \theta}{1 - \tan \theta \tan \theta}$$

$$= \frac{2 \tan \theta}{1 - \tan^2 \theta}$$

If θ represents the measure of an angle, then the following identities hold for all values of θ.

$$\sin 2\theta = 2 \sin \theta \cos \theta$$
$$\cos 2\theta = \cos^2 \theta - \sin^2 \theta$$
$$= 1 - 2 \sin^2 \theta$$
$$= 2 \cos^2 \theta - 1$$
$$\tan 2\theta = \frac{2 \tan \theta}{1 - \tan^2 \theta} \qquad (\tan^2 \theta \neq 1)$$

Double Angle Identities

Example

1   If $\sin \theta = \dfrac{2}{\sqrt{5}}$ and θ terminates in the first quadrant, find each of the following.

a. cos 2θ   **b. sin 2θ**   **c. tan 2θ**

$$\sin^2 \theta + \cos^2 \theta = 1 \qquad \text{\textit{Substituting }} \frac{2}{\sqrt{5}} \text{ \textit{for sin }} \theta.$$

$$\frac{4}{5} + \cos^2 \theta = 1 \qquad \text{\textit{Solving.}}$$

$$\cos \theta = \frac{1}{\sqrt{5}} \qquad \text{\textit{Since }} \tan \theta = \frac{\sin \theta}{\cos \theta} \text{ \textit{or }} \frac{\frac{2}{\sqrt{5}}}{\frac{1}{\sqrt{5}}}.$$

Thus, $\tan \theta = 2$.

a. $\cos 2\theta = \cos^2 \theta - \sin^2 \theta$

$$= \left(\frac{1}{\sqrt{5}}\right)^2 - \left(\frac{2}{\sqrt{5}}\right)^2$$

$$= -\frac{3}{5}$$

b. $\sin 2\theta = 2 \sin \theta \cos \theta$

$$= 2\left(\frac{2}{\sqrt{5}}\right)\left(\frac{1}{\sqrt{5}}\right)$$

$$= \frac{4}{5}$$

c. $\tan 2\theta = \dfrac{2 \tan \theta}{1 - \tan^2 \theta}$

$$= \frac{2(2)}{1 - (2)^2}$$

$$= -\frac{4}{3}$$

The formulas that were used to find the sine or cosine of half of a number may also be used to find the sine or cosine of half of an angle.

The formula for the tangent of half of an angle is found by dividing $\sin \frac{\alpha}{2}$ by $\cos \frac{\alpha}{2}$.

$$\tan \frac{\alpha}{2} = \frac{\pm\sqrt{\dfrac{1 - \cos \alpha}{2}}}{\pm\sqrt{\dfrac{1 + \cos \alpha}{2}}}$$

$$= \pm\sqrt{\frac{1 - \cos \alpha}{1 + \cos \alpha}}$$

If α represents the measure of an angle, then the following identities hold for all values of α.

$$\sin \frac{\alpha}{2} = \pm\sqrt{\frac{1 - \cos \alpha}{2}} \qquad \cos \frac{\alpha}{2} = \pm\sqrt{\frac{1 + \cos \alpha}{2}}$$

$$\tan \frac{\alpha}{2} = \pm\sqrt{\frac{1 - \cos \alpha}{1 + \cos \alpha}}$$

Half Angle Identities

The sign of the radical is chosen according to the quadrant in which the terminal side of $\frac{\alpha}{2}$ lies.

Example

2 Find the value of each of the following.

a. cos 15°

b. sin 15°

a. $\cos 15° = \cos \dfrac{30°}{2}$

$$= +\sqrt{\frac{1 + \cos 30°}{2}}$$

$$= +\sqrt{\frac{1 + \dfrac{\sqrt{3}}{2}}{2}}$$

$$= \frac{\sqrt{2 + \sqrt{3}}}{2}$$

b. $\sin 15° = \sin \dfrac{30°}{2}$

$$= +\sqrt{\frac{1 - \cos 30°}{2}}$$

$$= +\sqrt{\frac{1 - \dfrac{\sqrt{3}}{2}}{2}}$$

$$= \frac{\sqrt{2 - \sqrt{3}}}{2}$$

The double angle and half angle identities may also be used to verify other identities.

Example

3 Verify that $\cot A = \dfrac{\sin 2A}{1 - \cos 2A}$ is an identity.

$\cot A = \dfrac{\sin 2A}{1 - \cos 2A}$

$\cot A = \dfrac{2 \sin A \cos A}{1 - (2 \cos^2 A - 1)}$ $\sin 2A = 2 \sin A \cos A$
                                      $\cos 2A = 2 \cos^2 A - 1$

$\cot A = \dfrac{2 \sin A \cos A}{2 - 2 \cos^2 A}$ *Simplify.*

$\cot A = \dfrac{2 \sin A \cos A}{2(1 - \cos^2 A)}$ *Factor.*

$\cot A = \dfrac{\sin A \cos A}{\sin^2 A}$ $1 - \cos^2 A = \sin^2 A$

$\cot A = \dfrac{\cos A}{\sin A}$ *Simplify.*

$\cot A = \cot A$ $\frac{\cos A}{\sin A} = \cot A$

Exploratory Exercises

Solve each of the following.

1. x is a first quadrant angle. In which quadrant does the terminal side for $2x$ lie?

2. x is a second quadrant angle. In which quadrant does the terminal side for $2x$ lie?

3. $2x$ is a third quadrant angle. In which quadrant does the terminal side for x lie?

4. $2x$ is a fourth quadrant angle. In which quadrant does the terminal side for x lie?

5. $\frac{x}{2}$ is a first quadrant angle. In which quadrant does the terminal side for x lie?

6. $\frac{x}{2}$ is a second quadrant angle. In which quadrant does the terminal side for x lie?

7. x is a third quadrant angle. In which quadrant does the terminal side for $\frac{x}{2}$ lie?

8. x is a fourth quadrant angle. In which quadrant does the terminal side for $\frac{x}{2}$ lie?

9. $\frac{x}{2}$ is a first quadrant angle. In which quadrant does the terminal side for $2x$ lie?

10. $2x$ is a second quadrant angle. In which quadrant does the terminal side for $\frac{x}{2}$ lie?

Simplify each expression.

11. $1 - 2 \sin^2 10°$

12. $2 \cos^2 15° - 1$

13. $2 \sin 35° \cos 35°$

14. $\cos^2 25° - \sin^2 25°$

15. $\dfrac{2 \tan 50°}{1 - \tan^2 50°}$

16. $\sqrt{\dfrac{1 - \cos 40°}{2}}$

17. $\sqrt{\dfrac{1 + \cos 62°}{2}}$

18. $\sqrt{\dfrac{1 - \cos 16°}{1 + \cos 16°}}$

19. $\cos^2 3x - \sin^2 3x$

Written Exercises

If $\sin r = \dfrac{3}{5}$ and r is in the first quadrant, find each of the following.

1. $\sin 2r$
2. $\cos 2r$
3. $\tan 2r$
4. $\sin \dfrac{r}{2}$
5. $\cos \dfrac{r}{2}$
6. $\tan \dfrac{r}{2}$

If $\tan y = \dfrac{5}{12}$ and y is in the third quadrant, find each of the following.

7. $\sin 2y$
8. $\cos 2y$
9. $\tan 2y$
10. $\sin \dfrac{y}{2}$
11. $\cos \dfrac{y}{2}$
12. $\tan \dfrac{y}{2}$

Use the half-angle identities to find each of the following.

13. $\sin 22°30'$
14. $\cos 22°30'$
15. $\tan 22°30'$
16. $\sin 7°30'$
17. $\cos 7°30'$
18. $\tan 7°30'$

If $P(-3, -4)$ is on the terminal side of an angle in standard position with measure θ, find each of the following.

19. $\sin \theta$
20. $\cos \theta$
21. $\tan \theta$
22. $\sin 2\theta$
23. $\cos 2\theta$
24. $\tan 2\theta$
25. $\sin \dfrac{\theta}{2}$
26. $\cos \dfrac{\theta}{2}$
27. $\tan \dfrac{\theta}{2}$

Verify each identity.

28. $\dfrac{1}{2} \sin 2A = \dfrac{\tan A}{1 + \tan^2 A}$

29. $1 + \cos 2A = \dfrac{2}{1 + \tan^2 A}$

30. $\cot \dfrac{x}{2} = \dfrac{1 + \cos x}{\sin x}$

31. $\tan 2x \tan x + 2 = \dfrac{\tan 2x}{\tan x}$

32. $\sin 2B (\cot B + \tan B) = 2$

33. $\csc A \sec A = 2 \csc 2A$

34. $\dfrac{1 - \tan^2 \theta}{1 + \tan^2 \theta} = \cos 2\theta$

35. $\cot X = \dfrac{\sin 2X}{1 - \cos 2X}$

36. $1 - \sin A = \left(\sin \dfrac{A}{2} - \cos \dfrac{A}{2} \right)^2$

37. $\cos^4 A = \dfrac{2 \cos 2A + \cos^2 2A + 1}{4}$

38. $\dfrac{\sin \alpha + \sin 3\alpha}{\cos \alpha + \cos 3\alpha} = \tan 2\alpha$

39. $\dfrac{\cos 2A}{1 + \sin 2A} = \dfrac{\cot A - 1}{\cot A + 1}$

40. $\dfrac{\cos A + \sin A}{\cos A - \sin A} = \dfrac{1 + \sin 2A}{\cos 2A}$

41. $\tan \dfrac{x}{2} = \dfrac{1 - \cos x}{\sin x}$

42. $\tan \dfrac{x}{2} = \dfrac{\sin x}{1 + \cos x}$

43. $\cot \dfrac{\alpha}{2} = \dfrac{\sin \alpha}{1 - \cos \alpha}$

Challenge Exercises

Derive a formula for each of the following.

44. $\sin 3\alpha$ in terms of $\sin \alpha$
45. $\cos 3\alpha$ in terms of $\cos \alpha$

For the Scholar

What is the shortest distance from the center of the circle to the longest chord if three parallel chords of lengths 4, 8, and 10 lie in a circle on the same side of its center and the distance between them is the same?

1. Trigonometric Functions of an Angle in Standard Position: For any angle with measure α, point $P(x, y)$ on its terminal side, and $r = \sqrt{x^2 + y^2}$, the trigonometric functions of α are as follows. (125)

$$\sin \alpha = \frac{y}{r} \qquad \cos \alpha = \frac{x}{r} \qquad \tan \alpha = \frac{y}{x}$$

$$\csc \alpha = \frac{r}{y} \qquad \sec \alpha = \frac{r}{x} \qquad \cot \alpha = \frac{x}{y}$$

2. Trigonometric Functions in a Right Triangle: For an acute angle A in right triangle ABC, the trigonometric functions are as follows.   (126)

$$\sin A = \frac{\text{side opposite}}{\text{hypotenuse}} = \frac{a}{c} \qquad \cos A = \frac{\text{side adjacent}}{\text{hypotenuse}} = \frac{b}{c}$$

$$\tan A = \frac{\text{side opposite}}{\text{side adjacent}} = \frac{a}{b} \qquad \cot A = \frac{\text{side adjacent}}{\text{side opposite}} = \frac{b}{a}$$

$$\sec A = \frac{\text{hypotenuse}}{\text{side adjacent}} = \frac{c}{b} \qquad \csc A = \frac{\text{hypotenuse}}{\text{side opposite}} = \frac{c}{a}$$

3. Cofunction Identities: The following trigonometric identities hold for all values of A when $0° \leq A \leq 90°$.   (132)

$$\sin A = \cos (90° - A) \qquad \cos A = \sin (90° - A)$$
$$\tan A = \cot (90° - A) \qquad \cot A = \tan (90° - A)$$
$$\sec A = \csc (90° - A) \qquad \csc A = \sec (90° - A)$$

4. Reciprocal Identities: The following trigonometric identities hold for all values of A, except those for which any function is undefined.   (132)

$$\sin A = \frac{1}{\csc A} \qquad \cos A = \frac{1}{\sec A}$$

$$\tan A = \frac{1}{\cot A} \qquad \cot A = \frac{1}{\tan A}$$

$$\sec A = \frac{1}{\cos A} \qquad \csc A = \frac{1}{\sin A}$$

5. Quotient Identities: The following trigonometric identities hold for all values of A, except those for which any function is undefined.   (133)

$$\frac{\sin A}{\cos A} = \tan A \qquad \sin A = \cos A \tan A$$

$$\frac{\cos A}{\sin A} = \cot A \qquad \cos A = \sin A \cot A$$

6. Pythagorean Identities: The following trigonometric identities hold for all values of A, except those for which any function is undefined.   (133)

$$\sin^2 A + \cos^2 A = 1$$
$$\tan^2 A + 1 = \sec^2 A$$
$$1 + \cot^2 A = \csc^2 A$$

7. Suggestions for Verifying Identities: (135)
   1. Transform the more complicated side of the equation into the form of the simpler side.
   2. Substitute one or more basic trigonometric identities to simplify the expression.
   3. Factor or multiply to simplify the expression.
   4. Multiply both numerator and denominator by the same trigonometric expression.
8. The Degree/Radian Proportion: Let R represent a number of radians. Let D represent a number of degrees. (138)
$$\frac{R}{\pi} = \frac{D}{180°}$$
9. Length of an Arc: The length of any circular arc, s, is equal to the product of the radius of the circle, r, and the radian measure of the central angle it subtends. (139)
$$s = r\theta$$
10. The trigonometric function of an angle of any size may be reduced to function of an acute angle. This acute angle is called the reference angle. (141)
11. Sum and Difference Identities for Sine and Cosine Functions: If α and β represent the measures of two angles, then the following identities hold for all values of α and β. (147)
$$\sin (\alpha \pm \beta) = \sin \alpha \cos \beta \pm \cos \alpha \sin \beta$$
$$\cos (\alpha \pm \beta) = \cos \alpha \cos \beta \mp \sin \alpha \sin \beta$$
12. Sum and Difference Identities for the Tangent Function: If α and β represent the measures of two angles, then the following identities hold for all values of α and β. (148)
$$\tan (\alpha \pm \beta) = \frac{\tan \alpha \pm \tan \beta}{1 \mp \tan \alpha \tan \beta}$$
13. Double Angle Identities: If θ represents the measure of an angle, then the following identities hold for all values of θ. (150)
$$\sin 2\theta = 2 \sin \theta \cos \theta$$
$$\cos 2\theta = \cos^2 \theta - \sin^2 \theta$$
$$= 1 - 2 \sin^2 \theta$$
$$= 2 \cos^2 \theta - 1$$
$$\tan 2\theta = \frac{2 \tan \theta}{1 - \tan^2 \theta} \qquad (\tan^2 \theta \neq 1)$$
14. Half Angle Identities: If α represents the measure of an angle, then the following identities hold for all values of α. (151)
$$\sin \frac{\alpha}{2} = \pm \sqrt{\frac{1 - \cos \alpha}{2}} \qquad \cos \frac{\alpha}{2} = \pm \sqrt{\frac{1 + \cos \alpha}{2}}$$
$$\tan \frac{\alpha}{2} = \pm \sqrt{\frac{1 - \cos \alpha}{1 + \cos \alpha}}$$

Chapter Review

Find the values of the six trigonometric functions of an angle in standard position if each of the following points lies on its terminal side. (5-1)

1. $(5, 3)$ **2.** $(12, 5)$ **3.** $(-6, 8)$ **4.** $(2, 0)$

Find the value of each expression without using tables or a calculator. (5-1)

5. $\sin 30° - \cos 60°$ **6.** $2 \sin 90° \cos 90°$ **7.** $\sin^2 30° + \cos 60°$

Use the table on page 531 to find each trigonometric value. Use interpolation when necessary. (5-2)

8. $\cos 38°$ **9.** $\csc 32°18'$ **10.** $\sin 79°42'$ **11.** $\tan 42°51'$

Find x to the nearest minute. (5-2)

12. $\cot x = 0.1234$ **13.** $\sin x = 0.1115$ **14.** $\cos x = 0.5132$

Solve each of the following for values of θ between 0° and 90°. (5-3)

15. If $\cos \theta = \dfrac{2}{3}$, find $\sin \theta$.   **16.** If $\sin \theta = \dfrac{1}{2}$, find $\csc \theta$.

17. If $\tan \theta = 4$, find $\sec \theta$.   **18.** If $\csc \theta = \dfrac{5}{3}$, find $\cos \theta$.

Verify each identity. (5-4)

19. $\dfrac{\sin \theta}{\sec \theta} = \dfrac{1}{\tan \theta + \cot \theta}$ **20.** $\dfrac{1}{\sec^2 \theta} + \dfrac{1}{\csc^2 \theta} = 1$

21. $\csc x \sec x = \cot x + \tan x$ **22.** $\cos^2 x + \tan^2 x \cos^2 x = 1$

23. $\dfrac{1 - \cos \theta}{1 + \cos \theta} = (\csc \theta - \cot \theta)^2$ **24.** $\dfrac{\sec \theta + 1}{\tan \theta} = \dfrac{\tan \theta}{\sec \theta - 1}$

Change each of the following to degree measure. (5-5)

25. $\dfrac{\pi}{3}$ **26.** $-\dfrac{5\pi}{12}$ **27.** $\dfrac{4\pi}{3}$ **28.** $\dfrac{7\pi}{4}$

Given the degree measure of a central angle, find the measure of its intercepted arc in a circle of radius 8 cm. (5-5)

29. $120°$ **30.** $40°$ **31.** $28°$ **32.** $64°$

Express each of the following in terms of a function of a positive angle less than 45°. (5-6)

33. $\cos 210°$ **34.** $\sin 355°$ **35.** $\sec (-128°)$ **36.** $\tan 96°$

37-40. Find the value of each expression in problems **33-36.**

Find the value of each of the following without using tables or a calculator. (5-7)

41. $\cos 360°$ **42.** $\sin (-\pi)$ **43.** $\cos 90°$ **44.** $\tan (-90°)$

Use the sum and difference identities to evaluate each of the following. (5-8)

45. $\sin 105°$ **46.** $\cos 240°$ **47.** $\cos 15°$ **48.** $\sin (-255°)$

If $P(-4, 3)$ is on the terminal side of an angle in standard position with measure α, find each of the following. (5-9)

49. $\cos \dfrac{\alpha}{2}$ **50.** $\tan 2\alpha$ **51.** $\sin \dfrac{\alpha}{2}$ **52.** $\cos 2\alpha$

Find the value of each of the following to four decimal places.

1. sin A
2. cos A
3. tan B
4. csc B
5. sec B
6. cot A

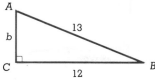

Show that each of the following statements is true.

7. $\cos 90° = 2 \cos^2 45° - 1$
8. $\cos^2 90° - \sin^2 90° = \cos 180°$
9. $1 + \tan^2 60° = \sec^2 60°$
10. $\tan^2 45° + \cot^2 45° = 2$

Use the table on page 531 to find each trigonometric value. Use interpolation when necessary.

11. $\sin 32°10'$
12. $\tan 79°16'$
13. $\sec 38°22'$

Find x to the nearest minute.

14. $\sin x = 0.9165$
15. $\csc x = 1.0175$
16. $\cot x = 0.2137$

Solve each of the following for values of θ between 0° and 90°.

17. If $\sin \theta = \frac{1}{2}$, find $\cos \theta$.
18. If $\csc \theta = \frac{5}{3}$, find $\cos \theta$.
19. If $\sec \theta = 3$, find $\tan \theta$.
20. If $\sin \theta = \frac{4}{5}$, find $\sec \theta$.

Verify each identity.

21. $\tan \beta(\cot \beta + \tan \beta) = \sec^2 \beta$
22. $\sin^2 A \cot^2 A = (1 - \sin A)(1 + \sin A)$
23. $\frac{\sec x}{\sin x} - \frac{\sin x}{\cos x} = \cot x$
24. $\frac{\cos x}{1 + \sin x} + \frac{\cos x}{1 - \sin x} = 2 \sec x$

Change each of the following to radian measure in terms of π.

25. $135°$
26. $275°$
27. $-150°$

Given the radian measure of a central angle, find the measure of its intercepted arc in a circle of radius 12 in.

28. $\frac{4\pi}{5}$
29. $\frac{5\pi}{12}$
30. 1.5

Find the value of each of the following.

31. $\cos (-50°)$
32. $\cot 240°$
33. $\sin 142°$

Find the value of each of the following without using tables or a calculator.

34. $\csc 180°$
35. $\sin \left(-\frac{\pi}{2}\right)$
36. $\sec 90°$

Use the sum and difference formulas to evaluate each of the following.

37. $\sin 255°$
38. $\cos 165°$
39. $\sin (-195°)$

If $\cos x = \frac{3}{4}$ and x is in the fourth quadrant, find each of the following.

40. $\sin 2x$
41. $\cos \frac{x}{2}$
42. $\tan 2x$

CHAPTER 6

Graphs and Inverses of the Trigonometric Functions

When sound waves are made visible by an oscilloscope, they have a regular pattern that repeats itself many times per second. Joseph Fourier (1768–1830) showed that every sound wave that repeats itself is related to a trigonometric curve called the sine curve.

6-1 Graphs of the Trigonometric Functions

The graphs of the trigonometric functions are identical to the graphs of the circular functions. The table of values for $0° \le \theta \le 90°$ or a calculator can be used to determine the set of ordered pairs $(\theta, f(\theta))$, for an angle θ and any trigonometric function f. Ordered pairs can be found for any value of θ by using the concept of the reference angle and the trigonometric tables. On a calculator, any value of θ can be entered followed by the trigonometric functions to determine $f(\theta)$ for the ordered pair. The measure of angle θ is plotted using the x-axis. Each trigonometric function of angle θ, that is, $f(\theta)$, is plotted using the y-axis.

The graphs of the six trigonometric functions for $-360° \le \theta \le 360°$ are shown.

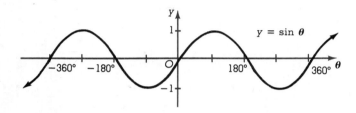

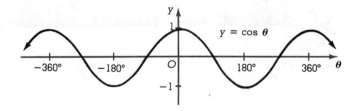

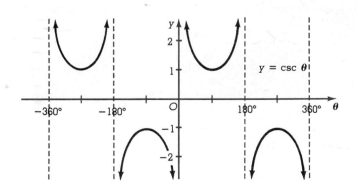

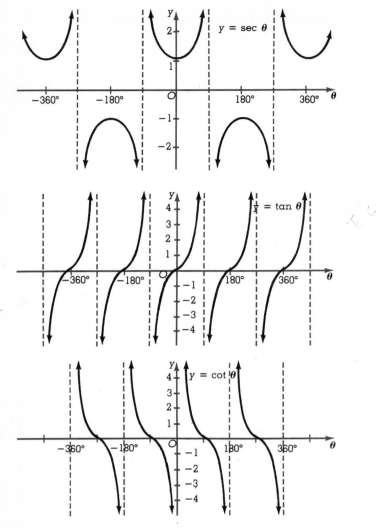

Note the resemblance of the cosine curve to the sine curve. Actually, since the sin $x = \cos(90° - x)$, the cosine curve is 90° out of phase with the sine curve. In other words, the cosine curve is a sine curve displaced 90° to the left along the x-axis.

Knowledge of the characteristics of the graphs of the functions can be used to quickly determine the quadrantal values of the functions. At a glance, it is obvious that the value of the sine function is 0 at $-360°$, $-180°$, $0°$, $180°$, $360°$, and at every integral multiple of 180°. The maximum value of the sine function is 1 at $x = 90°$ or $-270°$, and the minimum is -1 at $x = 270°$ or $-90°$. Since the graph is periodic and repeats itself every 360°, other zero, maximum and minimum points can be readily found. Similar special values of the other functions may be determined by an inspection of their graphs.

Example

1

Use the graph of the cosine function to find the values of θ for which $\cos \theta = 0$.

When $\cos \theta = 0$, the value of θ is $-270°$, $-90°$, $90°$, or $270°$. Since the cosine function has a period of $360°$, the values of θ for which $\cos \theta = 0$ are given by $90° + n \cdot 360°$ and $270° + n \cdot 360°$ where n is any integer.

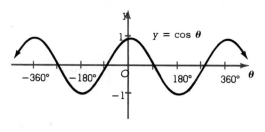

The graph of a trigonometric function may be drawn from the knowledge of its shape and the values of the function at integral multiples of $90°$.

A sketch of a complete sine or cosine curve requires only five key points.

Example

2

Graph the sine curve in the interval $-540° \le \theta \le 0°$.

Find the value of $\sin \theta$ for $\theta = -540°, -450°, -360°, -270°, -180°, -90°,$ and $0°$.

$$\sin (-540°) = 0 \qquad \sin (-450°) = -1$$
$$\sin (-360°) = 0 \qquad \sin (-270°) = 1$$
$$\sin (-180°) = 0 \qquad \sin (-90°) \; = -1$$
$$\sin 0° \qquad = 0$$

Plot the points from these ordered pairs.

$$(-540°, 0) \qquad (-450°, -1)$$
$$(-360°, 0) \qquad (-270°, 1)$$
$$(-180°, 0) \qquad (-90°, -1)$$
$$(0°, 0)$$

Connect these points with a smooth continuous curve.

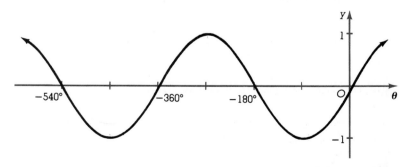

Exploratory Exercises

Evaluate each of the following by referring to the graphs of the sine and cosine functions.

1. sin 90°   **2.** cos 270°   **3.** sin 360°   **4.** cos 450°

5. cos 90°   **6.** cos (−90°)   **7.** sin 180°   **8.** sin 450°

State whether the value of each of the following is positive or negative.

9. sin 50°   **10.** cos 140°   **11.** tan 280°   **12.** csc 440°

13. sec 150°   **14.** cot 250°   **15.** sin 350°   **16.** cos (−500°)

State which value is greater.

17. cos 20° or cos 80°   **18.** sin 10° or sin 100°

19. sin 40° or sin 50°   **20.** cos 70° or cos 170°

Written Exercises

Find the values of θ for which each of the following is true.

1. cos θ = 1   **2.** sin θ = 1

3. tan θ = 1   **4.** cos θ = −1

5. sin θ = 0   **6.** sin θ = −1

State the domain for each of the following.

7. y = sin θ **8.** y = cos θ

9. y = cot θ **10.** y = sec θ

11. y = tan θ **12.** y = csc θ

13-18. State the range of each function in problems **7-12.**

Graph each function in the indicated interval.

19. y = sin x; −180° ≤ x ≤ 180°   **20.** y = cos x; 270° ≤ x ≤ 630°

21. y = tan x; 90° ≤ x ≤ 450°   **22.** y = csc x; −540° ≤ x ≤ 0°

23. y = sec x; −180° ≤ x ≤ 360°   **24.** y = cot x; −90° ≤ x ≤ 360°

Graph the sine and cosine functions on the same coordinate axes for 0° ≤ **x** ≤ 360°. Use the graph to find values of **x**, if any, for which each of the following is true.

25. sin x = −cos x **26.** sin x ≤ cos x

27. sin x · cos x > 1   **28.** sin x · cos x ≤ 0

29. sin x + cos x = 1   **30.** sin x − cos x = 0

For the Scholar

A rectangle has a length that is twice its width. A scalene triangle is drawn with its base on a diagonal of the rectangle. The area of the rectangle is $\frac{1}{5}$ the area of the triangle. What is the length of the altitude drawn to the base in the triangle?

6-2 Amplitude, Period, and Phase Shift

The graphs of the trigonometric functions can be modified by constants. Consider an equation of the form $y = A \sin \theta$. The maximum absolute value of $\sin \theta$ is 1. If every value of $\sin \theta$ is multiplied by A, the maximum value of $A \sin \theta$ is $|A|$. Similarly, the maximum value of $A \cos \theta$ is $|A|$. The absolute value of A, or $|A|$, is called the **amplitude** of the functions $y = A \sin \theta$ and $y = A \cos \theta$.

If $A < 0$, the curve is a reflection of the graph of the function on the x-axis for the coefficient having the same absolute value but opposite sign.

The amplitude of the functions, $y = A \sin \theta$ and $y = A \cos \theta$, is the absolute value of A, or $|A|$.	*Amplitude of a Sine or Cosine Function*

The tangent function does not have an amplitude because $y = \tan \theta$ increases without limit as θ approaches values such as $90°$.

Example

1 Graph $y = 2 \sin \theta$. State the amplitude.

Complete a table of values.

θ	0°	45°	90°	135°	180°	225°	270°	315°	360°
$\sin \theta$	0	$\dfrac{\sqrt{2}}{2}$	1	$\dfrac{\sqrt{2}}{2}$	0	$-\dfrac{\sqrt{2}}{2}$	-1	$-\dfrac{\sqrt{2}}{2}$	0
$2 \sin \theta$	0	$\sqrt{2}$	2	$\sqrt{2}$	0	$-\sqrt{2}$	-2	$-\sqrt{2}$	0

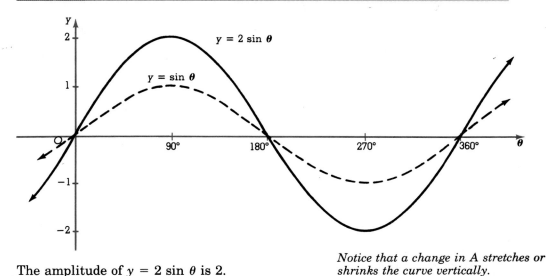

The amplitude of $y = 2 \sin \theta$ is 2.

Notice that a change in A stretches or shrinks the curve vertically.

Consider an equation of the form $y = \sin k\theta$, where k is a constant. Since the period of the sine function is $360°$, the following identity can be written.

$$y = \sin k\theta = \sin (k\theta + 360°)$$

or

$$y = \sin k\left(\theta + \frac{360°}{k}\right)$$

Thus, the period of $y = \sin k\theta$ is $\dfrac{360°}{k}$. Similarly, the period of $y = \cos k\theta$ is $\dfrac{360°}{k}$. The period of $y = \tan k\theta$ is $\dfrac{180°}{k}$ since the period of the tangent function is $180°$.

If the measure of angle θ is expressed in radians, the period of the sine and cosine functions is $\dfrac{2\pi}{k}$. The period of the tangent function is $\dfrac{\pi}{k}$.

The period of the functions, $y = \sin k\theta$ and $y = \cos k\theta$ is $\dfrac{360°}{k}$. The period of the function, $y = \tan k\theta$ is $\dfrac{180°}{k}$.	**Periods of a Sine, Cosine, or Tangent Function**

Example

2 Graph $y = \cos 2\theta$. State the period.

θ	0	30°	45°	60°	90°	120°	135°	150°	180°
2θ	0	60°	90°	120°	180°	240°	270°	300°	360°
$\cos 2\theta$	1	$\dfrac{1}{2}$	0	$-\dfrac{1}{2}$	-1	$-\dfrac{1}{2}$	0	$\dfrac{1}{2}$	1

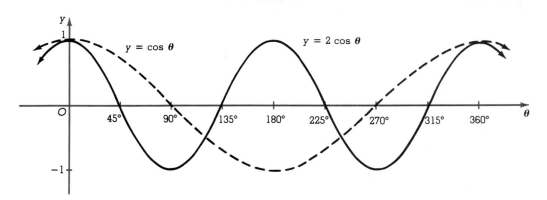

The period of $y = \cos 2\theta$ is $\dfrac{360°}{2}$ or $180°$.

Notice that a change in k stretches or shrinks the curve horizontally. As k becomes larger, the period becomes smaller.

Consider an equation of the form $y = A \sin (k\theta + c)$ where $A \neq 0$, $k \neq 0$, and $c \neq 0$. To find a zero of the function find the value of θ such that $0 = A \sin (k\theta + c)$. The value of θ is found by solving $k\theta + c = 0$ for θ.   *Why?*

$$k\theta + c = 0$$
$$\theta = -\frac{c}{k}$$

Thus, if $y = 0$, then $\theta = -\frac{c}{k}$. The value of $-\frac{c}{k}$ is called the **phase shift.** When $c > 0$, the graph of $y = A \sin (k\theta + c)$ is similar to the graph of $y = A \sin k\theta$, but is shifted $\left|\frac{c}{k}\right|$ units to the *left*. When $c < 0$, the graph of $y = A \sin (k\theta + c)$ is similar to the graph of $y = A \sin k\theta$, but is shifted $\left|\frac{c}{k}\right|$ units to the *right*.

The phase shift of the function, $y = A \sin (k\theta + c)$, is $-\frac{c}{k}$. If $c > 0$, the shift is to the left and if $c < 0$ the shift is to the right. This definition applies to all trigonometric functions.	*Phase Shift of All Trigonometric Functions*

Example

3   Graph $y = \tan (\theta - 45°)$. State the phase shift.

θ	0°	45°	90°	135°	180°	225°	270°	315°	360°
$\theta - 45°$	−45°	0°	45°	90°	135°	180°	225°	270°	315°
$\tan (\theta - 45°)$	−1	0	1	undefined	−1	0	1	undefined	−1

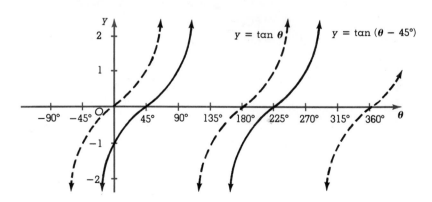

The phase shift of $y = \tan (\theta - 45°)$ is $-\dfrac{-45°}{1}$ or $45°$.

Example

4 Find the possible equations of a sine function with amplitude 2, period 180°, and phase shift 45°.

Find the possible values of the amplitude.	$\|A\| = 2$ $A = 2$ or $A = -2$
Find the period.	$\dfrac{360°}{k} = 180°$ $k = 2$
Find the phase shift.	$-\dfrac{c}{k}$ or $-\dfrac{c}{2} = 45°$ $c = -90°$

The possible equations are $y = 2 \sin (2x - 90°)$ and $y = -2 \sin (2x - 90°)$.

Exploratory Exercises

State the amplitude, period, and phase shift for each of the following.

1. $y = 2 \sin 5\theta$

2. $y = 4 \sin \theta$

3. $y = 3 \cos (\theta - 90°)$

4. $y = 2 \cos 2\theta$

5. $y = \tan (2\theta - 180°)$

6. $y = 10 \tan 4\theta$

7. $y = 110 \sin 20\theta$

8. $y = \tan 2(\theta - 180°)$

9. $y = 2 \sin \theta$

10. $y = 243 \sin (15\theta - 40°)$

11. $y = -7 \sin 6\theta$

12. $y = -6 \cos (180° - \theta)$

13. $y = \dfrac{1}{4} \cos \dfrac{\theta}{2}$

14. $y = 12 \cos 3(\theta - 90°)$

15. $y = 10 \sin \left(\dfrac{1}{3}\theta - 300°\right)$

Written Exercises

Write an equation of the sine function for each amplitude, period, and phase shift.

1. amplitude = 3, period = 720°, phase shift = 60°

2. amplitude = 5, period = 360°, phase shift = 60°

3. amplitude = $\dfrac{2}{3}$, period = 180°, phase shift = 45°

4. amplitude = 17, period = 45°, phase shift = −60°

5. amplitude = $\dfrac{1}{2}$, period = $\dfrac{3\pi}{2}$, phase shift = $-\dfrac{\pi}{4}$

6. amplitude = 7, period = 225°, phase shift = −90°

Write an equation of the cosine function for each amplitude, period, and phase shift.

7. amplitude = $\dfrac{1}{3}$, period = 180°, phase shift = 0°

8. amplitude = 3, period = 180°, phase shift = 120°

9. amplitude = 4, period = 720°, phase shift = 90°

10. amplitude = 100, period = 630°, phase shift = −90°

11. amplitude = $\frac{7}{3}$, period = 150°, phase shift = 270°

12. amplitude = 1, period = $\frac{3\pi}{4}$, phase shift = $-\frac{\pi}{3}$

Identify the amplitude, period, and phase shift of each sine curve.

13.
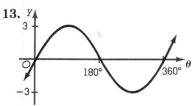

14.
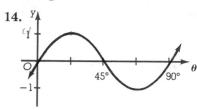

15.
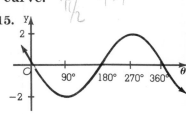

16.
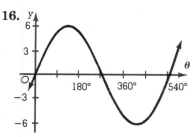

17.
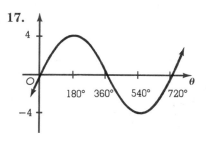

18.
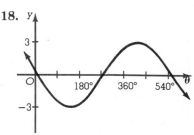

Graph each of the following.

19. $y = \frac{1}{2} \cos \theta$

20. $y = \frac{2}{3} \cos \theta$

21. $y = \sin \left(x + \frac{\pi}{3} \right)$

22. $y = \sin 4\theta$

23. $y = \cos 3\theta$

24. $y = 3 \sin \theta$

25. $y = 3 \sec \theta$

26. $y = \cos (\theta - 30°)$

27. $y = 2 \tan \theta$

28. $y = \cos (\theta + 30°)$

29. $y = -\cot \theta$

30. $y = \sin (\theta - 45°)$

31. $y = 4 \sin \frac{1}{2} \theta$

32. $y = -\frac{1}{2} \cos \frac{3}{4} \theta$

33. $y = -6 \sin \left(2x + \frac{\pi}{4} \right)$

Sound waves are registered as sine waves on an oscilloscope. Given on the vertical scale, each square represents 1, and on the horizontal scale, each square represents 20°, find the amplitude and period of each of the following.

34.
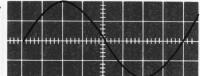

35.
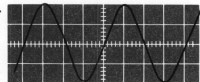

For the Scholar

Simplify the expression, finding the product of the positive numbers a, b, and c when

$$(a + b + c)^{-1}(a^{-1} + b^{-1} + c^{-1})(ab + bc + ac)^{-1}((ab)^{-1} + (bc)^{-1} + (ac)^{-1}) = \frac{1}{25}.$$

6-3 Graphing the Trigonometric Functions

A function of the form $y = A \sin(k\theta + c)$ can be graphed after finding the amplitude, period, and phase shift of the function. Once these values are known, a rough curve can be sketched using the general knowledge of the shape of the sine curve.

Example

1 **Graph $y = 4 \sin 2\theta$.**

Find the amplitude. $\qquad |A| = 4$ $\qquad$ *The values of the function vary from 4 to −4.*

Find the period. $\qquad \dfrac{360°}{k} = \dfrac{360°}{2}$ or 180° $\qquad$ *The curve repeats at each 180° interval.*

Find the phase shift. $\qquad -\dfrac{c}{k} = \dfrac{0}{2}$ or 0 $\qquad$ *There is no phase shift.*

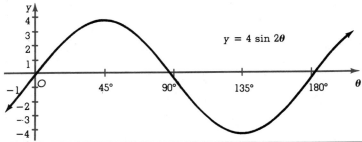

The functions $y = A \cos(k\theta + c)$ and $y = A \tan(k\theta + c)$ can be graphed in a similar manner.

Example

2 **Graph $y = 3 \cos(2\theta + 180°)$.**

Find the amplitude. $\qquad |A| = 3$

Find the period. $\qquad \dfrac{360°}{k} = \dfrac{360°}{2}$ or 180°

Find the phase shift. $\qquad -\dfrac{c}{k} = -\dfrac{180°}{2}$ or −90° $\qquad$ *Since $c > 0$, the graph is shifted 90° to the left.*

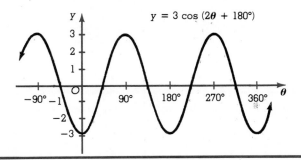

When graphing the tangent function, find the period and phase shift since the function does not have an amplitude.

Example

3 Graph $y = \tan\left(\dfrac{x}{2} - \dfrac{\pi}{6}\right)$.

Find the period. $\qquad \dfrac{\pi}{k} = \dfrac{\pi}{\frac{1}{2}}$ or 2π

Find the phase shift. $\qquad -\dfrac{c}{k} = -\left(\dfrac{-\frac{\pi}{6}}{\frac{1}{2}}\right)$ or $\dfrac{\pi}{3}$ *Since $c < 0$, the graph is shifted $\frac{\pi}{3}$ to the right.*

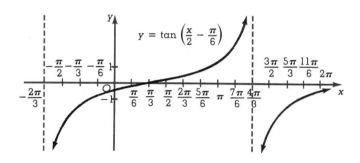

$$y = \tan\left(\dfrac{x}{2} - \dfrac{\pi}{6}\right)$$

Exploratory Exercises

State the amplitude, period, and phase shift for each of the following.

1. $y = \sin(\theta + 90°)$ **2.** $y = \sin(\theta - 180°)$ **3.** $y = 3\cos(\theta - 90°)$

4. $y = 2\cos\left(\dfrac{x}{2} + \pi\right)$ **5.** $y = -3\sin(6\theta - 180°)$ **6.** $y = -\dfrac{1}{3}\sin(2\theta + 45°)$

7. $y = \dfrac{1}{2}\cos\left(\dfrac{\theta}{2} - 180°\right)$ **8.** $y = \dfrac{1}{2}\sin 2(\theta - 180°)$ **9.** $y = \dfrac{1}{10}\sin\left(\dfrac{2}{3}x - \dfrac{\pi}{3}\right)$

10. $y = 6\sin\left(6x + \dfrac{3\pi}{2}\right)$ **11.** $\dfrac{1}{2}y = \sin(3\theta + 180°)$ **12.** $2y = 10\sin\left(\dfrac{\theta}{2} + 90°\right)$

Written Exercises

Graph each of the following.

1. $y = \dfrac{1}{2}\cos 2\theta$ **2.** $y = \tan\left(\dfrac{x}{2} + \dfrac{\pi}{2}\right)$ **3.** $y = 6\sin 4\theta$

4. $y = 5\cos(2\theta + 180°)$ **5.** $y = -\sin(\theta - 45°)$ **6.** $y = -3\sin(\theta - 45°)$

7-18. Graph each equation in problems **1-12** of the Exploratory Exercises.

Graph each of the following.

19. $y = \sec 3\theta$

20. $y = \tan (\theta + 90°)$

21. $y = \cot (\theta - 90°)$

22. $y = \csc (\theta + 60°)$

23. $y = \tan (2\theta - 90°)$

24. $y = \csc (3\theta + 180°)$

Challenge Exercise

25. Sketch the graph of $y = \sin \dfrac{1}{x}$. (Hint: Start with values of x greater than $\dfrac{1}{180}°$ and decrease the values.)

For the Scholar

Given $\odot P$ with $m\overset{\frown}{XY} = 120$, $m\overset{\frown}{YZ} = 72$, and point A on minor $\overset{\frown}{XZ}$ such that $\overline{PA} \perp \overline{XZ}$. What is the ratio of $m\angle PAY$ to $m\angle XZY$?

6-4 Graphing Compound Functions

Compound functions may consist of sums or products of trigonometric functions. They may also consist of sums or products of the trigonometric functions and other functions. For example, $y = x + \sin x$ is a compound function that is the sum of a linear function and a trigonometric function.

Some compound functions may be graphed by graphing each function separately on the same coordinate axes and adding the ordinates geometrically. After a few critical points are determined, the remainder of the curve of the compound function can be sketched.

A compass may be used to find the sum of the ordinates.

Example

1 Graph **y = x + sin x.**

First graph each function, $y = x$ and $y = \sin x$, separately on the same axes. Next add the ordinates of special values, such as zeros, for one of the functions or the points of intersection. Then, sketch the graph with a smooth curve.

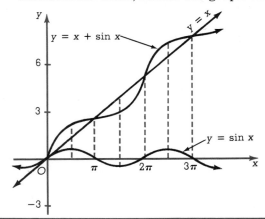

2   **Graph $y = \sin x + \cos x$.**

First graph each function, $y = \sin x$ and $y = \cos x$, separately on the same axes. Next, add the ordinates of special values. Then, sketch the graph with a smooth curve.

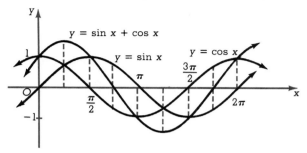

A table or a calculator may be used to find ordered pairs of the compound function as a check on geometric methods.

The following example shows the graph of a compound function which is the product of a linear function and a trigonometric function.

3   **Graph $y = x \sin x$.**

First graph each function, $y = x$ and $y = \sin x$, separately on the same axes. Then, find key points. Since the maximum or minimum points of $y = \sin x$ are ± 1, the values of $x \sin x$ are $\pm x$ at these points. At the points where $\sin x = 0$, $x \sin x = 0$. After these points are plotted, sketch the graph with a smooth curve.

Notice the values of $y = x \sin x$ that lie on $y = -x$.

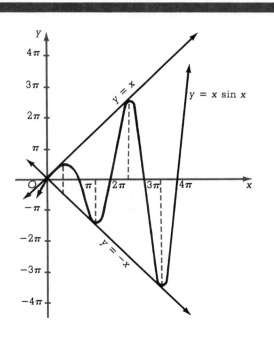

Exploratory Exercises

Find $f\left(\frac{\pi}{2}\right)$ for each of the following.

1. $f(x) = \sin x + \cos x$
2. $f(x) = \sin x - \cos x$
3. $f(x) = x + \cos x$
4. $f(x) = x + \sin x$
5. $f(x) = 3 \sin x$
6. $f(x) = \sin x + \sin 2x$
7. $f(x) = x \sin x$
8. $f(x) = x \cos x$
9. $f(x) = \cos x - \sin 2x$

10-18. Find $f\left(\frac{\pi}{4}\right)$ for problems 1-9.

Written Exercises

Graph each of the following.

1. $y = x + \cos x$
2. $y = \sin \frac{x}{3} + \frac{x}{3}$
3. $y = \cos x - 2$
4. $y = \sin x - \cos x$
5. $y = \sin x + \sin 2x$
6. $y = 2x + 2 \sin x$
7. $y = x - \sin x$
8. $y = 2 \sin x - \frac{1}{2}x$
9. $y = \cos x - \sin x$
10. $y = 2 \sin x - 3 \cos x$
11. $y = \cos 2x - \cos 3x$
12. $y = 2 \sin x + 3 \cos x$
13. $y = \frac{1}{2} \sin x - \cos 3x$
14. $y = 2 \sin x - \frac{1}{2} \cos x$
15. $y = \sin x + \sin \left(x + \frac{\pi}{2}\right)$
16. $y = x \cos x$
17. $y = 2x \sin 2x$
18. $y = \sin^2 x$

For the Scholar

Sue sold a small antique table for \$80. She determined her loss to be n percent of her cost. Three months later Sam, the new owner, sold the table at a profit equal to n percent of his cost. If the difference between Sam's selling price and Sue's cost is $\frac{10}{9}$ dollars, find Sam's percent of profit.

6-5 Inverse Trigonometric Functions

The **inverse** of a function may be found by interchanging the elements of the ordered pairs of the function. In other words, the domain of a function becomes the range of its inverse and the range of the function becomes the domain of its inverse. For example, the inverse of $y = 2x + 5$ is $y = \frac{x - 5}{2}$.

To find the inverse of $y = 2x + 5$, solve for x and switch the variables.

The inverse may *not* be a function. For example, if $f(x) = x^2$, the ordered pairs of f are of the form (x, x^2). The inverse of f has ordered pairs of the form (x^2, x) or $(x, \pm\sqrt{x})$ and is *not* a function.

Why?

The sine function is the set of all ordered pairs $(x, \sin x)$. Thus the inverse of this function, the **arcsine relation,** is the set of all ordered pairs $(\sin x, x)$. Note that $y = \arcsin x$ and $x = \sin y$ generate the same set of ordered pairs and therefore, describe the same relation. The domain of $y = \arcsin x$ is $-1 \leq x \leq 1$ or $|x| \leq 1$, and the range of the relation is the set of real numbers.

	Names of the Inverses of the Trigonometric Functions
The inverse of sin x is arcsin x. The inverse of cos x is arccos x. The inverse of tan x is arctan x.	

An equation such as sin $x = 0.3393$ can be written in the form $x = $ arcsin 0.3393. The last equation is read "x is an angle whose sine is 0.3393," or "x equals the arcsine of 0.3393." The solutions for x consist of all angles that have as their sine the number 0.3393. An infinite number of such angles exist.

An alternate notation for arcsin x is sin⁻¹ x. The inverses of the other trigonometric functions may be written in a similar manner.

Examples

1 **Find x if sin x = 0.5.**

If sin $x = 0.5$, then x is an angle whose sine is 0.5.
Thus, $x = 30°, 150°, 390°, 510°, \cdots$.

2 **Find all positive values of x less than 360° which satisfy the equation tan x = −1.**

$\tan x = -1$
$\quad x = \arctan(-1)$
$\quad x = 135°, 315°$

3 **Evaluate sin (arcsin 0.8660).**

Let $A = $ arcsin 0.8660.
Then sin $A = 0.8660$ and sin (arcsin 0.8660) $= 0.8660$.

4 **Evaluate** $\tan\left(\cos^{-1}\dfrac{3}{5}\right)$.

Let $A = \cos^{-1}\dfrac{3}{5}$.

Then, $\cos A = \dfrac{3}{5}$.
Draw a right triangle and call one acute angle A. Since $\cos A = \dfrac{3}{5}$, the adjacent side of angle A can be set equal to 3 and the hypotenuse equal to 5. Next, find the length of the opposite side.

$3^2 + x^2 = 5^2$ *Use the Pythagorean*
$\quad\quad x = 4$ *Theorem.*

$\tan\left(\cos^{-1}\dfrac{3}{5}\right) = \tan A$ $A = \cos\dfrac{3}{5}$

$\qquad\qquad = \dfrac{4}{3}$

Thus, $\tan\left(\cos^{-1}\dfrac{3}{5}\right) = \dfrac{4}{3}$.

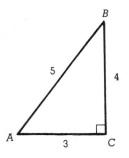

Exploratory Exercises

Write the inverse of each function.

1. $f = \{(3, 1), (2, 4), (1, 5)\}$

2. $f = \{(3, 8), (4, -2), (5, -3)\}$

3. $g = \{(3, 2), (4, 2)\}$

4. $g = \{(-3, 1), (2, 4), (7, 8)\}$

5. $h = \{(-1, -2), (-3, -2), (-1, -4), (0, 6)\}$

6. $h = \{(4, -2), (3, 7), (5, 7), (3, 8)\}$

Write each of the following in the form of an inverse relation.

7. $x = \sin \theta$

8. $\cos \alpha = \dfrac{1}{3}$

9. $\tan y = -3$

10. $y = \cos x$

11. $\dfrac{4}{3} = \tan \theta$

12. $\sin x = 2$

13. $n = \sin \theta$

14. $\sin \beta = 1$

15. $\cos \theta = y$

Written Exercises

Find values of x in the interval $0° \le x \le 360°$ that satisfy each equation.

1. $x = \arcsin 0$

2. $x = \cos^{-1} 0$

3. $x = \arctan 1$

4. $x = \arcsin \dfrac{\sqrt{3}}{2}$

5. $x = \arctan \dfrac{\sqrt{3}}{3}$

6. $x = \sin^{-1} \dfrac{1}{\sqrt{2}}$

7. $x = \sec^{-1} 2$

8. $x = \text{arccot } 2.1445$

9. $x = \arcsin (-0.5)$

Evaluate each of the following. Assume that angles are acute.

10. $\sin \left(\sin^{-1} \dfrac{1}{2} \right)$

11. $\cot \left(\arctan \dfrac{4}{5} \right)$

12. $\cos \left(\arcsin \dfrac{\sqrt{3}}{2} \right)$

13. $\tan \left(\arcsin \dfrac{5}{13} \right)$

14. $\sec \left(\cos^{-1} \dfrac{1}{2} \right)$

15. $\cos \left(\text{arccot } \dfrac{4}{3} \right)$

16. $\sin (\tan^{-1} 1) + \cos (\cos^{-1} 0.5)$

17. $\sin (\arctan \sqrt{3} + \text{arccot } \sqrt{3})$

18. $\tan \left(\arcsin \dfrac{\sqrt{2}}{2} \right) - \cot \left(\arccos \dfrac{\sqrt{2}}{2} \right)$

19. $\tan \left(\sin^{-1} \dfrac{\sqrt{3}}{2} - \cos^{-1} \dfrac{\sqrt{3}}{2} \right)$

Verify each expression. Assume that angles are acute.

20. $\sin^{-1} \dfrac{\sqrt{2}}{2} + \cos^{-1} \dfrac{\sqrt{2}}{2} = 90°$

21. $\arccos \dfrac{\sqrt{3}}{2} + \arcsin \dfrac{\sqrt{3}}{2} = \dfrac{\pi}{2}$

22. $\arcsin \dfrac{2}{5} + \arccos \dfrac{2}{5} = \dfrac{\pi}{2}$

23. $\tan^{-1} 1 + \cos^{-1} \dfrac{\sqrt{3}}{2} = \sin^{-1} \dfrac{1}{2} + \sec^{-1} \sqrt{2}$

24. $\tan^{-1} \dfrac{3}{4} + \tan^{-1} \dfrac{5}{12} = \tan^{-1} \dfrac{56}{33}$

25. $\arcsin \dfrac{3}{5} + \arccos \dfrac{15}{17} = \arctan \dfrac{77}{36}$

For the Scholar

Given $\overline{XY}$, the base of $\triangle XYZ$, is fixed in length, what is the path of the centroid as the vertex Z moves along a line parallel to the base?

Using Mathematics

The design of underwater diving equipment uses information about human breathing patterns. One complete cycle of a breathing pattern, inhaling and exhaling, can be represented by the sine curve.

The **vital capacity** is the maximum volume of air inhaled and exhaled at each breath for a given size lung. Note that the amplitude of the breathing cycle of a resting body is much smaller than that of the vital capacity. The lung capacity of a body at a resting state is approximately 20% of its vital capacity.

As a gaseous body, such as an aqualung tank, is submerged to various depths of water, the volume of the gas is affected by the pressure of the water. The volume can be found by using the following formula.

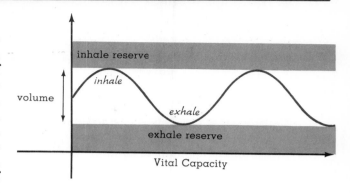

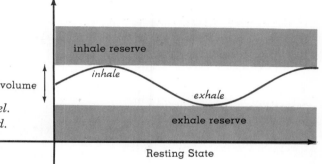

$$V_d = \frac{33V_S}{d + 33}$$

V_s is the volume of gas at sea level.
V_d is the volume of gas at depth d.

This information is used to solve problems about underwater diving.

An aqualung tank contains 70 ft³ of air. The diver who is breathing 12 breaths per minute in a resting state has a 0.21 ft³ vital capacity. Find the present lung capacity of the diver, the volume of air in the tank at a 66 ft depth, and the length of time the diver can remain at a depth of 66 ft.

lung capacity = 20% of 0.21 ft³   *volume of air* = 0.042 ft³/breath · 12 breaths/
                                                      needed/minute   minute

            = 0.042 ft³/breath   = 0.504 ft³/minute

volume of gas = $\frac{33 \cdot 70}{66 + 33}$ *time at 66 ft* = $\frac{23.3 \text{ ft}^3}{0.504 \text{ ft}^3/\text{minute}}$
at 66 ft

            = 23.3 ft³   = 46 minutes

Exercises **Find the resting state lung capacity of the diver, the volume of air in the tank at the given depth, and the possible length of time the diver can remain at the given depth. Assume 12 breaths per minute in the resting state.**

1. $V_S = 60$ ft³; $d = 45$ ft
   vital capacity = 0.158 ft³

2. $V_S = 65$ ft³; $d = 70$ ft
   vital capacity = 0.105 ft³

3. $V_S = 56$ ft³; $d = 60$ ft
   vital capacity = 0.21 ft³

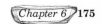

6-6 Principal Values of the Inverse Trigonometric Functions

The inverse of any trigonometric function is not a function since one value in the domain corresponds to more than one value in the range. The domains of the trigonometric functions may be limited so that their inverse relations are functions.

Consider only a part of the domain of the sine function, namely any x so that $-90° \leq x \leq 90°$. It is possible to define a new function, called Sine, whose inverse is a function.

Capital letters are used to distinguish the function with restricted domains from the usual trigonometric functions.

$$y = \text{Sin } x \text{ if and only if } y = \sin x \text{ and } -90° \leq x \leq 90°$$

The values in the domain of Sine are called **principal values.** Other new functions that have inverses can be defined as follows.

$y = \text{Cos } x$ if and only if $y = \cos x$ and $0 \leq x \leq 180°$
$y = \text{Tan } x$ if and only if $y = \tan x$ and $-90° < x < 90°$

The inverses of the Sine, Cosine, and Tangent functions are called the Arcsine, Arccosine, and Arctangent functions, respectively. They are defined as follows.

Note the capital "A" in the name of each inverse function.

Given $y = \text{Sin } x$, the inverse sine function is defined by the following equation. $$y = \text{Sin}^{-1} x \quad \text{or} \quad y = \text{Arcsin } x$$	**Arcsine Function**
Given $y = \text{Cos } x$, the inverse cosine function is defined by the following equation. $$y = \text{Cos}^{-1} x \quad \text{or} \quad y = \text{Arccos } x$$	**Arccosine Function**
Given $y = \text{Tan } x$, the inverse tangent function is defined by the following equation. $$y = \text{Tan}^{-1} x \quad \text{or} \quad y = \text{Arctan } x$$	**Arctangent Function**

Example

1 Find $\text{Arcsin}\left(-\frac{1}{2}\right)$.

$\theta = \text{Arcsin}\left(-\frac{1}{2}\right)$

$\text{Sin } \theta = -\frac{1}{2}$

$\theta = -30°$ *Why is θ not 210°?*

Thus, $\text{Arcsin}\left(-\frac{1}{2}\right) = -30°$.

2 **Find cos (Tan⁻¹ 1).**

Let $\theta = \text{Tan}^{-1} 1$.

Tan $\theta = 1$ $\qquad\qquad -90° < \theta < 90°$

$\qquad \theta = 45°$

$\cos (\text{Tan}^{-1} 1) = \cos 45°$

$$= \frac{\sqrt{2}}{2}$$

3 **Find $\cos \left(\text{Tan}^{-1} \sqrt{3} - \text{Sin}^{-1} \frac{1}{2} \right)$.**

Let $\alpha = \text{Tan}^{-1} \sqrt{3}$ and let $\beta = \text{Sin}^{-1} \frac{1}{2}$.

$\text{Tan } \alpha = \sqrt{3} \qquad \text{Sin } \beta = \frac{1}{2}$

$\qquad \alpha = 60° \qquad\qquad \beta = 30°$

$\cos \left(\text{Tan}^{-1} \sqrt{3} - \text{Sin}^{-1} \frac{1}{2} \right) = \cos (\alpha - \beta)$

$\qquad\qquad\qquad\qquad\qquad\quad = \cos (60° - 30°)$

$\qquad\qquad\qquad\qquad\qquad\quad = \cos 30°$

$\qquad\qquad\qquad\qquad\qquad\quad = \frac{\sqrt{3}}{2}$

Using Calculators

Find $\cos \left(\text{Arctan } \frac{5}{12} - \text{Arccot } \frac{4}{3} \right)$.

The least, or principal, value of the inverse function is always given by the calculator in decimal form.

ENTER: 5 | ÷ | 12 | = | 2ndF | | − | (| (| 4 | ÷ |

DISPLAY: 5 $\qquad$ 12 $\quad$ 0.41666666 $\qquad$ 22.61986495 $\qquad$ 0 $\quad$ 4

ENTER: 3 |) | 1/x | 2ndF | |) | = |

DISPLAY: 3 $\quad$ 1.33333333 $\quad$ 0.75 $\qquad$ 36.86989764 $\qquad$ −14.25003269

ENTER:

DISPLAY: 0.96230769

Example

4 Find x if $x = \arcsin \frac{1}{2}$.

Since $\arcsin \frac{1}{2}$ is not capitalized, general values of x must be given.

$$\sin x = \frac{1}{2}$$
$$x = 30° \text{ and } x = 150° \text{ for } 0° \le x \le 360°$$

General values are given by $x = 30° + n \cdot 360°$ and $x = 150° + n \cdot 360°$ where n is any integer.

Exploratory Exercises

Evaluate each of the following.

1. $\text{Cos}^{-1} \frac{1}{2}$

2. $\text{Sin}^{-1} \left(-\frac{\sqrt{3}}{2} \right)$

3. $\text{Arctan } 1$

4. $\text{Sin}^{-1} \left(-\frac{1}{2} \right)$

5. $\text{Arctan } 0.8693$

6. $\text{Arccos } 0.8910$

7. $\text{Sin}^{-1} 0$

8. $\text{Tan}^{-1} 1$

9. $\text{Cos}^{-1} \left(-\frac{\sqrt{3}}{2} \right)$

10. $\text{Arcsin } \frac{\sqrt{3}}{2}$

11. $\text{Arcsin } \left(-\frac{\sqrt{2}}{2} \right)$

12. $\text{Arctan } \frac{3}{4}$

13. $\text{Sin}^{-1} \frac{\sqrt{3}}{2}$

14. $\text{Tan}^{-1} \left(\frac{\sqrt{3}}{3} \right)$

15. $\text{Sin}^{-1} 1$

16. $\text{Sin}^{-1} (-1)$

17. $\text{Arctan } (-0.3443)$

18. $\text{Arccos } \left(-\frac{\sqrt{2}}{2} \right)$

19. $\text{Cos}^{-1} 0$

20. $\text{Arccos } (-0.5746)$

Written Exercises

Evaluate each of the following.

1. $\text{Tan}^{-1} (-1)$

2. $\text{Arccos } \frac{\sqrt{3}}{2}$

3. $\arcsin \frac{\sqrt{3}}{2}$

4. $\text{Cos}^{-1} \left(-\frac{1}{2} \right)$

5. $\arctan (-1)$

6. $\text{Arctan } \sqrt{3}$

7. $\arccos \frac{\sqrt{2}}{2}$

8. $\sin \left(\text{Sin}^{-1} \frac{1}{2} \right)$

9. $\text{Sin}^{-1} \left(\cos \frac{\pi}{2} \right)$

10. $\text{Sin}^{-1} \left(\tan \frac{\pi}{4} \right)$

11. $\arcsin \frac{3}{4}$

12. $\cos \left(\text{Cos}^{-1} \frac{1}{2} \right)$

13. $\cos \left(\text{Cos}^{-1} \frac{4}{5} \right)$

14. $\sin \left(\text{Sin}^{-1} \frac{\sqrt{3}}{2} \right)$

15. $\arctan 5$

16. $\tan \left(\text{Sin}^{-1} \frac{5}{13} \right)$

17. $\tan \left[\text{Cos}^{-1} \left(-\frac{3}{5} \right) \right]$

18. $\sin \left[\text{Arctan } \left(-\sqrt{3} \right) \right]$

19. $\arccos \left(-\frac{1}{2} \right)$

20. $\sin \left(2 \text{ Cos}^{-1} \frac{3}{5} \right)$

21. $\cos \left(\text{Tan}^{-1} \sqrt{3} \right)$

22. $\cos \left[\text{Arcsin } \left(-\frac{1}{2} \right) \right]$

23. $\arctan \frac{1}{2}$

24. $\sin \left(2 \text{ Sin}^{-1} \frac{1}{2} \right)$

25. $\cos \left(\text{Tan}^{-1} 1 \right)$

26. $\sin \left(2 \text{ Sin}^{-1} \frac{\sqrt{3}}{2} \right)$

27. $\arcsin (-1)$

28. $\tan \left(\frac{1}{2} \text{ Sin}^{-1} \frac{15}{17} \right)$

29. $\sin \left(\frac{1}{2} \text{ Arctan } \frac{3}{5} \right)$

30. $\cos \left(2 \text{ Tan}^{-1} \sqrt{3} \right)$

31. $\sin\left(\text{Sin}^{-1}\,1 - \text{Cos}^{-1}\frac{1}{2}\right)$

32. $\cos\left(\text{Cos}^{-1}\,0 + \text{Sin}^{-1}\frac{1}{2}\right)$

33. $\cos\left(\text{Tan}^{-1}\,\sqrt{3} - \text{Sin}^{-1}\frac{1}{2}\right)$

34. $\sin\left[\text{Arctan}\left(-\frac{3}{4}\right) + \text{Arccot}\left(-\frac{4}{3}\right)\right]$

35. $\sin\left(\text{Tan}^{-1}\,1 - \text{Sin}^{-1}\,1\right)$

36. $\cos\left[\text{Cos}^{-1}\left(-\frac{1}{2}\right) - \text{Sin}^{-1}\,1\right]$

37. $\cos\left[\text{Cos}^{-1}\left(-\frac{\sqrt{2}}{2}\right) - \frac{\pi}{2}\right]$

38. $\cos\left[\frac{4}{3}\pi - \text{Cos}^{-1}\left(-\frac{1}{2}\right)\right]$

39. $\tan\left(\text{Cos}^{-1}\frac{3}{5} - \text{Sin}^{-1}\frac{5}{13}\right)$

40. $\sin\left[\frac{\pi}{2} - \text{Cos}^{-1}\left(\frac{1}{2}\right)\right]$

Challenge Exercises

Express each of the following in terms of u and v.

41. $\sin\left(\text{Arcsin}\,u - \text{Arccos}\,v\right)$

42. $\cos\left(\text{Arcsin}\,u + \text{Arccos}\,v\right)$

For the Scholar

Find the fourth term in the expression of $\left(\dfrac{\sqrt{x}}{y^2} - \dfrac{y}{\sqrt{x}}\right)^6$.

6-7 Graphing Inverses of Functions

The inverse of a function can be found by reversing the elements of each ordered pair in the given function. For example, if a function consists of the ordered pairs $(5, 3)$, $(6, -2)$, $(4, 3)$, $\left(3, -\frac{1}{2}\right)$, its inverse consists of $(3, 5)$, $(-2, 6)$, $(3, 4)$, $\left(-\frac{1}{2}, 3\right)$.

In this case, is the inverse a function?

The graph of the inverse of a function may be drawn by reflecting the graph of the given function over the line $x = y$.

Example

1 **Draw the graph of the inverse of $y = 2x - 2$.**

First draw the graph of $y = 2x - 2$. Then reflect this graph over the line $x = y$ to get the graph of its inverse.
The inverse of $y = 2x - 2$
is $y = \frac{1}{2}x + 1$.

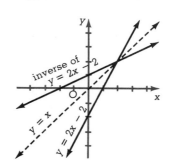

The inverse trigonometric relations can be illustrated by means of the graphs of the relations.

Let x assume all permissable values in the relation $y = \arcsin x$. Thus, $-1 \le x \le 1$. If general values are plotted for y, the graph of $y = \arcsin x$ is obtained. Notice that the graph of $y = \arcsin x$ has the same relation to the y-axis that the graph of $y = \sin x$ has to the x-axis.

Values of Arcsin x are shown as a color portion of the curve. Note that $y = $ Arcsin x is a function because each value of x determines only one value of y. The range is $-90° \le$ Arcsin $x \le 90°$.

But $y = \arcsin x$ is *not* a function. A vertical line drawn on the graph would pass through more than one point.

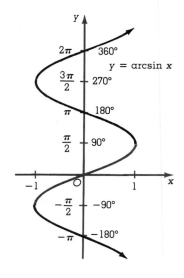

The inverse of the cosine function may be graphed in a similar way. The graph of the principal values is shown as a color portion of the curve at the right. Although there are an unlimited number of values of the arccos x for a given value of x, there is only one value of Arccos x for each x. The range of Arccos x is $0° \le$ Arccos $x \le 180°$.

On the graph of the inverse of the tangent function shown below, notice its similarity to the graph of $y = \tan x$ with the axes interchanged. Values of Arctan x are shown as a color portion of the curve. For each value of x, there is only one value of Arctan x, but an unlimited number of values for arctan x. The range of Arctan x is $-90° <$ Arctan $x < 90°$.

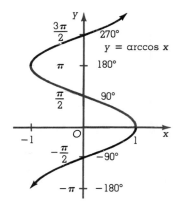

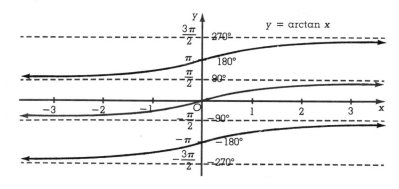

Examples

1 **Determine if Tan^{-1} (tan x) = x for all x. If false, give a counterexample.**

Let $x = 135°$.

$$\text{Tan}^{-1} (\text{tan } 135°) = \text{Tan}^{-1} (-1) \quad \textit{Substituting}$$
$$= -45°$$

Therefore, Tan^{-1} (tan x) = x is not true for all x.

2 **Graph y = Cot^{-1} x for 0 < y < π.**

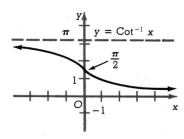

Exploratory Exercises

State the domain of each function or relation.

1. $y = \sin x$ 2. $y = \cos x$ 3. $y = \tan x$ 4. $y = \text{Sin } x$

5. $y = \text{Cos } x$ 6. $y = \text{Tan } x$ 7. $y = \arcsin x$ 8. $y = \arccos x$

9. $y = \arctan x$ 10. $y = \text{Arcsin } x$ 11. $y = \text{Arccos } x$ 12. $y = \text{Arctan } x$

13-24. State the range of each function or relation in problems **1-12.**

Written Exercises

Write the equation for the inverse of each function.

1. $y = x + 2$ 2. $y = \cos x$ 3. $y = 3$ 4. $y = \text{Arctan } x$

5. $y = \text{Arcsin } x$ 6. $y = \frac{1}{2}x + 4$ 7. $y = x$ 8. $y = \frac{x - 3}{5}$

9. $y = -3x - 1$ 10. $y = x^2$ 11. $y = \text{Sin } x$ 12. $y = (x - 4)^2$

13-24. Graph each function and its inverse in problems **1-12.**

Determine if the inverse of each relation graphed below is a function.

25.

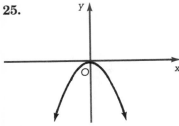

26.

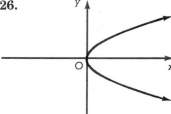

27.

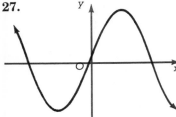

28.

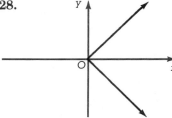

29.

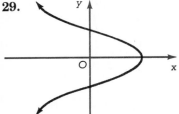

30.

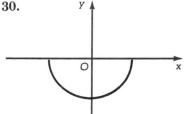

Determine if each of the following is true or false. If false, give a counterexample.

31. $\tan (\mathrm{Tan}^{-1} x) = x$ for all x

32. $\mathrm{Sin}^{-1} x = -\mathrm{Sin}^{-1} (-x)$, $-1 \leq x \leq 1$

33. $\mathrm{Cot}^{-1} (\cot x) = x$ for all x

34. $\mathrm{Cos}^{-1} (-x) = -\mathrm{Cos}^{-1} x$, $-1 \leq x \leq 1$

35. $\mathrm{Sin}^{-1} x + \mathrm{Cos}^{-1} x = \dfrac{\pi}{2}$, $-1 \leq x \leq 1$

36. $\mathrm{Arccos}\, x = \mathrm{Arccos}\, (-x)$, $-1 \leq x \leq 1$

37. $\mathrm{Cos}^{-1} x = \dfrac{1}{\mathrm{Cos}\, x}$

38. $\mathrm{Tan}^{-1} x = \dfrac{1}{\mathrm{Tan}\, x}$

Sketch the graph of each of the following.

39. $y = \tan (\mathrm{Tan}^{-1} x)$

40. $y = \sin (\mathrm{Tan}^{-1} x)$

Challenge Exercise

41. Sketch $y = \arcsin x$ and $y = \arccos x$ on the same coordinate axes. Give four values of y corresponding to points of intersection of the graphs.

For the Scholar

If $0° < \theta < 90°$, $x > y > 0$, and $\cot \theta = \dfrac{x^2 - y^2}{2xy}$, find the value of $\sec \theta$.

Chapter Summary

1. The curve of a trigonometric function can be drawn from the knowledge of its shape and the values of the function at integral multiples of 90°. (161)

2. **Amplitude of a Sine or Cosine Function:** The amplitude of the functions, $y = A \sin \theta$ and $y = A \cos \theta$ is the absolute value of A, or $|A|$. (163)

3. **Periods of a Sine, Cosine, or Tangent Function:** The period of the functions, $y = \sin k\theta$ and $y = \cos k\theta$ is $\dfrac{360°}{k}$. The period of the function, $y = \tan k\theta$ is $\dfrac{180°}{k}$. (164)

4. **Phase Shift of All Trigonometric Functions:** The phase shift of the function, $y = A \sin (k\theta + c)$, is $-\dfrac{c}{k}$. If $c > 0$, the shift is to the left and if $c < 0$, the shift is to the right. This definition applies to all trigonometric functions. (165)

5. Compound functions can be graphed by graphing each function separately on the same coordinate axes and adding or multiplying the ordinates. (170)

6. **Inverses of the Trigonometric Functions:**

> The inverse of sin x is arcsin x.
> The inverse of cos x is arccos x.
> The inverse of tan x is arctan x. (173)

7. **Arcsine Function:** Given $y = \text{Sin } x$, the inverse sine function is defined by the following equation.

$$y = \text{Sin}^{-1} x \quad \text{or} \quad y = \text{Arcsin } x \quad (176)$$

8. **Arccosine Function:** Given $y = \text{Cos } x$, the inverse cosine function is defined by the following equation.

$$y = \text{Cos}^{-1} x \quad \text{or} \quad y = \text{Arccos } x \quad (176)$$

9. **Arctangent Function:** Given $y = \text{Tan } x$, the inverse tangent function is defined by the following equation.

$$y = \text{Tan}^{-1} x \quad \text{or} \quad y = \text{Arctan } x \quad (176)$$

10. The graph of the inverse of a function can be drawn by reflecting the graph of the given function over the line $x = y$. (179)

State which value is greater. (6-1)

1. sin 20° or sin 50°
2. cos 90° or cos 190°
3. cos 28° or cos 29°
4. sin 120° or sin 240°

Graph each function in the indicated interval. (6-1)

5. $y = \sin x$; $90° \leq x \leq 450°$
6. $y = \cos x$; $-90° \leq x \leq 360°$
7. $y = \tan x$; $-180° \leq x \leq 180°$
8. $y = \cot x$; $-180° < x < 360°$

State the amplitude, period, and phase shift for each of the following. (6-2)

9. $y = 4 \cos 2x$
10. $y = 15 \sin \left(\frac{3}{2}x + 90°\right)$
11. $y = 5 \cot \left(\frac{x}{2} - 45°\right)$
12. $y = -\sqrt{3} \cos (x - 180°)$
13. $y = 2 \tan 5x$
14. $y = -7 \sin 5x$

Write an equation of a sine function for each amplitude, period, and phase shift. (6-2)

15. amplitude = 3, period = 360°, phase shift = 45°
16. amplitude = 17, period = 270°, phase shift = -90°
17. amplitude = $\frac{1}{3}$, period = 180°, phase shift = 90°

Graph each of the following. (6-2, 6-3, 6-4)

18. $y = \frac{1}{2} \sin 2\theta$
19. $y = 3 \cos \frac{\theta}{2}$
20. $y = 2 \tan (3\theta + 90°)$
21. $y = \sin (4\theta + 60°)$
22. $y = 4 \cos (\theta + 180°)$
23. $y = -3 \sin (\theta - 45°)$
24. $y = 2 \sin x - \cos x$
25. $y = x + 2 \sin 2x$

Write each of the following in the form of an inverse trigonometric relation. (6-5)

26. $y = \sin \alpha$
27. $\tan y = x$
28. $n = \cos \theta$

Evaluate each of the following. Assume that angles are acute. (6-5)

29. $\cos \left(\arccos \frac{1}{2}\right)$
30. $\tan \left(\text{arccot} \frac{4}{5}\right)$
31. $\cot \left(\cos^{-1} \frac{3}{5}\right)$
32. $\sin (\tan^{-1} 1) + \cos (\sin^{-1} 1)$
33. $\tan \left(\arcsin \frac{\sqrt{3}}{2} + \arccos \frac{\sqrt{3}}{2}\right)$

Evaluate each of the following. (6-6)

34. $\sin \left(\text{Arcsin} \frac{1}{2}\right)$
35. $\cos (\text{Tan}^{-1} 1)$
36. $\sin 2 \left(\text{Arcsin} \frac{1}{2}\right)$
37. $\cos \left(\frac{\pi}{2} - \text{Cos}^{-1} \frac{\sqrt{2}}{2}\right)$
38. $\cos \left(\text{Sin}^{-1} \frac{1}{2}\right)$
39. $\sin \left(3 \text{Sin}^{-1} \frac{\sqrt{3}}{2}\right)$
40. $\sin \left[\text{Cos}^{-1} \left(-\frac{1}{2}\right) + \text{Tan}^{-1} 1\right]$
41. $\cos \left(\text{Arctan} \sqrt{3} + \text{Arcsin} \frac{1}{2}\right)$

Write the equation for the inverse of each function or relation. (6-7)

42. $y = \arcsin x$
43. $y = x^2 + 1$
44. $y = \text{Cos } x$

45-47. Graph each function and its inverse in problems **42-44**.

48-50. Determine if each inverse in problems **42-44** is a function.

Chapter Test

Find the values of x in degrees for which each of the following is true.

1. $\cos x = 1$

2. $\tan x = 0$

3. $\sin x = -1$

4. $\cos x = \dfrac{\sqrt{2}}{2}$

Graph each function in the indicated interval.

5. $y = \sin x;\ -180° \le x \le 180°$

6. $y = \tan x;\ 0° \le x \le 360°$

State the amplitude, period, and phase shift for each of the following.

7. $y = 2 \sin 2\theta$

8. $y = 3 \cos 4\theta$

9. $y = 110 \sin(15\theta - 40°)$

10. $y = 10 \sin(180° - \alpha)$

Graph each of the following.

11. $y = 3 \cos \dfrac{\theta}{2}$

12. $y = 2 \sin(4\theta + 90°)$

13. $y = \tan(2\theta - 45°)$

14. $y = 2 \cos x - x$

Evaluate each of the following. Assume that angles are acute.

15. $\sin\left(\arccos \dfrac{\sqrt{3}}{2}\right)$

16. $\tan\left(\cos^{-1} \dfrac{5}{13}\right)$

17. $\sec\left(\sin^{-1} \dfrac{1}{2}\right)$

18. $\cos(\arctan \sqrt{3} + \text{arccot } \sqrt{3})$

Evaluate each of the following.

19. $\sin\left(\text{Arccos } \dfrac{1}{2}\right)$

20. $\tan\left[\text{Sin}^{-1}\left(-\dfrac{\sqrt{2}}{2}\right)\right]$

21. $\cos\left(\dfrac{1}{2} \text{Tan}^{-1} \dfrac{3}{4}\right)$

22. $\tan\left(\pi + \text{Arcsin } \dfrac{2}{3}\right)$

Write the equation for the inverse of each function.

23. $y = 3x - 7$

24. $y = \tan x$

25-26. Graph each function and its inverse in problems **23-24**.

27-28. Determine if each inverse in problems **23-24** is a function.

CHAPTER 7

Applications of Trigonometry

FAIRCHILD AERIAL SU

When a highway is designed, the designer studies the curves to be included, the inclination of any curves, the type of surfaces on which the highway will be built, and the speeds that will be expected. Trigonometric functions are used by the designer to determine the best location and placement of the highway.

7-1 Solving Trigonometric Equations

A **trigonometric equation** is an equation involving a trigonometric function. If the equation is true for all defined values of the variable, it is an **identity.**

Trigonometric equations may be solved by the same methods used to solve other equations. For example, the use of algebraic techniques such as factoring and substitution may be helpful in solving trigonometric equations.

Example

1 **Solve $2 \sin^2 x - 3 \sin x + 1 = 0$ for principal values of x.**

$2 \sin^2 x - 3 \sin x + 1 = 0$

$(2 \sin x - 1)(\sin x - 1) = 0$ *Factor.*

$2 \sin x - 1 = 0$ or $\sin x - 1 = 0$

$\sin x = \dfrac{1}{2}$ $\sin x = 1$

$x = \text{Arcsin } \dfrac{1}{2}$ $x = \text{Arcsin } 1$

$x = 30°$ $x = 90°$

The solutions are 30° and 90°.

Usually trigonometric equations are solved for principal values of the variable. However, there are other solutions that differ by integral multiples of the period of the function.

Example

2 **Solve $2 \tan x \sin x + 2 \sin x = \tan x + 1$ for all values of x.**

$2 \tan x \sin x + 2 \sin x = \tan x + 1$

$2 \tan x \sin x + 2 \sin x - \tan x - 1 = 0$

$(\tan x + 1)(2 \sin x - 1) = 0$

$\tan x + 1 = 0$ or $2 \sin x - 1 = 0$

$\tan x = -1$ $\sin x = \dfrac{1}{2}$

$x = \arctan (-1)$ $x = \arcsin \dfrac{1}{2}$

$x = -45° + n \cdot 180°$ $x = 30° + n \cdot 360°$ and $x = 150° + n \cdot 360°$

The solutions are $-45° + n \cdot 180°$, $30° + n \cdot 360°$, and $150° + n \cdot 360°$ where n is any integer.

Example

3 Solve sin (x + 30°) = cos 2x if 0 ≤ x ≤ 90°.

$$\sin (x + 30°) = \cos 2x$$
$$(x + 30°) + 2x = 90°$$
$$3x = 60°$$
$$x = 20°$$

If sin A = cos B, then A + B = 90° since the sine and cosine are cofunctions.

The solution is 20°.

If an equation cannot be easily solved by factoring, try writing the expressions in terms of only one trigonometric function.

Example

4 Solve 2 sin² x − cos x − 1 = 0 for all values of x.

$$2 \sin^2 x - \cos x - 1 = 0$$
$$2(1 - \cos^2 x) - \cos x - 1 = 0$$
$$2 - 2 \cos^2 x - \cos x - 1 = 0$$
$$-2 \cos^2 x - \cos x + 1 = 0$$
$$2 \cos^2 x + \cos x - 1 = 0$$
$$(2 \cos x - 1)(\cos x + 1) = 0$$

$$\sin^2 x = 1 - \cos^2 x$$

$$2 \cos x - 1 = 0 \qquad \text{or} \qquad \cos x + 1 = 0$$
$$\cos x = \frac{1}{2} \qquad\qquad\qquad \cos x = -1$$
$$x = \arccos \frac{1}{2} \qquad\qquad\qquad x = \arccos (-1)$$
$$x = 60° + n \cdot 360° \text{ and } 300° + n \cdot 360° \qquad x = 180° + n \cdot 360°$$

The solutions are $60° + n \cdot 360°$, $300° + n \cdot 360°$, and $180° + n \cdot 360°$ for any integer n.

Some trigonometric equations have no solutions. In other words, there is no replacement for the variable that will result in a true sentence. For example, the equation sin x = 2 has no solution.   *Why?*

It is important to always check your solutions. Some algebraic operations may introduce answers that are *not* solutions to the original equation.

Example

5

Solve $2 \sin^2 x + 3 \sin x - 2 = 0$ for principal values of x.

$$2 \sin^2 x + 3 \sin x - 2 = 0$$
$$(2 \sin x - 1)(\sin x + 2) = 0$$

$2 \sin x - 1 = 0$ or $\sin x + 2 = 0$

$\sin x = \dfrac{1}{2}$ $\sin x = -2$

$x = \text{Arcsin } \dfrac{1}{2}$ $x = \text{Arcsin } (-2)$ *There is no solution since sin x is*

$x = 30°$ *in the interval $-1 \leq \sin x \leq 1$.*

The solution is 30°.

Exploratory Exercises

Solve each equation for principal values of x.

1. $2 \cos x - 1 = 0$
2. $2 \sin x + 1 = 0$
3. $\sqrt{2} \sin x - 1 = 0$
4. $2 \cos x - \sqrt{3} = 0$
5. $2 \cos x + 1 = 0$
6. $\sqrt{3} \tan x + 1 = 0$
7. $\sin 2x - 1 = 0$
8. $\cos 3x - 0.5 = 0$
9. $\tan 2x - \sqrt{3} = 0$

How many solutions does each equation have if $0° \leq \theta \leq 360°$?

10. $\sin \theta = 1$
11. $\cos \theta = -\dfrac{\sqrt{3}}{2}$
12. $\tan \theta = -3$
13. $\sin 2\theta = \dfrac{1}{2}$
14. $\sin 2\theta = -\dfrac{\sqrt{3}}{2}$
15. $\sin 3\theta = -2$
16. $\sin^2 2\theta = \dfrac{1}{2}$
17. $\tan^2 2\theta = 3$
18. $\sin \dfrac{1}{2}\theta = -\dfrac{\sqrt{3}}{2}$

Written Exercises

Solve each equation for general values of x.

1. $2 \sin^2 x - \sin x - 1 = 0$
2. $\sin x + \sin x \cos x = 0$
3. $2 \sin^2 x - 1 = 0$
4. $2 \sin x + \sqrt{3} = 0$
5. $\tan^2 x - 1 = 0$
6. $\cos x - 2 \cos x \sin x = 0$
7. $4 \cos^2 x = 1$
8. $\sqrt{3} \cot x + 1 = 0$
9. $2 \cos^2 x - 5 \cos x + 2 = 0$
10. $\sin (x + 10°) = \cos 3x$

Solve each equation for principal values of x.

11. $2 \sin^2 x + \sin x = 0$
12. $\sqrt{2} \cos x - 1 = 0$
13. $4 \sin^2 x - 3 = 0$
14. $\tan 2x = \cot x$
15. $2 \cos^2 x = \sin x + 1$
16. $2 \tan x - 4 = 0$
17. $\sin^2 x - 3 \sin x + 2 = 0$
18. $\sin x + \cos x = 0$
19. $\sin 2x = \cos x$
20. $\cos^2 x - \dfrac{7}{2} \cos x - 2 = 0$
21. $\tan x + \cot x = 2$
22. $\sin 2x = 2 \cos x$

23. $\sin^2 x - \sin x = 0$

24. $\cos x \tan x - \sin^2 x = 0$

25. $\sin^2 x - 2 \sin x - 3 = 0$

26. $\sin^2 x - 2 \sin x - 1 = 0$

27. $\sqrt{3} \cot x \sin x + 2 \cos^2 x = 0$

28. $3 \cos 2x - 5 \cos x = 1$

29. $\sin^2 x = \cos x - 1$

30. $\tan x + \sec x = \sqrt{3}$

31. $\tan^2 x = 3 \tan x$

32. $3 \tan^2 x + 4 \sec x + 4 = 0$

33. $3 \sin^2 x - \cos^2 x = 0$

34. $4 \tan x + \sin 2x = 0$

35. $\sin 2x \sin x + \cos 2x \cos x = 1$

36. $\cos 2x + 3 \cos x - 1 = 0$

37. $\sin 2x = \cos 3x$

38. $\cos 2x + \sin x = 1$

39. $\sin 2x = 2 \sin x$

40. $2 \sin x \cos x + 4 \sin x = \cos x + 2$

For the Scholar

Let x and y be consecutive integers whose product is z. What kind of integer is $3\sqrt{k}$, when $k = x^2 + y^2 + z^2$?

7-2 Right Triangles

Trigonometric functions can be used to solve problems involving right triangles. Usually, two measures such as a side and an angle or two sides are known and the measure of a side or an angle is to be found.

Recall the definitions of the trigonometric functions using right triangle ABC.

$\sin A = \dfrac{a}{c}$ $\csc A = \dfrac{c}{a}$

$\cos A = \dfrac{b}{c}$ $\sec A = \dfrac{c}{b}$

$\tan A = \dfrac{a}{b}$ $\cot A = \dfrac{b}{a}$

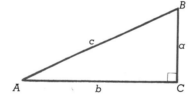

SOH-CAH-TOA is a helpful mnemonic device for remembering the first three equations.

$sin = \dfrac{opposite}{hypotenuse}$

$cos = \dfrac{adjacent}{hypotenuse}$

$tan = \dfrac{opposite}{adjacent}$

Example

1   **Solve right triangle ABC. Round measures to the nearest tenth.**

$49° + B = 90°$ *Angles A and B are complementary.*
$B = 41°$

$\dfrac{7}{c} = \sin 49°$ $\dfrac{7}{b} = \tan 49°$

$\dfrac{7}{c} = 0.7547$ $\dfrac{7}{b} = 1.1504$

$c = 9.3$ $b = 6.1$

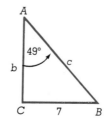

To solve a right triangle means to find all measures of the sides and angles.

Therefore, $B = 41°$, $c = 9.3$, and $b = 6.1$.

There are many useful applications of trigonometry.

Example 2

A utility pole is braced by a cable attached to it at the top and anchored in a concrete block at ground level a distance of 4 meters from the base of the pole. If the angle between the cable and the ground is 73°, find the height of the pole and the length of the cable. Round the length measurements to the nearest tenth and angle measurements to the nearest minute.

Write an equation using a trigonometric function.

$$\frac{h}{4} = \tan 73°$$

$$\frac{h}{4} = 3.2709 \qquad \textit{Solve for h.}$$

$$h = 13.1$$

Find the length of the cable in a similar manner.

$$\frac{4}{\ell} = \cos 73°$$

$$\frac{4}{\ell} = 0.2924$$

$$\ell = 13.8$$

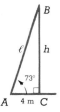

The height of the pole is about 13.1 meters and the length of the cable is about 13.8 meters.

Using Calculators

A metal fitting makes a 30° angle with the horizontal as shown. Find the measures of x and y.

First, find the measure of the hypotenuse.

$$c = \frac{15}{16} + \frac{5}{16} = \frac{20}{16} \text{ or } \frac{5}{4}$$

Then, find the measure of x and y.

$$\frac{y}{\frac{20}{16}} = \cos 30° \qquad \frac{x}{\frac{20}{16}} = \sin 30°$$

Roofing Improvement

top view

metal fitting

side view

0.09"

| ENTER: | 20 | ÷ | 16 | × | 30 | cos | = |

| DISPLAY: | 20 | | 16 | 1.25 | 30 | 0.866025403 | 1.082531755 |

| ENTER: | 20 | ÷ | 16 | × | | 30 | sin | = |

| DISPLAY: | 20 | | 16 | 1.25 | | 30 | 0.5 | 0.625 |

Thus, x is about 0.63 inches and y is about 1.08 inches.

3 A 7 meter ladder leans against a building. It forms an angle with the building measuring 16°. How far is the foot of the ladder from the base of the building? Round the length measurement to the nearest tenth.

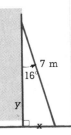

$$\frac{x}{7} = \sin 16°$$

$$\frac{x}{7} = 0.2756$$

$$x = 1.9$$

The foot of the ladder is about 1.9 meters from the building.

In problems where an observer is involved, an angle of elevation or an angle of depression is frequently given. An **angle of elevation** is the angle between a horizontal line and the line of sight from the observer to an object at a higher level. An **angle of depression** is the angle between a horizontal line and the line of sight from the observer to an object at a lower level.

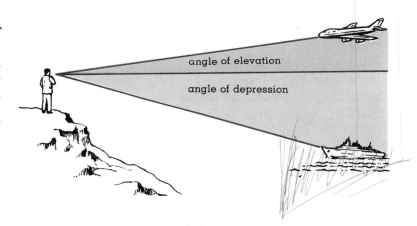

4 When the angle of elevation of the sun is 27°, the shadow of a tree is 25 meters long. How tall is the tree? Round the height of the tree to the nearest tenth.

$$\frac{h}{25} = \tan 27°$$

$$\frac{h}{25} = 0.5095$$

$$h = 12.7$$

The tree is about 12.7 meters tall.

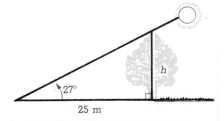

Example

5 Felipe is standing on top of a 200-foot cliff above a lake. The measurement of the angle of depression to a boat on the lake is 21°. How far is the boat from the base of the cliff? Round the distance to the nearest tenth.

$$\frac{200}{x} = \tan 21°$$ *The angle of elevation from the boat to the top of the cliff is also 21°. Why?*

$$\frac{200}{x} = 0.3839$$

$$x = 521.0$$

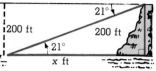

The boat is about 521 feet from the base of the cliff.

Exploratory Exercises

State equations that would enable you to solve each problem. Use the given triangle.

1. If $A = 20°$ and $c = 35$, find a.
2. If $b = 13$ and $A = 76°$, find a.
3. If $a = 6$ and $c = 12$, find B.
4. If $a = 21.2$ and $b = 9$, find A.
5. If $B = 16°$ and $c = 13$, find a.
6. If $A = 49°13'$ and $a = 10$, find b.

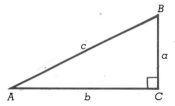

7. If $c = 16$ and $a = 7$, find b.
8. If $a = 7$ and $b = 12$, find A.
9. If $a = 5$ and $b = 6$, find c.
10. If $B = 78°8'$ and $a = 4.1$, find c.
11. The base angles of an isosceles triangle are 57°30', and the base is 7.5 cm long. Find the equal sides and the altitude to the base.
12. A tower, 250 meters high, casts a shadow 176 meters long. Find the angle of elevation of the sun to the nearest minute.

Written Exercises

Suppose $\triangle ABC$ is a right triangle. Let A and B be the acute angles, and a and b be the measures of the sides opposite these angles. Solve each triangle.

1. $A = 41°$, $b = 7.44$
2. $B = 42°10'$, $a = 9$
3. $b = 22$, $A = 22°22'$
4. $a = 21$, $c = 30$
5. $A = 45°$, $c = 7\sqrt{2}$
6. $a = 31.2$, $c = 42.4$
7. $A = 37°15'$, $b = 11$
8. $a = 11$, $b = 21$
9. $A = 55°55'$, $c = 16$

10-19. Solve each triangle for the exploratory exercises **1-10.**

Solve each of the following. Round to the nearest hundredth or the nearest minute.

20. A ladder, 6 meters long, stands on level ground and rests against a wall at a point 4 meters from the ground. How far from the wall is the foot of the ladder?

21. A regular hexagon is inscribed in a circle with diameter 7.52 cm. Find the length of its apothem (the distance from the center to the midpoint of a side).

22. A regular pentagon has an apothem of 7.43 centimeters. Find the length of a side of the pentagon and the radius of the circumscribed circle.

23. A monument is 112.5 meters high and casts a shadow 201.2 meters long. Find the angle of elevation of the sun.

24. Find the bearing of a road that runs directly from A to B, with B being 3 miles north and 1.7 miles east of A. (The bearing of B from A is the positive angle with vertex at A measured clockwise from north to B.)

25. A flagpole 40 feet high stands on top of a building. From a point P on the street, the angle of elevation of the top of the pole is 54°54′ and the angle of elevation of the bottom of the pole is 47°30′. How high is the building?

26. A rectangle is 17.5 cm by 26.2 cm. Find the angle made by the longer side and a diagonal.

27. A 7.4 cm chord subtends a central angle of 41° in a circle. Find the radius of the circle.

28. The diameter of a circle is 13.4 cm. Find the length of a chord that subtends a central angle of 26°20′.

29. Find the area of a regular pentagon that is inscribed in a circle whose diameter is 7.3 cm.

30. To find the height of a mountain peak two points, A and B, were located on a plain in line with the peak and the angles of elevation were measured from each point. The angle at A was 36°40′ and the angle at B was 21°10′. The distance from A to B was 570 feet. How high is the peak above the level of the plain?

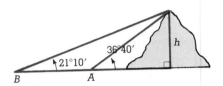

31. A mountain peak stands near a level plain on which are two farm houses C and D that are in a straight line from the peak. The angle of depression from the peak to C is 49°42′, and the angle of depression to D is 26°27′. The peak is known to be 1004 feet above the level of the plain. Find the distance from C to D.

32. Mr. Riegle observes that the angle of elevation of the top of a building is 41°30′. After moving back a distance of 265 feet and in the same vertical plane with the building, Mr. Riegle finds that the angle of elevation of the top of the building is now 28°10′. Find the height of the building.

33. In order to find the height of a chimney CT, the angle of elevation of the top T is measured by means of a transit from point A, whose distance from the chimney is not known. Then the transit is turned through a horizontal angle of 90° and point B is located. At B the angle of elevation of the top of the chimney is measured again. Find the height of the chimney if $m\angle CAT$ is 37°17′, $m\angle CBT$ is 24°42′, and AB is 73 meters.

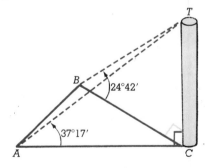

For the Scholar

In $\triangle ABC$, four lines are drawn parallel to the base, $\overline{AB}$, such that $\overline{AC}$ and $\overline{BC}$ are each separated into five congruent segments. The interior of $\triangle ABC$ is divided into five distinct parts, the largest has an area of 90 square units. Find the area of $\triangle ABC$ and the area of the smallest part.

Using Mathematics

Radio transmission is propagated in two modes, FM (Frequency Modulation) and AM (Amplitude Modulation). An audio frequency, 20 to 30 thousand waves per second, is superimposed on a radio carrier wave, 30 thousand to 30 billion waves per second.

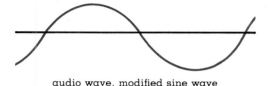

audio wave, modified sine wave

radio carrier wave, high frequency sine waves

AM means that the amplitude of the carrier wave is altered by the audio wave.

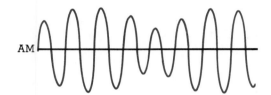

AM

$$y = \underbrace{(A_0 + A_1 \sin 2\pi\, nt)}_{amplitude\ factor} \sin 2\pi\, vt$$

FM means that the frequency of the carrier wave is varied with narrow limits by the audio wave.

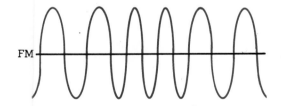

FM

$$y = A_0 \sin 2\pi \underbrace{(v_0 + v_1 \sin 2\pi\, nt)}_{frequency\ or\ period\ factor} t$$

A television picture carrier wave is amplitude modulated while the sound is frequency modulated. In the equation, $y = A \sin kx$, the value of A determines amplitude and the value of k determines period (or frequency).

Exercises
Use a calculator to find a table of values for $0 \le x \le 1$ for each of the following in increments of 0.05 radians. Then, graph the functions.

1. $y = (\sin x) \sin 10x$

2. $y = \sin (10 \sin x)x$

7-3 The Law of Sines

The trigonometric functions also can be used to solve problems involving triangles that are not right triangles.

Consider $\triangle ABC$ that is inscribed in $\odot O$ with diameter DB. Let $2r$ be the length of the diameter. Draw $\overline{AD}$. Then, $\angle D \cong \angle C$ and $\sin C = \sin D$. But $\angle BAD$ is a right angle, so $\sin D = \frac{c}{2r}$. Thus, $\sin C = \frac{c}{2r}$ or $\frac{c}{\sin C} = 2r$. Similarly, by drawing diameters through A and C, $\frac{b}{\sin B} = 2r$ and $\frac{a}{\sin A} = 2r$. The following equations can be written.

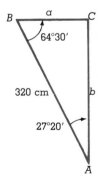

$$\frac{a}{\sin A} = \frac{b}{\sin B} = \frac{c}{\sin C}$$

These equations are known as the Law of Sines. It states that the ratio of any side of a triangle to the sine of the angle opposite that side is a constant for a given triangle. For example, in a $30°$–$60°$ right triangle with sides 1, $\sqrt{3}$, and 2, the ratios are

$$\frac{1}{\sin 30°} = \frac{\sqrt{3}}{\sin 60°} = \frac{2}{\sin 90°}. \qquad \text{\textit{The ratio is 2 to 1 in this case.}}$$

Let $\triangle ABC$ be any triangle with a, b, and c representing the measures of sides opposite angles with measurements A, B, and C respectively. Then, the following equations are true. $$\frac{a}{\sin A} = \frac{b}{\sin B} = \frac{c}{\sin C}$$	*Law of Sines*

Example

1 **Solve $\triangle ACB$ if $B = 64°20'$, $A = 27°20'$, and $BA = 320$ cm.**

Find the measurement of $\angle C$.

$27°20' + 64°30' + C = 180°$
$C = 180° - 27°20' - 64°30'$ or $88°10'$

Use the Law of Sines to find a and b.

$$\frac{c}{\sin C} = \frac{a}{\sin A}$$

$$\frac{320}{\sin 88°10'} = \frac{a}{\sin 27°20'}$$

$$a = \frac{320 \sin 27°20'}{\sin 88°10'}$$

$$= \frac{320(0.4592)}{0.9995}$$

$$= 147.0$$

$$\frac{c}{\sin C} = \frac{b}{\sin B}$$

$$\frac{320}{\sin 88°10'} = \frac{b}{\sin 64°30'}$$

$$b = \frac{320 \sin 64°30'}{\sin 88°10'}$$

$$= \frac{320(0.9026)}{0.9995}$$

$$= 289.0$$

Therefore, $C = 88°10'$, a is 147 cm and b is 289 cm.

When the lengths of two sides of a triangle and the measurement of the angle opposite one of them is given, one solution does not always exist. In such a case, one of the following will be true.

1. No triangle exists.
2. Exactly one triangle exists.
3. Two triangles exist.

In other words, there may be no solution, one solution, or two solutions.

Suppose a, b, and A are given. Consider the case where $A < 90°$.

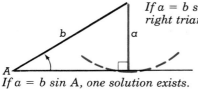

If a = b sin A, the solution is a right triangle.

If a = b sin A, one solution exists.

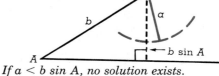

If a < b sin A, no solution exists.

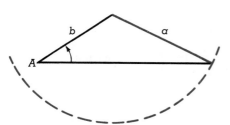

If a > b sin A and a > b, one solution exists.

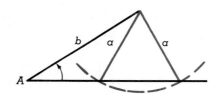

If b sin A < a < b, two solutions exist.

Consider the case where $A \geq 90°$.

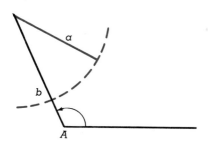

If a ≤ b, no solution exists.

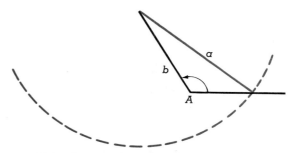

If a > b, one solution exists.

2   **Solve △ABC if A = 63°10′, b = 18, and a = 17.**

To determine the number of solutions, use $a = b \sin A$.

$$b \sin A = 18 \sin 63°10′$$
$$= 18(0.8923)$$
$$= 16.1$$

Since $63°10′ < 90°$ and $16.1 < 17 < 18$, two solutions exist.

$$\frac{17}{\sin 63°10′} = \frac{18}{\sin B}$$
$$\sin B = \frac{18 \sin 63°10′}{17}$$
$$= \frac{18(0.8923)}{17}$$
$$= 0.9448$$
$$B = 70°52′ \qquad \text{or} \qquad B = 109°8′ \qquad \textit{Round to the nearest minute.}$$

Solution 1

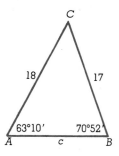

$$63°10′ + 70°52′ + C = 180°$$
$$C = 180° - (63°10′ + 70°52′)$$
$$= 45°58′$$
$$\frac{17}{\sin 63°10′} = \frac{c}{\sin 45°58′}$$
$$c = \frac{17 \sin 45°58′}{\sin 63°10′}$$
$$= \frac{17(0.7189)}{0.8923}$$
$$= 13.70$$

One solution is $B = 70°52′$, $C = 45°58′$, and $c = 13.70$.

Solution 2

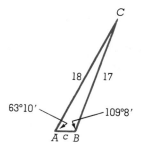

$$63°10′ + 109°8′ + C = 180°$$
$$C = 180° - (63°10′ + 109°8′)$$
$$= 7°42′$$
$$\frac{17}{\sin 63°10′} = \frac{c}{\sin 7°42′}$$
$$c = \frac{17 \sin 7°42′}{\sin 63°10′}$$
$$= \frac{17(0.1340)}{0.8923}$$
$$= 2.55$$

Another solution is $B = 109°8′$, $C = 7°42′$, and $c = 2.55$.

Example

3 Solve $\triangle ABC$ if $A = 40°$, $b = 16$, and $a = 9$.

$$b \sin A = 16 \sin 40°$$
$$= 16(0.6428)$$
$$= 10.28$$

Since $40° < 90°$ and $9 < 10.28$, no solution exists.

Exploratory Exercises

State if the given information determines one triangle, two triangles, or no triangle.

1. $A = 140°$, $b = 10$, $a = 3$
2. $C = 17°$, $a = 10$, $c = 11$
3. $B = 160°$, $a = 10$, $A = 41°$
4. $A = 30°$, $a = 4$, $b = 8$
5. $A = 43°$, $b = 20$, $a = 11$
6. $A = 60°$, $b = 2$, $a = \sqrt{3}$
7. $a = 20$, $b = 19$, $A = 90°$
8. $A = 38°$, $b = 10$, $a = 8$
9. $A = 118°$, $b = 11$, $a = 17$
10. $A = 58°$, $a = 17$, $b = 13$
11. $c = 4$, $C = 30°$, $b = 10$
12. $b = 2$, $B = 140°$, $a = 3$

State an equation which would enable you to solve each triangle described below. Do not solve.

13. If $A = 40°$, $B = 60°$, and $a = 20$, find b.
14. If $b = 2.8$, $A = 53°$, and $B = 61°$, find a.
15. If $b = 10$, $a = 14$, and $A = 50°$, find B.

Written Exercises

Determine the number of possible solutions. If a solution exists, solve the triangle.

1. $a = 8$, $A = 49°$, $B = 57°$
2. $a = 6$, $b = 8$, $A = 150°$
3. $A = 37°20'$, $B = 51°30'$, $c = 125$
4. $a = 26$, $b = 29$, $A = 58°$
5. $A = 40°$, $B = 60°$, $c = 20$
6. $A = 29°10'$, $B = 62°20'$, $c = 11.5$
7. $b = 40$, $a = 32$, $A = 125°20'$
8. $B = 70°$, $C = 58°$, $a = 84$
9. $a = 12$, $b = 14$, $A = 90°$
10. $A = 107°13'$, $a = 17.2$, $c = 12.2$
11. $A = 25°$, $a = 125$, $b = 150$
12. $A = 76°$, $a = 5$, $b = 20$

13-15. Solve each triangle in exploratory exercises **13-15**.

Solve each of the following. Round all answers to the nearest hundredth or the nearest minute.

16. A triangular lot faces two streets that meet at an angle measuring 85°. The sides of the lot facing the street are each 160 feet in length. Find the perimeter of the lot.

17. A flower bed is in the shape of an obtuse triangle. One angle is 45°, the side opposite is 28 feet, and another side is 36 feet. Find the remaining angles and side.

18. A building 60 feet tall is on top of a hill. A surveyor is at a point on the hill and observes the angle of elevation to the top of the building has measurement 42° and to the bottom of the building has measurement 18°. How far is the surveyor from the bottom of the building?

19. A 35 foot pole stands vertically on a uniformly sloped hillside. At a time when the angle of elevation of the sun is 37°12′ the shadow of the pole extends directly down the slope. If the hillside has an angle of inclination of 6°40′, find the length of the shadow.

Use the Law of Sines to show that each statement is true.

20. $\dfrac{a - c}{c} = \dfrac{\sin A - \sin C}{\sin C}$

21. $\dfrac{b + c}{b - c} = \dfrac{\sin B + \sin C}{\sin B - \sin C}$

22. $\dfrac{a}{b} = \dfrac{\sin A}{\sin B}$

23. $\dfrac{b}{a + b} = \dfrac{\sin B}{\sin A + \sin B}$

24. Use the Law of Sines to show the bisector of an interior angle of a triangle separates the opposite side into parts that have the same ratio as the sides adjacent to the angle bisected.

For the Scholar

Find the product of all the real values of a that satisfy the equation $4|a - 4| = |a + 4|$.

7-4 The Law of Cosines

If two sides and the included angle or three sides of a triangle are given, the Law of Sines *cannot* be used to solve the triangle. Another formula is needed.

Consider $\triangle ABC$ with height measuring h units and sides measuring a units, b units, and c units. Suppose segment DC is x units long. Then, segment BD is $(a - x)$ units long.

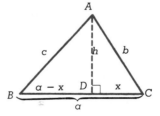

The Pythagorean Theorem and the definition of the cosine function can be used to show how $\angle C$, a, b, and c are related.

$$
\begin{aligned}
c^2 &= (a - x)^2 + h^2 \\
&= a^2 - 2ax + x^2 + h^2 \\
&= a^2 - 2ax + b^2 \\
&= a^2 - 2a(b \cos C) + b^2 \\
&= a^2 + b^2 - 2ab \cos C
\end{aligned}
$$

Use the Pythagorean Theorem.
Expand $(a - x)^2$.
$b^2 = x^2 + h^2$
$\cos C = \frac{x}{b}$, so $x = b \cos C$

By drawing altitudes from B and C, similar formulas for a^2 and b^2 can be found. All three formulas, the Law of Cosines, can be summarized as follows.

Let $\triangle ABC$ be any triangle with a, b, and c representing the measures of sides opposite angles with measurements A, B, and C respectively. Then, the following equations are true.

$$a^2 = b^2 + c^2 - 2bc \cos A$$
$$b^2 = a^2 + c^2 - 2ac \cos B$$
$$c^2 = a^2 + b^2 - 2ab \cos C$$

Law of Cosines

Example

1 Solve $\triangle SRT$ if $S = 128°40'$, $r = 32.4$, and $t = 26.7$

$$
\begin{aligned}
s^2 &= r^2 + t^2 - 2rt \cos S \qquad \textit{Use the Law of Cosines.}\\
&= (32.4)^2 + (26.7)^2 - 2(32.4)(26.7) \cos 128°40'\\
&= (32.4)^2 + (26.7)^2 - 2(32.4)(26.7)(-0.6248)\\
&= 2843.65\\
s &= 53.3
\end{aligned}
$$

$$
\dfrac{53.3}{\sin 128°40'} = \dfrac{32.4}{\sin R} \qquad \textit{Use the Law of Sines}
$$

$$
\begin{aligned}
\sin R &= \dfrac{32.4 \sin 128°40'}{53.3}\\[2mm]
&= \dfrac{32.4(0.7808)}{53.3}\\[2mm]
&= 0.4746\\
R &= 28°20' \qquad \textit{Round to the nearest 10 minutes.}
\end{aligned}
$$

$$128°40' + 28°20' + T = 180°$$

Therefore, $s = 24.9$, $R = 28°20'$ and $T = 23°$.

Using Calculators

Solve $\triangle ABC$ for a if $A = 24°49'$, $b = 251.3$, and $c = 318.7$. Round to the nearest tenth. $a = \sqrt{(251.3)^2 + (318.7)^2 - 2(251.3)(318.7) \cos 24°49'}$ *Use the Law of Cosines.*

ENTER:	251.3	x^2	$+$	318.7	x^2	$-$	24.49
DISPLAY:	251.3	63151.69		318.7	101569.69	164721.38	24.49

ENTER:	→DEG	cos	$\times$	2	$\times$	251.3	$\times$
DISPLAY:	24.81666666	0.90755426		2	1.815310853	251.3	456.1876174

ENTER:	318.7	$=$	
DISPLAY:	318.7	19334.38635	139.048144

Thus, $a \approx 139.0$.

Example

2 Solve $\triangle ABC$ if $a = 7.23$, $b = 5.81$, and $c = 4.93$.

$(7.23)^2 = (5.81)^2 + (4.93)^2 - 2(5.81)(4.93) \cos A$ *Use the Law of Cosines.*

$\cos A = \dfrac{(5.81)^2 + (4.93)^2 - (7.23)^2}{2(5.81)(4.93)}$

$\qquad = 0.1010$

$\qquad A = 84°10'$ *Round to the nearest 10 minutes.*

$\dfrac{\sin 84°10'}{7.23} = \dfrac{\sin B}{5.81}$ *Use the Law of Sines.*

$\sin B = \dfrac{5.81 \sin 84°10'}{7.23}$

$\sin B = \dfrac{5.81(0.9948)}{7.23}$

$\qquad = 0.7994$

$\qquad B = 53°$ *Round to the nearest 10 minutes.*

$84°10' + 53° + C = 180°$

$\qquad\qquad C = 180° - 84°10' - 53°$

$\qquad\qquad\quad = 42°50'$

Therefore, $A = 84°10'$, $B = 53°$, and $C = 42°50'$.

Exploratory Exercises

In each of the following, three parts of a triangle are given. Determine whether the Law of Sines or the Law of Cosines would be used first to solve the triangle.

1. $a = 14$, $b = 15$, $c = 16$
2. $C = 35°$, $a = 11$, $b = 10.5$
3. $a = 10$, $A = 40°$, $c = 8$
4. $A = 40°$, $b = 6$, $c = 7$
5. $c = 21$, $a = 14$, $B = 60°$
6. $A = 40°$, $C = 70°$, $c = 14$
7. $c = 10.3$, $a = 21$, $b = 16.7$
8. $c = 14.1$, $A = 29°$, $b = 7.8$
9. $b = 17$, $B = 45°28'$, $a = 12$
10. $A = 28°50'$, $b = 4$, $c = 2.9$

Written Exercises

Solve each of the following triangles.

1. $A = 52°10'$, $b = 6$, $c = 8$
2. $a = 4$, $b = 5$, $c = 7$
3. $b = 7$, $c = 10$, $A = 51°$
4. $A = 52°40'$, $b = 540$, $c = 490$
5. $a = 5$, $b = 6$, $c = 7$
6. $C = 105°18'$, $a = 6.11$, $b = 5.84$
7. $A = 61°25'$, $b = 191$, $c = 205$
8. $a = 3$, $b = 7$, $c = 5$
9. $b = 13$, $a = 21.5$, $C = 39°20'$
10. $a = 11.4$, $b = 13.7$, $c = 12.2$
11. $A = 40°$, $B = 59°$, $c = 14$
12. $a = 9$, $c = 5$, $B = 120°$

13-22. Solve each triangle in exploratory exercises **1-10.**

Solve each of the following.

23. The sides of a triangle are 6.8 cm, 8.4 cm, and 4.9 cm. Find the measure of the smallest angle.

24. The sides of a parallelogram are 55 cm and 71 cm. Find the length of each diagonal if the larger angle is 106°.

25. Nathan is flying from Chicago to Columbus, a distance of 300 miles. He starts his flight 15° off course and flies on this course for 75 miles. How far is he from Columbus?

26. Two ships leave San Francisco at the same time. One travels 40° west of north at a speed of 20 knots. The other travels 10° west of south at a speed of 15 knots. How far apart are they after 11 hours?

27. A 40 foot television antenna stands on top of a building. From a point on the ground, the angles of elevation of the top and bottom of the antenna, respectively have measurements of 56° and 42°. How tall is the building?

28. From a point of observation on a level plain the distance to one of two houses is 253 meters and to the other house is 319 meters. What is the distance between the houses if the angle subtended by them at the point of observation is 42°12′?

For the Scholar

A closed figure is bound by the following system:

$$\begin{cases} x = 0 \\ y = 10 \\ y = -x, \text{ when } -6 \le x \le 0 \\ 2x + 3y = 6, \text{ when } -12 \le x \le -6 \end{cases}$$

What is the area of the closed figure?

7-5 Area of a Triangle

The area of a triangle can be expressed in terms of two sides of the triangle and the measure of the included angle.

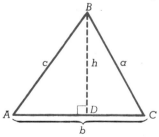

Suppose lengths b and c and the measure of the included angle A in $\triangle ABC$ are given. Let K represent the area of $\triangle ABC$ and let h represent the length of the altitude from B. Then, $K = \frac{1}{2}bh$. But, $\frac{h}{c} = \sin A$ or $h = c \sin A$. By substituting $c \sin A$ for h, the following formula is obtained.

$$K = \frac{1}{2}bc \sin A$$

Similarly, if altitudes are drawn from A and C, the formulas, $K = \frac{1}{2}ab \sin C$ and $K = \frac{1}{2}ac \sin B$, can be developed.

Example

1 **Find the area of $\triangle ABC$ if $a = 17.7$, $b = 21.0$, and $C = 78°10'$.**

$K = \frac{1}{2}ab \sin C$

$ = \frac{1}{2}(17.7)(21.0) \sin 78°10'$

$ = \frac{1}{2}(17.7)(21.0)(0.9787)$

$ = 181.9$

To the nearest whole unit, the area is 182 square units.

The area of a triangle also can be expressed in terms of one side of the triangle and two angles.

By the Law of Sines, $\dfrac{b}{\sin B} = \dfrac{c}{\sin C}$ or $b = \dfrac{c \sin B}{\sin C}$. Substituting this expression for b in $K = \frac{1}{2}bc \sin A$ gives the following formula.

$$K = \frac{1}{2}c^2 \frac{\sin A \sin B}{\sin C}$$

Similarly, $K = \frac{1}{2}a^2 \dfrac{\sin B \sin C}{\sin A}$ and $K = \frac{1}{2}b^2 \dfrac{\sin A \sin C}{\sin B}$.

Example

2 **Find the area of $\triangle ABC$ if $a = 10$, $A = 75°20'$, and $B = 49°40'$.**

Find the measurement of angle C.

$180° = 75°20' + 49°40' + C$

$ C = 180° - 75°20' - 49°40'$

$ = 55°$

Use $K = \frac{1}{2}a^2 \frac{\sin B \sin C}{\sin A}$.

$K = \frac{1}{2}(10)^2 \dfrac{\sin 49°40' \sin 55°}{\sin 75°20'}$

$ = \frac{1}{2}(100) \dfrac{(0.7623)(0.8192)}{(0.9674)}$

$ = 32.3$

To the nearest whole unit, the area is 32 square units.

If the lengths of three sides of a triangle are given, the area can be found by using the Law of Cosines and the formula $K = \frac{1}{2}ab \sin C$.

Example

3 Find the area of $\triangle ABC$ if $a = 17$, $b = 13$, and $c = 19$.

Solve for A using
The Law of Cosines.

$$(17)^2 = (13)^2 + (19)^2 - 2(13)(19) \cos A$$

$$\cos A = \frac{(17)^2 - (13)^2 - (19)^2}{-2(13)(19)}$$

$$= \frac{-241}{-494}$$

$$= 0.4879$$

$$A = 60°50' \qquad \text{Round to the nearest 10 minutes.}$$

Use $K = \frac{1}{2}bc \sin A$.

$$K = \frac{1}{2}(13)(19) \sin 60°50'$$

$$= \frac{1}{2}(13)(19)(0.8732)$$

$$= 107.8$$

To the nearest whole unit, the area is 108 square units.

Hero's formula also can be used when finding the area of a triangle given the lengths of three sides.

If the measures of the sides of a triangle are a, b, and c, then the area, K, of the triangle is found as follows. $$K = \sqrt{s(s - a)(s - b)(s - c)} \text{ where } s = \frac{1}{2}(a + b + c)$$	***Hero's Formula***

Example

4 Use Hero's formula to find the area of $\triangle ABC$ if $a = 17$, $b = 13$, and $c = 19$.

$$s = \frac{1}{2}(17 + 13 + 19)$$

$$= 24.5$$

$$K = \sqrt{(24.5)(24.5 - 17)(24.5 - 13)(24.5 - 19)}$$

$$= \sqrt{11,622.19}$$

$$= 107.8$$

To the nearest whole unit, the area is 108 square units.

Exploratory Exercises

State an equation that can be used to find the area of each triangle described below.

1. $a = 3$, $b = 4$, $C = 120°$

2. $c = 20$, $A = 45°$, $B = 30°$

3. $a = 4$, $b = 6$, $c = 8$

4. $A = 43°$, $b = 16$, $c = 12$

5. $A = 19°20'$, $a = 18.6$, $C = 63°50'$

6. $a = 20$, $b = 30$, $c = 40$

7. $a = 6$, $B = 52°$, $c = 4$

8. $b = 12$, $B = 135°$, $C = 30°$

Written Exercises

Find the area of each of the following triangles to the nearest whole unit.

1. $a = 7.5$, $b = 9$, $C = 100°$
2. $c = 3.2$, $A = 16°$, $B = 31°45'$
3. $a = 2$, $b = 7$, $c = 8$
4. $b = 146.2$, $c = 209.3$, $A = 61°12'$
5. $A = 60°$, $a = 2$, $B = 75°$
6. $a = \sqrt{2}$, $b = 2$, $c = 3$
7. $a = 19.42$, $c = 19.42$, $B = 31°16'$
8. $a = 174$, $b = 138$, $c = 188$
9. $a = 8$, $B = 60°$, $C = 75°$
10. $a = 11$, $B = 50°6'$, $c = 5$

11-18. Find the area of each triangle described in exploratory exercises **1-8.**

Solve each of the following.

19. A triangular plot of land has two sides that have lengths of 400 feet and 600 feet. The measurement of the angle between those sides is 46°20'. Find its perimeter and area.

20. The adjacent sides of a parallelogram are 8 cm and 12 cm and one angle is 60°. Find the area of the parallelogram.

21. The sides of a rhombus are 5 cm each and one diagonal is 6 cm. Find the area of the rhombus.

22. A regular pentagon is inscribed in a circle whose radius is 7 cm. Find the area of the pentagon.

23. A regular octagon is inscribed in a circle whose radius is 5 cm. Find the area of the octagon.

24. The area of $\triangle ABC$ is 24 cm², $a = 6$ cm, and $b = 10$ cm. Find the measure of angle C.

25. The diagonals of a quadrilateral are x and y units long. Their intersection forms angle A. Show that the area of the quadrilateral is $\frac{1}{2}xy \sin A$.

26. Find a formula for the area enclosed by a circle of radius r and a regular inscribed hexagon.

7-6   Vector Triangles

Vectors can be used to represent quantities having magnitude and direction. Common quantities that can be represented by vectors are velocity, acceleration, weight, force, and an electrical field.

Graphically, vectors can be added by forming a triangle or parallelogram with the given vectors as sides. Trigonometric solutions of vector triangles usually provide more accurate results than graphical solutions.

The vector sum of two or more vectors is called the resultant, usually denoted by $\bar{r}$.

Examples

1 **A plane is flying due east at 245 km/h. A 22 km/h wind is blowing from the northeast. Find the ground speed and the direction of the plane.**

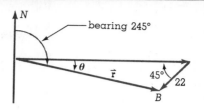

Make a sketch showing the given vector quantities and the resultant. Let $\vec{r}$ be the resultant velocity and let the bearing of the plane be $90° + \theta$.

Use the Law of Cosines to find the magnitude of $\vec{r}$.

$|\vec{r}|^2 = 245^2 + 22^2 - 2(245)(22)\cos 45°$
$\phantom{|\vec{r}|^2} = 245^2 + 22^2 - 2(245)(22)(0.7071) \text{ or } 52{,}886$
$|\vec{r}| = 230 \text{ km/h}$

Use the Law of Sines to find θ.

$$\frac{230}{\sin 45°} = \frac{22}{\sin \theta}$$

$$\sin \theta = \frac{22 \sin 45°}{230}$$

$$ = \frac{22(0.7071)}{230} \text{ or } 0.0676$$

$\theta = 3°50'$ *Round to the nearest 10 minutes.*

The bearing of the plane is $90° + 3°50'$ or $93°50'$.
Thus, the plane is actually flying 230 km/h $3°50'$ south of east or at a bearing of $93°50'$.

2 **Two forces, one of 30 N and the other of 50 N, act on an object. If the angle between the forces is 40°, find the magnitude and the direction of the resultant force.**   *N is the symbol for the metric unit of force, the newton.*

Make a sketch showing the given vector quantities and the resultant. Let the resultant be force $\vec{r}$ and let the angle it makes with the 50 N vector be θ.

Angle OAC is the supplement of 40°. So you know two sides and the included angle in $\triangle OAC$.

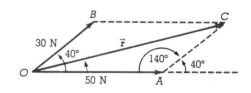

Use the Law of Cosines to find the magnitude of $\vec{r}$.

$|\vec{r}|^2 = 50^2 + 30^2 - 2(50)(30)\cos 140°$
$\phantom{|\vec{r}|^2} = 2500 + 900 - 3000(-0.7660) \text{ or } 5698$
$|\vec{r}| = 75.5 \text{ N}$

Use the Law of Sines to find the direction of $\vec{r}$.

$$\frac{75.5}{\sin 140°} = \frac{30}{\sin \theta}$$

$$\sin \theta = \frac{30 \sin 140°}{75.5}$$

$$ = \frac{30(0.6428)}{75.5} \text{ or } 0.2554$$

$\theta = 14°50'$ *Round to the nearest 10 minutes.*

Thus, $\vec{r}$ has a magnitude of 75.5 N and makes a $14°50'$ angle with the 50 N vector.

Example

3 An object with a mass of 3 N is attached to a length of string and whirled around in a circle. If the magnitude of the centripetal force is 5 N, find the angle that the string makes with a vertical line and the resultant force pulling the object inward.

The figure shows the given vector quantities and the resultant. $|\vec{\mathbf{r}}|$ is the force inward on the string and θ is the angle that the string makes with a vertical line.

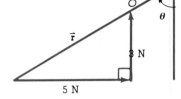

Find θ.

$$\tan \theta = \frac{5}{3}$$

$$= 1.6667$$

$$\theta = 59° \qquad \textit{Round to the nearest 10 minutes.}$$

Find $|\vec{r}|$.

$$\cos 59° = \frac{3}{|\vec{\mathbf{r}}|}$$

$$|\vec{\mathbf{r}}| = \frac{3}{\cos 59°}$$

$$|\vec{\mathbf{r}}| = 6 \qquad \textit{Round to the nearest newton.}$$

Thus, the string makes a 59° angle from the vertical line. The force pulling the object inward is 6 N.

Using Calculators

An object with a mass of 7 N is attached to a length of string and whirled around in a circle. If the magnitude of the centripetal force is 10 N, find the angle that the string makes with a vertical line and the resultant force pulling the object inward.

Find θ.

$$\tan \theta = \frac{10}{7}$$

ENTER: 10 [÷] 7 [=] [2ndF] [tan] [2ndF] [→DEG]

DISPLAY: 10   7   1.428571429   55.0079798   55

Therefore, $\theta = 55°$.

Find $|\vec{r}|$.

$$\cos 55° = \frac{7}{|\vec{\mathbf{r}}|}$$

$$|\vec{\mathbf{r}}| = \frac{7}{\cos 55°}$$

ENTER: 7 [÷] 55 [COS] [=]

DISPLAY: 7   55   0.573576436   12.20412757

Thus, the string makes a 55° angle from the vertical line. The force pulling the object inward is about 12 N.

Exploratory Exercises

Make a sketch to show the given vectors.

1. A plane headed due west at a velocity of 320 mph.

2. A force of 35 N acting on an object at an angle of 30° with the level ground.

3. A boat traveling at 16 knots at an angle of 25° with the current.

4. A force of 18 N acting on an object while another force of 51 N acts on the same object at an angle of 45° from the first.

Find the magnitude and direction of the resultant of the vectors shown in each diagram.

5.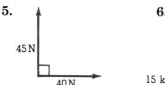

6.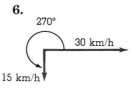

7.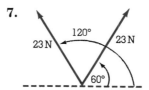

8.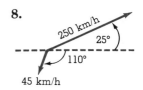

Written Exercises

Two 10-lb forces act on the same object at the same time. Find the magnitude of their resultant if each of the following is the measurement of the angle between them.

1. 30°   2. 90°   3. 120°   4. 180°

Solve each of the following.

5. A 100-N force and a 50-N force act on the same object. The angle between the forces measures 90°. Find the magnitude and direction of the resultant force.

6. An airplane flies at 150 km/h and heads 30° south of east. A 50 km/h wind blows in the direction 25° west of south. Find the ground speed and direction of the plane.

7. An airplane is heading due north at 260 mph. A wind from the east is 16 mph. Find the ground speed and direction of the plane.

8. An airplane is heading due north at 260 mph. A 16-mph wind blows from the northwest at an angle of 110° clockwise from north. Find the ground speed and direction of the plane.

9. One force of 125 N acts on an object. Another force of 85 N acts on the same object at an angle of 72° from the first. Find the magnitude and direction of the resultant force.

10. A wagon is pulled along level ground by a force of 18 N in the handle at an angle of 30° to the horizontal. Find the horizontal and vertical components of this vector.

11. Points C and D are directly across from each other on the opposite banks of a river. A boat traveling at a speed of 12 mph crosses the river from C to D. If the current of the river has a speed of 4 mph, at what angle must the skipper head to travel directly from C to D?

12. A force F_1 of 36 N acts at an angle of 20° above the horizontal. Pulling in the opposing direction is a force F_2 of 48 N acting at an angle of 42° below horizontal. Find the magnitude and direction of the resultant force.

13. Three forces in a horizontal plane act on an object. The forces are 7 N, 11 N, and 15 N. The angle between the 7 N and 11 N forces is 105°, between the 11 N and the 15 N forces is 147°, and between the 15 N and the 7N forces is 108°. Find the magnitude and direction of the resultant force.

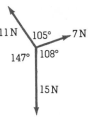

A boat heads directly across a river 320 m wide at 40 m/s. The current is flowing at 8 m/s.

14. Find the resultant velocity of the boat.

15. How long does it take the boat to reach the opposite shore?

A boat heads directly across a river 40 m wide at 8 m/s. The current is flowing at 3.8 m/s.

16. Find the resultant velocity of the boat.

17. How far downstream is the boat when it reaches the other side?

18. An airplane flies east for 210 km. It then flies 70° south of east for 100 km. Find the distance and direction of the plane from its starting place.

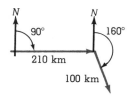

For the Scholar

A circular metal disk rolls on its edge at a speed of x miles per hour. Since its circumference is 33 feet, it rolls 5 miles per hour faster when the time of a complete rotation is shortened by $\frac{1}{2}$ a second. Find the value of x.

7-7 Area of a Circular Sector and Segment

A **sector** of a circle is the region bounded by an arc of a circle and the radii drawn to its endpoints. For example, figure *ORTS* is a sector of $\odot O$.

The ratio of the area of a sector to the area of the circle is equal to the ratio of its arc to the circumference. Let A represent the area of the sector. Then, $\dfrac{A}{\pi r^2} = \dfrac{\text{length of } \overset{\frown}{RTS}}{2\pi r}$. But, the length of $\overset{\frown}{RTS}$ is $r \cdot \alpha$. Thus, the following formula is true.

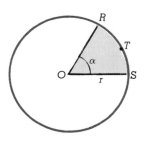

If α is the measure of the central angle expressed in radians and r is the radius of the circle, then the area of the sector, A, is as follows.

$$A = \frac{1}{2}r^2\alpha$$

Area of a Circular Sector

1 **A sector has arclength 6 cm and central angle 0.8 radians. Find the radius of the circle and the area of the sector.**

Find the radius of the circle.	arclength $= r \cdot \alpha$
	6 cm $= r \cdot 0.8$
	$r = 7.5$
Find the area of the sector.	$A = \frac{1}{2}r^2\alpha$
	$= \frac{1}{2}(7.5)^2(0.8)$
	$= 22.5$

Thus, the radius is 7.5 cm and the area is 22.5 cm².

A **segment** of a circle is the region bounded by an arc and its chord. If the arc is a minor arc, then the area of the segment can be found by subtracting the area of $\triangle OAB$ from the area of sector $OACB$. Let S represent the area of the segment.

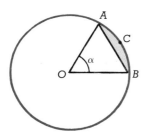

$S = $ (area of sector $OACB$) $-$ (area of $\triangle OAB$)

$\quad = \frac{1}{2}r^2\alpha - \frac{1}{2}ab \sin C$

$\quad = \frac{1}{2}r^2\alpha - \frac{1}{2}r \cdot r \sin \alpha \qquad a = r, \, b = r, \, and \, C = \alpha$

$S = \frac{1}{2}r^2(\alpha - \sin \alpha)$

If α is the measure of the central angle expressed in radians and r is the radius of the circle, then the area of the segment, S, is as follows.

$$S = \frac{1}{2}r^2(\alpha - \sin \alpha)$$

Area of a Circular Segment

Example

2

A sector has a central angle of 100° in a circle of radius 3 cm. Find the area of the circular sector and the area of the corresponding circular segment.

Convert 100° to radian measure.
$$\frac{R}{\pi} = \frac{D}{180°}$$

$$\frac{R}{\pi} = \frac{100°}{180°}$$

$$R = \frac{5}{9}\pi \text{ or } 1.7453 \text{ radians} \qquad \textit{Round to 4 decimal places.}$$

Find the area of the sector.
$$A = \frac{1}{2}r^2\alpha$$

$$= \frac{1}{2}(3)^2(1.7453)$$

$$= 7.9 \qquad \textit{Round to the nearest tenth.}$$

Find the area of the segment.
$$S = \frac{1}{2}r^2(\alpha - \sin \alpha)$$

$$= \frac{1}{2}(3)^2(1.7453 - \sin 1.7453)$$

$$= \frac{1}{2}(3)^2(1.7453 - 0.9848)$$

$$= 3.4 \qquad \textit{Round to the nearest tenth.}$$

Thus, the area of the circular sector is 7.9 cm² and the area of the corresponding circular segment is 3.4 cm².

Exploratory Exercises

Change the following degree measures to radian measures.

1. 225°   2. 60°   3. 90°   4. 330°

5. 62°   6. 28°   7. 171°   8. 143°

Find the arclength of each of the following.

9.   10.   11.   12.

Written Exercises

Find the area of each sector, given its central angle, θ, and the radius of the circle.

1. $\theta = \frac{\pi}{8}, r = 7$ 2. $\theta = \frac{5\pi}{12}, r = 10$ 3. $\theta = 48°, r = 22$

4. $\theta = 54°, r = 6$ 5. $\theta = \frac{2\pi}{3}, r = 1.36$ 6. $\theta = 82°, r = 7.3$

7. $\theta = 45°, r = 9.75$ 8. $\theta = 12°, r = 14$ 9. $\theta = \frac{\pi}{9}, r = 5.2$

Find the area of each circular segment, given its central angle, θ, and the radius of the circle.

10. $\theta = \dfrac{5\pi}{6}$, $r = 15$

11. $\theta = \dfrac{3\pi}{4}$, $r = 24$

12. $r = 120°$, $r = 8$

13. $\theta = 81°$, $r = 16$

14. $\theta = \dfrac{5\pi}{8}$, $r = 6$

15. $\theta = 85°$, $r = 2.1$

16. $\theta = 26°$, $r = 42$

17. $\theta = 150°$, $r = 11.5$

18. $\theta = \dfrac{\pi}{5}$, $r = 16.25$

Solve each of the following.

19. A sector has arclength 6 cm and central angle 1.2 radians. Find the radius and area of the circle.

20. A sector has area of 15 cm² and central angle of 0.2 radians. Find the radius of the circle and arclength of the sector.

21. A sector has a central angle of 20° and arclength of 3.5 cm. Find the radius and area of the circle.

22. A sector has a central angle of 24° and arclength of 8.3 cm. Find the radius and area of the circle.

23. Find the area swept over by the spoke of a wheel of radius 15 cm as the wheel rotates through an angle of 270°.

24. Find the area of the circular segment between a 4.8 cm chord and its arc if the diameter of the circle is 7.2 cm.

The change of the direction in a highway is given by the central angle, θ, subtended by the arc of the curve.

25. A highway curve, in the shape of an arc of a circle, is 0.25 miles. The direction of the highway changes 45° from one end of the curve to the other. Find the radius of the circle in feet which the curve follows.

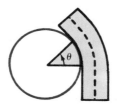

26. A highway curve, in the shape of an arc of a circle, is 500 ft. The radius of the circle that the curve follows is 2500 ft. Find the change in direction of the highway in degrees formed by the curve.

Challenge Exercise

27. The radius of a circle is 20.4 cm. In the circle is inscribed a polygon of five sides. Four of the central angles subtended by the sides are $\dfrac{\pi}{6}, \dfrac{\pi}{4}, \dfrac{2\pi}{3}$, and $\dfrac{2\pi}{5}$. Find the area of the polygon.

For the Scholar

How many sides does a convex polygon have when the sum of all but one of its interior angles is 3080°?

Chapter Summary

1. A trigonometric equation is an equation involving a trigonometric function. It is solved by the same methods used to solve other equations.   (187)
2. Trigonometric functions can be used to solve problems involving right triangles.   (190)
3. Law of Sines: Let $\triangle ABC$ be any triangle with a, b, and c representing the measures of sides opposite angles with measurements A, B, and C respectively. Then, the following equations are true.

$$\frac{a}{\sin A} = \frac{b}{\sin B} = \frac{c}{\sin C} \qquad (196)$$

4. When the measures of two sides of a triangle and the measurement of the angle opposite one of them is given, one solution does not always exist. No triangle may exist, one triangle may exist, or two triangles may exist.   (197)
5. Law of Cosines: Let $\triangle ABC$ be any triangle with a, b, and c representing the measures of sides opposite angles with measurements A, B, and C respectively. Then, the following equations are true.

$$a^2 = b^2 + c^2 - 2bc \cos A$$
$$b^2 = a^2 + c^2 - 2ac \cos B$$
$$c^2 = a^2 + b^2 - 2ab \cos C \qquad (201)$$

6. If the measures of two sides of a triangle and the measurement of the included angle are given, the area of the triangle, K, is found as follows.

$$K = \frac{1}{2}bc \sin A \qquad K = \frac{1}{2}ab \sin C \qquad K = \frac{1}{2}ac \sin B \qquad (203)$$

7. If the measure of one side of a triangle and the measurements of two angles are given, the area of the triangle, K, is found as follows.

$$K = \frac{1}{2}c^2 \frac{\sin A \sin B}{\sin C}$$
$$K = \frac{1}{2}a^2 \frac{\sin B \sin C}{\sin A}$$
$$K = \frac{1}{2}b^2 \frac{\sin A \sin C}{\sin B} \qquad (204)$$

8. Hero's Formula: If the measures of the sides of a triangle are a, b, and c, then the area, K, of the triangle is found as follows.

$$K = \sqrt{s(s-a)(s-b)(s-c)} \text{ where } s = \frac{1}{2}(a + b + c) \qquad (205)$$

9. Vector triangles can be solved by using the trigonometric functions.   (206)

10. **Area of a Circular Sector:** If α is the measure of the central angle expressed in radians and r is the radius of the circle, then the area of the sector, A, is as follows.

$$A = \frac{1}{2}r^2\alpha \qquad (210)$$

11. **Area of a Circular Segment:** If α is the measure of the central angle expressed in radians and r is the radius of the circle, then the area of the segment, S, is as follows.

$$S = \frac{1}{2}r^2(\alpha - \sin \alpha) \qquad (211)$$

Chapter Review

Solve each equation for general values of x. (7-1)

1. $2 \cos^2 x - 1 = 0$
2. $\tan x + 1 = \sec x$
3. $\sin^2 x + \cos 2x - \cos x = 0$
4. $\sin x \tan x - \tan x = 0$

Solve each equation for principal values of x. (7-1)

5. $\tan^2 x - 2 \tan x = 3$
6. $\cos x = 3 \cos x - 2$
7. $\cos 2x + \sin x = 1$
8. $4 \sin^2 x - 4 \sin x + 1 = 0$

Solve each of the following right triangles. Angle C is the right angle. (7-2)

9. $A = 63°, a = 9.7$
10. $a = 2, b = 7$
11. $B = 83°, b = \sqrt{31}$
12. $a = 44, B = 44°44'$

Solve each of the following. Round answers to the nearest hundredth or the nearest minute. (7-2)

13. A flagpole casts a shadow 40 feet long when the measurement of the angle of the sun is 31°20'. How tall is the flagpole?

14. In a parking garage, the floors are 20 feet apart. The ramp to each floor is 120 feet long. Find the measurement of the angle of elevation of the ramp.

15. A 24-foot ladder leans against a building. It forms an angle with the building measuring 18°. How far is the foot of the ladder from the base of the building?

16. A train travels 5000 meters along a track whose angle of elevation has a measurement of 6°. How much did it rise during this distance?

Determine the number of possible solutions. If a solution exists, solve the triangle. (7-3)

17. $A = 38°42', a = 172, c = 203$
18. $a = 12, b = 19, A = 57°$
19. $A = 29°, a = 12, b = 15$
20. $A = 45°, a = 83, b = 79$

Solve each of the following. Round answers to the nearest hundredth. (7-3)

21. A triangular piece of sheet metal has sides 23.4 cm and 29.6 cm long with the angle opposite the shorter side 47°15'. Find the length of the third side.

22. Two planes leave an airport at the same time. Each flies at a speed of 110 miles per hour. One flies in the direction 60° east of north. The other flies in the direction 40° east of south. How far apart are the planes after 3 hours?

Solve each of the following triangles. (7-4)

23. $A = 51°$, $b = 40$, $c = 45$

24. $a = 5$, $b = 12$, $c = 13$

25. $B = 19°$, $a = 51$, $c = 61$

26. $A = 25°26'$, $a = 13.7$, $B = 78°$

27. $a = 11$, $b = 13$, $c = 20$

28. $B = 24°$, $a = 42$, $c = 6.5$

Solve each of the following. Round answers to the nearest hundredth or the nearest minute. (7-4)

29. The sides of a triangular city lot have lengths of 50 meters, 70 meters, and 85 meters. Find the measurement of the angle opposite the shortest side.

30. The sides of a parallelogram are 3 cm and 5 cm. If the parallelogram has a 120° angle, how long are its diagonals?

Find the area of each triangle described below. (7-5)

31. $a = 6$, $B = 54°$, $c = 4$

32. $A = 20°$, $a = 19$, $C = 64°$

33. $a = 5$, $b = 7$, $c = 9$

34. $a = 11.7$, $b = 13.5$, $C = 81°20'$

35. $a = 2$, $b = 3$, $C = 70°$

36. $A = 42°$, $B = 65°$, $a = 63$

Solve each of the following. (7-5)

37. The diagonals of a parallelogram are 60 cm and 40 cm. They intersect at an angle of 60°. Find the area of the parallelogram.

38. The area of $\triangle ABC$ is 90 cm², $b = 12$ cm, and $c = 15$ cm. Find the measure of angle A.

Solve each of the following. (7-6)

39. An airplane flies due south at 265 km/h. It flies against a headwind of 60 km/h from a direction 30° east of south. Find the ground speed and direction of the airplane.

40. Steve and Rachel are moving a stove. They are applying forces of 70 N and 90 N at an angle of 30° to each other. Find the resultant force and the angle it makes with the larger force.

A metal ball with a mass of 12 N is attached to the end of a rope and whirled in a circle. The centripetal force at a given velocity is 60 N. (7-6)

41. Find the angle that the rope makes with a vertical line.

42. Find the force on the rope.

Find the area of each sector, given its central angle, θ, and the radius of the circle. (7-7)

43. $\theta = \dfrac{3\pi}{5}$, $r = 13$

44. $\theta = \dfrac{\pi}{6}$, $r = 4$

45. $\theta = 45°$, $r = 8$

46. $\theta = 19°$, $r = 19$

Find the area of each circular segment, given its central angle, θ, and the radius of the circle. (7-7)

47. $\theta = \dfrac{4\pi}{7}$, $r = 17$

48. $\theta = \dfrac{2\pi}{5}$, $r = 51$

49. $\theta = 73°$, $r = 7$

50. $\theta = 41°$, $r = 0.5$

Chapter Test

Solve each equation for principal values of x.

1. $\sin x - \cos x = 0$
2. $\sin^2 x - \cos^2 x = 0$
3. $2 \cos^2 x + 3 \sin x - 3 = 0$
4. $\sin 3x = \sin x$
5. $\tan^2 x - \sqrt{3} \tan x = 0$
6. $\tan 2x \cot x - 3 = 0$

Solve each of the following right triangles. Angle C is the right angle.

7. $b = 42, A = 77°$
8. $c = 13, a = 12$

Solve each of the following. Round answers to the nearest hundredth.

9. At ground level, the measurement of the angle of elevation of a kite is 70°. It is held by a string 65 meters long. How far is the kite above the ground?

10. A ship sails due north from port for 90 kilometers, then 40 kilometers east, and then 70 kilometers north. How far is the ship from port?

Determine the number of possible solutions. If a solution exists, solve the triangle.

11. $a = 64, c = 90, C = 98°$
12. $a = 9, b = 20, A = 31°$
13. $a = 13, b = 7, c = 15$
14. $a = 20, c = 24, B = 47°$

Solve each of the following. Round answers to the nearest hundredth.

15. An isosceles triangle has a base of 22 centimeters and a vertex angle measuring 36°. Find its perimeter.

16. A ship at sea is 70 miles from one radio transmitter and 130 miles from another. The measurement of the angle between signals is 130°. How far apart are the transmitters?

Find the area of each triangle described below.

17. $A = 70°11', B = 43°55', b = 16.7$
18. $b = 11.5, c = 14, A = 20°$

A boat that travels at 16 knots in calm water is moving across a current of 3 knots in a river 250 m wide. The boat makes an angle of 35° with the current (heading into the current).

19. Find the resultant velocity of the boat.

20. How far upstream is the boat when it reaches the other shore?

Find the area of each sector given its central angle, θ, and the radius of the circle.

21. $\theta = \frac{\pi}{3}, r = 21$
22. $\theta = 27°, r = 5$

23-24. Find the area of the corresponding circular segment for problems **21-22**.

CHAPTER 8

Sequences and Series

The numbers in the following sequence are often found in nature.

$$1, 1, 2, 3, 5, 8, 13, 21, 34, \cdots$$

For example, the number of spirals on a sunflower is usually a number of the sequence. How might the next number of the sequence be determined?

8-1 Arithmetic Sequences and Series

A **sequence** is a set of numbers in a specific order. The **terms** of a sequence are the numbers in it. The first term of a sequence is denoted a_1 or a, the second term a_2, and so on up to the nth term, a_n.

A sequence is sometimes called a progression.

symbol	a_1	a_2	a_3	a_4	a_5	a_6
term	14.2	20.4	26.6	32.8	39.0	45.2

How might a_7 be determined?

The sequence above is an arithmetic **sequence.** The difference between successive terms is a constant, which is called the **common difference.**

> An arithmetic sequence is a sequence in which each term after the first, a, is equal to the sum of the preceding term and the common difference, d. The general form of the sequence, either finite or infinite, is represented as follows.
>
> $$a, a + d, a + 2d, \cdots$$

Arithmetic Sequence

$d = \dfrac{a}{2}$

Example

1 Find the next three terms of the arithmetic sequence $-2, 3, 8, \cdots$.

Find the common difference.
$3 - (-2) = 5 \qquad 8 - 3 = 5 \qquad d = 5$

Add 5 to the third term to get the fourth, and so on.
$8 + 5 = 13 \qquad 13 + 5 = 18 \qquad 18 + 5 = 23$

The next three terms are 13, 18, and 23.

The nth term of an arithmetic sequence can be found if the first term and the common difference are known. Consider the sequence having $a = 3$ and $d = 2$. Notice the pattern in the way the terms are formed.

first term	a	3
second term	$a + d$	$3 + 2 = 5$
third term	$a + 2d$	$3 + 2(2) = 7$
fourth term	$a + 3d$	$3 + 3(2) = 9$
fifth term	$a + 4d$	$3 + 4(2) = 11$
nth term	$a + (n - 1)d$	$3 + (n - 1)2 = a_n$

Since $a = a_1$, $a_n = a_1 + (n - 1)d$.

> The nth term of an arithmetic sequence with the first term a and the common difference d is given by the following formula.
>
> $$a_n = a + (n - 1)d$$

The nth Term of an Arithmetic Sequence

Notice that the preceding formula has four variables, a_n, a, n, and d. If any three of these are known, the fourth can be found.

Examples

2 **Find the 79th term of the sequence $-7, -4, -1, \cdots$.**

$$a = -7 \qquad d = -4 - (-7) = 3 \qquad n = 79$$
$$a_{79} = -7 + (79 - 1)3 \text{ or } 227$$

3 **Find the first term of the sequence for which $a_{15} = 38$ and $d = -3$.**

$$a_{15} = a + (15 - 1)d$$
$$38 = a + 14(-3)$$
$$38 = a - 42$$
$$a = 80$$

The terms between any two nonconsecutive terms of an arithmetic sequence are called **arithmetic means**. In the following sequence, 76 and 85 are the arithmetic means between 67 and 94.

$$49, 58, 67, 76, 85, 94$$

Example

4 **Form an arithmetic sequence that has seven arithmetic means between 7 and -2.**

$$a = 7 \qquad a_9 = -2$$
$$-2 = 7 + (9 - 1)d \qquad \textit{Why does } n = 9?$$
$$d = -\frac{9}{8}$$

One such sequence is $7, 5\frac{7}{8}, 4\frac{3}{4}, 3\frac{5}{8}, 2\frac{1}{2}, 1\frac{3}{8}, \frac{1}{4}, -\frac{7}{8}, -2.$ *This sequence can be extended in either direction.*

An **arithmetic series** is the indicated sum of the terms of an arithmetic sequence. The symbol S_n is used to represent the sum of n terms. To find an expression for S_n, a series can be written in two ways and simplified by adding term by term, as shown below. The second equation is obtained by reversing the order of the terms in the series.

$$S_n = \quad a \quad + (a + d) + (a + 2d) + \cdots + (a_n - 2d) + (a_n - d) + a_n$$
$$+ (S_n = \quad a_n \quad + (a_n - d) + (a_n - 2d) + \cdots + (a + 2d) + (a + d) + a)$$
$$\overline{2S_n = (a + a_n) + (a + a_n) + (a + a_n) + \cdots + (a + a_n) + (a + a_n) + (a + a_n)}$$
$$2S_n = n(a + a_n) \qquad \textit{There are n terms in the series.}$$

Therefore, $S_n = \dfrac{n(a + a_n)}{2}$.

The sum of the first n terms of an arithmetic series is given by the following formula.

$$S_n = \frac{n}{2}(a + a_n)$$

Sum of an Arithmetic Series

Example

5 Find the sum of the first 63 terms of the series $-19 - 13 - 7 - \cdots$.

$$a = -19 \qquad d = 6 \qquad n = 63$$
$$S_{63} = \frac{63}{2}[-19 + a_{63}]$$
$$= \frac{63}{2}[-19 + (-19 + 62(6))] \qquad \text{Since } a_n = a_1 + (n - 1)d,$$
$$\qquad\qquad\qquad\qquad\qquad\qquad\qquad a_{63} = -19 + 62(6).$$
$$= \frac{63}{2}(-19 - 19 + 372)$$
$$= 10{,}521$$

Exploratory Exercises

Find the next five terms of each arithmetic sequence.

1. $5, 9, 13, \cdots$
2. $17, 29, 41, \cdots$
3. $19, 25, 31, \cdots$
4. $0, 7, 14, \cdots$
5. $-9, -2, 5, \cdots$
6. $27, 23, 19, \cdots$
7. $1.5, 3, 4.5, \cdots$
8. $5, -1, -7, \cdots$
9. $a, a + 3, a + 6, \cdots$
10. $-n, 0, n, \cdots$
11. $x, 2x, 3x, \cdots$
12. $n + 5, n + 11, \cdots$
13. $b, -b, -3b, \cdots$
14. $5k, -k, \cdots$
15. $r + 15, r + 8, \cdots$

Written Exercises

$$a_n = a + (n - 1)d$$

Solve each of the following.

1. Find the 19th term of the sequence for which $a = 11$ and $d = -2$.
2. Find the 16th term of the sequence for which $a = 1.5$ and $d = 0.5$.
3. Find n for the sequence for which $a_n = 37$, $a = -13$ and $d = 5$.
4. Find n for the sequence for which $a_n = 633$, $a = 9$, and $d = 24$.
5. Find the first term of the sequence for which $d = -2$ and $a_7 = 3$.
6. Find the first term of the sequence for which $d = \frac{2}{3}$ and $a_8 = 15$.
7. Find d for the sequence for which $a = 4$ and $a_{11} = 64$.
8. Find d for the sequence for which $a = -6$ and $a_{29} = 50$.
9. Find the sixth term in the sequence $-2 + \sqrt{3}, -1, -\sqrt{3}, \cdots$.
10. Find the seventh term in the sequence $1 + i, 2 - i, 3 - 3i, \cdots$.
11. Find the 43rd term of the sequence $-19, -15, -11, \cdots$.
12. Find the 58th term of the sequence $10, 4, -2, \cdots$.
13. Form a sequence that has one arithmetic mean between 12 and 21.
14. Form a sequence that has one arithmetic mean between 36 and 48.
15. Form a sequence that has two arithmetic means between -4 and 5.
16. Form a sequence that has two arithmetic means between $\sqrt{2}$ and 10.

17. Form a sequence that has three arithmetic means between 1 and 4.

18. Form a sequence that has seven arithmetic means between 5 and 17.

19. Find S_{14} for the series for which $a = 3.2$ and $d = 1.5$.

20. Find S_{23} for the series for which $a = -3$ and $d = 6$.

21. Find the sum of the first 11 terms of the series $-3 - 1 + 1 + 3 + \cdots$.

22. Find the sum of the first 32 terms of the series $0.5 + 0.75 + 1 + \cdots$.

23. Find n for a sequence for which $a = -7$, $d = 1.5$, and $S_n = -14$.

24. Find n for a sequence for which $a = 5$, $d = 3$, and $S_n = 440$.

25. Cylindrical tiles of uniform size are stacked in the form of a triangle. There are 21 tiles on the bottom row. Find the total number of tiles in the stack.

26. A person has $650 in a bank and is closing out the account by writing one check a week against it. The first check is $20, the second is $25, and so on. Each check exceeds the previous one by $5. In how many weeks will the account be closed if there is no service charge?

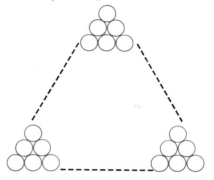

For the Scholar

Find the surface area of the regular tetrahedron *ABCD* whose vertices are vertices of the cube shown. The length of an edge of the cube is 4.

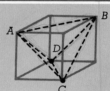

8-2 Geometric Sequences and Series

The following sequence is an example of a **geometric sequence.**   *Can you find the next term?*

$$1, 0.2, 0.04, 0.008, \cdots$$

The ratio of successive terms is a constant, called the **common ratio.**   *The common ratio is considered to be unequal to 1. (r ≠ 1)*

A geometric sequence is a sequence in which each term after the first, *a*, is the product of the preceding term and the common ratio, *r*. The general form of the sequence is $$a, ar, ar^2, \cdots.$$	*Geometric Sequence*

The common ratio of a geometric sequence can be found by dividing any term by the preceding term.

Example

1 Find the common ratio and the next two terms of the geometric sequence 13, 91, 637, $\cdots$.

$91 \div 13 = 7 \qquad 637 \div 91 = 7 \qquad r = 7$
$637 \cdot 7 = 4459 \qquad 4459 \cdot 7 = 31{,}213$

The common ratio is 7 and the next two terms are 4459 and 31,213.

The terms of a geometric sequence for which $a = 3$ and $r = 2$ can be represented as follows.

first term	a	$3 = 3$
second term	ar	$3 \cdot 2 = 6$
third term	ar^2	$3 \cdot 2^2 = 12$
fourth term	ar^3	$3 \cdot 2^3 = 24$
nth term	ar^{n-1}	$3 \cdot 2^{n-1} = a_n$

The nth term of a geometric sequence with the first term a and the common ratio r is given by the following formula.

$$a_n = ar^{n-1}$$

The nth Term of a Geometric Sequence

By definition, the nth term is also equal to $a_{n-1}r$, where a_{n-1} is the $(n-1)$th term. $a_n = a_{n-1}r$.

Example

2 Find the 17th term of the sequence $1, \frac{1}{2}, \frac{1}{4}, \cdots$.

$\frac{1}{2} \div 1 = \frac{1}{2} \qquad \frac{1}{4} \div \frac{1}{2} = \frac{1}{2} \qquad r = \frac{1}{2}$

$a_n = ar^{n-1}$

$a_{17} = 1\left(\frac{1}{2}\right)^{17-1}$

$a_{17} = \left(\frac{1}{2}\right)^{16}$

$a_{17} = \frac{1}{2^{16}} \text{ or } \frac{1}{65{,}536}$

The terms between any two nonconsecutive terms of a geometric sequence are called **geometric means**.

$a_n = a + (n-1)d$

Example

3 Form a sequence that has two geometric means between 125 and 216.

$$a = 125 \qquad a_4 = 216$$
$$a_4 = ar^3$$
$$216 = 125r^3$$

Assume that 125 is the first term of a geometric sequence.

$$r^3 = \frac{216}{125} \qquad r = \frac{6}{5}$$

$$125 \cdot \frac{6}{5} = 150 \qquad 150 \cdot \frac{6}{5} = 180$$

One such sequence is 125, 150, 180, 216.

The sum of the terms of a geometric sequence is called a **geometric series.** A formula for the sum of a series, S_n, can be found by writing an expression for $S_n - rS_n$, then solving for S_n.

$$S_n = a + ar + ar^2 + \cdots + ar^{n-2} + ar^{n-1}$$
$$- (rS_n = \qquad ar + ar^2 + \cdots + ar^{n-2} + ar^{n-1} + ar^n)$$
$$S_n - rS_n = a \qquad\qquad\qquad\qquad - ar^n$$

$$S_n(1 - r) = a - ar^n$$
$$S_n = \frac{a - ar^n}{1 - r} \qquad r \neq 1$$

The sum of the first *n* terms of a geometric series is given by the following formula.

$$S_n = \frac{a - ar^n}{1 - r} \qquad (r \neq 1)$$

Sum of a Geometric Series

Example

4 Find the sum of the first 9 terms of the series $\frac{2}{3} + \frac{1}{3} + \frac{1}{6} + \cdots$.

$$\frac{1}{3} \div \frac{2}{3} = \frac{1}{2} \qquad \frac{1}{6} \div \frac{1}{3} = \frac{1}{2} \qquad r = \frac{1}{2}$$

$$S_9 = \frac{\dfrac{2}{3} - \dfrac{2}{3}\left(\dfrac{1}{2}\right)^9}{1 - \dfrac{1}{2}}$$

$$S_9 = \frac{511}{384}$$

Thus, the sum of the first 9 terms is $\frac{511}{384}$.

Exploratory Exercises

Find the next four terms of each geometric sequence.

1. $4, 2, 1, \cdots$
2. $2, 3, \cdots$
3. $\frac{1}{3}, \frac{2}{3}, \cdots$
4. $\frac{1}{2}, \frac{1}{4}, \cdots$
5. $7, 3.5, \cdots$
6. $1.2, 3.6, \cdots$
7. $2, 5, \cdots$
8. $4, 5.6, \cdots$

Determine whether the given terms form a geometric sequence. Write *yes* or *no*.

9. $\sqrt{2}, 2, \sqrt{8}, \cdots$
10. $\sqrt[3]{3^2}, 3, 3\sqrt[3]{3}, \cdots$
11. $t^{-2}, t^{-1}, 1, \cdots$
12. $\frac{1}{2}, \frac{1}{6}, \frac{1}{10}, \cdots$
13. $\frac{\sqrt{3}}{2}, \frac{\sqrt{3}}{4}, \frac{\sqrt{3}}{8}, \cdots$
14. $\frac{3}{4}, \frac{9}{8}, \frac{27}{12}, \cdots$

Written Exercises

Answer each of the following.

1. The first term of a geometric sequence is -3 and the common ratio is $\frac{2}{3}$. Find the next four terms.

2. The first term of a geometric sequence is 8 and the common ratio is $\frac{3}{2}$. Find the next three terms.

3. The first term of a geometric sequence is $\frac{1}{2}$ and the common ratio is $\frac{2}{3}$. Find the ninth term of the sequence.

4. If $r = 2$ and $a_5 = 24$, find the first term of the geometric sequence.

5. Find the ninth term of the geometric sequence $\sqrt{2}, 2, 2\sqrt{2}, \cdots$.

6. Find the sixth term of the geometric sequence $10, 0.1, 0.001, \cdots$.

7. Find the first four terms of the geometric sequence for which $a_5 = 32\sqrt{2}$ and $r = -\sqrt{2}$.

8. Find the first three terms of the geometric sequence for which $a_4 = 2.5$ and $r = 2$.

9. Form a sequence that has one geometric mean between $\frac{1}{4}$ and 4.

10. Form a sequence that has two geometric means between 1 and 27.

11. Form a sequence that has two geometric means between -2 and 54.

12. Form a sequence that has three geometric means between 2 and $\frac{1}{8}$.

13. Find the sum of the first seven terms of the series $\frac{1}{2} + \frac{1}{4} + \frac{1}{8} + \cdots$.

14. Find the sum of the first six terms of the series $2 + 3 + 4.5 + \cdots$.

15. Find the sum of the first five terms of the series $\frac{5}{3} + 5 + 15 + \cdots$.

16. Find the sum of the first eight terms of the series $3 + 6 + 12 + \cdots$.

17. Find the sum of the first nine terms of the series $0.5 + 1 + 2 + \cdots$.

18. Find the sum of the first ten terms of the series $1 + \sqrt{2} + 2 + 2\sqrt{2} + \cdots$.

For the Scholar

Find $\alpha + \beta$ in radians if $\tan \alpha = M$ and $\tan \beta = N$ and $(3M + 3)(2N + 2) = 12$.

The ratio of the circumference to the diameter of a circle is a constant, π. The number π is **irrational.** That is, the value is an infinite, non-repeating decimal. It has been proven that π is also **transcendental.** That is, π cannot be the root of a polynomial equation with rational coefficients.

In the history of mathematics, many expressions have been found that represent the value of π.

In 1593 a French mathematician, François Viète, found an infinite irrational product for π.

$$\frac{\pi}{2} = \frac{1}{\sqrt{\frac{1}{2}} \cdot \sqrt{\frac{1}{2} + \frac{1}{2}\sqrt{\frac{1}{2}}} \cdot \sqrt{\frac{1}{2} + \frac{1}{2}\sqrt{\frac{1}{2} + \frac{1}{2}\sqrt{\frac{1}{2}}}} \cdots}$$

In 1655 an English mathematician, John Wallis, found an infinite rational product for π.

$$\frac{\pi}{2} = \frac{2}{1} \cdot \frac{2}{3} \cdot \frac{4}{3} \cdot \frac{4}{5} \cdot \frac{6}{5} \cdot \frac{6}{7} \cdot \frac{8}{7} \cdot \frac{8}{9} \cdots$$

One of the simplest expressions for π was discovered by Wilhelm von Leibniz, a German mathematician and philosopher. In 1674 Leibniz expressed π as the limit of an infinite series.

$$\frac{\pi}{4} = 1 - \frac{1}{3} + \frac{1}{5} - \frac{1}{7} + \frac{1}{9} - \frac{1}{11} + \frac{1}{13} \cdots$$

Each of the expressions given above can be used to approximate π to any given number of decimal places. However, an accurate approximation requires lengthy calculations. More recently, other expressions have been found that can be used to approximate π more quickly.

Computers have been used to calculate over a million decimal places for π. The first 100 decimal places for π are given below.

π = 3.1415926535 8979323846 2643383279 5028841971 6939937510
5820974944 5923078164 0628620899 8628034825 3421170679 $\cdots$

Exercises Use a calculator for each approximation.

1. Use the first 3 products in Viète's expression to approximate π.
2. Use the first 4 products in Viète's expression to approximate π.
3. Use the first 10 products in Wallis's expression to approximate π.
4. Use the first 20 products in Wallis's expression to approximate π.
5. Use the first 5 terms of Leibniz's series to approximate π.
6. Use the first 10 terms of Leibniz's series to approximate π.

8-3   Infinite Sequences

An infinite sequence has an unlimited number of terms. For example, the sequence $1, \frac{1}{2}, \frac{1}{3}, \frac{1}{4}, \frac{1}{5}, \cdots, \frac{1}{n}, \cdots$ is an infinite sequence whose nth term is $\frac{1}{n}$. Several terms of this sequence are graphed below.

Notice that the terms approach zero as n increases in value. Zero is called the limit of the terms of this sequence. This can be expressed as follows.

$$\lim_{n \to \infty} \frac{1}{n} = 0$$

∞ *is the symbol for infinity.*

This is read "the limit of 1 over n as n approaches infinity equals zero."

If a general expression for the nth term of a sequence is known, the limit can usually be estimated by substituting large values for n. Consider the following examples.

Examples

1   **Find the limit of the sequence $\frac{1}{2}, \frac{1}{4}, \frac{1}{8}, \frac{1}{16}, \cdots$.**

The nth term of this sequence is $\frac{1}{2^n}$.

The 50th term is $\frac{1}{2^{50}}$, or about 1×10^{-15}. The 100th term is $\frac{1}{2^{100}}$, or about 1×10^{-30}. Notice that the values approach zero.

Therefore, $\lim_{n \to \infty} \frac{1}{2^n} = 0$.   *Zero is the limit of any geometric sequence for which $|r| < 1$. Why?*

2   **Find the limit of the sequence $\frac{1-2}{5}, \frac{1-4}{10}, \frac{1-6}{15}, \cdots, \frac{1-2n}{5n}, \cdots$.**

The 50th term is $\frac{1-100}{250}$, or $\frac{-99}{250}$. The 100th term is $\frac{1-200}{500}$, or $\frac{-199}{500}$.

Therefore, $\lim_{n \to \infty} \frac{1-2n}{5n} = -\frac{2}{5}$.

The form of the expression for the nth term of a sequence can be altered to make the limit easier to find.

Examples

3 Evaluate $\lim\limits_{n \to \infty} \dfrac{3n + 1}{n}$.

Since $\dfrac{3n + 1}{n} = 3 + \dfrac{1}{n}$, $\lim\limits_{n \to \infty} \dfrac{3n + 1}{n} = \lim\limits_{n \to \infty} \left(3 + \dfrac{1}{n}\right)$.

But, $\lim\limits_{n \to \infty} \dfrac{1}{n} = 0$.   Therefore, $\lim\limits_{n \to \infty} \left(3 + \dfrac{1}{n}\right) = 3 + 0$ or 3.

The limit is 3.

4 Evaluate $\lim\limits_{n \to \infty} \dfrac{4n^2 + n}{2n^2 + 1}$.   *Divide the numerator and denominator by the highest power of n that occurs in* ~~*either the numerator or*~~ *the denominator.*

$\lim\limits_{n \to \infty} \dfrac{4n^2 + n}{2n^2 + 1} = \lim\limits_{n \to \infty} \dfrac{\dfrac{4n^2}{n^2} + \dfrac{n}{n^2}}{\dfrac{2n^2}{n^2} + \dfrac{1}{n^2}}$ or $\lim\limits_{n \to \infty} \dfrac{4 + \dfrac{1}{n}}{2 + \dfrac{1}{n^2}}$

$= \dfrac{4 + 0}{2 + 0}$ or 2

The limit is 2.

Limits do not exist for all sequences. If the terms of a sequence become arbitrarily large or approach two different values, the sequence has no limit.

Examples

5 Evaluate $\lim\limits_{n \to \infty} \dfrac{3n^2 + 1}{n}$.

$\lim\limits_{n \to \infty} \dfrac{3n^2 + 1}{n} = \lim\limits_{n \to \infty} \left(3n + \dfrac{1}{n}\right)$ or $3n$ $\lim\limits_{n \to \infty} \dfrac{1}{n} = 0$

Since $3n$ becomes infinitely large as n approaches infinity, the sequence has no limit.

6 Evaluate $\lim\limits_{n \to \infty} (-1)^n \left(\dfrac{5n + 3}{n}\right)$.

$\lim\limits_{n \to \infty} (-1)^n \left(\dfrac{5n + 3}{n}\right) = \lim\limits_{n \to \infty} (-1)^n \left(5 + \dfrac{3}{n}\right)$

$= 5(-1)^n$

When n is even, $(-1)^n = 1$. When n is odd, $(-1)^n = -1$.

Thus, the odd-numbered terms approach -5 and the even-numbered terms approach 5. Therefore, the sequence has no limit.

Exploratory Exercises

Write an expression for the nth term of each given sequence.

1. $1, 2, 4, 8, \cdots$
2. $1, 3, 9, 27, \cdots$
3. $5, 7, 9, 11, \cdots$
4. $4, 7, 10, 13, \cdots$
5. $3, 2, \dfrac{4}{3}, \dfrac{8}{9}, \cdots$
6. $5, 2, \dfrac{4}{5}, \dfrac{8}{25}, \cdots$
7. $\dfrac{4}{2}, \dfrac{9}{4}, \dfrac{14}{6}, \dfrac{19}{8}, \cdots$
8. $3, \dfrac{5}{2}, \dfrac{7}{3}, \dfrac{9}{4}, \cdots$

Written Exercises

Evaluate each limit, or state that the limit does not exist.

1. $\lim\limits_{n \to \infty} \dfrac{n+1}{n}$
2. $\lim\limits_{n \to \infty} \dfrac{n-1}{n}$
3. $\lim\limits_{n \to \infty} \dfrac{3n-5}{n}$
4. $\lim\limits_{n \to \infty} \dfrac{4n+2}{n}$
5. $\lim\limits_{n \to \infty} \dfrac{1}{3^n}$
6. $\lim\limits_{n \to \infty} \dfrac{2}{5^n}$
7. $\lim\limits_{n \to \infty} \dfrac{3n^2+4}{2n}$
8. $\lim\limits_{n \to \infty} \dfrac{n^3+6n}{3n^3}$
9. $\lim\limits_{n \to \infty} \dfrac{2n^2-6n}{5n^2}$
10. $\lim\limits_{n \to \infty} \dfrac{n^2-4}{2n}$
11. $\lim\limits_{n \to \infty} \dfrac{(n+2)(2n-1)}{n^2}$
12. $\lim\limits_{n \to \infty} \dfrac{n^2+n-3}{n^2}$
13. $\lim\limits_{n \to \infty} \dfrac{3n+1}{n-3}$
14. $\lim\limits_{n \to \infty} \dfrac{4n^2+5}{3n^2+2n}$
15. $\lim\limits_{n \to \infty} \dfrac{5n}{n^2+2}$
16. $\lim\limits_{n \to \infty} \dfrac{2n^3}{n^2+4n}$
17. $\lim\limits_{n \to \infty} \dfrac{2n+(-1)^n}{n^2}$
18. $\lim\limits_{n \to \infty} \dfrac{(-1)^n n^3}{3n^3+4n}$

19-26. For each sequence in problems **1-8** in the exploratory exercises, find the limit as $n \to \infty$ or state that the limit does not exist.

For the Scholar

Simplify the following expression if $x < 0$.
$$\left| 4x - \sqrt{(3x-1)^2} \right|$$

$x - 1 = 0 \quad -x + 1 = 0$
$y = 1 \qquad -x = -1$
$\qquad\qquad x = 1$

8-4 Sum of an Infinite Series

The indicated sum of the terms of an infinite sequence is an **infinite series.** Consider the geometric series $\dfrac{1}{2} + \dfrac{1}{4} + \dfrac{1}{8} + \dfrac{1}{16} \cdots$. Since this is a geometric series, the sum of the first n terms, S_n, can be found using the formula $\dfrac{a - ar^n}{1 - r}$.

1 Find the sum of the first 100 terms of the series $\frac{1}{2} + \frac{1}{4} + \frac{1}{8} + \cdots$.

$$r = \frac{1}{2}$$

$$S_{100} = \frac{\frac{1}{2} - \frac{1}{2}\left(\frac{1}{2}\right)^{100}}{1 - \frac{1}{2}} = \frac{\frac{1}{2} - \left(\frac{1}{2}\right)^{101}}{\frac{1}{2}} = \frac{\frac{1}{2}}{\frac{1}{2}} - \frac{\left(\frac{1}{2}\right)^{101}}{\frac{1}{2}} = 1 - \left(\frac{1}{2}\right)^{100}$$

Since $\left(\frac{1}{2}\right)^{100}$ is very small, S_{100} is nearly equal to 1.

In the preceding example, the sum of the first 100 terms was shown to be very close to 1. No matter how many terms are added, the sum will never exceed 1. Therefore, 1 is called the **sum of the infinite series.** The sum of an infinite series is defined as follows.

> If S_n is the sum of n terms of a series, and S is a number such that $S > S_n$ for all n, and $S - S_n$ approaches zero as n increases without limit, then the sum of the infinite series is S.
>
> $$\lim_{n \to \infty} S_n = S$$

Sum of an Infinite Series

If an infinite series has a limit, or sum, the nth term of the series, a_n, must approach zero as $n \to \infty$. Thus, if $\lim_{n \to \infty} a_n \neq 0$, the series has no limit. If $\lim_{n \to \infty} a_n = 0$, the series may or may not have a limit.

Since the terms of an arithmetic series do not approach zero as $n \to \infty$, no limit exists for an infinite arithmetic series. However, limits do exist for certain geometric series, such as the one in the preceding example.

Infinite Arithmetic series do not have limits.

The formula for the sum of the first n terms of a geometric sequence can be written as follows.

$$S_n = \frac{a(1 - r^n)}{1 - r} \qquad r \neq 1$$

Suppose $n \to \infty$, that is, the number of terms increases without limit. If $|r| > 1$, r^n increases without limit as $n \to \infty$. However, when $|r| < 1$, $r^n \to 0$ as $n \to \infty$. Then, S_n approaches the value $\frac{a}{1 - r}$, called the **sum of an infinite geometric series.**

The sum, S, of an infinite geometric series for which $|r| < 1$ is given by the following formula.
$$S = \frac{a}{1 - r}$$

Sum of an Infinite Geometric Series

Examples

2 **Find a and r for the following series. Then, find the sum of the series, if it exists.**
$$1 - \frac{1}{3} + \frac{1}{9} - \frac{1}{27} + \cdots$$

$a = 1 \qquad r = -\frac{1}{3}$

$$S = \frac{1}{1 - \left(-\frac{1}{3}\right)}$$

$$= \frac{1}{\frac{4}{3}} \text{ or } \frac{3}{4}$$

The sum of the series is $\frac{3}{4}$.

The Pascal program finds the sum of the first 20 terms of the series.

```
PROGRAM SERIES;
USES TRANCEND;
VAR  N : INTEGER;
     SUM, X : REAL;
BEGIN
  SUM : = 1;
  FOR N : = 2 TO 20 DO
    BEGIN
    X : = 1/EXP((N − 1) * LN(3));
    IF (N/2) = (N DIV 2)
      THEN SUM := SUM − X
      ELSE SUM := SUM + X;
    WRITELN ('FOR X = ', N, ' THE SUM OF THE SERIES IS ', SUM ,'.');
    END
END.
```

Other Pascal programming exercises can be found in the appendix

3 **Write the repeating decimal $0.454545 \cdots$ or $0.\overline{45}$ as a fraction.**

Write $0.\overline{45}$ as an infinite geometric series.
$$0.\overline{45} = \frac{45}{100} + \frac{45}{10,000} + \frac{45}{1,000,000} + \cdots \qquad r = \frac{1}{100}$$

$$S = \frac{\frac{45}{100}}{1 - \frac{1}{100}}$$

$$= \frac{45}{99} \text{ or } \frac{5}{11}$$

Thus, $0.454545 \cdots = \frac{5}{11}$.

4 **A rubber ball dropped 30 feet bounces 0.4 of the height from which it fell on each bounce. How far will it travel before coming to rest?**

The distance is given by the following series.
$$a, ar, ar, ar^2, \cdots .$$
Thus, the sum of the series can be found by S_n.
$$S_n = a + \frac{2ar}{1 - r}$$
Therefore, $S_n = 30 + \frac{2(30)(0.4)}{1 - (0.4)}$ or 70.

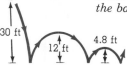

The distance travelled is the actual path of the ball.

30 ft 12 ft 4.8 ft

Exploratory Exercises

Write an expression for the sum of the first 10 terms of each series.

1. $4 + 1 + \frac{1}{4} + \frac{1}{16} + \cdots$

2. $4 + 3 + \frac{9}{4} + \cdots$

3. $20 + 2 + 0.2 + \cdots$

4. $300 + 30 + 3 + \cdots$

5. $25 + 5 + 1 + \cdots$

6. $36 + 6 + 1 + \cdots$

7-12. For problems **1-6,** guess the sum of the infinite series.

Written Exercises

Find the sum of each infinite geometric series, if it exists.

1. $\frac{2}{3} + \frac{1}{3} + \frac{1}{6} + \frac{1}{12} + \cdots$

2. $1 + \frac{2}{5} + \frac{4}{25} + \cdots$

3. $\sqrt{3} + 1 + \frac{\sqrt{3}}{3} + \cdots$

4. $2\sqrt{2} + 8 + 16\sqrt{2} + \cdots$

5. $\frac{1}{20} + \frac{1}{40} + \frac{1}{80} + \cdots$

6. $\frac{2}{7} + \frac{4}{7} + \frac{8}{7} + \cdots$

7. $0.2 + 0.02 + 0.002 + \cdots$

8. $\frac{1}{25} + \frac{1}{250} + \frac{1}{2500} + \cdots$

9. $2 + 3 + \frac{9}{2} + \cdots$

10. $10 + 5 + 2.5 + \cdots$

Write each repeating decimal as a fraction.

11. $0.555 \cdots$

12. $0.888 \cdots$

13. $0.2727 \cdots$

14. $0.370370370 \cdots$

15. $0.123123 \cdots$

16. $0.3636 \cdots$

17. $2.205205205 \cdots$

18. $3.242424 \cdots$

19. $0.3181818 \cdots$

20. $7.259259 \cdots$

A silicon ball is dropped from a height and bounces. Find the distance the ball travels before coming to rest for each of the following.

21. A ball dropped from a height of 12 feet rebounds 0.7 of the height from which it fell on each bounce.

22. A ball dropped from a height of 40 feet rebounds 0.75 of the height from which it fell on each bounce.

For the Scholar

The measures of the angles of a convex polygon form an arithmetic sequence. The least measurement in the sequence is 129°. The greatest measurement is 159°. Find the number of sides in this polygon.

8-5 Convergence and Divergence

Convergence and **divergence** are terms that relate to the existence of a limit, or sum, of an infinite series.

If an infinite series has a sum, or limit, the series is convergent. If an infinite series is not convergent, it is divergent.

Convergent and Divergent Series

1 Determine whether each series is convergent or divergent.

a. $\frac{2}{3} + \frac{1}{3} + \frac{1}{6} + \cdots$

b. $-5 - 3 - 1 + 1 + 3 + \cdots$

c. $1 + 4 + 16 + 64 + \cdots$

a. This is a geometric series, $r = \frac{1}{2}$. Since $|r| < 1$, the series has a limit. Therefore, the series is convergent.

b. This is an arithmetic series, $d = 2$. Since an arithmetic series has no limit, the series is divergent.

c. This is a geometric series, $r = 4$. Since $|r| > 1$, the series has no limit. Therefore, the series is divergent.

When a series is neither arithmetic nor geometric, it is more difficult to determine whether the series is convergent or divergent. Several different techniques can be used.

One test for convergence is the ratio test. This test can be used when all terms of a series are positive. The test depends upon the ratio of consecutive terms of a series, which must be expressed in general form.

Let a_n and a_{n+1} represent two consecutive terms of a series of positive terms. Suppose r is defined as follows. $$r = \lim_{n \to \infty} \frac{a_{n+1}}{a_n}$$ The series is convergent if $r < 1$ and divergent if $r > 1$. If $r = 1$, the test fails.

Ratio Test for Convergence

To use this test, all terms must be positive.

Example

2 Use the ratio test to determine whether the following series is convergent or divergent.

$$10 + \frac{10^2}{1 \cdot 2} + \frac{10^3}{1 \cdot 2 \cdot 3} + \cdots + \frac{10^n}{1 \cdot 2 \cdot 3 \cdots n} + \cdots$$

$$a_n = \frac{10^n}{1 \cdot 2 \cdot 3 \cdots n}, \ a_{n+1} = \frac{10^{n+1}}{1 \cdot 2 \cdot 3 \cdots (n+1)}$$

$$\lim_{n \to \infty} \frac{\dfrac{10^{n+1}}{1 \cdot 2 \cdot 3 \cdots (n+1)}}{\dfrac{10^n}{1 \cdot 2 \cdot 3 \cdots n}} = \lim_{n \to \infty} \frac{10}{n+1} = 0$$

Thus, the series is convergent.

When the ratio test fails, other methods can be used to determine if a series is convergent or divergent. Study the methods used in the next two examples.

Examples

3 **Determine whether the following series is convergent or divergent.**

$$1 + \frac{1}{2} + \frac{1}{3} + \frac{1}{4} + \frac{1}{5} + \cdots + \frac{1}{n} + \cdots$$

Suppose the terms are grouped as follows. Beginning after the second term, the number of terms in each successive group is doubled.

$$(1) + \left(\frac{1}{2}\right) + \left(\frac{1}{3} + \frac{1}{4}\right) + \left(\frac{1}{5} + \frac{1}{6} + \frac{1}{7} + \frac{1}{8}\right) + \left(\frac{1}{9} + \cdots + \frac{1}{16}\right) + \cdots.$$

Notice that the first enclosed expression is greater than $\frac{1}{2}$, and the second is equal to $\frac{1}{2}$.

Beginning with the third expression, each sum of enclosed terms is greater than $\frac{1}{2}$. There are an unlimited number of such expressions, so the series is unlimited. Therefore, the series is divergent.

4 **Determine whether the following series is convergent or divergent.**

$$1 + \frac{1}{2^p} + \frac{1}{3^p} + \frac{1}{4^p} + \frac{1}{5^p} + \frac{1}{6^p} + \frac{1}{7^p} + \frac{1}{8^p} + \cdots + \frac{1}{n^p} \cdots, \text{ where } (p > 1).$$

The terms can be grouped as shown.

$$1 + \left(\frac{1}{2^p} + \frac{1}{3^p}\right) + \left(\frac{1}{4^p} + \frac{1}{5^p} + \frac{1}{6^p} + \frac{1}{7^p}\right) + \left(\frac{1}{8^p} + \cdots + \frac{1}{15^p}\right) + \cdots$$

Notice that the first term of each group is greater than the successive terms. Therefore, the sum of a group of t terms is less than t times the first term.

$$\left(\frac{1}{2^p} + \frac{1}{3^p}\right) < \left(\frac{1}{2^p} + \frac{1}{2^p}\right) = \frac{2}{2^p} = \frac{1}{2^{p-1}} \text{ and}$$

$$\left(\frac{1}{4^p} + \frac{1}{5^p} + \frac{1}{6^p} + \frac{1}{7^p}\right) < \frac{1}{4^{p-1}} = \left(\frac{1}{2^{p-1}}\right)^2, \text{ and so on.}$$

Thus, another series can be formed that is greater than the given series.

$$\left[1 + \frac{1}{2^p} + \frac{1}{3^p} + \cdots\right] < \left[1 + \frac{1}{2^{p-1}} + \frac{1}{(2^{p-1})^2} + \frac{1}{(2^{p-1})^3} + \cdots\right]$$

The second series is geometric and the common ratio is $\frac{1}{2^{p-1}}$. Since $p > 1$, $\left|\frac{1}{2^{p-1}}\right| < 1$. Thus, the second series has a limit. Since the sum of the given series must be less than that limit, the given series must also be convergent.

As shown in example **4,** a series can be compared to a series known to be convergent or divergent. The following list of series can be used for reference.

1. **Convergent:** $a + ar + ar^2 + \cdots + ar^{n-1} + \cdots,\ |r| < 1$
2. **Divergent:** $a + ar + ar^2 + \cdots + ar^{n-1} + \cdots,\ |r| > 1$
3. **Divergent:** $a + (a + d) + (a + 2d) + (a + 3d) + \cdots$
4. **Divergent:** $1 + \dfrac{1}{2} + \dfrac{1}{3} + \dfrac{1}{4} + \dfrac{1}{5} + \cdots + \dfrac{1}{n} + \cdots$
5. **Convergent:** $1 + \dfrac{1}{2^p} + \dfrac{1}{3^p} + \cdots + \dfrac{1}{n^p} + \cdots,\ p > 1$

Summary of Series for Reference

If a series has all positive terms, the **comparison test** can be used to determine whether the series is convergent or divergent.

All terms must be positive.

A series of positive terms is convergent if each term of the series is equal to or less than the value of the corresponding term of some convergent series of positive terms. The series is divergent if each term is equal to or greater than the corresponding term of some divergent series of positive terms.

Comparison Test

Example

5 Use the comparison test to determine whether the following series is convergent or divergent.

$$\frac{1}{2} + \frac{2}{3} + \frac{3}{4} + \cdots + \frac{n}{n + 1} + \cdots$$

The general term of this series is $\dfrac{n}{n + 1}$. The general term of the divergent series $1 + \dfrac{1}{2} + \dfrac{1}{3} + \dfrac{1}{4} + \cdots$ is $\dfrac{1}{n}$. You can show that $\dfrac{n}{n + 1} > \dfrac{1}{n}$ for $n > 2$, as follows.

If $n > 2$, then $n - 1 > 1$.

$$n(n - 1) > 1 \text{ or } n^2 - n > 1$$
$$n^2 > n + 1$$
$$\frac{n^2}{n + 1} > 1$$
$$\frac{n}{n + 1} > \frac{1}{n}$$

Thus, the series is divergent.

The series is divergent for $n > 2$. Therefore, it is also divergent for $n > 0$. Why?

Example

6 Use the comparison test to determine whether the following series is convergent or divergent.

$$\frac{1}{2 + 1^2} + \frac{1}{2 + 2^2} + \frac{1}{2 + 3^2} + \cdots$$

The general term of this series is $\frac{1}{2 + n^2}$. The general term of the convergent series $1 + \frac{1}{2^2} + \frac{1}{3^2} + \frac{1}{4^2} + \cdots$ is $\frac{1}{n^2}$. Since $\frac{1}{2 + n^2} < \frac{1}{n^2}$ for any n, the series $\frac{1}{2 + 1^2} + \frac{1}{2 + 2^2} + \frac{1}{2 + 3^2} + \cdots$ is also convergent.

Exploratory Exercises

Determine whether each series is convergent or divergent.

1. $1 + 3 + 5 + \cdots$

2. $\frac{1}{4} + \frac{5}{16} + \frac{3}{8} + \frac{7}{16} + \cdots$

3. $\frac{1}{9} + \frac{1}{27} + \frac{1}{81} + \cdots + \frac{1}{3^{n+1}} + \cdots$

4. $1 + \frac{1}{5} + \frac{1}{25} + \cdots + \frac{1}{5^{n-1}} + \cdots$

5. $\frac{1}{2} + \frac{1}{8} + \frac{1}{32} + \cdots + \frac{1}{2^{2n-1}} + \cdots$

6. $\frac{8}{3} + \frac{32}{9} + \frac{128}{27} + \cdots + \frac{2^{2n+1}}{3^n} + \cdots$

Written Exercises

Use the ratio test to determine whether each series is convergent or divergent.

1. $\frac{1}{2} + \frac{2}{2^2} + \frac{3}{2^3} + \cdots + \frac{n}{2^n} + \cdots$

2. $1 + \frac{1}{2^2} + \frac{1}{3^3} + \frac{1}{4^4} + \cdots + \frac{1}{n^n} + \cdots$

3. $1 + \frac{1}{1 \cdot 2} + \frac{1}{1 \cdot 2 \cdot 3} + \frac{1}{1 \cdot 2 \cdot 3 \cdot 4} + \cdots$

4. $\frac{1}{1 \cdot 2} + \frac{1}{2 \cdot 2^2} + \frac{1}{3 \cdot 2^3} + \cdots + \frac{1}{n \cdot 2^n} + \cdots$

5. $1 + \frac{2}{1 \cdot 2 \cdot 3} + \frac{3}{1 \cdot 2 \cdot 3 \cdot 4 \cdot 5} + \cdots$

6. $1 + \frac{1}{1 \cdot 2 \cdot 3} + \frac{1}{1 \cdot 2 \cdot 3 \cdot 4 \cdot 5} + \cdots$

7. $\frac{1}{1 \cdot 2} + \frac{1}{3 \cdot 4} + \frac{1}{5 \cdot 6} + \cdots$

8. $\frac{1}{1 \cdot 2} + \frac{1}{1 \cdot 2 \cdot 3 \cdot 4} + \frac{1}{1 \cdot 2 \cdot 3 \cdot 4 \cdot 5 \cdot 6} + \cdots$

Determine whether each series is convergent or divergent.

9. $\frac{1}{1^2} + \frac{1}{3^2} + \frac{1}{5^2} + \cdots + \frac{1}{(2n - 1)^2} + \cdots$

10. $\frac{2}{1} + \frac{3}{2} + \frac{4}{3} + \cdots + \frac{n + 1}{n} + \cdots$

11. $\frac{1}{2 \cdot 1} + \frac{1}{2 \cdot 2} + \frac{1}{2 \cdot 3} + \cdots + \frac{1}{2n} + \cdots$

12. $\frac{3}{4} + \frac{3}{5} + \frac{3}{6} + \frac{3}{7} + \cdots + \frac{3}{n + 3} + \cdots$

For the Scholar

Find the sum of the first 102 terms of the sequence 5, 7, 2, $\cdots$ where the nth term $a_n = a_{n-1} - a_{n-2}$ for all $n > 2$.

The following sequence is called the **Fibonacci sequence.**

$$1, 1, 2, 3, 5, 8, 13, 21, 34, 55, \cdots$$

Each term after the second is the sum of the two previous terms. The numbers in the sequence are called **Fibonacci numbers.**

Fibonacci numbers are often found in nature. For example, the seeds of a sunflower are arranged in spirals, 34 in one direction and 55 in the other direction.

Leonardo Fibonacci first discovered this sequence while studying rabbits. He wanted to know how many pairs of rabbits would be produced in n months, starting with a single pair of newborn rabbits. He made the following assumptions.

1. Newborn rabbits become adults in one month.
2. Each pair of adult rabbits produces one pair each month.
3. No rabbits die.
4. There are an equal number of male and female rabbits.

Let F_n represent the number of pairs of rabbits at the end of n months. If to begin there is one pair of newborn rabbits, $F_0 = F_1 = 1$. This pair of rabbits would produce one pair at the end of the second month, so $F_2 = 1 + 1$, or 2. At the end of the third month, the first pair of rabbits would produce another pair. Thus, $F_3 = 2 + 1$, or 3.

The chart below shows the number of rabbits each month for several months. Do you see the pattern?

Month	Adult Pairs	Newborn Pairs	Total
F_0	0	1	1
F_1	1	0	1
F_2	1	1	2
F_3	2	1	3
F_4	3	2	5
F_5	5	3	8

In general, at the end of the nth month, all pairs of rabbits that were alive at the end of the $(n - 2)$nd month would produce one pair. Thus, there would be F_{n-1} adult pairs and F_{n-2} newborn pairs.

Exercises Solve each of the following.

1. Write the first 20 terms of the Fibonacci sequence.

2. Starting with a single pair of newborn rabbits, how many rabbits would there be at the end of 12 months?

3. Write the first 10 terms of the sequence for which $F_0 = 3$, $F_1 = 4$, and $F_n = F_{n-2} + F_{n-1}$.

4. Write the first 10 terms of the sequence for which $F_0 = 1$, $F_1 = 5$, and $F_n = F_{n-2} + F_{n-1}$.

8-6 Sigma Notation and the nth Term

In mathematics, the Greek letter sigma, Σ, is used to indicate a sum or series. For example, $\displaystyle\sum_{k=1}^{3} 4k$ represents a series of terms that are obtained by multiplying 4 times k, first for $k = 1$, then for $k = 2$, and finally for $k = 3$.

This is read "the summation from $k = 1$ to 4 of 4 times k."

$$\sum_{k=1}^{3} 4k = 4(1) + 4(2) + 4(3)$$
$$= 4 + 8 + 12$$
$$= 24$$

The variable used with the summation symbol, Σ, is called the **index of summation.** In the example above, the index of summation is k.

Any variable can be used for the index.

Examples

1 Write $\displaystyle\sum_{S=4}^{9} (2S - 1)$ in expanded form and find the sum.

$$\sum_{S=4}^{9} (2S - 1) = \underbrace{(2\cdot4 - 1)} + \underbrace{(2\cdot5 - 1)} + \underbrace{(2\cdot6 - 1)} + \underbrace{(2\cdot7 - 1)} + \underbrace{(2\cdot8 - 1)} + \underbrace{(2\cdot9 - 1)}$$
$$= \quad 7 \quad + \quad 9 \quad + \quad 11 \quad + \quad 13 \quad + \quad 15 \quad + \quad 17$$
$$= 72$$

2 Find the sum of the infinite geometric series $\displaystyle\sum_{r=0}^{\infty} 5(0.2)^r$, if it exists.

$$\sum_{r=0}^{\infty} 5(0.2)^r = 5 + 1 + 0.2 + 0.04 + \cdots \qquad a = 5 \text{ and } r = 0.2$$

The sum, S, equals $\dfrac{a}{1 - r}$, for $|r| < 1$. Therefore, $S = \dfrac{5}{1 - 0.2}$ or 6.25.

A series in expanded form can be written using sigma notation if a general formula can be written for the nth term of the series.

Example

3 Write the series $3 + 5 + 7 + \cdots + 53$ using sigma notation.

The nth term of the series is $2n + 1$.
Since $53 = 2(26) + 1$, the series has 26 terms.

Notice that $\displaystyle\sum_{n=2}^{27} (2n - 1)$ represents the same series. Why?

$$3 + 5 + 7 + \cdots + 53 = \sum_{n=1}^{26} (2n + 1)$$

Exploratory Exercises

Write each expression in expanded form and find the sum.

1. $\displaystyle\sum_{j=1}^{4} (j + 2)$

2. $\displaystyle\sum_{r=1}^{3} (r - 3)$

3. $\displaystyle\sum_{a=4}^{7} 2a$

4. $\displaystyle\sum_{k=5}^{8} 3k$

5. $\displaystyle\sum_{n=0}^{5} (2n - 1)$

6. $\displaystyle\sum_{n=0}^{6} (-n - 1)$

7. $\displaystyle\sum_{p=5}^{7} (3p + 2)$

8. $\displaystyle\sum_{b=4}^{8} (4 - 2b)$

Written Exercises

Write each expression in expanded form and find the sum.

1. $\displaystyle\sum_{p=3}^{7} (2p - 1)$

2. $\displaystyle\sum_{z=1}^{9} (10 - z)$

3. $\displaystyle\sum_{r=3}^{6} (r + 2)$

4. $\displaystyle\sum_{j=-3}^{3} (2j + 2)$

5. $\displaystyle\sum_{r=6}^{10} (r + 4)$

6. $\displaystyle\sum_{k=2}^{7} (5 - 2k)$

7. $\displaystyle\sum_{m=1}^{4} 4^m$

8. $\displaystyle\sum_{n=3}^{6} (3^n + 1)$

9. $\displaystyle\sum_{b=2}^{5} (b^2 + b)$

10. $\displaystyle\sum_{b=3}^{5} (2^b - b)$

11. $\displaystyle\sum_{a=0}^{4} (0.5 + 2^a)$

12. $\displaystyle\sum_{p=1}^{4} \left(3^{p-1} + \frac{1}{2}\right)$

13. $\displaystyle\sum_{k=1}^{\infty} 4\left(\frac{1}{2}\right)^k$

14. $\displaystyle\sum_{n=1}^{\infty} 3\left(\frac{1}{2}\right)^{n+1}$

15. $\displaystyle\sum_{b=0}^{\infty} 6\left(\frac{2}{3}\right)^b$

16. $\displaystyle\sum_{j=0}^{\infty} 5\left(\frac{3}{4}\right)^j$

17. $\displaystyle\sum_{r=2}^{\infty} \left(\frac{9}{10}\right)^r$

18. $\displaystyle\sum_{b=3}^{\infty} 2\left(\frac{3}{8}\right)^b$

Write each series using sigma notation.

19. $3 + 6 + 9 + 12$

20. $10 + 20 + 30 + 40 + 50$

21. $2 + 4 + 8 + \cdots + 64$

22. $3 + 6 + 12 + \cdots + 48$

23. $\frac{1}{2} + \frac{1}{3} + \frac{1}{4} + \cdots + \frac{1}{10}$

24. $\frac{1}{2} + \frac{1}{4} + \frac{1}{6} + \cdots + \frac{1}{14}$

25. $30 + 300 + 3000 + 30,000$

26. $16 + 8 + 4 + 2 + 1$

27. $11 + 9 + 7 + 5$

28. $19 + 18 + 16 + 12 + 4$

29. $-8 + 4 - 2 + 1$

30. $10 + 17 + 26 + 37$

31. $2 + 4 + 6 + \cdots$

32. $4 + 9 + 14 + \cdots$

33. $\frac{2}{5} + \frac{3}{5} + \frac{4}{5} + \cdots$

34. $\frac{2}{3} + \frac{2}{4} + \frac{2}{5} + \cdots$

35. $3 + 9 + 27 + \cdots$

36. $5 + 25 + 125 + \cdots$

Challenge Exercises

Determine whether the given equations are *true* or *false*.

37. $\displaystyle\sum_{k=0}^{5} a^k + \sum_{n=6}^{10} a^n = \sum_{b=0}^{10} a^b$

38. $\displaystyle\sum_{r=3}^{7} 3^r + \sum_{a=7}^{9} 3^a = \sum_{j=3}^{9} 3^j$

39. $\displaystyle\sum_{n=1}^{10} (5 + n) = \sum_{m=0}^{9} (4 + m)$

40. $\displaystyle\sum_{r=2}^{8} (2r - 3) = \sum_{s=3}^{9} (2s - 5)$

41. $2 \sum\limits_{k=3}^{7} k^2 = \sum\limits_{k=3}^{7} 2k^2$

42. $3 \sum\limits_{n=1}^{5} (n + 3) = \sum\limits_{n=1}^{15} (n + 3)$

43. $\sum\limits_{a=1}^{12} (-a) + \sum\limits_{a=1}^{12} (2a + 9) = \sum\limits_{a=1}^{12} (a + 9)$

44. $2 \sum\limits_{b=2}^{9} b^3 + \sum\limits_{b=1}^{8} \dfrac{1}{b} = \sum\limits_{b=1}^{8} \left[2(b + 1)^3 + \dfrac{1}{b} \right]$

For the Scholar

Equilateral triangle ABC and square $APQR$ have a common vertex A with points B and C between P and Q, and Q and R, respectively. If the area of square $APQR$ is 4 square meters, find the area of $\triangle QBC$.

8-7   The Binomial Theorem

The binomial expression $(x + y)$ can be raised to various powers. An important series is generated when $(x + y)^n$ is expanded. Consider the special cases where n is a small positive integer.

$(x + y)^0 = 1$

$(x + y)^1 = x + y$

$(x + y)^2 = x^2 + 2xy + y^2$

$(x + y)^3 = x^3 + 3x^2y + 3xy^2 + y^3$

$(x + y)^4 = x^4 + 4x^3y + 6x^2y^2 + 4xy^3 + y^4$

The following patterns are seen in the above expansions.

1. The expansion of $(x + y)^n$ has $n + 1$ terms.

2. The first term is x^n and the last term is y^n.

3. In successive terms the exponent of x decreases by 1 and the exponent of y increases by 1.

4. The degree of each term is n.

5. In any term, if the coefficient is multiplied by the exponent of x and the product is divided by the number of that term, the result is the coefficient of the following term.

6. The coefficients are symmetric. They increase at the beginning and decrease at the end of the expansion.

1 **Use the patterns to write $(x + y)^6$ in expanded form.**

First, write the series, omitting coefficients. The exponents of x decrease from 6 to 0 while the exponents of y increase from 0 to 6.

$$x^6 + x^5y + x^4y^2 + x^3y^3 + x^2y^4 + xy^5 + y^6 \qquad y^0 = 1, x^0 = 1$$

Then, find the coefficients of each term. The first coefficient is 1. Pattern **5** listed on the previous page can be used to find successive coefficients.

Second Coefficient   Third Coefficient   Fourth Coefficient

$$\frac{6 \cdot 1}{1} = 6 \qquad\qquad \frac{5 \cdot 6}{2} = 15 \qquad\qquad \frac{4 \cdot 15}{3} = 20$$

Since the coefficients are symmetric, the coefficients of the last three terms are 15, 6, and 1.

Thus, $(x + y)^6 = x^6 + 6x^5y + 15x^4y^2 + 20x^3y^3 + 15x^2y^4 + 6xy^5 + y^6$.

The general form of the expansion of $(x + y)^n$ is given by the **binomial theorem.**

If n is a positive integer, then the following is true. $$(x+y)^n = x^n + nx^{n-1}y^1 + \frac{n(n-1)}{1 \cdot 2}x^{n-2}y^2 + \frac{n(n-1)(n-2)}{1 \cdot 2 \cdot 3}x^{n-3}y^3 + \cdots + y^n$$	***The Binomial Theorem***

Example

2 **Use the binomial theorem to expand $(3a^2 - 2b)^4$.**

$$(3a^2 - 2b)^4 = (3a^2)^4 + 4(3a^2)^3(-2b) + \frac{4 \cdot 3(3a^2)^2(-2b)^2}{1 \cdot 2} + \frac{4 \cdot 3 \cdot 2(3a^2)(-2b)^3}{1 \cdot 2 \cdot 3} +$$

$$\frac{4 \cdot 3 \cdot 2(-2b)^4}{1 \cdot 2 \cdot 3 \cdot 4}$$

$$= 81a^8 - 216a^6b + 216a^4b^2 - 96a^2b^3 + 16b^4$$

When using the binomial theorem, often it is necessary to find the product of consecutive integers. The product $1 \cdot 2 \cdot 3 \cdot 4 \cdot 5$ is called **5 factorial** and symbolized **5!**

The expression $n!$ (n factorial) is defined as follows if n is an integer greater than zero. $$n! = n(n - 1)(n - 2) \cdots (1)$$	***Definition of n Factorial***

By definition, $0! = 1$.

Examples

3 **Evaluate 7!.**

$7! = 7 \cdot 6 \cdot 5 \cdot 4 \cdot 3 \cdot 2 \cdot 1 = 5040$

4 **Evaluate $\frac{6!}{4!}$.**

Notice that in the expansion of n!, you can stop writing the individual factors with any number d, and write as the final factor $(d - 1)!$.

$\frac{6!}{4!} = \frac{6 \cdot 5 \cdot 4!}{4!}$

$= 30$

An equivalent form of the binomial theorem uses both sigma notation and factorial notation. It is written as follows.

$$(x + y)^n = \sum_{r=0}^{n} \frac{n!}{r!(n - r)!} x^{n-r} y^r$$

Here n is a positive integer, and r is a positive integer or zero.

Example

5 **Find the fifth term of $(2a - 3b)^8$.**

$$(2a - 3b)^8 = \sum_{r=0}^{8} \frac{8!}{r!(8 - r)!} (2a)^{8-r}(-3b)^r$$

Since r increases from 0 to n, r is one less than the number of the term.

The fifth term, $\frac{8!}{4!(8 - 4)!}(2a)^{8-4}(-3b)^4$, is $\frac{8 \cdot 7 \cdot 6 \cdot 5}{4 \cdot 3 \cdot 2 \cdot 1}(2a)^4(-3b)^4$, or $90{,}720a^4b^4$.

The coefficients of the terms in the expansion of $(x + y)^n$ can be arranged in the form of a number pyramid called **Pascal's triangle.** In the first row, $n = 0$.

```
                1
              1   1
            1   2   1
          1   3   3   1
        1   4   6   4   1
      1   5  10  10   5   1
    1   6  15  20  15   6   1
```

The triangle may be extended indefinitely.

If two consecutive numbers in any row are added, the sum is a number in the following row. The three numbers form a triangle, as shown. In any row, the second number indicates the power to which the binomial is raised.

Example

6 Use Pascal's triangle to expand $(2a + b)^7$.

Extend the triangle to the row that has a seven as the second number.
1   7   21   35   35   21   7   1

Then, write the expansion and simplify each term.

$(2a + b)^7 = (2a)^7 + 7(2a)^6 b + 21(2a)^5 b^2 + 35(2a)^4 b^3 + 35(2a)^3 b^4 + 21(2a)^2 b^5 + 7(2a)b^6 + b^7$

$(2a + b)^7 = 128a^7 + 448a^6 b + 672a^5 b^2 + 560a^4 b^3 + 280a^3 b^4 + 84a^2 b^5 + 14ab^6 + b^7$

Exploratory Exercises

Write each product in factorial notation.

1. $1 \cdot 2 \cdot 3 \cdot 4 \cdot 5 \cdot 6$

2. $5 \cdot 4 \cdot 3 \cdot 2 \cdot 1$

3. $1 \cdot 3 \cdot 5 \cdot 7 \cdot 8 \cdot 6 \cdot 4 \cdot 2$

4. $9 \cdot 4 \cdot 5 \cdot 6 \cdot 8 \cdot 3 \cdot 2 \cdot 7 \cdot 1$

5. $8 \cdot 7 \cdot 6 \cdot 5$

6. $7 \cdot 6 \cdot 5 \cdot 4$

7. $17 \cdot 16 \cdot 15$

8. $12 \cdot 11 \cdot 10 \cdot 9 \cdot 8$

Written Exercises

Evaluate each expression.

1. $5!$

2. $9!$

3. $7!$

4. $4!$

5. $3(6!)$

6. $2(5!)$

7. $3!4!$

8. $5!3!$

9. $\dfrac{6!}{4!3!}$

10. $\dfrac{9!}{5!3!}$

11. $\dfrac{10!}{8!}$

12. $\dfrac{12!}{11!}$

Use the binomial theorem to expand each binomial.

13. $(n + 2)^7$

14. $(x + 3)^6$

15. $(2 + d)^4$

16. $(4 - b)^4$

17. $(2x - 3y)^3$

18. $(x - 2y)^4$

19. $(2x + y)^6$

20. $(3x - y)^5$

21. $(2x + \sqrt{3})^4$

22. $\left(\dfrac{x}{y} + v\right)^5$

23. $\left(3v - \dfrac{1}{2}w\right)^5$

24. $\left(\dfrac{1}{2}a + \dfrac{2}{3}b\right)^5$

Find the designated term of each binomial.

25. 4th term of $(a + b)^7$

26. 5th term of $(2x - y)^9$

27. 3rd term of $(x - 3y)^5$

28. 7th term of $\left(x - \dfrac{1}{2}y\right)^{10}$

29. 4th term of $(a - \sqrt{2})^8$

30. 6th term of $(3x - 2y)^{11}$

Use Pascal's triangle to expand each binomial.

31. $(x + y)^5$

32. $(a + b)^7$

33. $(r - s)^6$

34. $(x - 2)^7$

Simplify each of the following as far as possible. Assume x and y are positive integers, $x > y$, $x > 2$.

35. $\dfrac{x!}{(x - 2)!}$

36. $\dfrac{x!}{(x - y)!}$

37. $\dfrac{(x + 1)!}{(x - 1)!}$

38. $\dfrac{x!}{(x - y)!y!}$

39. $\dfrac{(x - y)!}{(x - y - 1)!}$

40. $\dfrac{x!(x - 3)!}{(x - 2)!(x - 1)!}$

41. Assume the binomial theorem is true for all rational values of n. Find an approximate value of $\sqrt{6}$ by applying the binomial theorem to the form of $\sqrt{6}$ derived below.

$$\sqrt{6} = \sqrt{4 + 2} = 2\sqrt{1 + \frac{2}{4}} = 2\left(1 + \frac{1}{2}\right)^{\frac{1}{2}}$$

For the Scholar

A cattle rancher estimated that one of his two best branding teams would take 15 hours to brand his herd of Angus; the other team would take 20 hours. However, from past experience, he knew that when working together their combined output decreased by 10 cattle per hour. In a hurry to get the cattle to the summer range, he decided to put both teams on the job of branding. It took them exactly 10 hours to brand the herd. How many Angus were in the herd headed for the summer range?

8-8 Mathematical Induction

A method of proof called **mathematical induction** can be used to prove a formula or conjecture.

Mathematical induction is a proof that depends on a process that is much like climbing a ladder. First, you must get on the first step. Then, you must show that you can always advance from one step to the next. Thus, if you can get onto the first step, you can certainly climb to the second. If you are on the second step, you can climb to the third. If you are on the third step, you can climb to the fourth; and so on, indefinitely, for all steps.

Consider the series $1 + 3 + 5 + 7 + \cdots$. What is the sum of the first two terms? The first three terms? The first four terms? Notice that the sum seems to be the square of the number of terms being added. Mathematical induction can be used to prove that the sum of n terms of this sequence is indeed n^2. The proof is based on two essential steps.

1. Verify that $S_n = n^2$ is the correct formula for the sum of n terms when $n = 1$, the first possible case.

Certainly the sum is 1 and $n^2 = 1$, so the formula, $S_n = n^2$, is valid for the first case. You are on the first step of the ladder.

When proving the second part, always replace n by either k or (k + 1).

2. Show that if S_n is valid for any special case (say $n = k$) then it is necessarily valid for the next case ($n = k + 1$). Notice that the kth term of the series $1 + 3 + 5 + \cdots$ is $2k - 1$. It must be proven that if $1 + 3 + 5 + \cdots + (2k - 1) = k^2$, then the formula is also valid for $n = k + 1$.

$$1 + 3 + 5 + \cdots + (2k - 1) + (2k + 1) = (k + 1)^2$$
The (k + 1)th term is 2k + 1.

This means that the sum S_k is given by $1 + 3 + 5 + \cdots + (2k - 1)$ $= k^2$, and you must prove that $S_{k+1} = (k + 1)^2$. From the assumption that $S_k = k^2$, you can write a formula for S_{k+1} by adding the next term $(2k + 1)$ to both sides.

$$S_{k+1} = 1 + 3 + 5 + \cdots + (2k - 1) + (2k + 1) = k^2 + (2k + 1)$$

When the formula $S_n = n^2$ is applied for $n = k + 1$, the result is $S_{k+1} = (k + 1)^2$. Is the result obtained by direct addition, $k^2 + (2k + 1)$, equal to $(k + 1)^2$? This can be verified as follows.

$$k^2 + (2k + 1) = k^2 + 2k + 1$$
$$= (k + 1)^2$$

$$(k + 1)^2 = k^2 + 2k + 1 \text{ or } k^2 + (2k + 1)$$

Since the formula for the sum for $n = k + 1$ gives the same result as the direct computation of the sum of the series, the formula is valid for $n = k + 1$ if it is valid for $n = k$. Thus, it can be concluded that since the formula is valid for $n = 1$, it is also valid for $n = 2$. Since it is valid for $n = 2$, it is valid for $n = 3$, and so on, indefinitely. Therefore, the following formula is valid for any positive integer n.

$$S_n = 1 + 3 + 5 + \cdots + (2n - 1) = n^2$$

In general, the following steps must be included in any proof by mathematical induction.

1. **First, verify that S_n is valid for the first possible case, usually $n = 1$.**

2. **Then, assume that S_n is valid for $n = k$ and prove that it is also valid for $n = k + 1$. Usually the result obtained by some direct method of arriving at the $(k + 1)$ case from the k case is compared with the result obtained by the formula to be verified.**

3. **Since S_n is valid for $n = 1$ (or other first case), it is valid for $n = 2$. Since it is valid for $n = 2$, it is valid for $n = 3$, and so on, indefinitely.**

Proof by Mathematical Induction

Example

1 **Prove that S_n for the sum of the first n positive integers is $\dfrac{n(n + 1)}{2}$.**

To prove S_n, $1 + 2 + 3 + \cdots + n = \dfrac{n(n + 1)}{2}$, first verify that S_n is valid for $n = 1$. Since $S_1 = 1$ and $\dfrac{1(1 + 1)}{2} = 1$, S_n is valid for $n = 1$.

Then, assume that S_n is valid for $n = k$, and show that it must also be valid for $n = k + 1$. Write S_k. Then, add the $(k + 1)$ term to both sides. Simplify the result.

$$S_k: 1 + 2 + 3 + \cdots + k = \frac{k(k + 1)}{2}$$

$$1 + 2 + 3 + \cdots + k + (k + 1) = \frac{k(k + 1)}{2} + (k + 1) \qquad \textit{Add (k + 1) to}$$
$$\textit{both sides of } S_k.$$
$$= \frac{k^2 + k}{2} + \frac{2k + 2}{2}$$
$$= \frac{k^2 + 3k + 2}{2}$$

Now, evaluate S_n for $n = k + 1$.

$$S_{k+1}: 1 + 2 + 3 + \cdots + k + (k + 1) = \frac{(k + 1)(k + 2)}{2} \text{ or } \frac{k^2 + 3k + 2}{2}$$

The formula gives the same result as adding the $(k + 1)$ term directly. Thus, if S_n is valid for $n = k$, it is also valid for $n = k + 1$.

Since S_n is valid for $n = 1$, it is also valid for $n = 2$. Since it is valid for $n = 2$, it is valid for $n = 3$, and so on, indefinitely.

Therefore, the formula $S_n = 1 + 2 + 3 + \cdots + n = \frac{n(n + 1)}{2}$ is valid for all positive integral values of n.

Mathematical induction can be used to prove that the expansion formula for the binomial $(x + y)^n$ is valid for all positive integral values of n.

Example

2 **Prove that the Binomial Theorem is valid for all positive integral values of n.**

$$S_n: (x + y)^n = x^n + nx^{n-1}y^1 + \frac{n(n - 1)}{2!}x^{n-2}y^2 + \frac{n(n - 1)(n - 2)}{3!}x^{n-3}y^3 + \cdots + y^n$$

First, show that S_n is valid for $n = 1$.

Since $(x + y)^1 = x^1 + 1x^0y^1$, or $x + y$, S_n is valid for $n = 1$.

Next, assume that S_n is valid for $n = k$ and prove that it is also valid for $n = k + 1$. By substituting k for n, S_k is obtained.

$$S_k: (x + y)^k = x^k + kx^{k-1}y + \frac{k(k - 1)}{2!}x^{k-2}y^2 + \cdots + y^k$$

To find the value for $n = k + 1$ directly, you can multiply each side of S_k by $(x + y)$.

$$S_{k+1}: (x + y)^k(x + y) = (x + y)\left(x^k + kx^{k-1}y + \frac{k(k - 1)}{2!}x^{k-2}y^2 + \cdots + y^k\right)$$

This can be simplified.

$$(x + y)^{k+1} = x\left(x^k + kx^{k-1}y + \frac{k(k-1)}{2!}x^{k-2}y^2 + \cdots + y^k\right) +$$
$$y\left(x^k + kx^{k-1}y + \frac{k(k-1)}{2!}x^{k-2}y^2 + \cdots + y^k\right) \quad \boxed{\begin{array}{c}\textit{Show that}\\ \frac{k(k-1)}{2!} + k = \frac{k(k+1)}{2!}\end{array}}$$
$$= x^{k+1} + kx^k y + \frac{k(k-1)}{2!}x^{k-1}y^2 + \cdots + xy^k +$$
$$x^k y + kx^{k-1}y^2 + \frac{k(k-1)}{2!}x^{k-2}y^3 + \cdots + y^{k+1}$$

The following result is obtained when like terms are combined.

$$(x + y)^{k+1} = x^{k+1} + (k + 1)x^k y + \frac{k(k+1)}{2!}x^{k-1}y^2 + \cdots + y^{k+1}$$

If $(k + 1)$ is substituted into S_n, the same result is obtained. Thus, if it is valid for $n = k$, it is also valid for $n = k + 1$.

Since S_n is valid for $n = 1$, it is also valid for $n = 2$. If it is valid for $n = 2$, it is valid for $n = 3$, and so on. Thus, S_n is valid for all positive integral values of n.

Written Exercises

Use mathematical induction to prove that the following formulas are valid for all positive integral values of n.

1. $2 + 4 + 6 + \cdots + 2n = n(n + 1)$

2. $1 + 4 + 7 + \cdots + (3n - 2) = \dfrac{n(3n - 1)}{2}$

3. $1 + 3 + 6 + \cdots + \dfrac{n(n + 1)}{2} = \dfrac{n(n + 1)(n + 2)}{6}$

4. $1^2 + 2^2 + 3^2 + \cdots + n^2 = \dfrac{n(n + 1)(2n + 1)}{6}$

5. $1^3 + 2^3 + 3^3 + \cdots + n^3 = \dfrac{n^2(n + 1)^2}{4}$

6. $1^2 + 3^2 + \cdots + (2n - 1)^2 = \dfrac{n(2n - 1)(2n + 1)}{3}$

7. $1 + 2 + 4 + 8 + \cdots + 2^{n-1} = 2^n - 1$
        8. $2 + 2^2 + 2^3 + \cdots + 2^n = 2^{n+1} - 2$

9. $\dfrac{1}{2} + \dfrac{1}{2^2} + \dfrac{1}{2^3} + \cdots + \dfrac{1}{2^n} = 1 - \dfrac{1}{2^n}$
        10. $-\dfrac{1}{2} - \dfrac{1}{4} - \dfrac{1}{8} - \cdots - \dfrac{1}{2^n} = \dfrac{1}{2^n} - 1$

Use the preceding formulas to solve each problem.

11. Find the sum of the series $2 + 4 + 6 + \cdots + 48$.

12. Find the sum of the series $1 + 4 + 7 + \cdots + 148$.

13. Find the sum of the even integers between 19 and 41.

14. Find the sum of the even integers between 29 and 51.

15. Find the sum of the first ten terms of the series $1^3 + 2^3 + \cdots$.

16. Find the sum of the first nine terms of the series $1^2 + 3^2 + 5^2 + \cdots$.

17. Find the sum of the first six terms of the series $2^5 + 2^6 + 2^7 + \cdots$.

18. Find the sum of the first seven terms of the series $3^2 + 4^2 + 5^2 + \cdots$.

Challenge Exercises

Use mathematical induction to prove that the following formulas are valid for all positive integral values of n.

19. $1^4 + 2^4 + \cdots + n^4 = \dfrac{6n^5 + 15n^4 + 10n^3 - n}{30}$

20. $1^5 + 2^5 + \cdots + n^5 = \dfrac{2n^6 + 6n^5 + 5n^4 - n^2}{12}$

21. $a + (a + d) + (a + 2d) + \cdots + (a + (n - 1)d) = \dfrac{n}{2}(2a + (n - 1)d)$

22. $\dfrac{1}{1 \cdot 2} + \dfrac{1}{2 \cdot 3} + \dfrac{1}{3 \cdot 4} + \cdots + \dfrac{1}{n(n + 1)} = \dfrac{n}{n + 1}$

For the Scholar

Find $P(6)$ if $P(x)$ is a function for which $P(1) = 1$, $P(2) = 2$, $P(3) = 3$, and $P(x + 1) = \dfrac{P(x - 2)P(x - 1) + 1}{P(x)}$ for $x \geq 3$.

Chapter Summary

1. An arithmetic sequence is a sequence in which each term after the first, a, is equal to the sum of the preceding term and the common difference, d. The general form of the sequence, either finite or infinite, is $a, a + d, a + 2d, \cdots$. (219)

2. The nth term of an arithmetic sequence with the first term a and the common difference d is given by $a_n = a + (n - 1)d$. (219)

3. The sum of the first n terms of an arithmetic series is given by the formula $S_n = \dfrac{n}{2}(a + a_n)$. (221)

4. A geometric sequence is a sequence in which each term after the first, a, is the product of the preceding term and the common ratio, r. The general form of the sequence is
$$a, ar, ar^2, ar^3, \cdots. \quad (222)$$

5. The nth term of a geometric sequence is given by the formula $a_n = ar^{n-1}$. (223)

6. The sum of the first n terms of a geometric series is given by the formula $S_n = \dfrac{a - ar^n}{1 - r}$ $(r \neq 1)$. (224)

7. Definition of the Sum of an Infinite Series: If S_n is the sum of n terms of a series, and S is a number such that S is greater than S_n for all n, and $S - S_n$ approaches zero as n increases without limit, then the sum of the infinite series is S. $\lim\limits_{n \to \infty} S_n = S$ (230)

8. The sum, S, of an infinite geometric series for which $|r| < 1$ is given by the formula $S = \dfrac{a}{1 - r}$.   (231)

9. Definition of Convergent and Divergent Series: If an infinite series has a sum, or limit, the series is convergent. If an infinite series is not convergent, it is divergent.   (232)

10. Ratio Test for Convergence: Let a_n and a_{n+1} represent two consecutive terms of a series of positive terms. Suppose r is defined as follows.

$$r = \lim_{n \to \infty} \frac{a_{n+1}}{a_n}$$

The series is convergent if $r < 1$ and divergent if $r > 1$. If $r = 1$, the test fails.   (233)

11. Comparison Test: A series of positive terms is convergent if each term of the series is equal to or less than the value of the corresponding term of some convergent series of positive terms. The series is divergent if each term is equal to or greater than the corresponding term of some divergent series of positive terms.   (235)

12. The Binomial Theorem: If n is a positive integer, then $(x + y)^n = x^n + nx^{n-1}y^1 + \dfrac{n(n - 1)}{1 \cdot 2}x^{n-2}y^2 + \dfrac{n(n - 1)(n - 2)}{1 \cdot 2 \cdot 3}x^{n-3}y^3 + \cdots + y^n$.   (241)

13. Definition of n Factorial: $n! = n(n - 1)(n - 2) \cdots (1)$ (241)

14. Proof by Mathematical Induction:
    1. Verify that S_n is valid for $n = 1$.
    2. Assume that S_n is valid for $n = k$ and prove that it is also valid for $n = k + 1$.
    3. Since S_n is valid for $n = 1$, it is valid for $n = 2$. Since it is valid for $n = 2$, it is valid for $n = 3$, and so on, indefinitely. (245)

Chapter Review

Solve each of the following.   (8-1)

1. Find the next six terms of the sequence 3, 4.3, 5.6, $\cdots$.

2. Find the 20th term of the arithmetic sequence for which $a = 7$ and $d = -4$.

3. Form a sequence that has three arithmetic means between 6 and -4.

4. Find the sum of the first 23 terms of the series $-3 + 3 + 9 + \cdots$.

Solve each of the following. (8-2)

5. Find the next four terms of the sequence 343, 49, 7, $\cdots$.

6. Find the 7th term of the geometric sequence for which $a = 2.2$ and $r = 2$.

7. Form a sequence that has three geometric means between 0.2 and 125.

8. Find the sum of the first 9 terms of the series $1.5 + 3 + 6 + \cdots$.

Evaluate each limit, or state that the limit does not exist. (8-3)

9. $\displaystyle\lim_{n\to\infty} \frac{2n}{5n + 1}$

10. $\displaystyle\lim_{n\to\infty} \frac{4n + 1}{n}$

11. $\displaystyle\lim_{n\to\infty} \frac{n^2 + 3}{2n}$

12. $\displaystyle\lim_{n\to\infty} \frac{3n^2 + n}{n^2 - n}$

13. $\displaystyle\lim_{n\to\infty} \frac{(-1)^n n^2}{5n^2}$

14. $\displaystyle\lim_{n\to\infty} \frac{4n^3 - 3n}{n^4 - 4n^3}$

Find the sum of each infinite geometric series, if it exists. (8-4)

15. $3 + 1 + \dfrac{1}{3} + \dfrac{1}{9} + \cdots$

16. $\dfrac{3}{16} + \dfrac{3}{8} + \dfrac{3}{4} + \cdots$

Write each repeating decimal as a fraction. (8-4)

17. $0.727272\ldots$

18. $3.\overline{45}$

Determine whether each series is convergent or divergent. (8-5)

19. $\dfrac{2}{3} + \dfrac{1}{9} + \dfrac{1}{54} + \dfrac{1}{324} + \cdots$

20. $1 + \dfrac{3}{2} + 2 + \dfrac{5}{2} + \cdots$

21. $\dfrac{1}{4} + 1 + 4 + 16 + \cdots$

22. $2 + 1 + \dfrac{2}{3} + \dfrac{1}{2} + \dfrac{2}{5} + \dfrac{1}{3} + \dfrac{2}{7} + \cdots$

Write each expression in expanded form and find the sum. (8-6)

23. $\displaystyle\sum_{a=5}^{11} (2a - 4)$

24. $\displaystyle\sum_{k=1}^{\infty} (0.4)^k$

Write each series using sigma notation. (8-6)

25. $-1 + 1 + 3 + 5 + \cdots$

26. $2 + 5 + 10 + 17 + \cdots + 82$

Evaluate each expression. (8-7)

27. $6!$

28. $8!$

29. $\dfrac{7!}{4!}$

30. $\dfrac{12!}{9!3!}$

Expand each binomial. (8-7)

31. $(a - x)^6$

32. $(2r + 3s)^4$

33. $(2x - y)^7$

Find the designated term of each binomial. (8-7, 8-8)

34. 5th term of $(x - 1)^{15}$

35. 10th term of $(x + 1)^{15}$

36. 8th term of $(x + 3y)^{10}$

37. Use mathematical induction to prove that the following formula is valid for all positive integral values of n.

$$1 \cdot 3 + 2 \cdot 4 + 3 \cdot 5 + \cdots + n(n + 2) = \frac{n(n + 1)(2n + 7)}{6}$$

Solve each of the following.

1. Find the next five terms of the sequence 3, 4.5, 6, · · · .

2. Find the next four terms of the sequence $\frac{1}{4}, \frac{1}{10}, \frac{1}{25}, \frac{2}{125}, \cdots$.

3. Form a sequence that has 3 arithmetic means between -4 and 8.

4. Form a sequence that has three geometric means between 16 and 1.

5. Find the 24th term of the sequence -6, -1, 4, · · · .

6. Find the 8th term of the sequence $\frac{1}{2}, \frac{3}{4}, \frac{9}{8}, \frac{27}{16}, \cdots$.

7. Find n for an arithmetic sequence for which $S_n = 345$, $a = 12$, and $d = 5$.

8. Find the sum of the first 10 terms of the geometric series $\frac{5}{2} + 5 + 10 + \cdots$.

Evaluate each limit, or state that the limit does not exist.

9. $\lim\limits_{n\to\infty} \dfrac{n^3 + 3}{3n^2 + 1}$

10. $\lim\limits_{n\to\infty} \dfrac{n^3 + 4}{2n^3 + 3n}$

Find the sum of each infinite geometric series, if it exists.

11. $\dfrac{1}{4} + \dfrac{1}{8} + \dfrac{1}{16} + \cdots$

12. $1 + \dfrac{4}{3} + \dfrac{16}{9} + \cdots$

Write each repeating decimal as a fraction.

13. 0.324324324 . . .

14. 1.91919 . . .

Determine whether each series is convergent or divergent.

15. $\dfrac{1}{6} + \dfrac{1}{3} + \dfrac{1}{2} + \dfrac{2}{3} + \cdots$

16. $1 + \dfrac{2}{3} + \dfrac{3}{3^2} + \dfrac{4}{3^3} + \cdots$

Write each expression in expanded form and find the sum.

17. $\sum\limits_{n=3}^{8} (n^2 + 1)$

18. $\sum\limits_{k=2}^{7} (2^k - k)$

Write each series using sigma notation.

19. $5 + 10 + 15 + \cdots + 95$

20. $7 + 9 + 11 + 13 + \cdots$

Evaluate each expression.

21. $\dfrac{9!}{4!5!}$

22. $\dfrac{11!}{8!2!}$

Find the designated term of each binomial.

23. 6th term of $(a + 2)^{10}$

24. 5th term of $(3x - y)^8$

25. Use mathematical induction to prove that the following formula is valid for all positive integral values of n.

$$2 \cdot 3 + 4 \cdot 5 + 6 \cdot 7 + \cdots + 2n(2n + 1) = \frac{n(n + 1)(4n + 5)}{3}$$

CHAPTER 9

Polar Coordinates and Complex Numbers

A nautilus has chambers spiraling inside its shell. The chambers are connected by a tube that absorbs gases from the chambers allowing the shell to act as a float. Spirals like the one in this shell can be drawn on a graph using polar coordinates.

9-1 Polar Coordinates

Points in a plane can be identified using **polar coordinates** of the form (r, θ). A fixed point O in the plane is called the **pole** or origin. The **polar axis** is a ray whose initial point is the pole. The distance from the pole to a point P with polar coordinates (r, θ) is $|r|$.

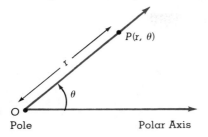

The polar axis is usually a horizontal line directed toward the right from the pole.

If r is positive, θ (theta) is the measure of any angle in standard position having $\overrightarrow{OP}$ as terminal side, as shown below. If r is negative, θ is the measure of any angle having the ray opposite $\overrightarrow{OP}$ as terminal side. The angle can be measured in degrees or radians.

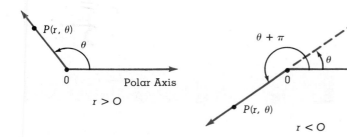

When θ is positive, the angle is measured counterclockwise from the polar axis.

Example

1 **Graph the point P that has polar coordinates $\left(2, \frac{\pi}{3}\right)$.**

$\frac{\pi}{3} = 60°$ *Remember*, $\frac{R}{\pi} = \frac{D}{180°}$.

Draw the terminal side of a 60° angle that has the polar axis as its initial side. Then, find the point on the ray that is 2 units from the pole.

Step 1

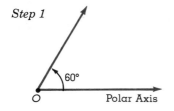

Step 2

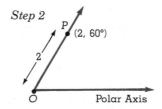

Either r or θ can be negative. If r is negative, the point (r, θ) is $|r|$ units from the pole on the ray opposite the terminal side of the angle with measure θ. If θ is negative, the angle is measured clockwise from the polar axis.

Example

2 **Graph the point P that has polar coordinates $(-2, -60°)$.**

First, draw the terminal side of the angle. Negative angles are measured clockwise.

Since r is negative, the point $(-2, -60°)$ is 2 units from the pole along the ray opposite the terminal side of the angle.

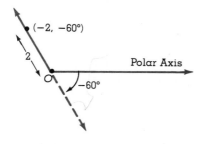

A point can be represented by more than one pair of polar coordinates. For example, the polar coordinates $(3, 150°)$, $(-3, -30°)$, $(-3, 330°)$, and $(3, -210°)$ all represent the same point, as shown below.

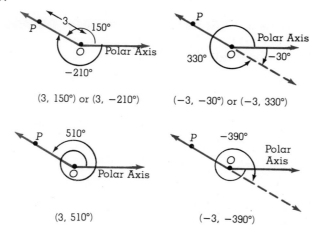

(3, 150°) or (3, −210°)   (−3, −30°) or (−3, 330°)

(3, 510°)   (−3, −390°)

In general, any point (r, θ) can also be represented by $(-r, \theta \pm 180°)$ or $(r, \theta + n \cdot 360°)$ where n is any integer.

3 **Name four different pairs of polar coordinates that represent point *R* shown below. Suppose −360° ≤ *θ* ≤ 360°.**

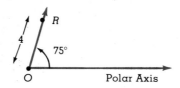

Point *R* can be represented by (4, 75°), (−4, −105°), (−4, 255°), or (4, −285°).

An equation that uses polar coordinates is called a **polar equation.** For example, *r* = 2*θ* is a polar equation. A **polar graph** represents the set of all points (*r*, *θ*) that satisfy a given equation.

Examples

4 **Graph *θ* = 30°.**

In this equation, *r* can have any value while *θ* must always be 30°. Thus, the graph is a line through the origin that forms an angle of 30° with the polar axis.

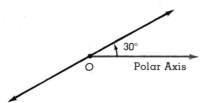

5 **Graph *r* = 3.**

In this equation *θ* can have any value while *r* must always equal 3. Thus, the graph is a circle with radius 3.

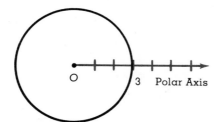

Compare this to the graph of r = −3.

Example

6 Name four different pairs of polar coordinates that represent point R. Suppose $-360° \leq \theta \leq 360°$.

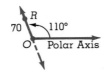

Four different pairs could be $(70, 110°)$, $(-70, -70°)$, $(70, -250°)$, and $(-70, 290)$.

Exploratory Exercises

Change each of the following radian measures to degrees. Round answers to the nearest degree.

1. π

2. $-\dfrac{\pi}{2}$

3. $-\dfrac{\pi}{4}$

4. $\dfrac{5\pi}{4}$

5. $-\dfrac{8}{3}\pi$

6. $\dfrac{5}{6}\pi$

7. $\dfrac{11\pi}{6}$

8. $\dfrac{7\pi}{4}$

9. 2

10. 5

11. -3

12. -4

Graph the point represented by the given polar coordinates. Then, name three other pairs of polar coordinates that represent the same point. Suppose $-360° \leq \theta \leq 360°$.

13. $\left(3, \dfrac{\pi}{6}\right)$

14. $\left(-2, -\dfrac{\pi}{3}\right)$

15. $(-2.4, 55°)$

16. $(3.1, -100°)$

Written Exercises

Graph the point that has the given polar coordinates.

1. $(1, 0)$

2. $\left(2, \dfrac{\pi}{2}\right)$

3. $\left(0.25, \dfrac{2\pi}{3}\right)$

4. $\left(0.5, -\dfrac{3\pi}{2}\right)$

5. $\left(-1, \dfrac{\pi}{3}\right)$

6. $\left(-3, \dfrac{5\pi}{6}\right)$

7. $\left(\dfrac{1}{2}, 1\right)$

8. $(4, -3)$

9. $(5, -45°)$

10. $(6, 225°)$

11. $(3, 315°)$

12. $(1, 330°)$

Name four different pairs of polar coordinates that represent point R. Suppose $-360° \leq \theta \leq 360°$.

13.

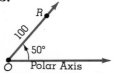

14.

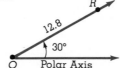

15.

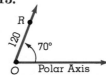

16.

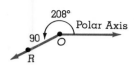

17.

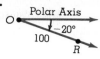

18.

Graph each polar equation.

19. $r = 2$

20. $r = -5$

21. $r = \sqrt{5}$

22. $r = 2^3$

23. $\theta = \dfrac{\pi}{2}$

24. $\theta = \dfrac{3\pi}{2}$

25. $\theta = -\dfrac{5\pi}{6}$

26. $\theta = -\pi$

27. $\theta = 135°$

28. $\theta = 80°$

29. $\theta = -95°$

30. $\theta = -220°$

For the Scholar

How many distinct integral divisors exist for 42^3 excluding 1 and 42^3?

9-2   Graphs of Polar Equations

Many interesting curves are obtained when polar equations are graphed. Study the following examples.

Example

1   **Graph $r = 8 \cos \theta$.**

First, make a table of values. Round values to the nearest tenth.

θ	$\cos \theta$	$8 \cos \theta$	(r, θ)
0°	1	8	(8, 0°)
30°	0.9	6.9	(6.9, 30°)
60°	0.5	4	(4, 60°)
90°	0	0	(0, 90°)
120°	−0.5	−4	(−4, 120°)
150°	−0.9	−6.9	(−6.9, 150°)
180°	−1	−8	(−8, 180°)
210°	−0.9	−6.9	(−6.9, 210°)
240°	−0.5	−4	(−4, 240°)
270°	0	0	(0, 270°)
300°	0.5	4	(4, 300°)
330°	0.9	6.9	(6.9, 330°)
360°	1	8	(8, 360°)

Then, graph each point and connect the points with a smooth curve.

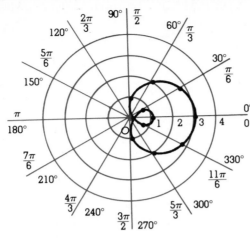

Notice that the entire graph is determined for $0° \le \theta \le 180°$.

The graph of any polar equation of the form $r = 2a \cos \theta$ forms a circle centered at $(a, 0)$, as in the previous example.

Example

2   **Graph $r = 1 + 2 \cos \theta$.**

θ	$1 + 2 \cos \theta$	(r, θ)
0°	3	(3, 0°)
30°	2.7	(2.7, 30°)
60°	2	(2, 60°)
90°	1	(1, 90°)
120°	0	(0, 120°)
150°	−0.7	(−0.7, 150°)
180°	−1	(−1, 180°)
210°	−0.7	(−0.7, 210°)
240°	0	(0, 240°)
270°	1	(1, 270°)
300°	2	(2, 300°)
330°	2.7	(2.7, 330°)
360°	3	(3, 360°)

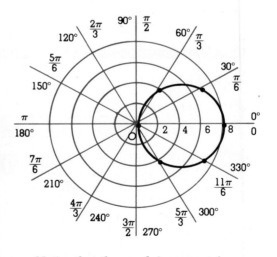

Notice that the graph is symmetric with respect to the polar axis.

The curve that represents the equation $r = 1 + 2 \cos \theta$ is called a **limaçon.** The limaçon is one of several **classical curves,** which can be formed by graphing polar equations. The equations, which distinguish other classical curves, are listed in the following chart.

Classical Curves				
Rose $r = a \cos n\theta$ $r = a \sin n\theta$ n is an integer greater than 0.	**Lemniscate** $r^2 = a^2 \cos 2\theta$ $r^2 = a^2 \sin 2\theta$	**Limaçon** $r = a + b \cos \theta$ $r = a + b \sin \theta$	**Cardioid** $r = a + a \cos \theta$ $r = a + a \sin \theta$	**Spiral of Archimedes** $r = a\theta$

Lemniscate

Cardioid

Spiral

To determine the exact shape of a classical curve you may need to graph many polar coordinates.

Roses

Limaçons

Example

3   **Graph $r = 2\theta$.**

θ	2θ	r
$\dfrac{\pi}{6}$	$\dfrac{\pi}{3}$	1.0
$\dfrac{\pi}{3}$	$\dfrac{2\pi}{3}$	2.1
$\dfrac{\pi}{2}$	π	3.1
$\dfrac{2\pi}{3}$	$\dfrac{4\pi}{3}$	4.2
$\dfrac{5\pi}{6}$	$\dfrac{5\pi}{3}$	5.2
π	2π	6.3
$\dfrac{7\pi}{6}$	$\dfrac{7\pi}{3}$	7.3
$\dfrac{4\pi}{3}$	$\dfrac{8\pi}{3}$	8.4
$\dfrac{3\pi}{2}$	3π	9.4
$\dfrac{5\pi}{3}$	$\dfrac{10\pi}{3}$	10.5
$\dfrac{11\pi}{6}$	$\dfrac{11\pi}{3}$	11.5
2π	4π	12.6

In this example, θ must be expressed in radians since r is a real number.

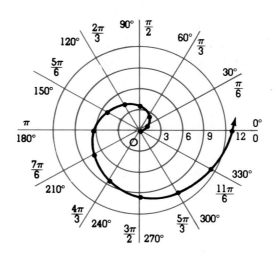

This curve is a spiral of Archimedes.

More than one polar equation can be graphed on the same polar coordinate system. However, the points where the graphs intersect do not always represent common solutions to the equations. This is possible since points in the polar coordinate system are not uniquely represented.

Example

4 Solve the following system of polar equations. Then, compare the common solutions to the points of intersection of the polar graphs.

$$r = 3 \cos 2\theta \qquad r = -3$$

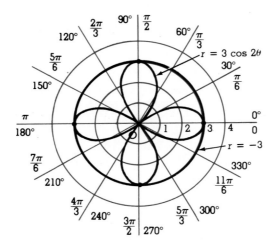

To solve the system of equations, eliminate r and solve for θ.

$3 \cos 2\theta = -3$
  $\cos 2\theta = -1$
    $2\theta = \arccos(-1)$
    $2\theta = 180°$ or $-180°$
    $\theta = 90°$ or $-90°$

Thus, the common solutions are $(-3, 90°)$ and $(-3, -90°)$.

The graphs of $r = 3 \cos 2\theta$ and $r = -3$ intersect at the points $(3, 0°)$, $(3, 90°)$, $(3, 180°)$, and $(3, 270°)$. The point $(3, 90°)$ is the same point as $(-3, -90°)$. The point $(3, 270°)$ is the same point as $(-3, 90°)$. Thus, two points of intersection, $(3, 0°)$ and $(3, 180°)$, do not represent common solutions to the polar equations.

Exploratory Exercises

Copy and complete the following chart for the equation $r = 3 + 3 \cos \theta$.

	θ	$\cos \theta$	$3 + 3 \cos \theta$	(r, θ)
1.	0°			
2.	30°			
3.	60°			
4.	90°			
5.	120°			
6.	150°			

	θ	$\cos \theta$	$3 + 3 \cos \theta$	(r, θ)
7.	180°			
8.	210°			
9.	240°			
10.	270°			
11.	300°			
12.	330°			

13. Graph the equation $r = 3 + 3 \cos \theta$.

Written Exercises

Graph each polar equation. In exercises 11 and 12, use radian measure for θ.

1. $r = 3 + 2 \sin \theta$ (limaçon)

2. $r = 10 \sin 3\theta$ (rose)

3. $r = 5 + 5 \sin \theta$ (cardioid)

4. $r^2 = 9 \cos 2\theta$ (lemniscate)

5. $r = 5 \cos 2\theta$ (rose)

6. $r = 1 + 4 \cos \theta$ (limaçon)

7. $r^2 = 8 \sin 2\theta$ (lemniscate)

8. $r = 2 + 2 \cos \theta$ (cardioid)

9. $r = 6 \cos 3\theta$ (rose)

10. $r = 4 \cos 4\theta$ (rose)

11. $r = \theta$ (spiral of Archimedes)

12. $r = \frac{1}{2}\theta$ (spiral of Archimedes)

Solve each system of equations. Then, graph each system of equations and determine the points of intersection.

13. $r = 6$
$r = 6 \cos \theta$

14. $r = \sin \theta$
$r = 1 - \sin \theta$

15. $r = 2 \sin \theta$
$r = 2\sqrt{3} \cos \theta$

16. $r = 2$
$r = 4 \cos \theta$

For the Scholar

Convex quadrilateral $PQRS$ has obtuse angles at vertex Q and vertex R. If $PQ = 9$, $RS = 5$, $QR = 5$, and $\sin Q = -\cos R = \frac{4}{5}$, find PS.

9-3 Polar and Rectangular Coordinates

Suppose a rectangular coordinate system is superimposed on a polar coordinate system. Let the two origins coincide and let the positive x-axis of the rectangular system coincide with the polar axis of the polar system.

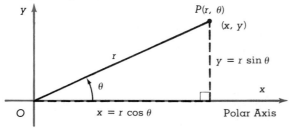

Let P be any point in the plane. In polar coordinates, P is identified by the ordered pair (r, θ). In rectangular coordinates, P is identified by the ordered pair (x, y). Suppose the polar coordinates of a point are known. The trigonometric functions can be used to find the rectangular coordinates of the point. Assume the unit distances are the same in each coordinate system.

The rectangular coordinates (x, y) of a point named by polar coordinates (r, θ) can be found by the following formulas. $$x = r \cos \theta \qquad y = r \sin \theta$$	*Conversion from Polar to Rectangular Coordinates*

Examples

1 **Find the rectangular coordinates of $A\left(-3, \dfrac{2\pi}{3}\right)$.** *Notice that θ is given in radians.*

$$x = r \cos \theta \qquad\qquad y = r \sin \theta$$
$$ = -3 \cos \frac{2\pi}{3} \qquad\qquad = -3 \sin \frac{2\pi}{3}$$
$$ = -3\left(-\frac{1}{2}\right) \text{ or } \frac{3}{2} \qquad = -3\left(\frac{\sqrt{3}}{2}\right) \text{ or } -\frac{3\sqrt{3}}{2}$$

The rectangular coordinates of A are $\left(\dfrac{3}{2}, \dfrac{-3\sqrt{3}}{2}\right)$ or $(1.5, -2.6)$.

2 **Find the rectangular coordinates of $B(4, -70°)$.**

$$x = r \cos \theta \qquad\qquad y = r \sin \theta$$
$$ = 4 \cos (-70°) \qquad\qquad = 4 \sin (-70°)$$
$$ = 4 \cos 70° \qquad\qquad = 4(-\sin 70°) \qquad \textit{Why?}$$
$$ = 4(0.3420) \qquad\qquad = 4(-0.9397)$$
$$ = 1.37 \qquad\qquad = -3.76 \qquad \textit{Round to the nearest hundredth.}$$

The rectangular coordinates of B are $(1.37, -3.76)$.

If a point is identified by rectangular coordinates (x, y), the polar coordinates (r, θ) of the point can be determined using the Pythagorean theorem and the Arctangent function. Recall that the Arctangent function determines angles in the first or fourth quadrants. Therefore, $\theta = \text{Arctan} \dfrac{y}{x}$ when (x, y) is in the first or fourth quadrant, as shown below. However, when (x, y) is in the second or third quadrant it is necessary to add π radians or $180°$ to $\text{Arctan} \dfrac{y}{x}$.

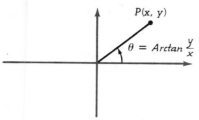

When $x > 0$, $\theta = \text{Arctan}\,\dfrac{y}{x}$.

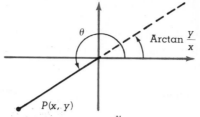

When $x < 0$, $\theta = \text{Arctan}\,\dfrac{y}{x} + \pi$.

When x is zero, $\theta = \pm\dfrac{\pi}{2}$. Why?

The polar coordinates (r, θ) of a point named by the rectangular coordinates (x, y) can be found by the following formulas.

$$r = \sqrt{x^2 + y^2} \qquad \theta = \text{Arctan}\,\frac{y}{x} \text{ when } x > 0$$

$$\theta = \text{Arctan}\,\frac{y}{x} + \pi \text{ when } x < 0$$

Conversion from Rectangular to Polar Coordinates

Example

3 Find the polar coordinates of the point named by the rectangular coordinates $(-2, 5)$.

$r = \sqrt{x^2 + y^2}$ $\qquad \theta = \text{Arctan}\,\dfrac{y}{x} + \pi$ *Here θ is expressed in radians.*

$\quad = \sqrt{(-2)^2 + 5^2} \qquad\quad = \text{Arctan}\,\dfrac{5}{-2} + \pi$

$\quad = \sqrt{29} \qquad\qquad\qquad\quad = -1.19 + 3.14$

$\quad = 5.39 \qquad\qquad\qquad\quad = 1.95$

The polar coordinates are $(5.39, 1.95)$.   *Other polar coordinates can name the same point.*

Equations in rectangular coordinates can be written as polar equations and vice versa. Study the following example.

Example

4 Change the equation $x^2 + y^2 = 9$ into a polar equation.

$$x^2 + y^2 = 9$$
$$(r \cos \theta)^2 + (r \sin \theta)^2 = 9$$
$$r^2(\cos^2 \theta + \sin^2 \theta) = 9$$
$$r^2 = 9 \text{ or } r = \pm 3.$$

The polar equation is $r = 3$ or $r = -3$.

Exploratory Exercises

Evaluate each of the following. Express θ in radians.

1. Arctan $\sqrt{3}$ 2. Arctan 1   3. Arctan 3.5   4. Arctan 1.4

Written Exercises

Find the polar coordinates of the point with the given rectangular coordinates.

1. $(3, 4)$ 2. $(5, 12)$ 3. $(1, 1)$ 4. $(-2, -2)$

5. $(2, -5)$ 6. $(-1, -3)$ 7. $(3, -2)$ 8. $(-\sqrt{3}, 3)$

Find the rectangular coordinates of the point with the given polar coordinates.

9. $\left(1, \dfrac{\pi}{6}\right)$ 10. $\left(1.5, \dfrac{\pi}{2}\right)$ 11. $\left(-3, -\dfrac{\pi}{2}\right)$ 12. $\left(-2, \dfrac{\pi}{4}\right)$

13. $(2, 0)$ 14. $(0.25, \pi)$ 15. $(2.5, 2)$ 16. $(3, 3.5)$

Change each equation into a polar equation.

17. $x = 5$ 18. $y = -2$ 19. $x = y$

20. $-y = x$ 21. $x^2 + y^2 = 25$ 22. $2x^2 + 2y^2 - 5y = 0$

Change each polar equation into an equation in rectangular coordinates.

23. $r = -7$ 24. $r = 6$ 25. $\theta = 45°$ 26. $\theta = \pi$

27. $r \sin \theta = 2$ 28. $r = 5 \csc \theta$ 29. $r = -2 \sec \theta$ 30. $r = \cos \theta + \sin \theta$

For the Scholar

With a constant throttle setting, a motorboat travels 36 miles downstream and then returns. The downstream trip takes 6 hours less than the return trip. When the speed of the motorboat is doubled, the trip downstream is one hour less than the return trip. What is the rate of the stream's current?

9-4 Simplifying Complex Numbers

A complex number can be written in the form $a + bi$ where a and b are real numbers and i is defined by $i^2 = -1$. Since $i^1 = i$ and $i^2 = -1$, higher powers of i can be found by multiplication. The first few powers of i are given below.

$$i^3 = -i \qquad i^5 = i \qquad i^7 = -i$$
$$i^4 = 1 \qquad i^6 = -1 \qquad i^8 = 1$$

Notice that the values i, -1, $-i$, and 1 repeat in cycles of four.

In general, i^n, where n is a whole number, can be simplified to 1, i, -1, or $-i$. Thus, to simplify i^n, divide n by 4 and express the result as 1, i, -1, or $-i$ if the remainder is 0, 1, 2, or 3, respectively. For example, i^{35} can be simplified as shown below.

Complex numbers are called imaginary numbers when $b \neq 0$ and pure imaginary numbers when $a = 0$ and $b \neq 0$.

$$i^{35} = i^{4(8)+3}$$
$$= (i^4)^8 \cdot i^3$$
$$= 1 \cdot -i \text{ or } -i$$

The real part of the complex number $a + bi$ is a, and the imaginary part is bi. Complex numbers can be added by adding their real parts and adding their imaginary parts.

Examples

1 **Find $(4 + 5i) + (3 + 2i)$.**

$$(4 + 5i) + (3 + 2i) = (4 + 3) + (5 + 2)i$$
$$= 7 + 7i$$

2 **Find $(8 + 3i) - (1 - 6i)$.**

$$(8 + 3i) - (1 - 6i) = (8 - 1) + (3 - (-6))i \qquad \textit{Subtract the real parts and the}$$
$$= 7 + 9i \qquad\qquad\qquad \textit{imaginary parts.}$$

The product of two or more complex numbers can also be found.

Example

3 **Find $(3 + 7i)(2 - 4i)$.**

$$(3 + 7i)(2 - 4i) = 6 - 12i + 14i - 28i^2$$
$$= 6 + 2i + 28$$
$$= 34 + 2i$$

Multiply the complex numbers as binomials using the FOIL method (First, Outer, Inner, Last).

Complex numbers of the form $a + bi$ and $a - bi$ are called **conjugates** of each other. The product of complex conjugates is always a real number. Thus, when a fraction has a complex number as the denominator, conjugates can be used to **rationalize the denominator.** This will produce a real number in the denominator.

Example

4 **Simplify $\dfrac{1 + i}{3 + 2i}$.**

$$\frac{1 + i}{3 + 2i} = \frac{(1 + i)(3 - 2i)}{(3 + 2i)(3 - 2i)}$$

$$= \frac{3 - 2i + 3i - 2i^2}{9 - 6i + 6i - 4i^2}$$

$$\frac{5 + i}{13} \text{ or } \frac{5}{13} + \frac{1}{13}i$$

The following chart summarizes the basic operations with complex numbers.

For any complex numbers $a + bi$ and $c + di$,
$(a + bi) + (c + di) = (a + c) + (b + d)i$
$(a + bi) - (c + di) = (a - c) + (b - d)i$
$(a + bi)(c + di) = (ac - bd) + (ad + bc)i$
$\dfrac{(a + bi)}{(c + di)} = \dfrac{(ac + bd) + (bc - ad)i}{c^2 + d^2}$

Exploratory Exercises

Simplify.

1. i^{15}

2. i^{46}

3. $(2 + 5i) + (-8 - i)$

4. $(3 - 7i) + (2 + 5i)$

5. $(9 + 6i) - (i + 5)$

6. $(-12 + 3i) - (7 - 5i)$

7. $(-6 - 2i) - (-8 - 3i)$

8. $(2 + 3i)(4 - i)$

9. $(1 + 3i)(2 + 4i)$

10. $(2 + i)^2$

11. $(i - 5)^2$

12. $(3i + 5)^2$

Find the product of each complex number and its conjugate.

13. $3 - 2i$

14. $12 + i$

15. $7i$

16. $-5i$

Written Exercises

Simplify.

1. i^{24}

2. i^{61}

3. $i^2(2 + 7i)$

4. $4(1 + i^3)$

5. $(1 - 4i) + (-3 + 3i)$

6. $(9 + 7i) - (-1 - 2i)$

7. $(2 + 3i\sqrt{2}) - i\sqrt{2}$

8. $4i + (6 + 3i)$

9. $(3i - 2) - (-3 + 2i)$

10. $(6 - 3i) - (7 + 3i)$

11. $(\sqrt{2} + i)(4\sqrt{2} + i)$

12. $(4 - 3i)(-4 + 3i)$

13. $(\sqrt{2} + i)(\sqrt{2} - i)$

14. $2(4 - 3i)(7 - 2i)$

15. $(2 + i)(3 - 4i)(1 + 2i)$

16. $(2 + i\sqrt{3})^2$

17. $(3 - 2i)^3$

18. $(1 - i)^4$

19. $\dfrac{3 + 7i}{2i}$

20. $\dfrac{4 - 3i}{2 + i}$

21. $\dfrac{-15 + i}{4 + 2i}$

22. $\dfrac{4}{\sqrt{3} + 2i}$

23. $\dfrac{2 + i\sqrt{3}}{2 - i\sqrt{3}}$

24. $\dfrac{2 - i\sqrt{7}}{2 + i\sqrt{7}}$

25. $\dfrac{7}{\sqrt{2} - 3i}$

26. $\dfrac{(1 - i)^2}{(1 + i)^2}$

27. $\dfrac{(4 + 3i)^2}{(3 - i)^2}$

For the Scholar

In $\triangle ABC$, $\overline{DF} \parallel \overline{AB}$, $\overline{AE}$ bisects $\angle CAB$, $\overline{BE}$ bisects $\angle ABC$, $AB = 20$, $BC = 18$, and $AC = 16$. Find the perimeter of $\triangle DCF$.

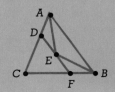

Polar transformations are sometimes used to simulate growth patterns or to alter the shape of an object. The following transformation formulas were used to alter the shape of a butterfly.

$$\theta' = \theta \qquad\qquad \theta'' = \theta$$
$$r' = r(1 + \tfrac{1}{3}(1 + \sin\,\theta)) \qquad r'' = r(1 + \tfrac{1}{2}(1 + \sin\,\theta))$$

The original outline is shown as a solid black line. The (r', θ') transformation is shown as a colored line. The (r'', θ'') transformation is shown as a broken line.

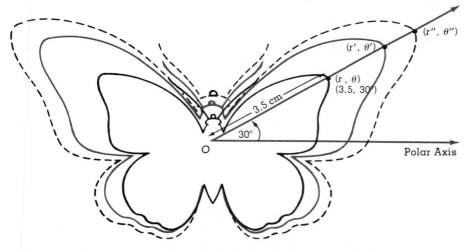

Consider the (r', θ') transformation. The image of any point (r, θ) on the black line is (r', θ') on the colored line. For example, the image, (r', θ'), of $(3.5, 30°)$ was determined as follows.

$$\theta' = \theta \qquad r' = r(1 + \tfrac{1}{3}(1 + \sin\,\theta))$$
$$\theta' = 30° \qquad r' = 3.5(1 + \tfrac{1}{3}(1 + \sin\,30°))$$
$$= 5.25$$

The image of $(3.5, 30°)$ is $(5.25, 30°)$. The coordinates of the images of other points were determined in a similar manner.

Exercises   Use the formulas $\theta' = \theta + 45°$ and $r' = 2r$ to determine the image of each point whose polar coordinates (r, θ) are given.

1. $(3, 20°)$ **2.** $(1.3, 50°)$ **3.** $(7, 110°)$ **4.** $(5.6, 300°)$

9-5 Polar Form of Complex Numbers

Every complex number can be written in the form $x + yi$ where x is the real part and yi is the imaginary part. This form is called the **rectangular form** of a complex number. Sometimes the rectangular form is written as the ordered pair (x, y).

A complex number can be represented graphically. In the complex plane, the horizontal axis is the real axis and the vertical axis is the imaginary axis. Point P on the graph corresponds to the complex number $x + yi$.

The angle θ is called the **amplitude** and r is called the **modulus.** Two complex numbers are equal if and only if their moduli are equal and their amplitudes differ by integral multiples of 2π radians. Thus, θ can be replaced by $\theta + 2n\pi$, for any integer n.

In the figure, notice that $y = r \sin \theta$ and $x = r \cos \theta$. These values can be substituted for x and y in the rectangular form to obtain the **polar,** or **trigonometric form** of a complex number.

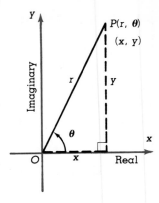

$x + yi = r(\cos \theta + i \sin \theta)$	**Polar Form of** $x + yi$

$r(\cos \theta + i \sin \theta)$ *is often written as* r *cis* θ

Values for r and θ can be obtained by the following.

$$r = \sqrt{x^2 + y^2} \qquad \theta = \text{Arctan } \frac{y}{x} \quad \text{when } x > 0$$

$$\theta = \text{Arctan } \frac{y}{x} + \pi \quad \text{when } x < 0$$

Thus, if x and y are known, r and θ can be found and the complex number $(x + yi)$ can be written in polar form $r(\cos \theta + i \sin \theta)$, and conversely. The amplitude θ is usually expressed in radian measure and the angle is placed in standard position.

Example

1 Express $-1 + i$ in polar form.

First, graph the complex number on the complex plane.

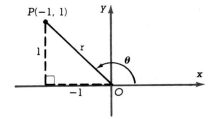

Notice that $x = -1$ *and* $y = 1$.

Next, find values for r and θ.

$r = \sqrt{x^2 + y^2}$ $\theta = \text{Arctan } \dfrac{y}{x} + \pi$ *Notice $x < 0$.*

$\quad = \sqrt{(-1)^2 + 1^2}$ $\quad = \text{Arctan } \dfrac{1}{-1} + \pi$

$\quad = \sqrt{2}$ $\quad = -\dfrac{\pi}{4} + \pi$ or $\dfrac{3\pi}{4}$

Therefore, $-1 + i = \sqrt{2}\left(\cos \dfrac{3\pi}{4} + i \sin \dfrac{3\pi}{4}\right)$.

2 **Express $4\left(\cos \dfrac{7\pi}{6} + i \sin \dfrac{7\pi}{6}\right)$ in rectangular form.**

First, graph the complex number
on the complex plane.

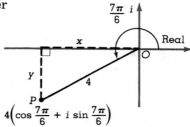

Then, find values for x and y.

$x = r \cos \theta$ $y = r \sin \theta$

$\quad = 4 \cos \dfrac{7\pi}{6}$ $\quad = 4 \sin \dfrac{7\pi}{6}$ *The reference angle for $\dfrac{7\pi}{6}$ is $\dfrac{\pi}{6}$.*

$\quad = -4 \cos \dfrac{\pi}{6}$ $\quad = -4 \sin \dfrac{\pi}{6}$

$\quad = -4\left(\dfrac{\sqrt{3}}{2}\right)$ or $-2\sqrt{3}$ $\quad = -4\left(\dfrac{1}{2}\right)$ or -2

Therefore, $4\left(\cos \dfrac{7\pi}{6} + i \sin \dfrac{7\pi}{6}\right) = -2\sqrt{3} - 2i$.

Exploratory Exercises

Graph each complex number. Then, express the number in polar form.

1. $1 - i$ **2.** $-2 + 2i$ **3.** $7i$ **4.** $4i$

5. -5 **6.** -3 **7.** $3 - i\sqrt{3}$ **8.** $2 - 2i\sqrt{3}$

Graph each complex number. Then, express the number in rectangular form.

9. $2(\cos 0 + i \sin 0)$ **10.** $3(\cos \pi + i \sin \pi)$ **11.** $\cos \dfrac{\pi}{2} + i \sin \dfrac{\pi}{2}$

12. $\cos \dfrac{3\pi}{2} + i \sin \dfrac{3\pi}{2}$ **13.** $\dfrac{1}{2}\left(\cos \dfrac{5\pi}{6} + i \sin \dfrac{5\pi}{6}\right)$ **14.** $2\left(\cos\left(-\dfrac{3\pi}{4}\right) + i \sin\left(-\dfrac{3\pi}{4}\right)\right)$

Written Exercises

Express each complex number in polar form.

1. $1 + i$ 2. $-3 - 3i$ 3. $3i$ 4. $6i$

5. $-5 - i$ 6. $3 + 4i$ 7. $-2 + 5i$ 8. $2\sqrt{3} - 3i$

9. $1 + \sqrt{3}i$ 10. $2 - 2i$ 11. $0 - i$ 12. $-1 + 0i$

Express each complex number in rectangular form.

13. $\sqrt{2}\left(\cos \dfrac{5\pi}{4} + i \sin \dfrac{5\pi}{4}\right)$ 14. $6\left(\cos \dfrac{3\pi}{2} + i \sin \dfrac{3\pi}{2}\right)$ 15. $12\left(\cos \dfrac{5\pi}{3} + i \sin \dfrac{5\pi}{3}\right)$

16. $\sqrt{3}\left(\cos \dfrac{\pi}{3} + i \sin \dfrac{\pi}{3}\right)$ 17. $2(\cos 3 + i \sin 3)$ 18. $3(\cos 2 + i \sin 2)$

19. $8\left(\cos \dfrac{\pi}{6} + i \sin \dfrac{\pi}{6}\right)$ 20. $\sqrt{2}\left(\cos \dfrac{-\pi}{2} + i \sin \dfrac{\pi}{2}\right)$ 21. $5\left(\cos \dfrac{5\pi}{6} + i \sin \dfrac{5\pi}{6}\right)$

For the Scholar

The function f is defined by $f(a) = \dfrac{ka}{4a + 2}$ where k is a constant and $a \neq -\dfrac{1}{2}$. What is the value of k when $f(f(a)) = a$ for all real numbers except $-\dfrac{1}{2}$?

9-6 Products and Quotients of Complex Numbers in Polar Form

When two complex numbers are written in polar form, their product and quotient can be easily computed.

Let $r_1(\cos \theta_1 + i \sin \theta_1)$ and $r_2(\cos \theta_2 + i \sin \theta_2)$ represent two complex numbers. A simple formula for the product of the two numbers can be obtained by multiplying the two numbers directly, then simplifying the result.

$r_1(\cos \theta_1 + i \sin \theta_1) \cdot r_2(\cos \theta_2 + i \sin \theta_2)$
$$= r_1 r_2(\cos \theta_1 \cos \theta_2 + \cos \theta_1 \, i \sin \theta_2 + i \sin \theta_1 \cos \theta_2 + i^2 \sin \theta_1 \sin \theta_2)$$
$$= r_1 r_2[(\cos \theta_1 \cos \theta_2 - \sin \theta_1 \sin \theta_2) + i(\sin \theta_1 \cos \theta_2 + \cos \theta_1 \sin \theta_2)]$$
$$= r_1 r_2[\cos (\theta_1 + \theta_2) + i \sin (\theta_1 + \theta_2)]$$

The product of two complex numbers $r_1(\cos \theta_1 + i \sin \theta_1)$ and $r_2(\cos \theta_2 + i \sin \theta_2)$ can be found by using the following formula. $$r_1(\cos \theta_1 + i \sin \theta_1) \cdot r_2(\cos \theta_2 + i \sin \theta_2)$$ $$= r_1 r_2[\cos (\theta_1 + \theta_2) + i \sin (\theta_1 + \theta_2)]$$	*Product of Complex Numbers in Polar Form*

Notice the modulus of the product of two complex numbers is the product of their moduli. The amplitude of the product is the sum of their amplitudes.

Example

1 **Find the product of** $6\left(\cos \frac{\pi}{6} + i \sin \frac{\pi}{6}\right)$ **and** $2\left(\cos \frac{2\pi}{3} + i \sin \frac{2\pi}{3}\right)$.

Find the modulus and amplitude of the product.

$$r = 6(2) \qquad\qquad \theta = \frac{\pi}{6} + \frac{2\pi}{3}$$

$$= 12 \qquad\qquad\quad = \frac{5\pi}{6}$$

Therefore, $6\left(\cos \frac{\pi}{6} + i \sin \frac{\pi}{6}\right) \cdot 2\left(\cos \frac{2\pi}{3} + i \sin \frac{2\pi}{3}\right) = 12\left(\cos \frac{5\pi}{6} + i \sin \frac{5\pi}{6}\right)$.

A formula for the quotient of two complex numbers $r_1(\cos \theta_1 + i \sin \theta_1)$ and $r_2(\cos \theta_2 + i \sin \theta_2)$ can be found by multiplying the numerator and denominator by $(\cos \theta_2 - i \sin \theta_2)$ as follows.

$$\frac{r_1(\cos \theta_1 + i \sin \theta_1)}{r_2(\cos \theta_2 + i \sin \theta_2)} = \frac{r_1(\cos \theta_1 + i \sin \theta_1)}{r_2(\cos \theta_2 + i \sin \theta_2)} \cdot \frac{(\cos \theta_2 - i \sin \theta_2)}{(\cos \theta_2 - i \sin \theta_2)}$$

$$= \frac{r_1}{r_2} \cdot \frac{(\cos \theta_1 \cos \theta_2 + \sin \theta_1 \sin \theta_2) + i(\sin \theta_1 \cos \theta_2 - \cos \theta_1 \sin \theta_2)}{\cos^2 \theta_2 + \sin^2 \theta_2}$$

$$= \frac{r_1}{r_2}[\cos (\theta_1 - \theta_2) + i \sin (\theta_1 - \theta_2)] \qquad \textit{Remember that } \cos^2 \theta + \sin^2 \theta = 1$$

The quotient of two complex numbers $r_1(\cos \theta_1 + i \sin \theta_1)$ and $r_2(\cos \theta_2 + i \sin \theta_2)$ can be found by using the following formula.

$$\frac{r_1(\cos \theta_1 + i \sin \theta_1)}{r_2(\cos \theta_2 + i \sin \theta_2)} = \frac{r_1}{r_2}[\cos (\theta_1 - \theta_2) + i \sin (\theta_1 - \theta_2)]$$

Quotient of Complex Numbers in Polar Form

Notice the modulus of the quotient of two complex numbers is the quotient of their moduli. The amplitude of the quotient is the difference of their amplitudes.

Example

2 **Find the quotient of** $6\left(\cos \frac{\pi}{6} + i \sin \frac{\pi}{6}\right)$ **and** $2\left(\cos \frac{2\pi}{3} + i \sin \frac{2\pi}{3}\right)$.

Find the modulus and amplitude of the quotient.

$$r = 6 \div 2 \qquad\qquad \theta = \frac{\pi}{6} - \frac{2\pi}{3}$$

$$= 3 \qquad\qquad\quad = -\frac{\pi}{2} \text{ or } \frac{3\pi}{2}$$

Therefore, $\dfrac{6\left(\cos \frac{\pi}{6} + i \sin \frac{\pi}{6}\right)}{2\left(\cos \frac{2\pi}{3} + i \sin \frac{2\pi}{3}\right)} = 3\left(\cos \frac{3\pi}{2} + i \sin \frac{3\pi}{2}\right)$.

Exploratory Exercises

Find each product or quotient.

1. $2(\cos \pi + i \sin \pi) \cdot 5(\cos 2\pi + i \sin 2\pi)$
2. $6(\cos 2\pi + i \sin 2\pi) \div 2(\cos \pi + i \sin \pi)$
3. $2\left(\cos \frac{\pi}{6} + i \sin \frac{\pi}{6}\right) \div \left(\cos \frac{\pi}{3} + i \sin \frac{\pi}{3}\right)$
4. $3\left(\cos \frac{\pi}{2} + i \sin \frac{\pi}{2}\right) \cdot 6\left(\cos \frac{3\pi}{4} + i \sin \frac{3\pi}{4}\right)$

5-8. Express the results of problems **1-4** in rectangular form.

Written Exercises

Find each product or quotient.

1. $8\left(\cos \frac{3\pi}{4} + i \sin \frac{3\pi}{4}\right) \cdot 2\left(\cos \frac{5\pi}{4} + i \sin \frac{5\pi}{4}\right)$
2. $3\left(\cos \frac{7\pi}{6} + i \sin \frac{7\pi}{6}\right) \cdot 6\left(\cos \frac{\pi}{6} + i \sin \frac{\pi}{6}\right)$
3. $3\sqrt{2}\left(\cos \frac{\pi}{4} + i \sin \frac{\pi}{4}\right) \div \sqrt{2}\left(\cos \frac{\pi}{6} + i \sin \frac{\pi}{6}\right)$
4. $6\left(\cos \frac{5\pi}{8} + i \sin \frac{5\pi}{8}\right) \div 12\left(\cos \frac{\pi}{2} + i \sin \frac{\pi}{2}\right)$
5. $2(\cos 0.8 + i \sin 0.8) \cdot 3.2(\cos 1.5 + i \sin 1.5)$
6. $9.24(\cos 1.8 + i \sin 1.8) \div 3.1(\cos 0.7 + i \sin 0.7)$
7. $5\left(\cos \frac{3\pi}{4} + i \sin \frac{3\pi}{4}\right) \cdot 2\left(\cos \frac{2\pi}{3} + i \sin \frac{2\pi}{3}\right)$
8. $\frac{1}{3}\left(\cos \frac{7\pi}{8} + i \sin \frac{7\pi}{8}\right) \cdot 3\sqrt{3}\left(\cos -\frac{\pi}{4} + i \sin -\frac{\pi}{4}\right)$
9. $6\sqrt{3}\left(\cos \frac{5\pi}{4} + i \sin \frac{5\pi}{4}\right) \div \sqrt{3}\left(\cos \frac{\pi}{6} + i \sin \frac{\pi}{6}\right)$
10. $8\left(\cos \frac{3\pi}{2} + i \sin \frac{3\pi}{2}\right) \div \frac{4}{5}\left(\cos \frac{\pi}{2} + i \sin \frac{\pi}{2}\right)$
11. $(1 + i)(-1 - i)$ 12. $(\sqrt{3} + i)(-2 + 2i)$ 13. $(-4 - 4\sqrt{3}i) \div 2i$
14. $(3 - 3i) \div (-2 + 2i)$ 15. $(2 - 2i)(1 - i)$ 16. $(6 + 6i) \div (-3i)$

17-26. Express the results of problems **1-10** in rectangular form.

For the Scholar

In $\triangle ABC$, where $a, b,$ and c are lengths of the sides, $\dfrac{a + b + c}{2 + \sqrt{3}} = \dfrac{ab}{a + b - c}$. Find the measure of $\angle C$.

9-7 Powers and Roots of Complex Numbers

The formula for the product of complex numbers can be used to find the square of a complex number.

$$[r(\cos \theta + i \sin \theta)]^2 = [r(\cos \theta + i \sin \theta)] \cdot [r(\cos \theta + i \sin \theta)]$$
$$= r^2[\cos (\theta + \theta) + i \sin (\theta + \theta)]$$
$$= r^2(\cos 2\theta + i \sin 2\theta)$$

Other powers of complex numbers can be found by using De Moivre's Theorem.

$[r(\cos \theta + i \sin \theta)]^n = r^n(\cos n\theta + i \sin n\theta)$	*De Moivre's Theorem*

Mathematical induction can be used to prove that De Moivre's Theorem is valid for any positive integer n. The formula has been shown to be valid when $n = 1$ and $n = 2$. Assume the formula is valid for $n = k$.

$$[r(\cos \theta + i \sin \theta)]^k = r^k(\cos k\theta + i \sin k\theta)$$

Then, multiply each side of the equation by $r(\cos \theta + i \sin \theta)$.

$$
\begin{aligned}
[r(\cos \theta + i \sin \theta)]^{k+1} &= [r^k(\cos k\theta + i \sin k\theta)][r(\cos \theta + i \sin \theta)] \\
&= r^{k+1}(\cos k\theta \cos \theta + (\cos k\theta)(i \sin \theta) + i \sin k\theta \cos \theta + i^2 \sin k\theta \sin \theta) \\
&= r^{k+1}[(\cos k\theta \cos \theta - \sin k\theta \sin \theta) + i(\sin k\theta \cos \theta + \cos k\theta \sin \theta)] \\
&= r^{k+1}[\cos (k + 1)\theta + i \sin (k + 1)\theta]
\end{aligned}
$$

Since the right side of the last equation gives the same result as can be obtained directly for $n = k + 1$, the formula is valid for all positive integral values of n.

Example

1 **Find $(1 + i)^5$.**

First, write $1 + i$ in polar form.

$$1 + i = \sqrt{2}\left(\cos \frac{\pi}{4} + i \sin \frac{\pi}{4}\right)$$

$r = \sqrt{1^2 + 1^2} \text{ or } \sqrt{2}$

$\theta = \text{Arctan } \frac{1}{1} \text{ or } \frac{\pi}{4}$

Then, use De Moivre's Theorem to find the 5th power of the complex number in polar form.

$$
\begin{aligned}
(1 + i)^5 &= \left[\sqrt{2}\left(\cos \frac{\pi}{4} + i \sin \frac{\pi}{4}\right)\right]^5 \\
&= (\sqrt{2})^5\left(\cos \frac{5\pi}{4} + i \sin \frac{5\pi}{4}\right) \\
&= 4\sqrt{2}\left(\cos \frac{5\pi}{4} + i \sin \frac{5\pi}{4}\right)
\end{aligned}
$$

Write the result in rectangular form.

$$
\begin{aligned}
4\sqrt{2}\left(\cos \frac{5\pi}{4} + i \sin \frac{5\pi}{4}\right) &= 4\sqrt{2}\left(-\frac{\sqrt{2}}{2} - i\frac{\sqrt{2}}{2}\right) \\
&= -4 - 4i.
\end{aligned}
$$

Thus, $(1 + i)^5 = -4 - 4i$.

The roots of $x^{}$ + 1 = 0 are $\frac{}{2}$ + $\frac{}{2}i$, $-\frac{}{2}$ + $\frac{}{2}i$, $-\frac{}{2}$ - $\frac{}{2}i$, and $\frac{}{2}$ - $\frac{}{2}i$.

It can be proven that De Moivre's Theorem is also valid when n is a rational number. Therefore, the roots of complex numbers can be found by letting $n = \frac{1}{2}, \frac{1}{3}, \frac{1}{4}, \cdots$. In general, the pth root of a complex number can be found by the following formula.

The roots of a complex number are cyclic in nature. Thus, when graphed on the complex plane, the pth roots of a complex number are equally spaced around a circle. The figures below show the three cube roots of 1 and the four fourth roots of -1.

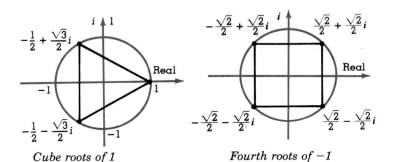

The cube roots of 1 form the vertices of an equilateral triangle. The fourth roots of -1 form the vertices of a square.

Cube roots of 1   Fourth roots of -1

If one pth root of a complex number is known, all the pth roots can be graphed on the complex plane. First, draw a circle of radius $r^{\frac{1}{p}}$ with its center at the origin of the complex plane. Then, graph the known root. Finally, separate the circle into p arcs of equal length to locate the other roots.

Example

6 **Graph the three cube roots of 8.**

The modulus of $8 + 0i$ is 8, and $8^{\frac{1}{3}} = 2$.

Draw a circle of radius 2 centered at the origin of the complex plane. Since $2^3 = 8$, one cube root of 8 is 2. Graph $2 + 0i$. Then, separate the circle into three arcs of equal length to locate the other two cube roots of 8.

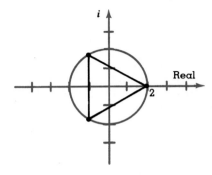

The other roots are $2\left(\cos\frac{2\pi}{3} + i \sin\frac{2\pi}{3}\right)$ and $2\left(\cos\frac{4\pi}{3} + i \sin\frac{4\pi}{3}\right)$.

Exploratory Exercises

Find each of the following powers. Express each result in rectangular form.

1. $[3(\cos \pi + i \sin \pi)]^3$

2. $\left[2\left(\cos \frac{\pi}{2} + i \sin \frac{\pi}{2}\right)\right]^5$

3. $\left(\cos \frac{\pi}{6} + i \sin \frac{\pi}{6}\right)^4$

4. $\left[3\left(\cos \frac{\pi}{3} + i \sin \frac{\pi}{3}\right)\right]^2$

5. $\left[2\left(\cos \frac{\pi}{4} + i \sin \frac{\pi}{4}\right)\right]^5$

6. $\left(\cos \frac{7\pi}{6} + i \sin \frac{7\pi}{6}\right)^3$

Find one of the indicated roots. Express the result in rectangular form.

7. $\left[4\left(\cos \frac{\pi}{2} + i \sin \frac{\pi}{2}\right)\right]^{\frac{1}{2}}$

8. $\left[4\left(\cos \frac{2\pi}{3} + i \sin \frac{2\pi}{3}\right)\right]^{\frac{1}{4}}$

9. $[-1(\cos \pi + i \sin \pi)]^{\frac{1}{3}}$

Written Exercises

Find each of the following powers. Express each result in rectangular form.

1. $(1 - i)^5$

2. $(-2 + 2i\sqrt{3})^4$

3. $(-3 + 3i)^3$

4. $(1 + i)^{10}$

5. $(3 + 4i)^4$

6. $(-5 + 12i)^2$

Find each indicated root.

7. $(1 + i)^{\frac{1}{3}}$

8. $(2\sqrt{3} + 2i)^{\frac{1}{5}}$

9. $(-2 - 2i)^{\frac{1}{4}}$

10. $(-4i)^{\frac{1}{10}}$

11. $\sqrt[5]{-1}$

12. $\sqrt[3]{i}$

Solve the following equations.

13. $x^3 + 1 = 0$

14. $x^3 - 8 = 0$

15. $x^5 - 1 = 0$

16. $x^4 - 1 = 0$

17. $x^6 + 1 = 0$

18. $x^5 + 1 = 0$

19-24. Graph the roots of each equation in problems 13-18.

For the Scholar

The sequence $\{a_n\}$ is defined by $a_1 = 3$ and $a_{n+1} = a_n + 3n$ for $n \geq 1$. Find the value of a_{50}.

Chapter Summary

1. Points in the plane can be identified using polar coordinates of the form (r, θ). The distance from a fixed point, called the **pole,** to a point $P(r, \theta)$ is $|r|$. The **polar axis** is a ray whose initial point is the pole. When r is positive, θ is the measure of any angle having the polar axis as its initial side and $\overrightarrow{OP}$ as its terminal side. (253)

2. **Classical Curves**

   Rose: $r = a \cos n\theta$ or $r = a \sin n\theta$, where n is a positive integer
   Lemniscate: $r^2 = a^2 \cos 2\theta$ or $r^2 = a^2 \sin 2\theta$
   Limaçon: $r = a + b \cos \theta$ or $r = a + b \sin \theta$
   Cardioid: $r = a + a \cos \theta$ or $r = a + a \sin \theta$
   Spiral of Archimedes: $r = a\theta$ (259)

3. Conversion from Polar to Rectangular Coordinates: The rectangular coordinates (x, y) of a point named by polar coordinates (r, θ) can be found by the following formulas.

$$x = r \cos \theta \qquad y = r \sin \theta \quad (262)$$

4. Conversion from Rectangular to Polar Coordinates: The polar coordinates (r, θ) of a point named by the rectangular coordinates (x, y) can be found by the following formulas.

$$r = \sqrt{x^2 + y^2} \qquad \theta = \text{Arctan } \frac{y}{x} \text{ when } x > 0$$

$$\theta = \text{Arctan } \frac{y}{x} + \pi \text{ when } x < 0 \quad (263)$$

5.

For any complex numbers $a + bi$ and $c + di$,
$(a + bi) + (c + di) = (a + c) + (b + d)i$
$(a + bi) - (c + di) = (a - c) + (b - d)i$
$(a + bi)(c + di) = (ac - bd) + (ad + bc)i$
$\dfrac{(a + bi)}{(c + di)} = \dfrac{(ac + bd) + (bc - ad)i}{c^2 + d^2}$

(266)

6. Polar Form of $x + yi$: $x + yi = r(\cos \theta + i \sin \theta)$ (268)

7. Values for r and θ can be obtained by using the following formulas.

$$r = \sqrt{x^2 + y^2} \qquad \theta = \text{Arctan } \frac{y}{x} \text{ when } x > 0$$

$$\theta = \text{Arctan } \frac{y}{x} + \pi \text{ when } x < 0 \quad (268)$$

8. The product of two complex numbers $r_1(\cos \theta_1 + i \sin \theta_1)$ and $r_2(\cos \theta_2 + i \sin \theta_2)$ can be found by using the following formula.

$$r_1(\cos \theta_1 + i \sin \theta_1) \cdot r_2(\cos \theta_2 + i \sin \theta_2) =$$
$$r_1 r_2[\cos (\theta_1 + \theta_2) + i \sin (\theta_1 + \theta_2)] \quad (270)$$

9. The quotient of two complex numbers $r_1(\cos \theta_1 + i \sin \theta_1)$ and $r_2(\cos \theta_2 + i \sin \theta_2)$ can be found by using the following formula.   (271)

$$\frac{r_1(\cos \theta_1 + i \sin \theta_1)}{r_2(\cos \theta_2 + i \sin \theta_2)} = \frac{r_1}{r_2}[\cos (\theta_1 - \theta_2) + i \sin (\theta_1 - \theta_2)]$$

10. De Moivre's Theorem: $[r(\cos \theta + i \sin \theta)]^n = r^n(\cos n\theta + i \sin n\theta)$ (273)

11. The p distinct roots of a complex number $x + yi$ can be found by replacing n by $0, 1, 2, \cdots, p - 1$, successively, in the following formula.   (274)

$$(x + yi)^{\frac{1}{p}} = r^{\frac{1}{p}}\left(\cos \frac{\theta + 2n\pi}{p} + i \sin \frac{\theta + 2n\pi}{p}\right)$$

Graph the point which has the given polar coordinates. (9-1)

1. $(-3, 50°)$ **2.** $(1.5, -110°)$ **3.** $\left(2, \dfrac{\pi}{4}\right)$ **4.** $\left(-3, -\dfrac{\pi}{2}\right)$

5-8. Name three other pairs of polar coordinates for each point named above.

Graph each polar equation. (9-1)

9. $r = \sqrt{7}$ **10.** $r = -2$ **11.** $\theta = 75°$

12. $\theta = -80°$ **13.** $\theta = -\dfrac{5\pi}{6}$ **14.** $\theta = \dfrac{3\pi}{4}$

Graph each polar equation. (9-2)

15. $r = 7 \cos \theta$ **16.** $r = 2 + 4 \cos \theta$

17. $r = 3 + 3 \sin \theta$ **18.** $r = 6 \sin 2\theta$

Find the polar coordinates of the point with the given rectangular coordinates. (9-3)

19. $(-\sqrt{3}, -3)$ **20.** $(5, 5)$ **21.** $(3, -2)$ **22.** $(-4, 2)$

Find the rectangular coordinates of the point with the given polar coordinates. (9-3)

23. $\left(6, \dfrac{\pi}{4}\right)$ **24.** $\left(2, -\dfrac{\pi}{6}\right)$ **25.** $(-2, 2.3)$ **26.** $(-1, -4.5)$

Simplify. (9-4)

27. i^{55} **28.** $i^{10} \cdot i^{25}$

29. $(2 + 3i) + (4 - 4i)$ **30.** $(-3 - i) - (2 + 7i)$

31. $i^3(4 - 3i)$ **32.** $(-i - 7)(i - 7)$

33. $(2 + 9i)(1 - 3i)$ **34.** $(5 + 6i)(-2 - 8i)$

35. $\dfrac{4 + i}{5 - 2i}$ **36.** $\dfrac{5}{\sqrt{2} - 4i}$

37. $\dfrac{7 + 5i}{7 - 5i}$ **38.** $\dfrac{8 - i}{2 + 3i}$

Express each complex number in polar form. (9-5)

39. $-6i$ **40.** $2 + 2i$

41. $-2 + 2i\sqrt{3}$ **42.** $6 - 8i$

43. $5 - 3i$ **44.** $-3 + i\sqrt{2}$

Express each complex number in rectangular form. (9-5)

45. $4\left(\cos \dfrac{5\pi}{6} + i \sin \dfrac{5\pi}{6}\right)$ **46.** $8\left(\cos \dfrac{7\pi}{4} + i \sin \dfrac{7\pi}{4}\right)$

47. $\sqrt{3}\left(\cos \dfrac{3\pi}{2} + i \sin \dfrac{3\pi}{2}\right)$ **48.** $2\left(\cos \dfrac{2\pi}{3} + i \sin \dfrac{2\pi}{3}\right)$

49. $3(\cos 1 + i \sin 1)$ **50.** $5(\cos 2 + i \sin 2)$

Find each product or quotient. Express each result in rectangular form. (9-6)

51. $2\left(\cos \frac{\pi}{3} + i \sin \frac{\pi}{3}\right) \cdot 4\left(\cos \frac{\pi}{3} + i \sin \frac{\pi}{3}\right)$

52. $3\left(\cos \frac{\pi}{2} + i \sin \frac{\pi}{2}\right) \cdot 2\left(\cos \frac{3\pi}{4} + i \sin \frac{3\pi}{4}\right)$

53. $1.9(\cos 2.1 + i \sin 2.1) \cdot 3(\cos 0.8 + i \sin 0.8)$

54. $8\left(\cos \frac{7\pi}{6} + i \sin \frac{7\pi}{6}\right) \div 2\left(\cos \frac{5\pi}{3} + i \sin \frac{5\pi}{3}\right)$

55. $6\left(\cos \frac{\pi}{2} + i \sin \frac{\pi}{2}\right) \div 4\left(\cos \frac{\pi}{6} + i \sin \frac{\pi}{6}\right)$

56. $2.2(\cos 1.5 + i \sin 1.5) \div 4.4(\cos 0.6 + i \sin 0.6)$

Find each product or quotient. Express each result in rectangular form. (9-6)

57. $\left(-3 + i\sqrt{3}\right)\left(2 + 2i\sqrt{3}\right)$ **58.** $(7 + 7i)(6 - 6i)$

59. $5i \div \left(1 + i\sqrt{3}\right)$ **60.** $(2 + 2i) \div (-6 - 6i)$

Find each of the following powers. (9-7)

61. $(2 + 2i)^8$ **62.** $\left(\sqrt{3} - i\right)^7$

63. $(-1 + i)^4$ **64.** $\left(-2 - 2i\sqrt{3}\right)^3$

Find each indicated root. (9-7)

65. $\sqrt[4]{i}$ **66.** $\left(\sqrt{3} + i\right)^{\frac{1}{3}}$

Solve the following equations. (9-7)

67. $x^5 - 32 = 0$ **68.** $x^6 - 1 = 0$

69-70. Graph the roots of each equation in problems **67-68**.

Graph the point that has the given polar coordinates. Then, name three other pairs of polar coordinates that represent the same point.

1. $\left(-2, \frac{5\pi}{4}\right)$ **2.** $\left(3, -\frac{\pi}{6}\right)$ **3.** $(2.5, 140°)$ **4.** $(-1.7, 25°)$

Graph each polar equation.

5. $r = -4$

6. $\theta = \frac{3\pi}{2}$

7. $r = 8 \sin \theta$

8. $r = 10 \sin 2\theta$

9. $r = 6 \cos 3\theta$

10. $r = 6 + \sin \theta$

Find the polar coordinates of the point with the given rectangular coordinates.

11. $(2, 2)$

12. $(-3, 1)$

Find the rectangular coordinates of the point with the given polar coordinates.

13. $\left(3, -\frac{5\pi}{4}\right)$

14. $(-4, 1.4)$

Simplify.

15. i^{93}

16. $(2 - 5i) + (-2 + 4i)$

17. $(-4 + i) - (4 - 2i)$

18. $(3 + 5i)(3 - 2i)$

19. $(7 + i)^2$

20. $\frac{6 - 2i}{2 + i}$

Express each complex number in polar form.

21. $-4 + 4i$

22. -5

23. $6 - 6i\sqrt{3}$

Express each complex number in rectangular form.

24. $2\left(\cos \frac{\pi}{3} + i \sin \frac{\pi}{3}\right)$

25. $\sqrt{2}\left(\cos \left(-\frac{\pi}{4}\right) + i \sin \left(-\frac{\pi}{4}\right)\right)$

Find each product or quotient. Express each result in rectangular form.

26. $4\left(\cos \frac{3\pi}{2} + i \sin \frac{3\pi}{2}\right) \cdot 3\left(\cos \frac{\pi}{4} + i \sin \frac{\pi}{4}\right)$

27. $2\sqrt{3}\left(\cos \frac{2\pi}{3} + i \sin \frac{2\pi}{3}\right) \div \sqrt{3}\left(\cos \frac{\pi}{6} + i \sin \frac{\pi}{6}\right)$

28. $(\sqrt{3} - 3i)(\sqrt{3} + i)$

Solve each of the following.

29. Find $(1 - i)^8$ by De Moivre's Theorem.

30. Solve the equation $x^8 - 1 = 0$ for all roots.

Exponential and Logarithmic Functions

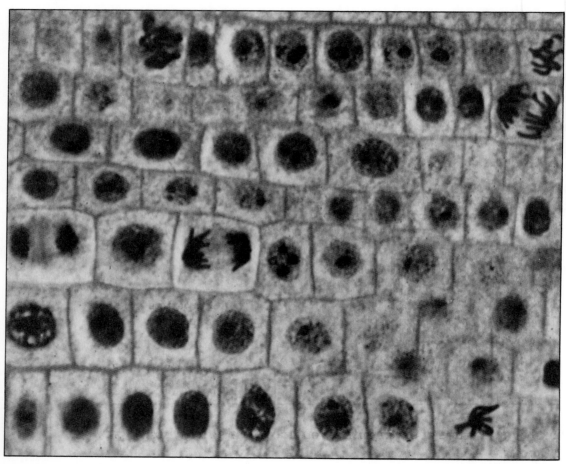

The photograph shows cells of an onion in various stages of cell division. Suppose a cell divides once each second. The number of cells created by one cell in n seconds can be found as follows.

Second	0	1	2	3	4	5	n
Number of Cells	1	2	4	8	16	32	2^n

The function $y = 2^n$ is an exponential function.

10-1 Rational Exponents

The definitions and properties of rational exponents are an extension of those for integral exponents. It is necessary to understand and be able to use the following definitions of x^n for any real number x and positive integer n.

$$\text{If } n = 1, \; x^n = x$$

$$\text{If } n > 1, \; x^n = \overbrace{x \cdot x \cdot x \cdots x}^{n \text{ factors}}$$

$$\text{If } x \neq 0, \; x^0 = 1$$

$$\text{If } x \neq 0, \; x^{-n} = \frac{1}{x^n}$$

These definitions can be used to verify the properties of exponents for positive integers m and n and real numbers a and b.

1. $a^m a^n = a^{m+n}$ **2.** $(a^m)^n = a^{mn}$ **3.** $\left(\dfrac{a}{b}\right)^m = \dfrac{a^m}{b^m}, \; b \neq 0$ **4.** $(ab)^m = a^m b^m$ **5.** $\dfrac{a^m}{a^n} = a^{m-n}, \; a \neq 0$	*Properties of Exponents*

Example

1 Verify that the five properties of exponents given above are valid when $m = 3$, $n = 2$, $a = 2$, and $b = 4$.

1. $a^m a^n = a^{m+n}$

$2^3 \cdot 2^2 \overset{?}{=} 2^{3+2}$

$8 \cdot 4 \overset{?}{=} 2^5$

$32 = 32$

2. $(a^m)^n = a^{mn}$

$(2^3)^2 \overset{?}{=} 2^{3 \cdot 2}$

$8^2 \overset{?}{=} 2^6$

$64 = 64$

3. $\left(\dfrac{a}{b}\right)^m = \dfrac{a^m}{b^m}$

$\left(\dfrac{2}{4}\right)^3 \overset{?}{=} \dfrac{2^3}{4^3}$

$\dfrac{8}{64} = \dfrac{8}{64}$

4. $(ab)^m = a^m b^m$

$(2 \cdot 4)^3 \overset{?}{=} 2^3 \cdot 4^3$

$8^3 \overset{?}{=} 8 \cdot 64$

$512 = 512$

5. $\dfrac{a^m}{a^n} = a^{m-n}$

$\dfrac{2^3}{2^2} \overset{?}{=} 2^{3-2}$

$\dfrac{8}{4} \overset{?}{=} 2^1$

$2 = 2$

Expressions with rational exponents can be defined such that the laws of exponents are still valid. Consider the expressions $7^{\frac{1}{2}}$ and $8^{\frac{1}{3}}$. According to the laws of exponents, the following must be true.

$$7^{\frac{1}{2}} \cdot 7^{\frac{1}{2}} = 7^{\frac{1}{2}+\frac{1}{2}}$$
$$= 7$$

But $\sqrt{7} \cdot \sqrt{7} = 7$.

Thus, $7^{\frac{1}{2}}$ and $\sqrt{7}$ must be equal.

$$8^{\frac{1}{3}} \cdot 8^{\frac{1}{3}} \cdot 8^{\frac{1}{3}} = 8^{\frac{1}{3}+\frac{1}{3}+\frac{1}{3}}$$
$$= 8$$

But $\sqrt[3]{8} \cdot \sqrt[3]{8} \cdot \sqrt[3]{8} = 8$.

Thus, $8^{\frac{1}{3}}$ and $\sqrt[3]{8}$ must be equal.

In general, let $y = b^{\frac{1}{n}}$ for a real number b and positive integer n. Then, $y^n = \left(b^{\frac{1}{n}}\right)^n = b^{\frac{n}{n}}$ or b. But, $y^n = b$ if and only if $y = \sqrt[n]{b}$. Therefore, $b^{\frac{1}{n}}$ is defined as follows.

For any real number $b \geq 0$ and any integer $n > 1$, $$b^{\frac{1}{n}} = \sqrt[n]{b}.$$ **This also holds when $b < 0$ and n is odd.**	*Definition of $b^{\frac{1}{n}}$*

What difficulties occur if $b < 0$ and n is even?

Examples

2 Evaluate $16^{\frac{1}{4}}$.

$16^{\frac{1}{4}} = (2^4)^{\frac{1}{4}}$ *Recall that $(a^m)^n = a^{mn}$.*

$= 2^{\frac{4}{4}}$ or 2

3 Evaluate $7^{\frac{1}{2}} \cdot 14^{\frac{1}{2}}$.

$7^{\frac{1}{2}} \cdot 14^{\frac{1}{2}} = 7^{\frac{1}{2}} \cdot 7^{\frac{1}{2}} \cdot 2^{\frac{1}{2}}$ *Recall that $(ab)^m = a^m b^m$.*

$= 7^{\frac{1}{2}+\frac{1}{2}} \cdot 2^{\frac{1}{2}}$

$= 7\sqrt{2}$

Next, consider the expression $8^{\frac{2}{3}}$.

$$8^{\frac{2}{3}} = (8^{\frac{1}{3}})^2 \qquad \text{or} \qquad (8^2)^{\frac{1}{3}}$$
$$(8^{\frac{1}{3}})^2 = (\sqrt[3]{8})^2 \qquad\qquad (8^2)^{\frac{1}{3}} = \sqrt[3]{8^2}$$

Thus, $(\sqrt[3]{8})^2$ and $\sqrt[3]{8^2}$ must be equal to $8^{\frac{2}{3}}$.

In general, $b^{\frac{m}{n}}$ is equal to $(b^{\frac{1}{n}})^m$ or $(b^m)^{\frac{1}{n}}$.

$$(b^{\frac{1}{n}})^m = (\sqrt[n]{b})^m \qquad (b^m)^{\frac{1}{n}} = \sqrt[n]{b^m}$$

Thus, $b^{\frac{m}{n}}$ is equal to $(\sqrt[n]{b})^m$ or $\sqrt[n]{b^m}$.

For any nonzero number b, and any integers m and n with $n > 1$, $$b^{\frac{m}{n}} = \sqrt[n]{b^m} = (\sqrt[n]{b})^m$$ **except when $\sqrt[n]{b}$ is not a real number.**	*Definition of Rational Exponents*

Examples

4 **Evaluate $81^{\frac{3}{4}}$.**

$$81^{\frac{3}{4}} = (3^4)^{\frac{3}{4}}$$
$$= 3^3$$
$$= 27$$

5 **Use radicals to express $(3m)^{\frac{2}{5}}n^{\frac{3}{5}}$.**

$$(3m)^{\frac{2}{5}}n^{\frac{3}{5}} = ((3m)^2 n^3)^{\frac{1}{5}}$$
$$= (3^2 m^2 n^3)^{\frac{1}{5}}$$
$$= \sqrt[5]{3^2 m^2 n^3}$$

6 **Use rational exponents to express $\sqrt{r^3 s^4}$.**

$$\sqrt{r^3 s^4} = (r^3 s^4)^{\frac{1}{2}}$$
$$= r^{\frac{3}{2}} s^2$$

7 **Simplify $\sqrt{a^3 b^5}$.**

$$\sqrt{a^3 b^5} = (a^3 b^5)^{\frac{1}{2}}$$
$$= a^{\frac{3}{2}} b^{\frac{5}{2}}$$
$$= a^{\frac{2}{2}} a^{\frac{1}{2}} b^{\frac{4}{2}} b^{\frac{1}{2}}$$
$$= |a|\, b^2 \sqrt{ab} \qquad \text{\textit{Why must $|a|$ be used?}}$$

Exploratory Exercises

Evaluate.

1. $7^{\frac{1}{4}} \cdot 7^{\frac{7}{4}}$

2. $81^{\frac{1}{2}}$

3. $27^{-\frac{2}{3}}$

4. $\sqrt[3]{125}$

5. $\sqrt[4]{16^2}$

6. $\left(5^{\frac{3}{4}}\right)^4$

7. $3^{-4} \cdot 3^8$

8. $64^{\frac{5}{6}}$

9. $\sqrt[5]{32}$

10. $\left(121^{\frac{1}{2}}\right)^0$

11. $2^{-8} \cdot 2^5$

12. $\left(8^{-\frac{1}{2}}\right)^{-\frac{2}{3}}$

13. $81^{\frac{1}{2}} - 81^{-\frac{1}{2}}$

14. $16^{\frac{3}{4}}$

15. $(3^{-1} + 3^{-2})^{-1}$

16. $\left(\sqrt[3]{216}\right)^2$

17. $\left(5^{\frac{2}{5}}\right)^{-5}$

18. $\left(\sqrt[3]{343}\right)^{-2}$

19. $\dfrac{64}{64^{\frac{2}{3}}}$

20. $\dfrac{25^{\frac{3}{4}}}{25^{\frac{1}{4}}}$

Written Exercises

Express each of the following using rational exponents.

1. $\sqrt{r^6 s^3}$

2. $\sqrt[3]{8x^3 y^6}$

3. $\sqrt[4]{a}$

4. $\sqrt{xy^3}$

5. $\sqrt[4]{x^{16} y^8}$

6. $\sqrt[6]{b^3}$

7. $\sqrt[3]{125a^2 b^3}$

8. $\sqrt{25a^4 b^{10}}$

9. $\sqrt[3]{64x^9 y^{15}}$

10. $\sqrt[6]{27}$

11. $\sqrt[5]{32x^5 y^8}$

12. $\sqrt{121a^5}$

13. $\sqrt[4]{24a^{12} b^{16}}$

14. $\sqrt[3]{ab^6 c^4}$

15. $\sqrt{16y^8 c}$

16. $\sqrt[3]{343x}$

17. $\sqrt[5]{y^3}$

18. $\sqrt[5]{15x^3 y^{15}}$

19. $\sqrt{20x^4 y^{12}}$

20. $\sqrt[4]{81x^4 ya}$

21. $\sqrt[6]{12a^4 b^2 c^3}$

22. $\sqrt[3]{8x^2 y^8}$

23. $\sqrt[5]{25a^{-5} b^{-10}}$

24. $\sqrt[6]{64a^6 b^{-2}}$

Express each of the following using radicals.

25. $64^{\frac{1}{6}}$

26. $25^{\frac{1}{3}}$

27. $15^{\frac{1}{5}}$

28. $a^{\frac{2}{3}}$

29. $a^{\frac{3}{4}} y^{\frac{1}{4}}$

30. $4^{\frac{1}{3}} a^{\frac{2}{3}} y^{\frac{4}{3}}$

31. $x^{\frac{4}{7}} y^{\frac{3}{7}}$

32. $a^{\frac{1}{6}} b^{\frac{4}{6}} c^{\frac{3}{6}}$

33. $r^{\frac{5}{2}} q^{\frac{3}{4}}$

34. $(c^3 b^2)^{\frac{1}{5}} x^{\frac{3}{5}}$

35. $a^{\frac{1}{5}} b^{\frac{1}{10}}$

36. $(4x)^{\frac{1}{3}} a^{\frac{1}{2}}$

37. $3^{\frac{5}{3}} x^{\frac{7}{3}}$

38. $(x^{10} y^2)^{\frac{1}{5}} a^{\frac{2}{5}}$

39. $(2^5 a^4 y)^{\frac{1}{3}}$

40. $ay^{\frac{2}{3}}\left(a^{\frac{1}{2}} y^2\right)$

41. $(2m)^{\frac{2}{5}} n^{\frac{3}{5}}$

42. $\dfrac{x^{\frac{2}{3}}}{x^{\frac{1}{3}}}$

43. $\dfrac{17^{\frac{3}{4}}}{17^{\frac{1}{4}}}$

44. $15x^{\frac{1}{3}} y^{\frac{1}{5}}$

Simplify each expression.

45. $x^6 \cdot x^{-3} \cdot x^2$

46. $4x^2 (4x)^{-2}$

47. $\left(5x^{\frac{1}{3}}\right)^3$

48. $(4y^4)^{\frac{3}{2}}$

49. $(y^{-2})^4 \cdot y^8$

50. $((2x)^4)^{-2}$

51. $\left(x^{\frac{1}{2}} y^{-2} a^{\frac{5}{4}}\right)^{-4}$

52. $\sqrt{a^3 b^2} \cdot \sqrt{a^4 b^5}$

53. $(5ac)^{\frac{1}{3}} (a^2 c^3)^{\frac{1}{3}}$

For the Scholar

If two convex polygons in the same plane intersect each other, find the maximum number of intersection points given that the polygons have no segment in common. Assume that the polygons have 19 and 20 vertices respectively.

10-2 Exponential Functions

The expression a^x has been defined for integral and rational exponents. The next step is to define irrational exponents such that the properties of exponents remain valid.

Consider the graph of $y = 2^x$, where x is an integer. This is a function, since for each value of x there is a unique y-value.

x	−4	−3	−2	−1	0	1	2	3	4	5
2^x	$\frac{1}{16}$	$\frac{1}{8}$	$\frac{1}{4}$	$\frac{1}{2}$	1	2	4	8	16	32

Notice that the vertical scale is condensed.

From the graph, it is clear that the function is increasing. That is, for any values x_1 and x_2, if $x_1 < x_2$ then $2^{x_1} < 2^{x_2}$.

Suppose the domain of $y = 2^x$ is expanded to include rational numbers. Notice the additional points graphed seem to "fill in" the graph of $y = 2^x$. That is, if a is between x_1 and x_2, then 2^a is between 2^{x_1} and 2^{x_2}. The graph of $y = 2^x$, when x is a rational number, is indicated by the broken line.

x	2^x
−3.5	0.09
−2.5	0.18
−1.5	0.35
−0.5	0.71
0.5	1.41
1.5	2.83
2.5	5.66
3.5	11.31
4.5	22.63

Values given in the table are approximate.

Use the $\boxed{y^x}$ key on a calculator to verify these values.

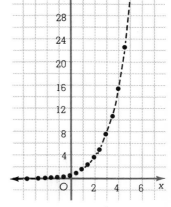

Since a^x has not been defined for irrational numbers, "holes" still remain in the graph of $y = 2^x$. How could you expand the domain of $y = 2^x$ to include both rational and irrational numbers? Consider a possible meaning for an expression such as $2^{\sqrt{3}}$. Since $1.7 < \sqrt{3} < 1.8$, it seems clear that $2^{1.7} < 2^{\sqrt{3}} < 2^{1.8}$. By using closer approximations for $\sqrt{3}$, closer approximations for $2^{\sqrt{3}}$ are possible.

$$2^{1.7} < 2^{\sqrt{3}} < 2^{1.8}$$
$$2^{1.73} < 2^{\sqrt{3}} < 2^{1.74}$$
$$2^{1.732} < 2^{\sqrt{3}} < 2^{1.733}$$
$$2^{1.7320} < 2^{\sqrt{3}} < 2^{1.7321}$$
$$2^{1.73205} < 2^{\sqrt{3}} < 2^{1.73206}$$

The sequence $2^{1.7}$, $2^{1.73}$, $2^{1.732}$, $\cdots$ converges to the value $2^{\sqrt{3}}$.
The sequence $2^{1.8}$, $2^{1.74}$, $2^{1.733}$, $\cdots$ converges to the same value.
Thus, $2^{\sqrt{3}}$ is **bounded** by the terms of the convergent sequences.

Therefore, it is now possible to determine a value for a^x, when x is an irrational number, by using rational approximations.

If x is an irrational number and $a > 0$, then a^x is the real number between a^{x_1} and a^{x_2}, for all possible choices of rational numbers x_1 and x_2 such that $x_1 < x < x_2$.	**Definition of Irrational Exponents**

Example

1 Use the graph of $y = 2^x$ and the properties of exponents to evaluate x or y to the nearest tenth.

a. $y = 2^{1.8}$ **b.** $y = 2^{3.1}$
c. $5.2 = 2^x$ **d.** $40 = 2^x$

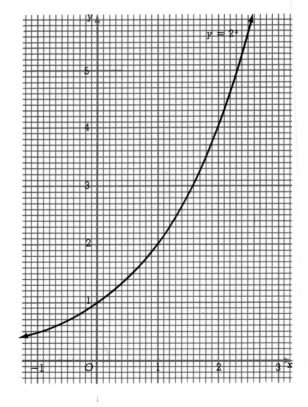

a. $y = 2^{1.8}$
From the graph, $y = 3.5$.

b. $y = 2^{3.1}$
$= 2^1 \cdot 2^{2.1}$
$= 2 \cdot 4.3$
$= 8.6$

c. $5.2 = 2^x$
From the graph, $x = 2.4$.

d. $\qquad 40 = 2^x$
$\qquad 8 \cdot 5 = 2^x$
$\quad 2^3 \cdot 2^{2.3} = 2^x$
$\qquad 2^{5.3} = 2^x$
$\qquad\quad x = 5.3$

An exponential function has the form $y = a^x$, where a is a positive real number. The figure shows graphs of several exponential functions. Notice the point $(0, 1)$ is common to each function. Compare the graph of $y = 2^x$ with the graph of $y = \left(\frac{1}{2}\right)^x$. What do you notice? When $a > 1$, is the graph of $y = a^x$ increasing or decreasing? When $a < 1$, is the graph increasing or decreasing?

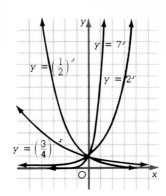

Example

2 **Graph the function $y = 3^x$.**

First, make a table of ordered pairs. Then, graph the ordered pairs and connect the points with a smooth curve.

x	3^x
-3	$\frac{1}{27}$
-2	$\frac{1}{9}$
-1	$\frac{1}{3}$
0	1
1	3
2	9
3	27

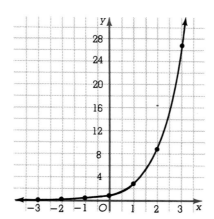

Using Calculators

Use a calculator to evaluate y to the nearest ten thousandth if $y = 2^{1.725}$.

		TAB					
ENTER:	2ndF	F↔E	4	2	y^x	1.725	=
DISPLAY:			0.000	2	2.0000	1.725	3.3058

Exploratory Exercises

Use the graph of $y = 2^x$ to evaluate each expression to the nearest tenth.

1. $2^{0.5}$ **2.** $2^{1.4}$ **3.** $2^{-1.5}$ **4.** $2^{2.5}$

5. $2^{0.8}$ **6.** $2^{\sqrt{2}}$ **7.** $2^{-0.1}$ **8.** $2^{2.1}$

Written Exercises

Use the graph of $y = 2^x$ to evaluate x or y to the nearest tenth.

1. $y = 2^{4.5}$ **2.** $y = 2^{3.8}$ **3.** $y = 2^{-2.6}$

4. $3.7 = 2^x$ **5.** $4.1 = 2^x$ **6.** $\sqrt{7} = 2^x$

7. $12 = 2^x$ **8.** $y = 2^{2.9}$ **9.** $48 = 2^x$

Graph each equation.

10. $y = 4^x$ **11.** $y = 3^x$ **12.** $y = 5^{-x}$

13. $y = \left(\dfrac{1}{4}\right)^x$ **14.** $y = \left(\dfrac{1}{3}\right)^x$ **15.** $y = 7^{-x}$

16. Compare the graphs for problems **10** and **13**. What do you notice?

Challenge Exercises

An amoeba divides once every hour. Beginning with a single amoeba, how many amoebae will there be after the given amount of time?

17. 3 hours   **18.** 7 hours   **19.** 10 hours   **20.** 1 day

For the Scholar

In the figure, $\overline{PQ}$ is a diameter of the circle with tangents $\overline{RP}$ and $\overline{SQ}$. The intersection of $\overline{RQ}$ and $\overline{SP}$ is point T on the circle. Find the length of $\overline{PQ}$ if $\overline{RP}$ and $\overline{SQ}$ measure 9 and 4 respectively.

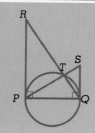

10-3 The Number e

Perhaps the most well-known and widely used irrational number is π. In 1748 Leonhard Euler, a Swiss mathematician, published a work in which he developed another irrational number which ranks along with π in importance. In his honor the number is called e, the **Euler number.** The number is the limit of the sum of the following infinite series.

$$e = 1 + \frac{1}{1!} + \frac{1}{2!} + \frac{1}{3!} + \frac{1}{4!} + \frac{1}{5!} + \cdots + \frac{1}{n!} + \cdots$$

The binomial theorem can be used to derive the series for e, as follows. Let v be any variable and apply the binomial theorem to $(1 + v)^n$.

Recall the binomial theorem from Chapter 8.

$$(1 + v)^n = 1 + nv + \frac{n(n-1)}{2!}v^2 + \frac{n(n-1)(n-2)}{3!}v^3 + \cdots$$

Now let k be a variable such that $v = \frac{1}{k}$ and let x be a variable such that $kx = n$. Then, substitute these values for v and n.

$$\left(1 + \frac{1}{k}\right)^{kx} = 1 + kx\left(\frac{1}{k}\right) + \frac{kx(kx-1)}{2!}\left(\frac{1}{k}\right)^2 + \frac{kx(kx-1)(kx-2)}{3!}\left(\frac{1}{k}\right)^3 + \cdots$$

$$= 1 + x + \frac{x\left(x - \frac{1}{k}\right)}{2!} + \frac{x\left(x - \frac{1}{k}\right)\left(x - \frac{2}{k}\right)}{3!} + \cdots$$

Then, find the limit as k increases without bound.

$$\lim_{k \to \infty} \left(1 + \frac{1}{k}\right)^{kx} = 1 + x + \frac{x^2}{2!} + \frac{x^3}{3!} + \frac{x^4}{4!} + \frac{x^5}{5!} + \cdots$$

Recall that $\lim\limits_{k \to \infty} \frac{1}{k} = 0$.

Let $x = 1$.

$$\lim_{k \to \infty} \left(1 + \frac{1}{k}\right)^{k} = 1 + 1 + \frac{1}{2!} + \frac{1}{3!} + \frac{1}{4!} + \cdots$$

Thus, e can be defined as follows.

$$e = \lim_{k \to \infty} \left(1 + \frac{1}{k}\right)^{k} = 1 + 1 + \frac{1}{2!} + \frac{1}{3!} + \cdots$$

Definition of e

The following computation for e is correct to three decimal places.

Verify these values by using a calculator.

$$e = 1 + 1 + \frac{1}{2!} + \frac{1}{3!} + \frac{1}{4!} + \frac{1}{5!} + \frac{1}{6!} + \frac{1}{7!} + \cdots$$

$$= 1 + 1 + \frac{1}{2} + \frac{1}{6} + \frac{1}{24} + \frac{1}{120} + \frac{1}{720} + \frac{1}{5040} + \cdots$$

$$= 1 + 1 + 0.5 + 0.16667 + 0.04167 + 0.00833 + 0.00138 + 0.000198 + \cdots$$

$$= 2.718$$

If x is a variable, then e^x can be approximated using the following series.

$$e^x = 1 + x + \frac{x^2}{2!} + \frac{x^3}{3!} + \frac{x^4}{4!} + \cdots$$

This series is often called the exponential series.

One of the most important exponential functions is $y = e^x$. It is often referred to as the **exponential function.** A graph of $y = e^x$, shown on the next page, can be used to find approximate values.

Example

1 Use the graph of $y = e^x$ to evaluate x or y to the nearest tenth.

   a. $y = e^{1.3}$ **b.** $y = e^{3.2}$

   c. $4 = e^x$ **d.** $y = 6^{0.8}$

a. $y = e^{1.3}$
   From the graph, $e^{1.3} = 3.7$

b. $y = e^{3.2}$
   $= e^{1.6}e^{1.6}$ *From the graph,*
   $= (4.9)^2$ $e^{1.6} = 4.9$
   $= 24.0$

c. $4 = e^x$
   From the graph, $x = 1.4$

d. $y = 6^{0.8}$
   $= (e^{1.8})^{0.8}$ $6 = e^{1.8}$
   $= e^{1.4}$
   $= 4.1$

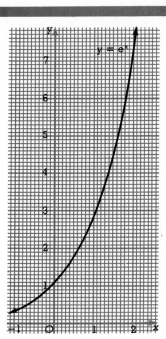

Values for $y = e^x$ and $y = e^{-x}$ are given in the table on page 540. Use this table to check the values found in example 1. Notice the graph is much less accurate than the table of values.

Use a calculator to check some of these values.

Example

2 Use the table of values on page 540 to graph $y = e^{-x}$.

x	e^{-x}
-1	2.7183
0	1
1	0.3679
2	0.1353

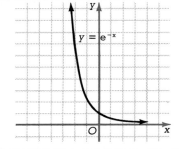

How would you find these values using your calculator?

Using Calculators

Find the value of y to the nearest ten thousandth for $y = e^{2.1450}$.

	TAB					e^x	
ENTER:			4	2.1450			
DISPLAY:			0.0000	2.1450		8.5420	

Exploratory Exercises

Use the graph of $y = e^x$ on page 292 to evaluate x or y to the nearest tenth.

1. $y = e^{1.1}$ **2.** $y = e^{1.4}$ **3.** $y = e^{0.5}$ **4.** $y = e^{0.8}$

5. $7 = e^x$ **6.** $y = e^{-0.5}$ **7.** $5.5 = e^x$ **8.** $y = e^{1.6}$

Written Exercises

Use the graph of $y = e^x$ on page 292 to evaluate x or y to the nearest tenth. Check your answers by using the table of values for e^x on page 540.

1. $y = e^{4.4}$ **2.** $y = e^{4.2}$ **3.** $y = e^{3.9}$ **4.** $y = \sqrt[3]{e}$

5. $y = 2\sqrt{e}$ **6.** $9 = e^x$ **7.** $6 = e^x$ **8.** $y = 5^{0.8}$

9. $y = 4^{0.5}$ **10.** $y = 2\sqrt[4]{e^3}$ **11.** $y = e^{6.4}$ **12.** $y = 4\sqrt[3]{e^2}$

Evaluate x to the nearest tenth given that $2 = e^{0.6932}$.

13. $32 = e^x$ **14.** $x = e^{2.0796}$ **15.** $x = e^{4.159}$

16. $x = e^0$ **17.** $16 = e^x$ **18.** $x = e^{0.346}$

19. Compute, correct to 5 decimal places, the values of $\frac{1}{8!}$ and $\frac{1}{9!}$ to verify that they do not affect the three-place value of e given.

Challenge Exercises

Use the first 5 terms of the exponential series $e^x = 1 + x + \dfrac{x^2}{2!} + \dfrac{x^3}{3!} + \dfrac{x^4}{4!} \cdots$ to approximate the following. Use your calculator.

20. $e^{1.5}$ **21.** $e^{0.45}$ **22.** $e^{4.6}$

23. $e^{2.3}$ **24.** $e^{0.8}$ **25.** $e^{1.9}$

Solve each problem. Use the table on page 540.

26. Graph $y = e^{-x^2}$. This graph approximates the bell-shaped curve. This curve is often used to represent the distribution of a particular trait in a normal population. It has many applications in statistics.

27. Graph $y = \dfrac{e^x + e^{-x}}{2}$. This graph is called the catenary curve. A flexible cable suspended between two points approximates this curve.

28. The exponential function $L(x) = 50 - 50e^{-0.3x}$ describes the learning curve for an assembly line worker in a factory. $L(x)$ represents the units of work produced by the worker during the xth day on the job after a training period. How many units are produced by this worker on the sixth day after the training period? What is the expected maximum production of this worker on any single day?

For the Scholar

> The sum of the first n terms of an arithmetic series is $5n + 3n^2$. Find the rth term.

Often money is lent with the understanding that when earnings accumulate they are to be added to the original investment at specified times and thus become part of a new principal. Interest computed on this basis is called **compound interest.** When interest is compounded, the effective annual yield from an investment is higher than the annual interest rate.

Federal Savings

12-month money market certificate

10.75%

Annual Interest Rate

11.35%

Effective Annual Yield

If P dollars are loaned at r percent for one interest period, the amount $A_1 = P + Pr = P(1 + r)$. This amount bears interest for the second period at r percent and the second amount $A_2 = P(1 + r) + rP(1 + r) = P(1 + r)^2$.

The accumulated amount of an investment at the end of a number of periods can be shown by means of a table.

End of Period	1	2	3	4	k
Accumulated Amount A	$P(1 + r)$	$P(1 + r)^2$	$P(1 + r)^3$	$P(1 + r)^4$	$\cdots P(1 + r)^k$

Thus, the compound interest formula is $A = P(1 + r)^k$.

When interest is compounded n times per year at rate r per year, then the rate per period is $\frac{r}{n}$ and the number of periods in t years is nt. The formula is then modified to the following form.

$$A = P\left(1 + \frac{r}{n}\right)^{nt}$$

Compound Interest Formula

Example Find the amount accumulated if $100 is invested for 1 year at 8% annual interest compounded quarterly.

In 1 year there are 4 quarters. The quarterly rate is 2%.   *Why?*
$A = 100(1 + 0.02)^4$
$\quad = 100(1.08243)$
$\quad = \$108.24$ *In this case, the effective annual yield is 8.24%. Why?*

Consider the special case where $rt = 1$. This could happen, for example, if money were invested for 20 years at 5%, or 1 year at 100%. Then, $r = \frac{1}{t}$.

$$A = P\left(1 + \frac{1}{nt}\right)^{nt}$$

Suppose the interest is compounded continuously. Then, n increases without limit. Thus, $nt \to \infty$, since t cannot equal zero. If the principal P is equal to 1, the value of A has the following limit as $nt \to \infty$.

$$A = \lim_{nt \to \infty} \left(1 + \frac{1}{nt}\right)^{nt} = e \qquad \textit{Recall that } e = \lim_{k \to \infty} \left(1 + \frac{1}{k}\right)^{k}.$$

That is, if \$1 is continuously compounded at rate r for t years where $rt = 1$, the amount accumulated will be \$2.71828 $\cdots$ or \$2.72.

Suppose the beginning principal is P, the annual interest rate is r, and the time in years is t. Then, the following formula can be used to find the final amount, A, when interest is compounded continuously.

$A = Pe^{rt}$	**Continuously Compounded Interest Formula**

Example If \$500 is invested at 6% continuously compounded for 40 years, what is the final amount?

$A = 500e^{0.06(40)}$ *Use the formula $A = Pe^{rt}$*

$\quad = 500e^{2.4}$

$\quad = 500(11.023)$

$\quad = \$5511.50$

Exercises Solve each of the following.

1. If interest is compounded annually, find the compound amount of \$1000 invested for 5 years at $9\frac{1}{2}\%$.

2. If interest is compound semiannually, find the compound amount of \$2500 invested for 3 years at 10% per year.

3. If interest is compounded semiannually, find the compound amount of \$1200 invested for $4\frac{1}{2}$ years at 12% per year.

4. If \$100 is invested at 7% continuously compounded for 15 years, what is the amount at the end of that time?

5. If \$350 is invested at $14\frac{1}{2}\%$ continuously compounded for 50 years, what is the amount at the end of that time?

6. If \$500 is invested at 6% continuously compounded for 20 years, how much more is the amount than if it were compounded annually?

7. If you invest \$3.00 at 15% annual interest, what is the amount you would have after one year if interest is compounded (**a**) quarterly (**b**) monthly (**c**) continuously?

8. Repeat exercise 7 using an annual rate of 12%.

9. One hundred dollars deposited in a bank that compounds interest quarterly yields \$115.00 at the end of one year. What is the annual rate of interest?

10. Which yields more, an amount invested at 12% compounded annually over a 10-year period, or the same amount invested at 11.5% compounded quarterly over a 10 year period?

10-4 Composition and Inverses of Functions

A function can be described as a mapping of the elements of one set, the domain, onto a second set, the range. Let function f map the elements in set R onto those in set S. Let function g map the elements in S onto those in T.

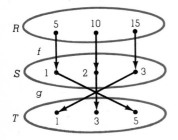

domain of f

$$f(x) = \frac{1}{5}x$$

range of f
domain of g

$$g(x) = -2x + 7$$

range of g

By combining f and g in this way, a function from R to T is defined, since each element of R is associated with exactly one element of T. For example, $f(15) = 3$ and $g(3) = 1$. This new function that maps R onto T is called the **composite** of f and g. It is denoted by $g \circ f$, as shown at the right. Composition of functions is *not* commutative.

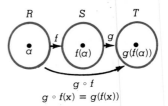

$$g \circ f$$
$$g \circ f(x) = g(f(x))$$

> Given functions f and g the composite function $f \circ g$ can be described by the following equation.
>
> $$f \circ g(x) = f(g(x))$$
>
> The domain of $f \circ g$ includes all elements x in the domain of g for which $g(x)$ is in the domain of f.

Composition of Functions

Example

1 If $f(x) = \dfrac{1}{x-1}$ and $g(x) = x + 1$, find $f \circ g(x)$.

$$f \circ g(x) = f(g(x))$$
$$= f(x + 1)$$
$$= \frac{1}{(x + 1) - 1} \text{ or } \frac{1}{x}$$

The composite function $f \circ g$ exists only when the range of g is a subset of the domain of f. Otherwise the composition is undefined. For example, $f \circ g(x)$ does not exist for the following functions.

$$g(x) = -\sqrt{x}$$
$$f(x) = \sqrt{x} + 1$$
$$f \circ g(x) = f(g(x)) = \sqrt{(-\sqrt{x})} + 1 \qquad \textit{Does } g \circ f(x) \textit{ exist?}$$

Consider two functions $f(x) = 5x - 3$ and $g(x) = \dfrac{x + 3}{5}$. Functions $f \circ g(x)$ and $g \circ f(x)$ can be found as follows.

$$
\begin{aligned}
f \circ g(x) &= f(g(x)) & g \circ f(x) &= g(f(x)) \\
&= f\left(\frac{x + 3}{5}\right) & &= g(5x - 3) \\
&= 5\left(\frac{x + 3}{5}\right) - 3 & &= \frac{(5x - 3) + 3}{5} \\
&= x & &= x
\end{aligned}
$$

Since $f(g(x)) = g(f(x)) = x$, the functions f and g are called **inverse functions.**

Two polynomial functions f and g are inverse functions if and only if both their compositions are the identity function. That is, $f \circ g(x) = g \circ f(x) = x$.	*Inverse Functions*

The inverse function of f, if it exists, is denoted by f^{-1}. If f and g are inverse functions, then $f = g^{-1}$ and $g = f^{-1}$.
The inverse of a function can be shown as a mapping.

The notation f^{-1} is read "f inverse," or "the inverse of f." The -1 is not an expo-nent.

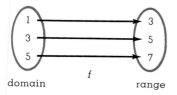
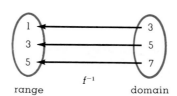

If $f = \{(1, 3), (3, 5), (5, 7)\}$, then $f^{-1} = \{(3, 1), (5, 3), (7, 5)\}$.

Notice the inverse is found by reversing the order of the coordinates of each ordered pair for the function. The mapping shown above is one-to-one. The mapping shown at the right is *not* one-to-one. The inverse of f is a function only if f represents a one-to-one mapping.   *Why?*

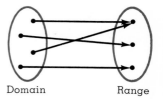

Suppose f and f^{-1} are inverse functions. Then, $f(a) = b$ if and only if $f^{-1}(b) = a$.	*Property of Inverse Functions*

The graphs of $f(x) = 5x - 3$ and $f^{-1}(x) = \dfrac{x + 3}{5}$ are shown on the graph. Notice the graph of f^{-1} is the reflection of f about the line $y = x$. Any two points (a, b) and (b, a) are symmetric with respect to the line $y = x$. The inverse of a function can be graphed by reflecting the graph of the function about the line $y = x$.

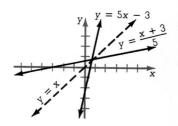

Example

2 **Suppose $f(x) = 2x + 5$. Find $f^{-1}(x)$, and show that f and f^{-1} are inverse functions.**

Recall that $f(a) = b$ if and only if $f^{-1}(b) = a$. Since $f(x) = 2x + 5$, $f(a) = 2a + 5$. Use $2a + 5 = b$ to find $f^{-1}(b)$.

Solve the equation for a.

$$2a = b - 5$$
$$a = \frac{b - 5}{2}$$
$$f^{-1}(b) = \frac{b - 5}{2}$$
$$f^{-1}(x) = \frac{x - 5}{2} \qquad \textit{Replace b by x.}$$

Now show that the compositions of f and f^{-1} are identity functions.

$$
\begin{aligned}
f \circ f^{-1}(x) &= f(f^{-1}(x)) \\
&= f\left(\frac{x - 5}{2}\right) \\
&= 2\left(\frac{x - 5}{2}\right) + 5 \\
&= x
\end{aligned}
\qquad
\begin{aligned}
f^{-1} \circ f(x) &= f^{-1}(f(x)) \\
&= f^{-1}(2x + 5) \\
&= \frac{(2x + 5) - 5}{2} \\
&= x
\end{aligned}
$$

So, $f \circ f^{-1}(x) = f^{-1} \circ f(x) = x$.

Not all functions have inverses that are functions.

Example

3 **Given $f(x) = x^2$, find $f^{-1}(x)$.**

Since $f(x) = x^2$, $f(a) = a^2$. Use $a^2 = b$ to find $f^{-1}(b)$. _Why?_

Solve the equation for a.

$$a^2 = b$$
$$a = \pm\sqrt{b}$$
$$f^{-1}(b) = \pm\sqrt{b} \qquad \textit{Replace a by } f^{-1}(b).$$
$$f^{-1}(x) = \pm\sqrt{x} \qquad \textit{Replace b by x.}$$

The equation does not define a function. Why?

To determine if a function will have an inverse function use the **horizontal line test.** If any horizontal line drawn on the graph of a function passes through no more than one point of the graph, then the function has an inverse that is also a function.

Exploratory Exercises

Find $f \circ g(4)$ and $g \circ f(4)$.

1. $f(x) = x + 2$
   $g(x) = x - 3$

2. $f(x) = x^2 + 7$
   $g(x) = x - 5$

3. $f(x) = x^2 - 1$ 24
   $g(x) = x + 1$ 16

4. $f(x) = 2x + 5$
   $g(x) = x - 6$

5. $f(x) = x^2$
   $g(x) = x^5$

6. $f(x) = x^2 + 2x + 1$ 6
   $g(x) = x - 1$ 24

7. $f(x) = 3x^2 - 4$
   $g(x) = 5x + 1$

8. $f(x) = x^2 - 4x + 5$
   $g(x) = x - .2$

9. $f(x) = 5x + 9$ 14
   $g(x) = \frac{1}{2}x - 1$ 13.5

Determine if the inverse of each relation graphed below is a function.

10.

11.

12.

Written Exercises

Find $f \circ g(x)$ and $g \circ f(x)$.

1. $f(x) = x + 3$
   $g(x) = 2x + 5$

2. $f(x) = x^2 - 9$
   $g(x) = x + 4$

3. $f(x) = \frac{1}{2}x - 7$
   $g(x) = x + 6$

4. $f(x) = x^2 + 3x + 2$
   $g(x) = x - 1$

5. $f(x) = 3x^2$
   $g(x) = x - 4$

6. $f(x) = x$
   $g(x) = 4x^2 - 7$

7. $f(x) = \frac{2}{5}x$
   $g(x) = 40x - 10$

8. $f(x) = x^3 + x^2 + 1$
   $g(x) = 2x$

9. $f(x) = 5x^2$
   $g(x) = x^2 - 1$

10. $f(x) = -2x + 11$
    $g(x) = x - 6$

11. $f(x) = x^2 + 5x + 6$
    $g(x) = x + 1$

12. $f(x) = x^3$
    $g(x) = x + 1$

For each of the following, determine whether the given functions are inverses of one another.

13. $y = 3x + 1$
    $y = \frac{x - 1}{3}$

14. $y = 5x - 6$
    $y = \frac{x + 6}{5}$

15. $y = \frac{1}{2}x - 5$
    $y = 2x + 5$

16. $y = x + 5$
    $y = x - 5$

17. $y = -x$
    $y = x$

18. $y = -3x + 7$
    $y = 3x - 7$

Graph each function and its inverse.

19. $y = x - 5$

20. $f = \{(0, 1), (2, 3), (4, 5)\}$

21. $y = 4x$

22. $f(x) = \frac{x - 3}{2}$

23. $y = -3x - 1$

24. $f(x) = (x - 2)^2$

For the Scholar

Find the values of n such that the linear factors of the form $x + ay + b$ and $x + cy + d$, with integer coefficients, have the product $x^2 + 5xy + x + ny - n$.

10-5 Logarithmic Functions

The exponential function $y = a^x$ is increasing for $a > 1$ and decreasing for $0 < a < 1$. Since the function is one-to-one, it has an inverse that is also a function. The inverse of $y = a^x$ is $x = a^y$. In the function $x = a^y$, y is called the **logarithm** of x. It is more conveniently written as $y = \log_a x$ and is read *y equals the log of x to the base a*. The logarithm is the exponent. The function $y = \log_a x$ is called a **logarithmic function**.

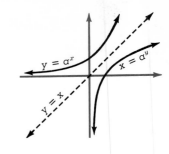

The logarithmic function $y = \log_a x$, $a > 0$ and $a \neq 1$, is the inverse of the exponential function $y = a^x$.

Definition of Logarithmic Function

Thus, $y = \log_a x$ if and only if $x = a^y$. *This is the definition of a logarithm.*

As a result, each logarithmic equation corresponds to an exponential equation. For example, the equation $y = \log_2 16$ can be written $2^y = 16$. Since $2^4 = 16$, $\log_2 16 = 4$.

Examples

1 Write the equation $\log_{27} 3 = \frac{1}{3}$ in exponential form.

$27^{\frac{1}{3}} = 3$

2 Solve the equation $\log_b 36 = -2$.

In exponential form, the equation is $b^{-2} = 36$.

Thus, $\frac{1}{b^2} = 36$, or $b^2 = \frac{1}{36}$.

Therefore, $b = \frac{1}{6}$.   *Why is b not equal to $-\frac{1}{6}$?*

Since the logarithmic function and the exponential function are inverses, both of their compositions yield the identity function.

$$a^{\log_a x} = x \qquad \log_a a^x = x$$

To show this, let $f(x) = \log_a x$ and $g(x) = a^x$. Then, find $f \circ g$ and $g \circ f$.

Since logarithms are exponents, the properties of logarithms can be derived from the properties of exponents.

Suppose m and n are positive numbers, b is a positive number other than 1, and p is any real number. Then the following properties hold.

Product Property: $\log_b mn = \log_b m + \log_b n$

Quotient Property: $\log_b \frac{m}{n} = \log_b m - \log_b n$

Power Property: $\log_b m^p = p \cdot \log_b m$

Properties of Logarithms

Examples

3   Use the properties of exponents to show that the product property of logarithms is valid.

Let $\log_b m = x$ and $\log_b n = y$.

$$b^x = m \quad \text{and} \quad b^y = n \qquad \text{\textit{Change to exponential form.}}$$
$$mn = b^x b^y \qquad\qquad\quad \text{\textit{Find the product of m and n.}}$$
$$= b^{x+y}$$
$$\log_b mn = \log_b b^{x+y} \qquad \text{\textit{Change to logarithmic form.}}$$
$$= x + y$$
$$= \log_b m + \log_b n \qquad \text{\textit{Substitute for x and y.}}$$

Thus, $\log_b mn = \log_b m + \log_b n$.

4   Solve the equation $\log_4 (2x - 3) = \log_4 (x + 2)$.

$$\log_4 (2x - 3) = \log_4 (x + 2)$$
$$2x - 3 = x + 2 \qquad \text{\textit{If } log_a x = log_a y, \text{ then } x = y.}$$
$$x = 5$$

The solution is 5.

5   Solve the equation $4 \log_5 x - \log_5 4 = \log_5 4$.

$$4 \log_5 x - \log_5 4 = \log_5 4$$
$$4 \log_5 x = 2 \log_5 4$$
$$2 \log_5 x = \log_5 4$$
$$\log_5 x^2 = \log_5 4 \qquad \text{\textit{Power property of logarithms}}$$
$$x^2 = 4$$
$$x = 2 \qquad \text{\textit{−2 is not a solution since} } log_a x \text{ \textit{has not been defined for negative numbers.}}$$

The solution is 2.

Exploratory Exercises

Change each equation to logarithmic form.

1. $2^3 = 8$ **2.** $5^2 = 25$ **3.** $10^4 = 10{,}000$

4. $6^{-2} = \dfrac{1}{36}$ **5.** $3^{-3} = \dfrac{1}{27}$ **6.** $49^{\frac{1}{2}} = 7$

Change each equation to exponential form.

7. $\log_2 16 = 4$ **8.** $\log_{10} 0.01 = -2$ **9.** $\log_2 32 = 5$

10. $\log_5 \dfrac{1}{25} = -2$ **11.** $\log_{16} 4 = \dfrac{1}{2}$ **12.** $\log_9 27 = \dfrac{3}{2}$

Evaluate each expression.

13. $\log_{10} 1000$ **14.** $\log_3 81$ **15.** $\log_{10} 0.001$

16. $\log_7 \dfrac{1}{343}$ **17.** $\log_2 \dfrac{1}{16}$ **18.** $\log_6 6^5$

19. $\log_a a^5$ **20.** $\log_8 16$ **21.** $8^{\log_8 3}$

Written Exercises

Solve each equation.

1. $\log_x 25 = 2$
2. $\log_x 36 = 2$
3. $\log_5 0.04 = x$
4. $\log_5 (3x) = \log_5 (2x + 7)$
5. $\log_6 (4x + 4) = \log_6 64$
6. $\log_3 (3x) = \log_3 36$
7. $\log_{\frac{1}{3}} x = -4$
8. $\log_3 27 = x$
9. $\log_x 16 = -4$
10. $\log_x \sqrt{3} = \frac{1}{4}$
11. $\log_{10} \sqrt[3]{10} = x$
12. $\log_{\sqrt{5}} 5 = x$
13. $\log_2 4 + \log_2 6 = \log_2 x$
14. $2 \log_6 4 - \frac{1}{4} \log_6 16 = \log_6 x$
15. $\log_3 12 - \log_3 x = \log_3 3$
16. $\log_5 x = 4 \log_5 3$
17. $3 \log_7 4 + 4 \log_7 3 = \log_7 x$
18. $\log_4 (x - 3) + \log_4 (x + 3) = 2$
19. $\log_2 (4x + 10) - \log_2 (x + 1) = 3$
20. $\log_6 x = \frac{1}{2} \log_6 9 + \frac{1}{3} \log_6 27$
21. $\log_{10} x + \log_{10} x + \log_{10} x = \log_{10} 8$
22. $\log_9 5x = \log_9 6 + \log_9 (x - 2)$

For the Scholar

How many points are there in the coordinate plane that are equally distant from the x-axis, the y-axis, and the line $x + y = 5$?

10-6 Common Logarithms

Logarithms that use 10 as a base are called **common logarithms.** When the base of a logarithm is not indicated, the base is assumed to be 10. Thus, log 25 means $\log_{10} 25$.

The common logarithms of integral powers of 10 can easily be determined.

$$
\begin{aligned}
\log 1000 &= 3 \text{ since } 1000 = 10^3 \\
\log 100 &= 2 \text{ since } 100 = 10^2 \\
\log 10 &= 1 \text{ since } 10 = 10^1 \\
\log 1 &= 0 \text{ since } 1 = 10^0 \\
\log 0.1 &= -1 \text{ since } 0.1 = 10^{-1} \\
\log 0.01 &= -2 \text{ since } 0.01 = 10^{-2}
\end{aligned}
$$

Notice log 1 = 0 and log 10 = 1. Thus, the logarithm of any number between 1 and 10 must be greater than zero and less than one. For example, log 5 = 0.6990.

The logarithms of numbers that differ by integral powers of ten are closely related.

The equals symbol (=) is used with the understanding that the numbers are approximate.

Example

1 Given that log 5 = 0.6990, evaluate each logarithm.

a. log 5000

b. log 0.05

a. log 5000 = log (1000 · 5)
$$= \log 1000 + \log 5$$
$$= 3 + 0.6990$$
$$= 3.6990$$

b. log 0.05 = $\log \left(\dfrac{5}{100} \right)$
$$= \log 5 - \log 100$$
$$= 0.6990 - 2$$
$$= -2 + 0.6990$$

The common logarithm of a number is composed of 2 parts, the **characteristic** and the **mantissa**. The characteristic precedes the decimal point. The mantissa is a positive decimal less than 1. For example, the characteristic of 3.6990 is 3 and the mantissa is .6990. The mantissa always represents the logarithm of a number between 1 and 10.

By using the table of common logarithms on pages 536–537, the logarithm of any number can be determined. First, write the number in scientific notation. The exponent of 10 in this form is always the characteristic of the logarithm of the number. Then, find the mantissa in the table of logarithms. To find log 1.23, read across the row labeled 12 and down the column labeled 3.

When using a calculator to find log n, n ≥ 1, the display gives a characteristic and a mantissa. When n < 1, this is not the case.

Common Logarithms of Numbers

n	0	1	2	3	4
10	0000	0043	0086	0128	0170
11	0414	0453	0492	0531	0569
12	0792	0828	0864	0899	0934
13	1139	1173	1206	1239	1271

log 1.23 = 0.0899

Remember that the logarithms are, in general, irrational numbers and the values given in the table are mantissas that have been rounded to four decimal places.

Most calculators give these values to seven decimal places.

Example

2 Find the common logarithm of each number. Use the table on pages 536–537.

a. 5280

b. 0.0351

a. log 5280 = log (5.28×10^3)
$$= \log 5.28 + \log 10^3$$
$$= 0.7226 + 3$$
$$= 3.7226$$

b. log 0.0351 = log (3.51×10^{-2})
$$= \log 3.51 + \log 10^{-2}$$
$$= 0.5453 + (-2)$$
$$= 0.5453 - 2$$

When the characteristic of a logarithm is negative, the logarithm can be written in many ways. To preserve the positive mantissa, the characteristic and mantissa are usually not added.

$$\log 0.0351 = -2 + 0.5453$$
$$= 8.5453 - 10$$

Two other ways are 2.5453 and 0.5453 − 2.

Most calculators display the sum of the characteristic and the mantissa. Thus, $\log 0.0351$ would be displayed as -1.4547.

If the logarithm of a number is known, then the number which corresponds to it is known as the **antilogarithm.** If $\log x = a$, then $x = $ antilog a.

Example

3 **If log x = 4.8825, find x.**

$\log x = 4.8825$
$\quad x = $ antilog 4.8825 *4 is the characteristic and 0.8825 is the mantissa.*
$\quad\quad = ($ antilog $0.8825) \times 10^4$
$\quad\quad = 7.63 \times 10^4$ *Find antilog 0.8825 in the table of mantissas.*
$\quad\quad = 76,300$

For years, problems involving powers and roots were easier to solve if logarithms were used. Now, the use of a calculator makes such computation simple indeed.

Example

4 **Use logarithms to evaluate the following expression.**
$$\frac{37.9\sqrt{488}}{(1.28)^3}$$

Let $A = \dfrac{37.9\sqrt{488}}{(1.28)^3}$

Then, $\log A = \log\left[\dfrac{37.9\sqrt{488}}{(1.28)^3}\right]$

$\quad\quad\quad\quad = \log 37.9 + \frac{1}{2}\log 488 - 3\log 1.28$ *Which properties are used here?*
$\quad\quad\quad\quad = 1.5786 + \frac{1}{2}(2.6884) - 3(0.1072)$
$\quad\quad\quad\quad = 2.6012$
Therefore, $A = $ antilog 2.6012
$\quad\quad\quad\quad = 399$

The value of the given expression is approximately 399.

Example

5 **Use logarithms to evaluate** $\sqrt[5]{0.0641}$.

Let $A = \sqrt[5]{0.0641}$

Then, $\log A = \log \sqrt[5]{0.0641}$
$= \frac{1}{5} \log 0.0641$
$= \frac{1}{5}(0.8069 - 2)$
$= \frac{1}{5}(3.8069 - 5)$ $0.8069 - 2 = 3.8069 - 5$ *Since the multiplying factor*
$= 0.7614 - 1$ *is $\frac{1}{5}$, the negative character-*
$A = \text{antilog } (0.7614 - 1)$ *istic should be a multiple*
$= (\text{antilog } 0.7614) \times 10^{-1}$ *of 5.*
$= 5.77 \times 10^{-1} \text{ or } 0.577$

The value of $\sqrt[5]{0.0641}$ is approximately 0.577.

Exploratory Exercises

Given that log 375 = 2.5740, find each of the following.

1. characteristic of log 375   **2.** mantissa of log 375   **3.** log 3750

4. log 37.5   **5.** antilog $\overline{1}.5740$ **6.** log 0.000375

7. antilog 4.5740   **8.** antilog 8.5740 − 10   **9.** antilog 0.5740 − 3

Written Exercises

Use the table on pages 536–537 to find the common logarithm of each number.

1. 64.8   **2.** 572   **3.** 8.91   **4.** 25,600

5. 0.00357   **6.** 0.654   **7.** 0.0123   **8.** 873,000

Use the table on pages 536–537 to find the antilogarithm of each number.

9. 3.8899   **10.** 1.8082   **11.** 0.7348 − 2   **12.** 5.3181

13. 8.9149 − 10   **14.** 2.5239   **15.** 0.9265   **16.** 0.7340 − 3

Evaluate each given expression using logarithms.

17. $24.5 \times 754 \times 0.0128$ **18.** $\dfrac{7.12 \times 5.43}{2.28}$ **19.** $(1.12)^3 \times 425$

20. $\sqrt{4.63 \times 54.8}$ **21.** $\sqrt[3]{(2.03)(612)}$ **22.** $6.73 \div \sqrt[4]{0.0063}$

23. $\left(\dfrac{1}{0.381}\right)^2$ **24.** $\sqrt[5]{45.8}$ **25.** $\dfrac{24.8\sqrt{451}}{(39.6)^3}$

For the Scholar

Suppose a number is generated by writing the integers 1 through 999 in order after the decimal point, that is, $N = 1986.12345678910111213 \cdots 998999$. Then, what is the 1986th digit to the right of the decimal point?

10-7 Exponential Equations

Logarithms can be used to solve equations in which variables appear as exponents. Such equations are called **exponential equations.** Solutions to equations involving exponential expressions are based on the fact that if $a^{x_1} = a^{x_2}$ for some base a and real numbers x_1 and x_2, then $x_1 = x_2$.

Examples

1 **Solve the equation $5^x = 100$.**

$$5^x = 100$$
$$\log 5^x = \log 100$$
$$x \log 5 = \log 100 \quad \textit{Power property}$$
$$x = \frac{\log 100}{\log 5}$$
$$= \frac{2}{0.6990} \text{ or } 2.8612$$

Set the tab on the calculator to round to 4 decimal places.

ENTER: 100   [log]   ÷   5   [log]   [=]

DISPLAY: 100   2.0000   5   0.6990   2.8614

The solution is approximately 2.8612.

2 **Express $\log_4 78$ in terms of common logarithms. Then, find its value.**

Let $x = \log_4 78$.
$$4^x = 78$$
$$\log 4^x = \log 78$$
$$x \log 4 = \log 78 \quad \textit{Power property}$$
$$x = \frac{\log 78}{\log 4}$$

The logarithm may be expressed as $\frac{\log 78}{\log 4}$.

$$\frac{\log 78}{\log 4} = \frac{1.8921}{0.6021} \text{ or } 3.1425$$

The value of $\log_4 78$ is approximately 3.1425.

Any logarithm can be expressed in terms of a different base. However, the base is usually changed to base e or base 10.

Suppose a, b, and n are positive numbers, and neither a nor b is 1. Then, the following equation is true.

$$\log_a n = \frac{\log_b n}{\log_b a}$$

Change of Bases

Examples

3 **Find the value of $\log_9 27$ using the formula above.**

$$\log_9 27 = \frac{\log_3 27}{\log_3 9} \qquad \text{\textit{log}}_3 \text{ was chosen because 27 and 9 are powers of 3.}$$

$$= \frac{3}{2} \qquad \textit{Why?}$$

The value of $\log_9 27$ is $\frac{3}{2}$.

4 **Solve the equation $5^{x-1} = 3^x$.**

$$5^{x-1} = 3^x$$
$$\log 5^{x-1} = \log 3^x$$
$$(x - 1) \log 5 = x \log 3$$
$$x \log 5 - \log 5 = x \log 3$$
$$x \log 5 - x \log 3 = \log 5$$
$$x (\log 5 - \log 3) = \log 5$$
$$x = \frac{\log 5}{\log 5 - \log 3}$$
$$= \frac{0.6990}{0.6990 - 0.4771} \text{ or } 3.1501$$

What base would be used to solve this equation using a calculator?

Exploratory Exercises

State x in terms of common logarithms.

1. $2^x = 46$
2. $3^x = 72$
3. $6^{2x} = 63$
4. $5^{3x} = 128$
5. $x = \log_5 121$
6. $x = \log_4 75$
7. $x = \log_3 16$
8. $x = \log_4 35$
9. $2^{-x} = 10$
10. $3^{-x} = 18$
11. $2^x = 14$
12. $3^x = 3\sqrt{2}$

Change each expression to an expression in terms of the given base.

13. $\log_4 7$, base 10
14. $\log_5 4.25$, base 10
15. $\log_{10} 5$, base 8
16. $\log_4 0.033$, base 10
17. $\log_a t$, base 10
18. $\log_2 6.7$, base 10

Written Exercises

Solve the following.

1-12. Evaluate x for problems **1-12** in the exploratory exercises.

Solve each equation using logarithms.

13. $3.6^x = 52.5$
14. $4.3^x = 76.2$
15. $6.7^{x-2} = 42$
16. $2.2^{x-5} = 9.32$
17. $9^{x-4} = 7.13$
18. $5^{x+2} = 14.5$
19. $x = \log_3 52.7$
20. $x = \log_4 19.5$
21. $x^{\frac{2}{3}} = 27.6$
22. $x^{\frac{3}{4}} = 89.8$
23. $5^{x-1} = 2^x$
24. $6^{x-2} = 4^x$
25. $3^{2x} = 7^{x-1}$
26. $12^{x-4} = 3^{x-2}$
27. $\log_2 x = -3$
28. $\log_x 6 = 1$
29. $\log_{27} \frac{1}{3} = x$
30. $\log_3 \sqrt[4]{5} = x$

The formula $y = y_0 \cdot c^{\frac{t}{T}}$ can be used to describe growth and decay in nature. The final count is y, the initial count is y_0, c is the constant of proportionality, t is time, and T is time per cycle of c.

31. The population of single-celled organisms in a pond doubles every 5 days. If the initial count of organisms is 5000 and the final count is 25,000, how many days have passed? (Hint: $c = 2$ because the population is doubling and $T = 5$ because the population doubles every 5 days).

32. A certain radioactive substance has a half-life of 5.5 years. If 0.0469 kilograms are remaining from an initial sample of 6 kilograms, how many years have passed? (Hint: $c = \frac{1}{2}$ because the population is halving and $T = 5.5$ because half of the sample remains after 5.5 years).

33. After 13 years there are 2.1 pounds of radioactive material remaining from an original sample of 7 pounds. What is the half-life of this material?

34. A single-celled animal divides every 3 hours. How many hours does it take for 1 organism to increase to 1000?

35. A certain strain of bacteria increases from an initial count of 1000 to a final count of 35,000 in 6 hours. If $c = 3$, how often does the strain triple?

36. A 5-pound sample of a radioactive substance has a half-life of 3.5 years. How many years have passed, if 0.078 pounds of the substance remains?

For the Scholar

The sum of all but one of the interior angles of a convex polygon equals 2525°. Find the measure of the exterior angle adjacent to the remaining interior angle.

10-8 Natural Logarithms

Logarithms to base e are called **natural logarithms** and are usually denoted **ln x.** Natural logarithms often are used to solve scientific and economic problems related to growth and decay.

The table on pages 538–539 gives values for ln x for values of x between 1 and 10, inclusive. For example, ln 5.63 = 1.7281.

Natural Logarithms of Numbers

n	0	1	2	3	4
5.5	1.7048	1.7066	1.7084	1.7102	1.71
5.6	1.7228	1.7246	1.7263	1.7281	1.72
5.7	1.7405	1.7422	1.7440	1.7457	1.74
5.8	1.7579	1.7596	1.7612	1.7630	1.7

ln 5.63 = 1.7281

Even though natural logarithms do not have a characteristic or mantissa, ln x can be determined for other values of x by using the properties of logarithms.

Example

1 **Find each natural logarithm. Use the table on pages 538–539.**
    a. ln 8.37   **b. ln 3.965**   **c. ln 2040**

    a. $\ln 8.37 = 2.1247$
    b. $\ln 3.965 = 1.3775$ (by interpolation)
    c. $\ln 2040 = \ln(2.04 \cdot 10^3)$ *Scientific notation*
                  $= \ln 2.04 + \ln 10^3$ *Product property*
                  $= \ln 2.04 + 3\ln 10$ *Power property*
                  $= 0.7129 + 3(2.3026)$ *ln 10 = 2.3026*
                  $= 7.6207$

If $\ln x = a$, then $x = \text{antiln } a$. The table of natural logarithms can also be used to find antilogarithms.

Example

2 **Find each antilogarithm. Use the table on pages 538–539.**
    a. antiln 2.2039   **b. antiln 1.3720**   **c. antiln 3.9824**

    a. $\text{antiln } 2.2039 = 9.06$
    b. $\text{antiln } 1.3720 = 3.943$ (by interpolation)
    c. $\text{antiln } 3.9824 = \text{antiln}(2.3026 + 1.6798)$ *ln 10 = 2.3026*
                      $= 10(5.364)$ *Product property*
                      $= 53.64$

Natural logarithms can be used to solve interest problems. The formula to calculate continuously compounded interest is $A = Pe^{rt}$. The final amount is A, the initial investment is P, r is the annual interest rate, and the time in years is t.

Example

3 **Suppose \$175 is deposited in a savings account. The interest rate is $9\frac{1}{2}\%$ compounded continuously. When will the original deposit be doubled?**

    $A = Pe^{rt}$
    $350 = 175e^{0.095t}$ *Substitute 350 for A, 175 for P, and 0.095 for r.*
    $2 = e^{0.095t}$
    $\ln 2 = \ln e^{0.095t}$
    $\ln 2 = 0.095t$ *Definition of Natural Logarithms*
    $\dfrac{\ln 2}{0.095} = t$
        $t = \dfrac{0.6932}{0.095}$ or about 7.3
        The original amount will double in about 7.3 years.

The general formula for growth and decay is $y = ne^{kt}$. The final amount is y, the initial amount is n, k is a constant, and t is time. For growth $k > 0$ and for decay $k < 0$.

Example

4 For a certain strain of bacteria, $k = 0.584$ when t is measured in hours. In how many hours will 4 bacteria increase to 2500 bacteria?

$$y = ne^{kt}$$
$$2500 = 4e^{0.584t} \quad \text{Substitute 2500 for } y, \text{ 4 for } n, \text{ and 0.584 for } k.$$
$$625 = e^{0.584t}$$
$$\ln 625 = \ln e^{0.584t}$$
$$\ln 625 = 0.584t$$
$$\frac{\ln 625}{0.584} = t$$
$$t = \frac{\ln (6.25 \cdot 10^2)}{0.584}$$
$$= \frac{\ln 6.25 + 2 \ln 10}{0.584}$$
$$= \frac{1.8326 + 2(2.3026)}{0.584}$$
$$\approx 11$$

The solution is approximately 11 hours.

Exploratory Exercises

Find each of the following. Use the table on pages 538–539.

1. $\ln 2.58$

2. $\ln 9.45$

3. $\ln 4.28$

4. $\ln 7.21$

5. antiln 0.4253

6. antiln 2.0807

7. antiln 1.5707

8. antiln 0.3788

9. antiln 1.7015

Written Exercises

Find each of the following.

1. $\ln 56.9$

2. $\ln 0.0543$

3. $\ln 650$

4. $\ln 0.0065$

5. $\ln 1$

6. $\ln \left(\dfrac{1}{0.61} \right)$

7. antiln 3.5674

8. antiln 4.6789

9. antiln 5.2094

10. antiln 0.28

11. antiln 0.847

12. antiln -1.847

Evaluate the variable for each of the following.

13. $2000 = 5e^{0.045t}$

14. $2 = e^{5k}$

15. $\ln 4.5 = \ln e^{0.031t}$

16. $732 = e^{6k}$

17. $45.9 = e^{0.075t}$

18. $\ln 60.3 = \ln e^{0.21t}$

Solve each of the following.

19. For a certain strain of bacteria $k = 0.658$ when t is measured in hours. How long will 15 bacteria take to increase to 250 bacteria?

20. Radium 226 decomposes radioactively. Its half-life (the time half the sample takes to decompose) is 1800 years. Find the constant k for the decay formula. Use 300 grams as the original amount.

21. Find k for a radioactive element for which half of a 45 milligram sample remains after 15 years.

22. In a certain solution bacteria can grow from 75 to 210 bacteria in 5 hours. Find the constant k for the growth formula.

23. For certain single-celled organisms, $k = 0.845$ when t is measured in days. How long will it take 14 organisms to increase to 600?

24. Bill has saved $2000 to buy a car which will cost about $5500. If his money is in a savings account paying $8\frac{1}{2}\%$ compounded continuously, when will he have enough money to buy the car?

25. Mr. Hammond invests a sum of money at 8% interest compounded continuously. If he makes his investment on January 1, 1981, and has $10,000 in his account by January 1, 2000, what was his original investment?

26. Assume $15 is invested at $10\frac{1}{2}\%$ compounded continuously. When will the investment be worth $45?

27. How much money must be invested at $11\frac{1}{2}\%$ interest compounded continuously to yield $3000 after 2 years?

28. For a radioactive substance $k = -0.048$. How much time does it take for a 3-pound sample to decrease to $1\frac{1}{2}$ pounds?

29. At what rate of interest compounded continuously will $200 triple in 25 years?

30. For a radioactive substance $k = -0.0954$. How long will it take for 365 grams of the substance to reduce to 45 grams?

31. In 7 days a sample of a radioactive substance decreases from 200 grams to 40 grams. Calculate k for this substance.

32. Jill invests a sum of money at 9% interest compounded continuously. How much must she invest now to have a total of $25,000 in 5 years?

Challenge Exercises

Solve each of the following for x.

33. $e^{2x} - 2e^x + 1 = 0$

34. $e^{-2x} - 4e^{-x} + 3 = 0$

Solve the following.

35. Suppose that in a certain experiment there are 1 million bacteria at $t = 0$ (time is in minutes) and at $t = 25$, there are 2 million bacteria. Under these conditions, determine n and k in the formula $y = ne^{kt}$. Then, determine the time when there will be 2 billion bacteria.

For the Scholar

Find the value of x, where x is positive and $a > 1$ such that

$$(3x)^{\log_a 3} - (5x)^{\log_a 5} = 0.$$

10-9 Euler's Formulas

Leonhard Euler was a very prolific writer on mathematics. His name is associated with a number of important mathematical relations. Among these is the relation between the trigonometric series and the exponential series. The **trigonometric series** for $\cos x$ and $\sin x$ are given below.

Evaluating this series using a computer program is a very easy task.

$$\cos x = 1 - \frac{x^2}{2!} + \frac{x^4}{4!} - \frac{x^6}{6!} + \frac{x^8}{8!} - \cdots$$

$$\sin x = x - \frac{x^3}{3!} + \frac{x^5}{5!} - \frac{x^7}{7!} + \frac{x^9}{9!} - \cdots$$

The two series are convergent for all values of x. By replacing x in the relations with any angle in radians and carrying out the computations as far as desired, approximate values of the trigonometric functions can be found to any desired degree of accuracy. The numbers in the tables of values were calculated in this manner.

Recall that the exponential series is the series for e^x.

$$e^x = 1 + x + \frac{x^2}{2!} + \frac{x^3}{3!} + \frac{x^4}{4!} + \cdots$$

Suppose x is replaced by $i\alpha$ in the exponential series.

$$e^{i\alpha} = 1 + i\alpha + \frac{(i\alpha)^2}{2!} + \frac{(i\alpha)^3}{3!} + \frac{(i\alpha)^4}{4!} + \cdots$$

$$= 1 + i\alpha - \frac{\alpha^2}{2!} - i\frac{\alpha^3}{3!} + \frac{\alpha^4}{4!} + \cdots$$

The terms can be grouped according to whether or not they contain the factor i.

$$e^{i\alpha} = \left(1 - \frac{\alpha^2}{2!} + \frac{\alpha^4}{4!} - \frac{\alpha^6}{6!} + \cdots\right) + i\left(\alpha - \frac{\alpha^3}{3!} + \frac{\alpha^5}{5!} - \frac{\alpha^7}{7!} + \cdots\right)$$

Notice the real part is exactly $\cos \alpha$ and the coefficient of i in the imaginary part is exactly $\sin \alpha$. This important relationship is called **Euler's formula.**

$e^{i\alpha} = \cos \alpha + i \sin \alpha$	**Euler's Formula**

If $-i\alpha$ had been substituted for x in this development the result would have been $e^{-i\alpha} = \cos \alpha - i \sin \alpha$.

Euler's formula can be used to write the **exponential form** of a complex number, θ in radians.

$$x + yi = r(\cos \theta + i \sin \theta)$$
$$= re^{i\theta}$$

$\cos \alpha + i \sin \alpha$ is often written cis α.

Example

1 **Write the exponential form of $1 + i\sqrt{3}$.**

First, write the polar form of $1 + i\sqrt{3}$.

$r = \sqrt{1^2 + \sqrt{3}^2}$ or 2 and $\theta = \text{Arctan } \dfrac{\sqrt{3}}{1}$ or $\dfrac{\pi}{3}$

$1 + i\sqrt{3} = 2\left(\cos \dfrac{\pi}{3} + i \sin \dfrac{\pi}{3}\right) = 2e^{\frac{i\pi}{3}}$

The exponential form of $1 + i\sqrt{3}$ is $2e^{\frac{i\pi}{3}}$.

The equations for $e^{i\alpha}$ and $e^{-i\alpha}$ can be used to derive the exponential values of $\sin \alpha$ and $\cos \alpha$.

$e^{i\alpha} - e^{-i\alpha} = (\cos \alpha + i \sin \alpha) - (\cos \alpha - i \sin \alpha)$ or $2i \sin \alpha$
$e^{i\alpha} + e^{-i\alpha} = (\cos \alpha + i \sin \alpha) + (\cos \alpha - i \sin \alpha)$ or $2 \cos \alpha$

$$\sin \alpha = \frac{e^{i\alpha} - e^{-i\alpha}}{2i} \qquad \cos \alpha = \frac{e^{i\alpha} + e^{-i\alpha}}{2}$$

From the study of logarithms it is known that there is no real number which is the logarithm of a negative number. However, a special case of Euler's formula can be used to find a complex number that is the logarithm of a negative number.

$$e^{i\alpha} = \cos \alpha + i \sin \alpha$$
$$e^{i\pi} = \cos \pi + i \sin \pi \qquad \textit{Let } \alpha = \pi.$$
$$e^{i\pi} = -1 + i(0)$$
$$e^{i\pi} = -1 \qquad \textit{So, } e^{i\pi} + 1 = 0.$$

This relation has been described as the most beautiful one in mathematics for it relates three of the most important mathematical numbers, e, π, and i.

If the logarithm to the base e is taken of both sides of $e^{i\pi} = -1$, a value for $\ln (-1)$ is obtained.

$$\ln e^{i\pi} = \ln (-1)$$
$$i\pi = \ln (-1)$$

The logarithm of a negative number $-k$ can be found since $\ln (-k) = \ln (-1)k = \ln (-1) + \ln k$, a complex number.

Example

2 **Evaluate $\ln (-8)$. Use $\ln (-1) = i\pi$.**

$\ln (-8) = \ln (-1) + \ln 8$
$\qquad = i\pi + 2.079$

Thus, $\ln (-8) = i\pi + 2.079$. *The logarithm is a complex number.*

Exploratory Exercises

Evaluate the following.

1. $\ln(-4)$ 2. $\ln(-7)$ 3. $\ln(-9)$ 4. $\ln(-6.2)$

5. $\ln(-7.85)$ 6. $\ln(-5.23)$ 7. $\ln(-2.01)$ 8. $\ln(-3.49)$

Write the exponential form of the following.

9. $2\left(\cos\frac{\pi}{3} + i\sin\frac{\pi}{3}\right)$ 10. $5\left(\cos\frac{5\pi}{3} + i\sin\frac{5\pi}{3}\right)$

11. $\sqrt{2}\left(\cos\frac{5\pi}{4} + i\sin\frac{5\pi}{4}\right)$ 12. $12\left(\cos\frac{\pi}{6} + i\sin\frac{\pi}{6}\right)$

13. $1\left(\cos\frac{\pi}{4} + i\sin\frac{\pi}{4}\right)$ 14. $3\left(\cos\frac{3\pi}{4} + i\sin\frac{3\pi}{4}\right)$

Written Exercises

Evaluate the following.

1. $\ln(-48.2)$ 2. $\ln(-0.036)$ 3. $\ln(-540)$ 4. $\ln(-21.6)$

5. $\ln(-68.7)$ 6. $\ln(-0.0082)$ 7. $\ln(-4320)$ 8. $\ln(-147)$

Write the exponential form of the following complex numbers.

9. $-1 + i$ 10. $4 - 4i$ 11. $6i$ 12. i

13. $-1 + i\sqrt{3}$ 14. $3 + 3i\sqrt{3}$ 15. $-2\sqrt{3} - 2i$ 16. $\sqrt{3} + i$

Challenge Exercises

Use the first 5 terms of the appropriate trigonometric series to approximate the value of each of the following. Then, compare the approximation to the actual value.

17. $\sin\pi$ 18. $\cos\pi$

For the Scholar

In right triangle ABC, points P_1 and P_2 trisect $\overline{AC}$. If $P_1B = 2\cos x$ and $P_2B = 2\sin x$, where $0 < x < \frac{\pi}{2}$ and x is real, find AC.

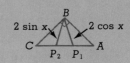

Chapter Summary

1. **Properties of Exponents:** For any numbers a, b, m, and n,
   1. $a^m a^n = a^{m+n}$
   2. $(a^m)^n = a^{mn}$
   3. $\left(\dfrac{a}{b}\right)^m = \dfrac{a^m}{b^m}$, $b \neq 0$
   4. $(ab)^m = a^m b^m$
   5. $\dfrac{a^m}{a^n} = a^{m-n}$, $a \neq 0$ (283)

2. **Definition of $b^{\frac{1}{n}}$:** For any real number $b \geq 0$ and any integer $n > 1$, $b^{\frac{1}{n}} = \sqrt[n]{b}$. This also holds when $b < 0$ and n is odd.   (284)

3. Definition of Rational Exponents: For any nonzero number b, and any integers m and n, with $n > 1$,
$$b^{\frac{m}{n}} = \sqrt[n]{b^m} = \left(\sqrt[n]{b}\right)^m$$
except when $\sqrt[n]{b}$ is not a real number. (285)

4. Definition of Irrational Exponents: If x is an irrational number and $a > 0$, then a^x is the real number between a^{x_1} and a^{x_2}, for all possible choices of rational numbers x_1 and x_2 such that $x_1 < x < x_2$. (288)

5. An exponential function has the form $y = a^x$, where a is a positive real number. (289)

6. Definition of e: $e = \lim\limits_{k \to \infty} \left(1 + \dfrac{1}{k}\right)^k = 1 + 1 + \dfrac{1}{2!} + \dfrac{1}{3!} + \cdots$ (291)

7. An important exponential function is $y = e^x$. (291)

8. Composition of Functions: Given functions g and f, the composite function $g \circ f$ can be described by the following equation.
$$g \circ f(x) = g(f(x))$$
The domain of $g \circ f$ includes all elements x in the domain of f for which $f(x)$ is in the domain of g. (296)

9. Inverse Functions: Two polynomial functions f and g are inverse functions if and only if both their compositions are the identity functions. That is, $f \circ g(x) = g \circ f(x) = x$. (297)

10. Property of Inverse Functions: Suppose f and f^{-1} are inverse functions. Then $f(a) = b$ if and only if $f^{-1}(b) = a$. (297)

11. The logarithmic function $y = \log_a x$, $a > 0$ and $a \neq 1$, is the inverse of the exponential function $y = a^x$. (300)

12. Properties of Logarithms: Suppose m and n are positive numbers, b is a positive number other than 1, and p is any real number. Then, the following properties hold.

Product Property: $\log_b mn = \log_b m + \log_b n$

Quotient Property: $\log_b \dfrac{m}{n} = \log_b m - \log_b n$

Power Property: $\log_b m^p = p \cdot \log_b m$ (300)

13. Logarithms to base 10 are called common logarithms. The characteristic of a common logarithm precedes the decimal point. The mantissa is a positive decimal less than 1. (303)

14. Change of Bases: Suppose a, b, and n are positive numbers, and neither a nor b is 1. Then the following equation is true.
$$\log_a n = \frac{\log_b n}{\log_b a} \quad (306)$$

15. Logarithms to base e are called natural logarithms. (308)
16. Euler's Formula: $e^{i\alpha} = \cos \alpha + i \sin \alpha$ (312)
17. The exponential form of a complex number $r(\cos \theta + i \sin \theta)$ is $re^{i\theta}$, where θ is expressed in radians. (312)
18. Since $e^{i\pi} = -1$, $\ln(-1) = i\pi$, and $\ln(-k) = i\pi + \ln k$. (313)

Chapter Review

Express each of the following using rational exponents. (10-1)

1. $\sqrt[5]{a^3}$

2. $\sqrt{9x^4y^5}$

3. $\sqrt[4]{16a^4b^3c^8}$

4. $\sqrt[3]{18x^3y^7}$

Express each of the following using radicals. (10-1)

5. $15^{\frac{1}{5}}$

6. $(2^4a^3b)^{\frac{1}{5}}$

7. $(4x)^{\frac{6}{5}}$

8. $(x^2y^3)^{\frac{1}{4}}$

Simplify the given expressions. (10-1)

9. $3x^2(3x)^{-2}$

10. $\left(6a^{\frac{1}{3}}\right)^3$

11. $\left(\frac{1}{2}x^4\right)^3$

12. $(2a)^{\frac{1}{3}}(a^2b)^{\frac{1}{3}}$

Graph each equation. (10-2)

13. $y = 3^{-x}$

14. $y = \left(\frac{1}{2}\right)^x$

15. $y = 2^x$

Evaluate x given that $1.5 \approx e^{0.4055}$. (10-3)

16. $(1.5)^3 = e^x$

17. $x = e^{0.811}$

18. $x = e^{0.2027}$

Find $f \circ g(x)$ and $g \circ f(x)$. (10-4)

19. $f(x) = 3x - 5$
    $g(x) = x + 2$

20. $f(x) = -3x^2$
    $g(x) = 2x^3$

21. $f(x) = x^2 + 2x + 3$
    $g(x) = x + 1$

Solve each equation for x. (10-5)

22. $\log_x 49 = 2$

23. $\log_3 (3x) = \log_3 45$

24. $\log_{\frac{1}{2}} x = -4$

Find the common logarithms of each of the following. (10-6)

25. 0.0459

26. 363

27. 42.8

Solve each equation using logarithms. (10-7)

28. $2.5^x = 65.7$

29. $x = \log_3 8.9$

30. $4^{y+3} = 28.4$

Find each of the following. (10-8)

31. $\ln 8.63$

32. $\ln 403$

33. antiln 3.7015

Solve each of the following. (10-8)

34. For certain single-celled organisms, $k = 0.732$ when t is measured in days. How long will it take 15 organisms to increase to 1000?

35. Joan has saved \$1500 for a new set of living room furniture that will cost \$3000. If her money is in a savings account paying 9% compounded continuously, when will she have enough money to buy the furniture?

Evaluate each of the following. (10-9)

36. $\ln (-8)$

37. $\ln (-46.2)$

38. $\ln (-234)$

Write the exponential form of the following. (10-9)

39. $3\left(\cos \frac{5\pi}{4} + i \sin \frac{5\pi}{4}\right)$

40. $1 + i$

Chapter Test ▰

Simplify each expression.

1. $((2a)^3)^{-2}$

2. $(x^{\frac{3}{2}}y^2 a^{\frac{5}{4}})^4$

3. $\sqrt{a^2 b} \cdot \sqrt{a^3 b^5}$

Evaluate x given that $3 \approx e^{1.0986}$.

4. $27 = e^x$

5. $x = e^{0.5493}$

6. $243 = e^x$

Find $f \circ g(x)$ and $g \circ f(x)$.

7. $f(x) = \sqrt{x}$
$g(x) = 2x^2 - 5$

8. $f(x) = 2x^2$
$g(x) = 5x + 6$

9. $f(x) = -x - 7$
$g(x) = -3x$

Solve each equation.

10. $\log_x \sqrt[3]{8} = \frac{1}{3}$

11. $\log_5 (2x) = \log_5 (3x - 4)$

12. $3.6^x = 72.4$

13. $4^{x+3} = 25.8$

Find each of the following.

14. $\log 542$

15. $\ln 0.248$

16. antiln 1.1217

17. $\log 0.00762$

18. antilog $(0.0899 - 2)$

19. $\ln (-5.4)$

Write the exponential form of the following.

20. $3\left(\cos \frac{\pi}{6} + i \sin \frac{\pi}{6}\right)$

21. $8i$

Solve each of the following.

22. In a certain solution, bacteria can grow from 50 to 250 in 6 hours. Find the constant k for the growth formula $y = ne^{kt}$.

23. How much money must be invested at 12% interest compounded continuously to yield $2500 after 2 years?

24. Graph the equation $y = 5^{-x}$.

CHAPTER 11

The Straight Line

Bridges, as well as other structures, are often composed of parts that follow straight paths or lines. The interaction of these lines with one another is an integral part of engineering design.

11-1 Parallel and Perpendicular Lines

Lines which are parallel or perpendicular can be studied by means of their equations.

A linear equation can be written in many forms. The **standard form** of a linear equation is $Ax + By + C = 0$, where A, B, and C represent real numbers and A and B are not both zero. The **slope-intercept form** is $y = mx + b$, where m is the slope and b is the y-intercept. The **point-slope form** is $y - y_1 = m(x - x_1)$ where m is the slope and (x_1, y_1) is a point on the line.

Lines that are **parallel** have the same slope. That is, if m_1 is the slope of ℓ_1 and m_2 is the slope of ℓ_2, then ℓ_1 and ℓ_2 are parallel if and only if $m_1 = m_2$. Vertical lines are also parallel. However, the slope of a vertical line is undefined.

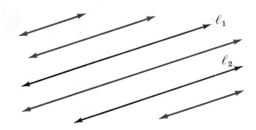

Two non-vertical lines are parallel if and only if their slopes are equal.	*Parallel Lines*

The slope of a line can be obtained directly from the standard form of the linear equation. By solving $Ax + By + C = 0$ for y, you obtain $y = -\frac{A}{B}x - \frac{C}{B}$. Therefore, the slope is $-\frac{A}{B}$. For example, the slope of the line $3x + 6y - 5 = 0$ is $-\frac{3}{6}$ or $-\frac{1}{2}$.

Since parallel lines have the same slope, the equation of a line parallel to a given line and through a given point can be written using point-slope form.

The expression "the line $Ax + By + C = 0$" means "the line which is the graph of $Ax + By + C = 0$."

Example

1 **Write the standard form of the equation of the line through $(3, -2)$ which is parallel to the line $3x - y + 7 = 0$.**

Since $-\frac{A}{B} = -\left(\frac{3}{-1}\right)$, the slope is 3.

$y - y_1 = m(x - x_1)$
$y + 2 = 3(x - 3)$ *Replace y_1 by -2 and x_1 by 3.*
$y + 2 = 3x - 9$
$3x - y - 11 = 0$

The equation is $3x - y - 11 = 0$.

In the figure, the angle of inclination of $\overleftrightarrow{P_1P_2}$ is α. The slope of the line through points $P_1(x_1, y_1)$ and $P_2(x_2, y_2)$ is $\dfrac{y_2 - y_1}{x_2 - x_1}$. Notice the tangent of the angle of inclination is equal to the slope. That is, $\tan \alpha = m$. The range of α is $0° \le \alpha < 180°$. Tan α is positive if $\alpha < 90°$ and negative if $90° < \alpha < 180°$. Tan a is undefined if $a = 90°$. *Why?*

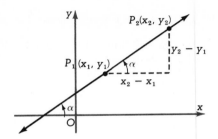

What relation do m_1 and m_2 have if ℓ_1 and ℓ_2 are perpendicular? Let α_1 be the angle of inclination of ℓ_1 and α_2 be the angle of inclination of ℓ_2. Since $\triangle ABC$ is a right triangle and α_2 is an exterior angle, $\alpha_2 = \alpha_1 + 90°$. Take the tangent of both sides of the equation.

The angle of inclination of a line is measured from the positive direction of the x-axis counterclockwise to the line. The angle of inclination of a horizontal line is zero.

$$\tan \alpha_2 = \tan(\alpha_1 + 90°)$$
$$\tan \alpha_2 = -\cot \alpha_1 \qquad \tan(\theta + 90°) = -\cot \theta$$
$$\frac{\tan \alpha_2}{\cot \alpha_1} = \frac{-\cot \alpha_1}{\cot \alpha_1} \qquad \textit{Divide both sides by } \cot \alpha_1.$$
$$\cot \alpha_1 \ne 0$$
$$\tan \alpha_1 \cdot \tan \alpha_2 = -1 \qquad \frac{1}{\cot \alpha_1} = \tan \alpha_1$$

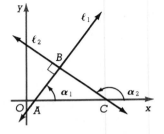

But, $m_1 = \tan \alpha_1$ and $m_2 = \tan \alpha_2$. Thus, when ℓ_1 is perpendicular to ℓ_2, the following is true.

$$m_1 m_2 = -1 \text{ or } m_1 = -\frac{1}{m_2}$$

Two non-vertical lines are perpendicular if and only if the slope of one is the negative reciprocal of the slope of the other.

Perpendicular Lines

Example

2 **Write the standard form of the equation of the line that passes through (1, 4) and is perpendicular to the line $3x - y + 4 = 0$.**

Since $m = -\dfrac{A}{B}$, the line $3x - y + 4 = 0$ has slope 3. Therefore the slope of the perpendicular line is $-\dfrac{1}{3}$.

$$y - y_1 = m(x - x_1)$$
$$y - 4 = -\frac{1}{3}(x - 1) \qquad \textit{x}_1 = 1 \textit{ and } \textit{y}_1 = 4$$
$$3y - 12 = -x + 1$$
$$x + 3y - 13 = 0$$

The equation is $x + 3y - 13 = 0$.

Exploratory Exercises

Find the slope of each line whose equation is given. Then, determine whether the lines are parallel, perpendicular, or neither.

1. $y = 3x - 2$
   $y = -3x + 2$

2. $y = 6x - 2$
   $y = 6x + 7$

3. $y = x - 9$
   $x + y + 9 = 0$

4. $y = 2x + 4$
   $x + 2y + 10 = 0$

5. $y + 4x - 2 = 0$
   $y + 4x + 1 = 0$

6. $y = 8x - 1$
   $7x - y - 1 = 0$

Write the standard form of the equation of the line that is parallel to $y = 2x - 3$ and passes through the given point.

7. $(4, 2)$

8. $(-3, 6)$

9. $(8, -2)$

10. $(-5, -7)$

11-14. For each point given in problems **7-10**, write the standard form of the equation of the line that passes through the point and is perpendicular to $y = 2x - 3$.

Written Exercises

Write the standard form of the equation of each line described below.

1. Parallel to $y = 3x - 5$, passes through $(0, 6)$

2. Parallel to $y = 2x + 6$, passes through $(-1, -2)$

3. Parallel to $y = 6x + 7$, passes through $(0, -3)$

4. Parallel to $y = -4x - 3$, passes through $(5, -7)$

5. Parallel to $2x + 3y - 5 = 0$, passes through $(2, 4)$

6. Parallel to $2x - 7y = 3$, passes through $(8, 0)$

7. Perpendicular to $y = -2x + 5$, passes through $(0, -3)$

8. Perpendicular to $y = 4x - 2$, passes through $(3, -4)$

9. Perpendicular to $5y = 4x - 10$, passes through $(-15, 8)$

10. Perpendicular to $3y = -2x + 3$, passes through $(-9, -6)$

11. Perpendicular to $6x - 4y + 8 = 0$, passes through $(2, 12)$

12. Perpendicular to $3x - y = 8$, passes through $(-1, 5)$

Solve each of the following.

13. Point $(5, 3)$ is joined to $(9, 1)$ and to $(2, -3)$. Show that the two lines formed are perpendicular.

14. Write the standard form of the equation of the line which passes through the intersection of $x - 3y + 2 = 0$ and $2x + y - 2 = 0$ and has slope $\frac{3}{2}$.

For the Scholar

Three circles are externally tangent to each other. If each circle has a radius of 4 units and each side of the triangle is tangent to two of the circles, find the area of the triangle.

11-2 Analytic Proofs

The study of certain functions geometrically, particularly those of first and second degree, by means of their graphs is called **analytic geometry.** Many theorems of plane geometry can be more easily proved by analytic methods. That is, they can be proved by algebraic operations in reference to a coordinate system.

A relation that is frequently needed is the distance formula. Recall that the distance between two points (x_1, y_1) and (x_2, y_2) is as follows.

$$d = \sqrt{(x_2 - x_1)^2 + (y_2 - y_1)^2}$$

The distance formula can be used to find the coordinates of the midpoint of a line segment. In the figure, the midpoint of $\overline{P_1P_2}$ is P_m.

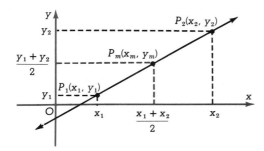

If the coordinates of P_1 and P_2 are (x_1, y_1) and (x_2, y_2), respectively, then the midpoint, P_m, of $\overline{P_1P_2}$ has coordinates

$$\left(\frac{x_1 + x_2}{2}, \frac{y_1 + y_2}{2}\right).$$

Midpoint Formula

Example

1 **Find the midpoint of the segment that has endpoints (5, 6) and (2, 8). Then, show that the midpoint is equidistant from the endpoints.**

The midpoint is $\left(\dfrac{5 + 2}{2}, \dfrac{6 + 8}{2}\right)$ or (3.5, 7).

Find the distance between the midpoint and each endpoint.

distance between (3.5, 7) and (5, 6)

$$\begin{aligned}d &= \sqrt{(3.5 - 5)^2 + (7 - 6)^2} \\ &= \sqrt{(-1.5)^2 + 1^2} \\ &= \sqrt{3.25}\end{aligned}$$

distance between (3.5, 7) and (2, 8)

$$\begin{aligned}d &= \sqrt{(3.5 - 2)^2 + (7 - 8)^2} \\ &= \sqrt{1.5^2 + (-1)^2} \\ &= \sqrt{3.25}\end{aligned}$$

Thus, the midpoint (3.5, 7) is equidistant from the endpoints (5, 6) and (2, 8).

When using the analytic method to prove theorems from geometry, the position of the figure in the coordinate plane can be arbitrarily selected as long as complete generality is preserved. Usually in straight line figures a vertex is located at the origin and one line is made to coincide with the x-axis as shown.

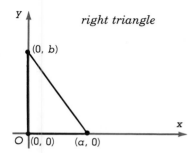

right triangle

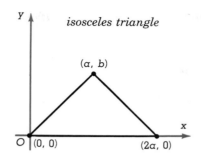

isosceles triangle

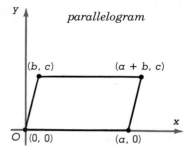

parallelogram

Example

2 **Prove that the line segment joining the midpoints of two sides of a triangle is parallel to the third side of the triangle.**

Let vertex A of $\triangle ABC$ be at $(0, 0)$ as shown in the figure. Let vertex B be located on the x-axis at $(a, 0)$ and let vertex C be at (b, c). Then, M and N are midpoints of $\overline{AC}$ and $\overline{BC}$, respectively. To prove that $\overline{MN}$ is parallel to $\overline{AB}$, show that their slopes are equal.

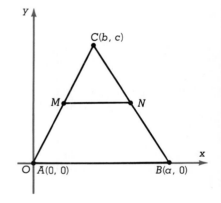

The slope of $\overline{AB}$ is $\dfrac{0}{a}$ or 0.

The coordinates of M and N are $\left(\dfrac{b}{2}, \dfrac{c}{2}\right)$ and $\left(\dfrac{a + b}{2}, \dfrac{c + 0}{2}\right)$, respectively.

Therefore, the slope of $\overline{MN}$ is as follows.

$$\frac{\dfrac{c + 0}{2} - \dfrac{c}{2}}{\dfrac{a + b}{2} - \dfrac{b}{2}} = \frac{\dfrac{c + 0 - c}{2}}{\dfrac{a + b - b}{2}} = \frac{\dfrac{0}{2}}{\dfrac{a}{2}} \text{ or } 0$$

Since $\overline{AB}$ and $\overline{MN}$ have the same slope, $\overline{AB}$ is parallel to $\overline{MN}$.

Therefore, the line segment joining the midpoints of two sides of a triangle is parallel to the third side of the triangle.

Exploratory Exercises

Name the midpoint of the segment that has the given endpoints.

1. $(8, 0)$, $(-6, 0)$
2. $(24, 0)$, $(0, -18)$
3. $(11, 7)$, $(5, 11)$
4. $(-3, -2)$, $(8, 4)$
5. $(0, 0)$, (a, b)
6. (a, b), (c, d)

Written Exercises

Solve each of the following analytically.

1. The vertices of a rectangle are $(-3, 1)$, $(-1, 3)$, $(3, -1)$, $(1, -3)$. Find the area of the rectangle.

2. Show that the points $(-1, 3)$, $(3, 6)$, $(6, 2)$, and $(2, -1)$ are the vertices of a square.

3. The vertices of a parallelogram are $(2, 4)$, $(5, 9)$, $(14, 9)$, and $(11, 4)$. Find the lengths of the diagonals.

4. The vertices of a triangle are $(5, 0)$, $(-3, 2)$, and $(-1, -4)$. Find the coordinates of the midpoints of the sides.

5. Show that the points $(-3, 1)$, $(9, -4)$, $(12, 0)$, and $(0, 5)$ are the vertices of a parallelogram.

6. Three vertices of a parallelogram are $(-2, -1)$, $(-1, 4)$, and $(5, 1)$. Find the coordinates of the fourth vertex. (three possibilities)

Prove each of the following analytically.

7. Given rectangle $ABCD$, prove that $\overline{AC} \cong \overline{BD}$. That is, prove that the diagonals of a rectangle are congruent.

8. Given rectangle $ABCD$, prove $\overline{AE} \cong \overline{EC}$ and $\overline{BE} \cong \overline{ED}$. What can you conclude about the diagonals of a rectangle?

9. The diagonals of a square are perpendicular.

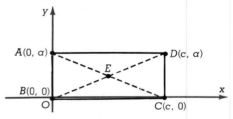

10. The diagonals of a parallelogram bisect each other.

11. The square of the hypotenuse of a right triangle is equal to the sum of the squares of the other sides.

12. The medians to the congruent sides of an isosceles triangle are congruent.

13. The line segment joining the midpoints of two sides of a triangle is equal in length to one-half the third side.

14. The line joining the midpoints of the non-parallel sides of a trapezoid is parallel to the bases of the trapezoid.

15. The median of a trapezoid is equal in length to one-half the sum of the lengths of the parallel sides.

16. The sum of the squares of the four sides of a parallelogram is equal to the sum of the squares of the diagonals.

Challenge Exercise

17. Prove the lines joining midpoints of successive sides of any quadrilateral form a parallelogram.

For the Scholar

Simplify the following expression when a is a positive number and $a \neq 1$.

$$\frac{2}{\log_3 a} + \frac{2}{\log_5 a} + \frac{2}{\log_7 a}$$

11-3 Angles of Intersecting Lines

The slope of a line is equal to the tangent of the angle of inclination. Thus, the formula $\tan \alpha = m$ can be used to find the angle of inclination of a line when the slope is known. Consider the line $4x - y + 3 = 0$. The slope of the line is 4. Why? Therefore $\tan \alpha = 4$ and $\alpha = \arctan 4$ or $76°$.

Let ℓ_1 and ℓ_2 be two non-vertical lines that intersect at C, and let the measures of their angles of inclination be α_1 and α_2, respectively. Let θ represent the measure of the angle of intersection of the lines. Then, θ can be expressed in terms of α_1 and α_2. Since α_2 is the measure of an exterior angle of $\triangle ABC$, it is equal to the sum of the measures of the non-adjacent opposite interior angles, α_1 and θ.

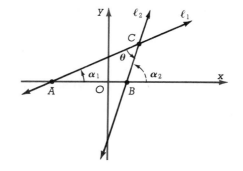

$$\alpha_2 = \alpha_1 + \theta$$
$$\theta = \alpha_2 - \alpha_1$$

Using this the following is true.

$$\tan \theta = \tan(\alpha_2 - \alpha_1)$$
$$\tan \theta = \frac{\tan \alpha_2 - \tan \alpha_1}{1 + \tan \alpha_2 \tan \alpha_1}$$

But, $\tan \alpha_1 = m_1$ and $\tan \alpha_2 = m_2$. Therefore,

$$\tan \theta = \frac{m_2 - m_1}{1 + m_1 m_2}.$$

If m_1 is the slope of ℓ_1 and m_2 is the slope of ℓ_2, then the angle of intersection, measured from ℓ_1 to ℓ_2, is θ and

$$\tan \theta = \frac{m_2 - m_1}{1 + m_1 m_2}.$$

Angle of Intersection

If either of the lines is vertical the formula fails. However, in this event the angle θ can be found directly. If the angle of inclination of ℓ_1 is α_1 and ℓ_2 is vertical, then $\theta = 90° - \alpha_1$. *Why?*

Example

1 **Find the acute angle formed by the intersection of the lines $y = 2x - 7$ and $y = -x + 1$.**

From the given equations, $m_1 = 2$ and $m_2 = -1$.

$$\tan \theta = \frac{m_2 - m_1}{1 + m_1 m_2}$$

$$= \frac{-1 - 2}{1 + 2(-1)} \text{ or } 3$$

$$\theta = \text{Arctan } 3 \text{ or approximately } 71°30'$$

If tan θ is a positive number, the acute angle from ℓ_1 to ℓ_2 is measured counterclockwise. If tan θ is a negative number, the acute angle from ℓ_1 to ℓ_2 is measured clockwise.

Exploratory Exercises

Find the angle of inclination of each line whose equation is given.

1. $y = 3x + 6$
2. $y = 2 - 5x$
3. $2x + y = 4$
4. $x - y = 6$
5. $y + 4x = 3$
6. $2x + 3y = 4$
7. $2y - 5x + 7 = 0$
8. $3x - 2y + 6 = 0$
9. $-2x + 3y + 7 = 0$

Find the acute angle formed by the intersection of lines with the given slopes.

10. $m_1 = 5, m_2 = 3$
11. $m_1 = 4, m_2 = 7$
12. $m_1 = -1, m_2 = -3$
13. $m_1 = -6, m_2 = -2$
14. $m_1 = 8, m_2 = -9$
15. $m_1 = -10, m_2 = 5$

Written Exercises

Find the acute angle formed by the intersection of the graphs of each pair of equations.

1. $y = -3x + 2$
$y = -x$
2. $y = -10x - 9$
$y = -6x + 4$
3. $y = 4x + 20$
$y = -8x - 15$
4. $2x - 5y = 4$
$3x - 2y = 0$
5. $y - 3x = 2$
$x = -4$
6. $9x - 2y + 5 = 0$
$x = 7$
7. $x - y = 2$
$2x + 3y = 9$
8. $3x - 2y = 10$
$x + y = 0$
9. $5x - 3y = 12$
$2x - 3y = 3$
10. $x + 5y - 2 = 0$
$y + x - 6 = 0$
11. $3x - y - 2 = 0$
$4x - y - 6 = 0$
12. $9x - 4y - 2 = 0$
$x + y - 6 = 0$

Solve each of the following.

13. Show that the lines $x - 7y - 2 = 0$ and $4x - 3y - 6 = 0$ intersect at a 45° angle.

14. Show that the lines $-4x + 2y - 5 = 0$ and $3x - y + 2 = 0$ intersect at an angle of 8°, to the nearest degree.

15. Find the acute angle between the diagonals of a parallelogram whose vertices are (3, 5), (7, 5), (9, 8), and (5, 8).

16. Find the acute angle between the diagonals of a parallelogram whose vertices are (4, 7), (10, 7), (2, 4), and (8, 4).

17. Find the angle of intersection between the two longer sides of a triangle whose vertices are (0, 0), (5, 0), and (7, 9).

18. Find the angle of intersection between the two longer sides of a triangle whose vertices are (2, 0), (9, 0), and (8, 9).

19. The angle between two lines is 60°. The slope of ℓ_1 is $\frac{2}{3}$. What is the slope of ℓ_2?

20. The angle between two lines is 60°. The slope of ℓ_2 is $\frac{2}{3}$. What is the slope of ℓ_1?

21. Write the equation of the line that passes through the origin and intersects the line $2x - y + 3 = 0$ at an angle of 45°. (two possibilities)

22. Write the equation of the line that passes through (2, 3) and intersects the line $3x + 2y - 1 = 0$ at an angle of 30°. (two possibilities)

For the Scholar

Polygon *ABCDEF* is formed by joining the midpoints of the sides of a regular hexagon whose apothem is 4 units. Find the area of polygon *ABCDEF*.

11-4   Normal Form of a Linear Equation

A **normal** is a line that is perpendicular to another line or surface. The **normal form** of the equation of a line is written in terms of the length of the normal from the line to the origin.

Let ℓ be a line that does not pass through the origin. Let p be the length of its normal to the origin. Let ϕ be the positive angle between the positive x-axis and p. Draw $\overline{MC}$ perpendicular to the x-axis. Then, $OM = p \cos \phi$, and $MC = p \sin \phi$.

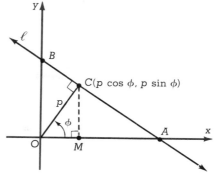

The equation of a line through the origin is of the form $y = mx$. Hence, the equation of $\overleftrightarrow{OC}$ is as follows.

$$y = \frac{MC}{OM} \cdot x = \frac{p \sin \phi}{p \cos \phi} \cdot x$$

$$\text{or}\quad x \sin \phi - y \cos \phi = 0$$

Since ℓ is perpendicular to $\overleftrightarrow{OC}$, its slope, $-\dfrac{\cos \phi}{\sin \phi}$, is the negative reciprocal of the slope of $\overleftrightarrow{OC}$. Then, the equation of ℓ is of the following form.

$$y = -\frac{\cos \phi}{\sin \phi} x + b \quad \text{or}$$

$$x \cos \phi + y \sin \phi - b \sin \phi = 0$$

Since the line passes through C, the equation is satisfied by the coordinates of C. Therefore, it is possible to replace x by $p \cos \phi$ and y by $p \sin \phi$.

The point C can be in any quadrant.
$0° \leq \phi < 360°$

$$p \cos \phi\,(\cos \phi) + p \sin \phi\,(\sin \phi) - b \sin \phi = 0$$
$$p \cos^2 \phi + p \sin^2 \phi - b \sin \phi = 0$$
$$p(\cos^2 \phi + \sin^2 \phi) - b \sin \phi = 0$$
$$p(1) - b \sin \phi = 0$$
$$p = b \sin \phi$$

Thus, replace $b \sin \phi$ by p in the equation of line ℓ to obtain the normal form of a linear equation.

The normal form of a linear equation is

$$x \cos \phi + y \sin \phi - p = 0$$

where p is the length of the normal from the line to the origin and ϕ is the positive angle between the positive x-axis and the normal.

Normal Form

1 **Write the equation of a line in standard form for which the normal p is 5, and makes an angle of 30° with the x-axis.**

$$x \cos \phi + y \sin \phi - p = 0 \qquad \textit{Normal form}$$
$$x \cos 30° + y \sin 30° - 5 = 0 \qquad \phi = 30° \text{ and } p = 5$$
$$\frac{\sqrt{3}}{2}x + \frac{1}{2}y - 5 = 0$$
$$\sqrt{3}x + y - 10 = 0$$

The equation is $\sqrt{3}x + y - 10 = 0$.

The standard form of a linear equation $Ax + By + C = 0$ can be transformed to normal form $x \cos \phi + y \sin \phi - p = 0$, if the relationship between the coefficients in the two forms is known. The equations will represent the same line if and only if their corresponding coefficients are proportional. That is, if $\dfrac{A}{\cos \phi} = \dfrac{B}{\sin \phi} = \dfrac{C}{-p}$, then $\sin \phi = \dfrac{-Bp}{C}$, and $\cos \phi = \dfrac{-Ap}{C}$.

The first equation can be divided by the second ($\cos \phi \neq 0$).

$$\frac{\sin \phi}{\cos \phi} = \frac{B}{A} = \tan \phi$$

Consider a right triangle with an acute angle ϕ such that $\tan \phi = \dfrac{B}{A}$. The length of the hypotenuse is $\sqrt{A^2 + B^2}$. Thus,

$$\sin \phi = \frac{B}{\pm\sqrt{A^2 + B^2}}, \cos \phi = \frac{A}{\pm\sqrt{A^2 + B^2}}, \text{ and } p = \frac{C}{\pm\sqrt{A^2 + B^2}}.$$

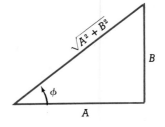

The double sign, $\pm$, is used since p must be positive in the equation $x \cos \phi + y \sin \phi - p = 0$. Thus, the sign must be chosen opposite the sign of C. That is, if C is positive use $-\sqrt{A^2 + B^2}$, and if C is negative use $\sqrt{A^2 + B^2}$.

The values for $\sin \phi$, $\cos \phi$, and p can be substituted into the normal form to obtain the following.

If $C = 0$, the sign is chosen so that $\sin \phi$ is positive, that is, the same sign as that of B.

$$\frac{Ax}{\pm\sqrt{A^2 + B^2}} + \frac{By}{\pm\sqrt{A^2 + B^2}} + \frac{C}{\pm\sqrt{A^2 + B^2}} = 0$$

Notice the standard form of an equation is closely related to the normal form.

> **The standard form of a linear equation, $Ax + By + C = 0$, can be changed to normal form by dividing each term by $\pm\sqrt{A^2 + B^2}$. The sign is chosen opposite the sign of C.**

Changing the Standard Form to Normal Form

If the equation of a line is in normal form, the length of the normal, p, can be obtained directly. The angle ϕ can be determined using the relation $\tan \phi = \dfrac{B}{A}$. The quadrant in which the normal lies must be determined so the correct angle can be found. When the equation of a line is in normal form, the coefficient of x is equal to $\cos \phi$ and the coefficient of y is equal to $\sin \phi$. Thus, the correct quadrant can be determined by studying the signs of $\cos \phi$ and $\sin \phi$. For example, if $\sin \phi$ is negative and $\cos \phi$ is negative the normal lies in the third quadrant.

Example

2 **Change $2x - 5y + 3 = 0$ to normal form. Then, find the length of the normal and the angle it makes with the x-axis.**

$2x - 5y + 3 = 0$ *Since C is positive, use $-\sqrt{A^2 + B^2}$, or $-\sqrt{29}$.*

The normal form is $\dfrac{2x}{-\sqrt{29}} - \dfrac{5y}{-\sqrt{29}} + \dfrac{3}{-\sqrt{29}} = 0$ or $-\dfrac{2x}{\sqrt{29}} + \dfrac{5y}{\sqrt{29}} - \dfrac{3}{\sqrt{29}} = 0.$

Thus, $\sin \phi = \dfrac{5}{\sqrt{29}}$, $\cos \phi = -\dfrac{2}{\sqrt{29}}$, and $p = \dfrac{3}{\sqrt{29}}$.

$\tan \phi = -\dfrac{5}{2}$ *Why?*

$\phi = \arctan(-2.5)$ *Since $\sin \phi$ is positive and $\cos \phi$ is negative, choose*
$\quad = 112°$ *an angle that terminates in quadrant II.*

Therefore, the angle is $112°$ and the length of the normal is $\dfrac{3}{\sqrt{29}}$, or about 0.56 units.

Exploratory Exercises

Find A, B, C, and $\sqrt{A^2 + B^2}$ for each of the following.

1. $2x + 3y + 4 = 0$ **2.** $3x + 4y - 6 = 0$ **3.** $5x + y = 7$

4. $3x - y = 4$ **5.** $y = 4x + 9$ **6.** $y = -7x - 6$

7-12. For problems **1-6**, write the equation in normal form. Then, find the length of the normal and name the quadrant in which the normal lies.

Simplify each of the following.

13. $x \cos 60° + y \sin 60° - 7 = 0$

14. $x \cos 45° + y \sin 45° - 11 = 0$

15. $x \cos 225° + y \sin 225° - 6 = 0$

16. $x \cos 135° + y \sin 135° - 3 = 0$

Written Exercises

Write the standard form of the equation of each line described below.

1. $p = 3,\ \phi = 60°$

2. $p = 5,\ \phi = 45°$

3. $p = 25,\ \phi = 225°$

4. $p = 8,\ \phi = 240°$

5. $p = 2,\ \phi = 150°$

6. $p = 32,\ \phi = 120°$

Write the normal form of each equation.

7. $x + y - 8 = 0$

8. $y = x + 6$

9. $2x - 3y - 1 = 0$

10. $6x - 8y - 15 = 0$

11. $3x + 4y - 1 = 0$

12. $x - 3y - 2 = 0$

13-16. For problems **9-12,** find the length of the normal (p) and the angle that the normal makes with the positive x-axis (ϕ).

Solve each of the following.

17. Write the equation of a line if the point on the line nearest the origin is (3, 3).

18. Write the equation of a line if the point on the line nearest the origin is (−4, 4).

19. What is the equation of a line that makes an angle of 150° with the positive x-axis and is 1 unit from the origin? (two solutions)

20. A line makes an angle of 135° with the positive x-axis and is 3 units from the origin. Find its equation in standard form. (two solutions)

For the Scholar

If $\log_x \cos a = 2y$, $x > 1$, and both the sin a and cos a are positive real numbers, then find $\log_x \sin a$.

11-5 Distance from a Point to a Line

Often it is necessary to find the distance from a point to a line. For example, finding the length of an altitude of a triangle requires that the distance from a vertex to the opposite side be determined.

Two cases must be considered. In one case, the point lies on the same side of the line as the origin and in the other the point lies on the opposite side of the line from the origin. If the line segment joining P to the origin does not intersect the line, point P is on the same side of the line as the origin. Let $\overleftrightarrow{RS}$ be a line in the coordinate plane and let $P(x_1, y_1)$ be a point not on $\overleftrightarrow{RS}$. Construct line TV parallel to $\overleftrightarrow{RS}$ and passing through P. The distance d between the parallel lines is the distance from $\overleftrightarrow{RS}$ to P.

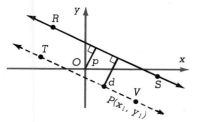

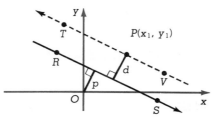

Let $x \cos \phi + y \sin \phi - p = 0$ be the equation of $\overleftrightarrow{RS}$ in normal form. If $\overleftrightarrow{TV}$ is parallel to $\overleftrightarrow{RS}$ then the equation of $\overleftrightarrow{TV}$ is $x \cos \phi + y \sin \phi - (p + d) = 0$. Solve for d.

$$d = x \cos \phi + y \sin \phi - p$$

Since $P(x_1, y_1)$ is on $\overleftrightarrow{TV}$ its coordinates satisfy the above equation.

$$d = x_1 \cos \phi + y_1 \sin \phi - p$$

An equivalent form of the expression above is used to find d when the equation of a line is given in standard form.

The following formula can be used to find the distance from a point (x_1, y_1) to a line $Ax + By + C = 0$.

$$d = \frac{Ax_1 + By_1 + C}{\pm\sqrt{A^2 + B^2}}$$

The sign of the radical is chosen opposite the sign of C.

Distance from a Point to a Line

The distance will be positive if the point and the origin are on opposite sides of the line. The distance will be negative if the point is on the same side of the line as the origin. In an application of the formula the absolute value of d is usually desired.

Example

1 Find the distance between $P(-1, 4)$ and the line $3x - 7y - 1 = 0$.

$$d = \frac{Ax_1 + By_1 + C}{\pm\sqrt{A^2 + B^2}}$$

$$= \frac{3x_1 + (-7)y_1 + (-1)}{\sqrt{3^2 + (-7)^2}} \qquad A = 3, B = -7, \text{ and } C = -1$$

$$= \frac{3(-1) + (-7)4 + (-1)}{\sqrt{9 + 49}}$$

$$= \frac{-32}{\sqrt{58}} \qquad \qquad \textit{Since C is negative, use } + \sqrt{A^2 + B^2}.$$
$$\textit{Remember to use } |d| \textit{ for the answer.}$$

$$= \frac{-16\sqrt{58}}{29} \text{ or about } -4.20 \qquad |d| = 4.20$$

Thus, the point P is $\dfrac{16\sqrt{58}}{29}$ or about 4.20 units from the line $3x - 7y - 1 = 0$ and is on the same side of the line as the origin.

The formula can also be used to find the distance between two parallel lines.

Example

2 **Find the distance between the lines $3x + 2y = 10$ and $y = -\frac{3}{2}x + 7$.**

The lines are parallel. Why? The distance between the lines can be found by choosing a point on one line, then finding the distance from the point to the other line. Since the second linear equation is in slope-intercept form, the line passes through the point $(0, 7)$. Find the distance from $(0, 7)$ to the line $3x + 2y = 10$.
Another point could have been chosen instead of $(0, 7)$.

$$3x + 2y = 10$$
$$3x + 2y - 10 = 0 \qquad \textit{Change the equation to standard form.}$$

$$d = \frac{Ax_1 + By_1 + C}{\pm\sqrt{A^2 + B^2}}$$

$$= \frac{3x_1 + 2y_1 - 10}{\sqrt{3^2 + 2^2}} \qquad \textit{Let A = 3, B = 2, and C = -10}$$

$$= \frac{3(0) + 2(7) - 10}{\sqrt{13}} \qquad \textit{Replace } x_1 \textit{ by 0 and } y_1 \textit{ by 7.}$$

$$= \frac{4}{\sqrt{13}} \text{ or } \frac{4\sqrt{13}}{13}$$

Thus, the parallel lines are $\frac{4\sqrt{13}}{13}$, or about 1.11 units apart.

Exploratory Exercises

State whether you would use a positive or negative value of $\pm\sqrt{A^2 + B^2}$ to find the distance from a point to the line that has the given equation.

1. $2x + 5y - 2 = 0$ **2.** $x - 7y + 4 = 0$ **3.** $2x - y + 6 = 0$

4. $4x + 3y - 6 = 0$ **5.** $x - y - 14 = 0$ **6.** $2x + 4y + 7 = 0$

Name the coordinates of one point that satisfy the first equation given. Then, find the distance from the point to the graph of the second equation.

7. $x + 2y + 4 = 0$ **8.** $y = 3x + 9$ **9.** $2x - 7y + 9 = 0$
     $2x + 4y - 7 = 0$ $2y = 6x - 4$ $2x - 7y - 9 = 0$

Written Exercises

Solve each of the following. Draw a graph for each problem.

1. Find the distance from the line $2x+5y-2 = 0$ to $(3, -1)$.

2. Find the distance from the line $x-7y+4 = 0$ to $(-4, 2)$.

3. Find the distance from the line $3x-y+1 = 0$ to $(0, 0)$.

4. Find and interpret the distance from the line $2x + 3y + 2 = 0$ to $(2, -2)$.

5. Find the distance between the lines $3x - 4y - 12 = 0$ and $6x - 8y - 48 = 0$.

6. Find the distance between the lines $x + y - 1 = 0$ and $y = -x + 6$.

7. Find the distance between the lines $3x - 5y + 7 = 0$ and $6x - 10y - 2 = 0$.

8. Find the distance between the lines $2x - 3y + 1 = 0$ and $3y - 2x = 5$.

9. Write equations for the lines which are at a distance of 3 units from the line $x - 5y + 10 = 0$.

10. Write equations for the lines which are at a distance of 4 units from the line $3x + 3y = 5$.

11. Find the lengths of the three altitudes of a triangle which has vertices at $(5, 3)$, $(1, -4)$, and $(-4, 1)$.

12. Find the lengths of the three altitudes of a triangle which has vertices at $(1, 1)$, $(4, 2)$, and $(3, 6)$.

For the Scholar

Solve the following equation for a.

$$2^{2a+3} - 2^{a+3} - 2^a + 1 = 0$$

11-6   Bisector of an Angle

The bisector of an angle is the set of points equidistant from the sides of the angle. Using this definition, the equations of the bisectors of the angles formed by two lines can be found.

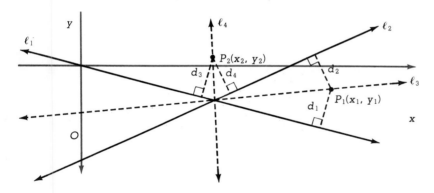

In the figure, ℓ_3 and ℓ_4 are the bisectors of the angles formed by ℓ_1 and ℓ_2. Also, $P_1(x_1, y_1)$ is a point on ℓ_3 and $P_2(x_2, y_2)$ is a point on ℓ_4. Let d_1 be the distance from ℓ_1 to P_1 and let d_2 be the distance from ℓ_2 to P_1.

Notice P_1 and the origin lie on opposite sides of ℓ_1. Therefore, d_1 is positive. Since the origin and P_1 are on opposite sides of ℓ_2, d_2 is also positive. Thus, for any point $P_1(x_1, y_1)$ on ℓ_3, $d_1 = d_2$. However, d_3 is positive and d_4 is negative. Why? Therefore, for any point $P_2(x_2, y_2)$ on ℓ_4, $d_3 = -d_4$.

The origin is in the interior of the angle that is bisected by ℓ_3 but in the exterior of the angle bisected by ℓ_4. Thus, a simple way to determine whether to equate distances or to let one distance equal the opposite of the other is to observe the position of the origin.

If the origin lies within the angle being bisected, the distances from each line to a point on the bisector have the same sign. If the origin does not lie within the angle being bisected, the distances have opposite signs.

To find the equation of a specific angle bisector, first graph the lines. Then, determine whether to equate the distances or to let one distance equal the opposite of the other.

Example

1 **Find the equation of the line that bisects the acute angle formed by the lines $2x - 3y + 6 = 0$ and $3x + y - 9 = 0$.**

As shown by the graph, the origin is in the interior of the acute angle. Therefore, $d_1 = d_2$.

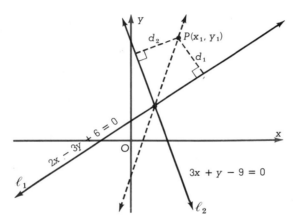

Write expressions for the distances from each line to $P_1(x_1, y_1)$.

$$d_1 = \frac{2x_1 - 3y_1 + 6}{-\sqrt{13}} \qquad \text{Use the formula } d = \frac{Ax_1 + By_1 + C}{\pm\sqrt{A^2 + B^2}}.$$

$$d_2 = \frac{3x_1 + y_1 - 9}{\sqrt{10}}$$

Since $d_1 = d_2$, use substitution to equate the previous expressions.

$$\frac{2x_1 - 3y_1 + 6}{-\sqrt{13}} = \frac{3x_1 + y_1 - 9}{\sqrt{10}}$$

The equation of the bisector can be obtained by simplifying and dropping the subscripts.

The equation is $(2\sqrt{10} + 3\sqrt{13})x + (-3\sqrt{10} + \sqrt{13})y + 6\sqrt{10} - 9\sqrt{13} = 0$.

Exploratory Exercises

Graph each pair of equations. Then, state whether it is necessary to equate the distance or let one distance be the opposite of the other to find the equation of a line that bisects the acute angle between them.

1. $x + 2y - 7 = 0$
   $4x + 5y + 2 = 0$

2. $7x + 4y - 5 = 0$
   $x - 2y + 3 = 0$

3. $x = y + 1$
   $y = 3x + 4$

Written Exercises

Find the equation of the line that bisects the acute angle formed by the graphs of each pair of equations.

1. $x - y + 2 = 0$
   $y - 5 = 0$

2. $2x - y - 4 = 0$
   $x + y - 8 = 0$

3. $2x + y - 1 = 0$
   $x - y + 3 = 0$

4. $4x + y + 3 = 0$
   $x + y + 2 = 0$

5. $3x + 2y - 2 = 0$
   $2x + 3y + 2 = 0$

6. $x - y + 4 = 0$
   $x + 4y + 6 = 0$

Find the equation of the line that bisects the obtuse angle formed by the graphs of each pair of equations.

7. $x + y - 5 = 0$
   $x - 5 = 0$

8. $2x - 3y + 9 = 0$
   $x + 4y + 4 = 0$

9. $2x + 5y + 3 = 0$
   $3x + y - 7 = 0$

10. $6x + y - 3 = 0$
    $x + 3y + 1 = 0$

11. $x + y + 2 = 0$
    $3x - y - 1 = 0$

12. $2x + 5y = 0$
    $5x + 2y = 0$

Find the equations of two lines that make a 45° angle with the graph of the given equation and pass through the given point.

13. $x - y + 3 = 0$, $(1, 4)$

14. $x - y = 0$, $(2, 2)$

15. $y = 2x + 4$, $(-2, 0)$

16. $3x + y - 7 = 0$, $(2, 1)$

Challenge Exercise

17. Find the equations of the bisectors of the interior angles of the triangle formed by $x + 2y = 1$, $2x + y = 3$, and $x - y + 5 = 0$. Show that these bisectors are concurrent by showing that their equations have a common solution.

For the Scholar

Find the length of an internal diagonal for a parallelepiped when the sum of the lengths of its edges is 36 units and the total surface area is 32 square units.

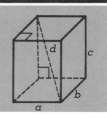

Using Mathematics

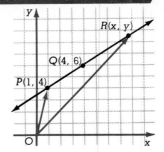

Lines in the coordinate plane can be described by vector equations. Consider the line that passes through $P(1, 4)$ and $Q(4, 6)$. A **direction vector** for the line is $\overrightarrow{PQ}$.

$$\overrightarrow{PQ} = (4 - 1, 6 - 4) \quad \text{or} \quad (3, 2)$$

Let $R(x, y)$ be any other point on the line. Then, $\overrightarrow{PR}$ is a scalar multiple of $\overrightarrow{PQ}$. That is, $\overrightarrow{PR} = t\overrightarrow{PQ}$ or $t(3, 2)$. The **vector equation** of the line can be written as follows.

$$\overrightarrow{OR} = \overrightarrow{OP} + \overrightarrow{PR} \quad \textit{Why?}$$
$$(x, y) = (1, 4) + t(3, 2)$$

By substituting specific values for t, points on the line can be determined.

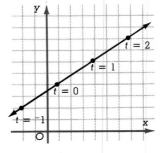

$$
\begin{aligned}
(1, 4) + t(3, 2) &= (x, y) \\
(1, 4) + 0(3, 2) &= (1, 4) \quad t(x, y) = (tx, ty) \\
(1, 4) + 1(3, 2) &= (4, 6) \\
(1, 4) + 2(3, 2) &= (7, 8) \\
(1, 4) + -1(3, 2) &= (-2, 2)
\end{aligned}
$$

Example Write a vector equation for the line through $P(-1, 3)$ and $Q(1, 7)$.

$$\overrightarrow{PQ} = (1 - (-1), 7 - 3) \quad \text{or} \quad (2, 4)$$

Therefore $(x, y) = (-1, 3) + t(2, 4)$ is a vector equation of the line.

A vector equation can be expressed as a pair of equations, called **parametric equations.** For example, the equation $(x, y) = (-1, 3) + t(2, 4)$ can be expressed as follows.

Vector and parametric equations are not unique.

$$x = -1 + 2t \qquad y = 3 + 4t$$

If the **parameter,** t, can be eliminated, then y can be expressed in terms of x. This can be accomplished by solving the first equation for t, then substituting for t in the second equation.

Exercises Write a vector equation of the line that passes through the given points.

1. $P(-1, 4)$, $Q(0, -3)$　　　　**2.** $P(4, 9)$, $Q(6, 2)$　　　　**3.** $P(-3, -2)$, $Q(1, 4)$

4-6. Write the parametric equations of each line for problems **1-3.**

Write the slope-intercept form of the equation of the line for each pair of parametric equations.

7. $x = 3 - t$
$\quad y = 2 + t$

8. $x = 1 + t$
$\quad y = -2 - 3t$

9. $x = 3 - 2t$
$\quad y = t + 5$

11-7   Polar Form of a Linear Equation

The polar form of a linear equation is closely related to the normal form, which is

$$x \cos \phi + y \sin \phi - p = 0.$$

But $x = r \cos \theta$ and $y = r \sin \theta$. Therefore, the polar form of the equation of a line can be obtained by substitution.

$$r \cos \theta \cos \phi + r \sin \theta \sin \phi - p = 0$$
$$\text{or } p = r \cos (\theta - \phi)$$

Recall that $\cos (\theta - \phi) = \cos \theta \cos \phi + \sin \theta \sin \phi.$

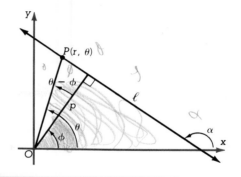

The polar form of a linear equation is $$p = r \cos (\theta - \phi)$$ where p is the length of the normal and ϕ is the positive angle between the positive x-axis and the normal.	*Polar Form of a Linear Equation*

θ and r are variables, and p and ϕ are constants for any specific line. Values for p and ϕ can be obtained from the normal form of the equation. Remember to choose the value for ϕ according to the quadrant in which the normal lies.

Example

1   **Change $3x - 5y + 5 = 0$ to polar form.**

First change to normal form.
$$\pm\sqrt{A^2 + B^2} = \pm\sqrt{3^2 + (-5)^2} = \pm\sqrt{34} \qquad \textit{Since C is positive, choose } -\sqrt{A^2 + B^2}.$$

The normal form is $-\dfrac{3x}{\sqrt{34}} + \dfrac{5y}{\sqrt{34}} - \dfrac{5}{\sqrt{34}} = 0.$

Therefore, $\sin \phi = \dfrac{5}{\sqrt{34}}$, $\cos \phi = -\dfrac{3}{\sqrt{34}}$, and $p = \dfrac{5}{\sqrt{34}}$.

$\phi = \arctan \dfrac{B}{A} \qquad \textit{The angle must terminate in the second quadrant. Why?}$

$\quad = \arctan \left(-\dfrac{5}{3}\right)$

$\quad \approx 121°$

Then, substitute the values for p and ϕ into the polar form.

$$p = r \cos (\theta - \phi)$$
$$\dfrac{5}{\sqrt{34}} = r \cos (\theta - 121°)$$

Thus, $\dfrac{5}{\sqrt{34}} = r \cos (\theta - 121°)$ is the polar form of $3x - 5y + 5 = 0$.

A polar equation can be graphed by preparing a table of coordinates as shown below.

Example

2 **Graph the equation $2 = r \cos (\theta + 20°)$.**

First, change the equation to $r = \dfrac{2}{\cos (\theta + 20°)}$.

Then, make a table of values and graph the equation on a polar grid.

θ	r
0°	2.1
10°	2.3
25°	2.8
40°	4
100°	−4

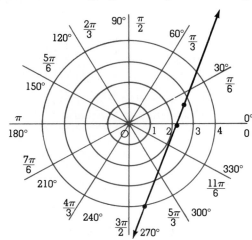

Using Calculators

Change $x - 3y - 4 = 0$ to polar form.

First, change to normal form.

The normal form is $\dfrac{x}{\sqrt{10}} - \dfrac{3y}{\sqrt{10}} - \dfrac{4}{\sqrt{10}} = 0$.

As a result, $\sin \phi \dfrac{-3}{\sqrt{10}}$, $\cos \phi = \dfrac{-1}{\sqrt{10}}$, and $p = \dfrac{-4}{\sqrt{10}}$.

Therefore, $\phi = \arctan \dfrac{-3}{1}$ or $\arctan -3$.

			tan⁻¹			
ENTER: 3				+	180	=
DISPLAY: 3	−3		−71.56505118		180	108.4349488

Therefore, ϕ is about 108°. Substitute the values for p and ϕ into the polar form.

$$p = r \cos (\theta - \phi)$$
$$\dfrac{-4}{\sqrt{10}} = r \cos (\theta - 108°)$$

Thus, $\dfrac{-4}{\sqrt{10}} = r \cos (\theta - 108°)$ is the polar form of $x - 3y - 4 = 0$.

An equation in polar form can be changed to an equation in rectangular coordinates.

Example

3 **Change $2 = r \cos\left(\theta - \frac{\pi}{4}\right)$ to an equation in rectangular coordinates.**

$$2 = r\left(\cos\theta \cos\frac{\pi}{4} + \sin\theta \sin\frac{\pi}{4}\right)$$

$$= r\left(\cos\theta \cdot \frac{\sqrt{2}}{2} + \sin\theta \cdot \frac{\sqrt{2}}{2}\right)$$

$$= r\cos\theta \cdot \frac{\sqrt{2}}{2} + r\sin\theta \cdot \frac{\sqrt{2}}{2}$$

$$= \frac{\sqrt{2}}{2}x + \frac{\sqrt{2}}{2}y$$

$$2\sqrt{2} = x + y$$

The standard form of the equation in rectangular coordinates is $x + y - 2\sqrt{2} = 0$.

Exploratory Exercises

Change each of the following to normal form.

1. $x - y + 4 = 0$ **2.** $2x + 3y - 5 = 0$ **3.** $2x - y + 6 = 0$

Evaluate each of the following. Assume the angle terminates in the first or fourth quadrant.

4. $\arctan\frac{3}{5}$ **5.** $\arctan\frac{5}{12}$ **6.** $\arctan\left(-\frac{12}{5}\right)$

Find ϕ and p for each of the following.

7. $3x - 2y + 4 = 0$ **8.** $x + 4y - 7 = 0$ **9.** $9x + y + 3 = 0$

For each equation complete the table that follows.

10. $r = \dfrac{1}{\cos(\theta + 15°)}$

θ	15°	30°	45°	60°
r				

11. $r = \dfrac{2}{\cos(\theta + 30°)}$

θ	0°	15°	30°	70°
r				

12. $r\cos(\theta + 10°) = 2$

θ	20°	25°	50°	60°
r				

13. $r\cos(\theta + 20°) = 3$

θ	10°	25°	40°	60°
r				

Written Exercises

Graph each of the following polar equations.

1. $5 = r \cos (\theta + 45°)$
2. $1.5 = r \cos (\theta - 10°)$
3. $3 = r \cos (\theta + 15°)$
4. $1.6 = r \cos (\theta - 15°)$
5. $2.5 = r \cos \left(\theta - \dfrac{\pi}{2}\right)$
6. $2.4 = r \cos \left(\theta + \dfrac{\pi}{3}\right)$

Change each of the following to polar form.

7. $x = 10$
8. $x = y$
9. $y = 3x + 4$
10. $y = -2x + 5$
11. $2x + 3y - 1 = 0$
12. $3x - 4y + 5 = 0$

Change each of the following to an equation in rectangular coordinates.

13. $0 = r \cos (\theta + 90°)$
14. $1 = r \cos (\theta + 30°)$
15. $1 = r \cos \theta$
16. $3 = r \cos \theta$
17. $4 = r \cos \left(\theta - \dfrac{\pi}{3}\right)$
18. $2 = r \cos \left(\theta + \dfrac{\pi}{2}\right)$

Find the polar form of the equation of the line that passes through each pair of points below.

19. $(0, 0)$ and $(4, 2)$
20. $(1, 3)$ and $(2, -4)$

Find the polar form of the equation of a line for which the slope and a point on the line are given below.

21. $\dfrac{3}{5}$ and $(0, 4)$
22. $-\dfrac{1}{2}$ and $(3, -2)$

For the Scholar

In the figure, if $\overline{NP}$ is extended to point Q such that $NP = NQ$ and $MN = NP$, find the measure of $\angle QMP$.

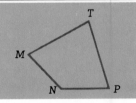

Chapter Summary

1. **Parallel Lines:** Two non-vertical lines are parallel if and only if their slopes are equal. (319)
2. The slope of a line is equal to the tangent of the angle of inclination. (320)
3. **Perpendicular Lines:** Two non-vertical lines are perpendicular if and only if the slope of one is the negative reciprocal of the slope of the other. (320)
4. **Midpoint Formula:** If the coordinates of P_1 and P_2 are (x_1, y_1) and (x_2, y_2), respectively, then the midpoint P_m has coordinates
$$\left(\dfrac{x_1 + x_2}{2}, \dfrac{y_1 + y_2}{2}\right). \qquad (322)$$

5. Many theorems of plane geometry can be proved by analytic methods. Usually in straight line figures a vertex is placed at the origin and one line is made to coincide with the x-axis. (323)

6. Angle of Intersection: If m_1 is the slope of ℓ_1 and m_2 is the slope of ℓ_2, then the angle of intersection, measured from ℓ_1 to ℓ_2, is θ and $\tan \theta = \dfrac{m_2 - m_1}{1 + m_1 m_2}$. (325)

7. The normal form of a linear equation is

$$x \cos \phi + y \sin \phi - p = 0$$

where p is the length of the normal from the line to the origin and ϕ is the positive angle between the positive x-axis and the normal. (327)

8. The standard form of a linear equation, $Ax + By + C = 0$, can be changed to normal form by dividing each term by $\pm\sqrt{A^2 + B^2}$. The sign is chosen opposite the sign of C. (329)

9. Distance from a Point to a Line: The distance from a point (x_1, y_1) to a line $Ax + By + C = 0$ is $\dfrac{Ax_1 + By_1 + C}{\pm\sqrt{A^2 + B^2}}$. The sign of the radical is chosen opposite to the sign of C. (331)

10. Relative Position of the Origin: If the origin lies within the angle being bisected, the distances from each line to a point on the bisector have the same sign. If the origin does not lie within the angle being bisected, the distances have opposite signs. (334)

11. To find the equation of a specific angle bisector, first graph the lines. Then, determine whether to equate the distances or to let one distance equal the opposite of the other. (334)

12. Polar Form of a Linear Equation: The polar form of a linear equation is $p = r \cos(\theta - \phi)$, where p is the length of the normal and ϕ is the angle between the positive x-axis and the normal. (337)

Chapter Review

Write the standard form of the equation of each line described below. (11-1)

1. Parallel to $y = 4x - 7$, passes through $(-2, 3)$.

2. Parallel to $-2x + 3y - 5 = 0$, passes through $(2, 4)$.

3. Perpendicular to $6x = 2y - 4$, y intercept 4.

4. Perpendicular to $5y = 4x + 2$, x intercept 5.

Prove the following analytically. (11-2)

5. If the diagonals of a parallelogram are perpendicular, then the parallelogram is a rhombus.

6. The midpoint of the hypotenuse of a right triangle is equidistant from the vertices.

Find the acute angle formed by the graphs of each pair of equations. (11-3)

7. $2x + y - 2 = 0$
   $3x + y + 1 = 0$

8. $-3x - 2y + 3 = 0$
   $2x + 5y - 2 = 0$

9. $2x - y = 6$
   $3x + y - 1 = 0$

10. $3x + y = 2$
    $x - 4y = 5$

11. $-x = 5y + 2$
    $y = 4x - 7$

12. $x = 6y - 5$
    $2y - x = 1$

Change the following linear equations to normal form. Then, find the length of the normal and the angle it makes with the positive x-axis. (11-4)

13. $3x + 2y - 6 = 0$

14. $7x + 3y - 8 = 0$

15. $6x = 4y - 5$

16. $9x = -5y + 3$

17. $-2x - 9y = -10$

18. $-x + 2y = 7$

Draw a graph for each of the following. Then, find the distance from the given point to the given line. (11-5)

19. $(5, 6)$; $2x - 3y + 2 = 0$

20. $(-1, 3)$; $-3x + 4y = -5$

21. $(-3, -4)$; $2y = -3x + 6$

22. $(-2, 4)$; $4y = 3x - 1$

Find the equation of the line that bisects the acute angle formed by the graphs of each pair of equations. (11-6)

23. $3x + y - 2 = 0$
    $x + 2y - 3 = 0$

24. $y = \frac{2}{3}x - 6$

    $y = \frac{3}{4}x + 2$

Change each of the following to an equation in rectangular coordinates. (11-7)

25. $3 = r \cos\left(\theta - \frac{\pi}{3}\right)$

26. $4 = r \cos\left(\theta + \frac{\pi}{2}\right)$

Change each of the following to polar form. (11-7)

27. $2x + y = -3$

28. $y = -3x - 4$

Chapter Test

Write the standard form of the equation of each line described below.

1. Parallel to $3x+2y-3=0$, passes through $(3, 4)$.

2. Perpendicular to $-x + 5y = -3$, passes through the origin.

Find the acute angle formed by the graphs of each pair of equations.

3. $y = -2x + 5$
   $y = -x$

4. $2y = -5x + 6$
   $3x + y - 5 = 0$

5. $y = \frac{2}{3}x - 1$
   $y = -\frac{4}{3}x + 2$

Change the following linear equations to normal form. Then, find the length of the normal and the angle it makes with the positive x-axis.

6. $-x + y - 3 = 0$

7. $-3x = 6y - 7$

8. $-10x + 5 = -5y$

Draw a graph for each of the following. Then, find the distance from the given point to the given line.

9. $(-5, 8); 2x + y - 6 = 0$

10. $(-6, 8); -3x - 4y = 2$

Find the equation of the line that bisects the acute angle formed by the graphs of each pair of equations.

11. $-x + 3y - 2 = 0$
    $y = \frac{3}{5}x + 3$

12. $7 = 5x + 2y$
    $y = -\frac{3}{4}x + 1$

Change each of the following to polar form.

13. $5x + 6y = -3$

14. $2x - 4y = 1$

15. $y = -\frac{1}{3}x + 2$

Change each of the following to an equation in rectangular coordinates.

16. $5 = r \cos \theta$

17. $3 = r \cos (\theta + 45°)$

18. $4 = r \cos \left(\theta - \frac{\pi}{2} \right)$

19. Prove analytically that the segment joining the midpoints of two sides of a triangle is parallel to the third side and one-half its length.

CHAPTER 12

Conics

The earth's orbit around the sun follows an elliptical path. The ellipse is one of the four conic sections. Equations of conic sections have the form $Ax^2 + Bxy + Cy^2 + Dx + Ey + F = 0$.

12-1 The Circle

A **circle** is a set of points in the plane at a given distance from a fixed point in the plane. The fixed point is the **center** of the circle and the given distance is the **radius.**

Let $C(h, k)$ be the center of a circle, and let $P(x, y)$ be any point on the circle. Thus, $r = CP$, as shown at the right. The distance formula can be used to write the equation for the circle.

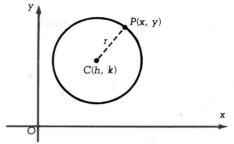

$$r^2 = (x - h)^2 + (y - k)^2$$

This is called the **standard form** of the equation of a circle.

The standard form of the equation of a circle with radius r and center (h, k) is $(x - h)^2 + (y - k)^2 = r^2$.	**Standard Form of the Equation of a Circle.**

Example

1 Write the equation of a circle that is tangent to the y-axis and has center $(-6, 7)$. Then, draw the graph.

Since the circle is tangent to the y-axis, the radius is 6. Thus, the equation of the circle can be found by substituting 6 for r, -6 for h, and 7 for k.

The equation is $(x + 6)^2 + (y - 7)^2 = 36$.

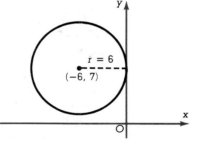

The standard form of the equation of a circle can be expanded to obtain another form of the equation.

$$(x - h)^2 + (y - k)^2 = r^2$$
$$x^2 - 2hx + h^2 + y^2 - 2ky + k^2 = r^2$$

If $r = 0$, the circle becomes a point. If $r < 0$, a real circle does not exist.

Since h, k, and r are constants, the equation can be written as $x^2 + y^2 + Dx + Ey + F = 0$. This equation is called the **general form** of the equation of a circle. Notice the coefficients of x^2 and y^2 must be equal. Also, there is no term containing xy, the product of the variables.

When the equation of a circle is given in general form, the equation can be transformed into standard form by completing the square for the terms in x and the terms in y.

If the coefficients of x^2 and y^2 are not 1, the equation can be transformed by division so that they are 1.

Example

2

The equation of a circle is $x^2 + y^2 - 4x + 6y - 12 = 0$. Find the coordinates of the center and the length of the radius of the circle. Then, draw the graph.

$$x^2 + y^2 - 4x + 6y - 12 = 0$$
$$(x^2 - 4x + \quad) + (y^2 + 6y + \quad) = 12 \qquad \textit{Complete the square.}$$
$$x^2 - 4x + \left(\frac{-4}{2}\right)^2 + y^2 + 6y + \left(\frac{6}{2}\right)^2 = 12 + \left(\frac{-4}{2}\right)^2 + \left(\frac{6}{2}\right)^2$$
$$(x - 2)^2 + (y + 3)^2 = 25$$

The center is $(2, -3)$ and the radius is 5 units.

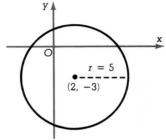

Any three non-collinear points in the plane determine a unique circle. The equation of the circle can be found by substituting the coordinates of each point into the general form of the equation. This will determine a system of three equations in three variables, D, E, and F. By solving the equations, the general form of the equation of the circle that passes through the three given points can be found.

The system can be solved by addition, substitution or matrices.

Example

3

Find the equation of the circle that passes through the points $(2, -1)$, $(-3, 0)$, and $(1, 4)$.

Substitute the coordinates of each point into the form $x^2 + y^2 + Dx + Ey + F = 0$.

$$4 + 1 \ + 2D - E \ + F = 0$$
$$9 + 0 \ - 3D \qquad + F = 0$$
$$1 + 16 + D \ + 4E + F = 0$$

Simplify the system of equations.

$$2D - E \ + F = -5$$
$$-3D \qquad + F = -9$$
$$D + 4E + F = -17$$

The solution to the system is $D = \frac{1}{3}$, $E = -\frac{7}{3}$, and $F = -8$.

Thus, the general form of the required equation is $x^2 + y^2 + \frac{1}{3}x - \frac{7}{3}y - 8 = 0$, or $3x^2 + 3y^2 + x - 7y - 24 = 0$.

Exploratory Exercises

Write the standard form of the equation of a circle with the given center and radius.

1. $(0, 0)$, 8
2. $(0, 0)$, $\sqrt{3}$
3. $(2, -7)$, 9
4. $(-2, 3)$, 5
5. $(-3, -5)$, 1
6. $(7, 4)$, $\sqrt{2}$

Find the coordinates of the center and the length of the radius of each circle whose equation is given. Then, graph the equation.

7. $(x - 2)^2 + (y - 3)^2 = 7$
8. $(x + 4)^2 + (y - 5)^2 = 9$
9. $(x - 2)^2 + (y - 6)^2 = 10$
10. $(x + 7)^2 + (y + 12)^2 = 36$
11. $4(x + 3)^2 + 4(y + 2)^2 = 7$
12. $9(x - 5)^2 = 4 - 9(y - 3)^2$

Written Exercises

Write the standard form of each equation. Then, graph the equation.

1. $x^2 + y^2 - 18 = 0$
2. $x^2 + y^2 - y = 0.75$
3. $x^2 + y^2 - 6x + 4y - 3 = 0$
4. $3x^2 + 3y^2 - 9 = 0$
5. $x^2 + y^2 + 8x + 2y - 8 = 0$
6. $x^2 + y^2 - 10x + 4y + 17 = 0$
7. $16x^2 + 16y^2 + 8x - 32y - 127 = 0$
8. $4x^2 + 4y^2 + x - 24y + 21 = 0$
9. $2x^2 - 4x + 2y^2 + 12y - 12 = 0$
10. $16x^2 + 16y^2 - 48x + 8y - 75 = 0$

Write the standard form of the equation of the circle that passes through the given points.

11. $(0, 0)$, $(3, 0)$, $(5, 2)$
12. $(-2, 3)$, $(6, -5)$, $(0, 7)$
13. $(5, 5)$, $(5, 3)$, $(1, 3)$
14. $(5, 0)$, $(1, -2)$, $(4, -3)$
15. $(5, 3)$, $(-2, 2)$, $(-1, -5)$
16. $(0, -9)$, $(7, -2)$, $(-5, -10)$
17. $(7, 5)$, $(1, -1)$, $(7, -1)$
18. $(-1, 7)$, $(-5, 11)$, $(-5, 3)$

Write the equation of each circle described below.

19. The circle passes through the origin and has center $(4, -3)$.
20. The circle passes through $(7, -1)$ and has center $(-2, 4)$.
21. The circle is tangent to the axes and has center $(5, -5)$.
22. The circle is tangent to the x-axis and has center $(2, -4)$.
23. The endpoints of a diameter are $(-2, -3)$ and $(4, 5)$.
24. The endpoints of a diameter are $(-3, 4)$ and $(1, 2)$.

Challenge Exercises

Solve each of the following.

25. The center of a circle is on the x-axis, the radius is 1 unit, and it passes through $\left(\frac{\sqrt{2}}{2}, \frac{\sqrt{2}}{2}\right)$. Write the equation of the circle.
26. A circle has center $(5, 12)$ and is tangent to the line $2x - y + 3 = 0$. Write the equation of the circle.
27. Write the equation of the family of circles in which $h = k$ and the radius is 7. Let k be any real number. Describe this family of circles.
28. In the equation $(x - h)^2 + (y - k)^2 = r^2$, what is true if $(h^2 + k^2 - r^2)$ is zero?

29. Write the equation of the line that passes through the center of the circle with equation $x^2 + y^2 - 8x - 4y + 11 = 0$ and is parallel to the graph of $3x - 4y = 7$.

30. Write the equation of the line that passes through the center of the circle with equation $x^2 + y^2 - 14x + 10y + 73 = 0$ and is parallel to the graph of $x + 2y = 5$.

For the Scholar

In $\triangle XYZ$, $\angle XYZ$ is obtuse and T is the midpoint of $\overline{XZ}$. If $XY = 6$, $YZ = 10$, and $YT = 4$, find XT.

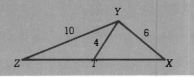

12-2 The Parabola

A **parabola** is the set of all points that are the same distance from a given point and a given line. The point is called the **focus.** The line is called the **directrix.**

In the figure at the right, F is the focus of the parabola and ℓ is the directrix. The parabola is symmetric with respect to the line $y = k$. This line is called the **axis of symmetry,** or **axis,** of the parabola. The point at which the axis intersects the parabola is called the **vertex.** Let the vertex, V, have the coordinates (h, k) and let $FV = p$. Thus, $VT = p$. Why? The coordinates of F are $(h + p, k)$ and the equation of the directrix is $x = h - p$.

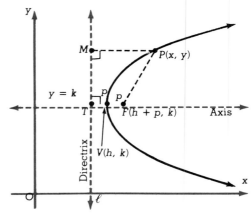

Consider any point $P(x, y)$ on the parabola. From the definition of a parabola, you know that $PF = PM$. The coordinates of M are $(h - p, y)$. Thus, the distance formula can be used to determine an equation for the parabola.

$$PF = PM$$
$$\sqrt{(x - (h + p))^2 + (y - k)^2} = \sqrt{(x - (h - p))^2 + (y - y)^2}$$
$$(x - (h + p))^2 + (y - k)^2 = (x - (h - p))^2$$
$$x^2 - 2x(h + p) + (h + p)^2 + (y - k)^2 = x^2 - 2x(h - p) + (h - p)^2$$

When p is positive, the parabola opens to the right or upward.

The above equation can be simplified to obtain the following equation.

$$(y - k)^2 = 4p(x - h)$$

If the directrix of the parabola is parallel to the x-axis, the equation of the parabola is $(x - h)^2 = 4p(y - k)$.

When p is negative, the parabola opens to the left or downward.

The standard form of the equation of a parabola with vertex (h, k) and directrix parallel to the y-axis, is

$$(y - k)^2 = 4p(x - h)$$

where p is the distance from the vertex to the focus.

The standard form of the equation of a parabola with vertex (h, k) and directrix parallel to the x-axis, is

$$(x - h)^2 = 4p(y - k)$$

where p is the distance from the vertex to the focus.

Standard Form of the Equation of a Parabola

Example

1 **Find the coordinates of the focus and the equation of the directrix of the parabola with equation $y^2 = 12x$. Then, draw the graph.**

Since the equation has the form $(y - k)^2 = 4p(x - h)$ with $h = 0$ and $k = 0$, the vertex is $(0, 0)$. Also, $4p = 12$, so $p = 3$. Since $p > 0$, the focus is 3 units to the right of the vertex and has coordinates $(3, 0)$. The equation of the directrix is $x = -3$.

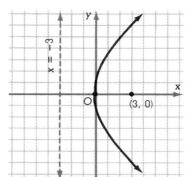

The standard form of the equation of a parabola may be transformed into the general form.

$$(y - k)^2 = 4p(x - h)$$
$$y^2 - 2ky + k^2 = 4px - 4ph$$
$$y^2 - 4px - 2ky + k^2 + 4ph = 0 \qquad \text{h, k, and p are constants.}$$
$$\mathbf{y^2 + Dx + Ey + F = 0} \qquad D = -4p,\ E = -2k,\ F = k^2 + 4ph$$

$$(x - h)^2 = 4p(y - k)$$
$$x^2 - 2hx + h^2 = 4py - 4pk$$
$$x^2 - 2hx - 4py + h^2 + 4pk = 0$$
$$\mathbf{x^2 + Dx + Ey + F = 0} \qquad D = -2h,\ E = -4p,\ F = h^2 + 4pk$$

Thus, the general form of the equation of a parabola is
$$y^2 + Dx + Ey + F = 0 \text{ or } x^2 + Dx + Ey + F = 0.$$

2   **The equation of a parabola is $x^2 + 4x + 2y + 10 = 0$. Write the equation in standard form.**

$$x^2 + 4x + 2y + 10 = 0$$
$$x^2 + 4x + 4 = -2y - 10 + 4 \qquad \textit{Complete the square.}$$
$$(x + 2)^2 = -2(y + 3)$$

The standard form of the equation is $(x + 2)^2 = -2(y + 3)$.

The **latus rectum** of a parabola is the line segment perpendicular to the axis through the focus with endpoints on the parabola. In the figure at the right, the latus rectum is $\overline{RS}$. Since $RU = RF$ and $RU = FT = 2p$, the length of the latus rectum is $4p$ units.

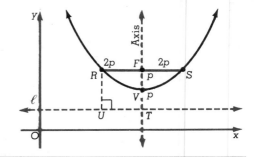

The length of the latus rectum of a parabola is $4p$ units, where p is the distance from the vertex to the focus.	*Latus Rectum of a Parabola*

Example

3   **Name the coordinates of the vertex and the focus, the equation of the directrix, and the equation of the axis of the parabola $x^2 - 4x - 12y - 32 = 0$. Then, find the length of the latus rectum and draw the graph.**

Write the equation in standard form. $(x - 2)^2 = 12(y + 3)$

Thus, the vertex is $(2, -3)$. Since $4p = 12$, $p = 3$. Therefore, the parabola opens upward and the focus is $(2, 0)$, or 3 units above the vertex. The equation of the directrix is $y = -6$ and the equation of the axis is $x = 2$. The length of the latus rectum is $4p$, or 12 units.

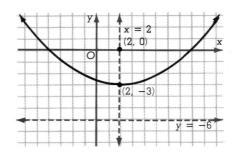

Parabolas have many applications. If a source of light is placed at the focus of a parabolic reflector, the rays will be reflected along parallel paths. In this way, a straight beam of light is formed. Also, the parabola is the path of an object given a velocity in a gravitational field. A thrown ball, or any projectile, will follow a parabolic path unless acted upon by additional forces or thrown directly upward.

Exploratory Exercises

Write the equation of each parabola described below.

1. Vertex (0, 0), focus (2, 0)
2. Vertex (0, 3), focus (0, 0)
3. Vertex (2, 4), focus (2, 6)
4. Vertex$(-2,5)$, focus$(-2,-8)$
5. Vertex $(-1, 4)$, focus (5, 4)
6. Vertex$(-3,4)$, focus$(-3,8)$

Name the vertex, focus, and directrix of the parabola whose equation is given. Then, draw the graph.

7. $y^2 = -2x$
8. $8y = x^2$
9. $(y - 3)^2 = 4x$
10. $(x + 5)^2 = 12y$
11. $(x - 2)^2 = 8(y + 1)$
12. $(y + 2)^2 = -16(x - 3)$

Write the standard form of each equation.

13. $x^2 - 11y = 0$
14. $3y^2 - 19x = 0$
15. $x^2 - 6x - 10y - 1 = 0$
16. $y^2 + 3x - 6y = 0$
17. $y^2 - 4x + 2y + 5 = 0$
18. $x^2 - 8x + 8y + 32 = 0$

Written Exercises

Solve each of the following.

1-6. Name the focus, vertex, directrix, and axis of each parabola for problems **13-18** in the exploratory exercises. Then, find the length of the latus rectum and draw the graph.

Write the equation of each parabola described below. Then, draw the graph.

7. Vertex (0, 0), focus (0, -3)
8. Vertex (6, -1), focus (3, -1)
9. Focus (3, 5), directrix $y = 3$
10. Focus (2, 5), directrix $x = 4$
11. Vertex $(-2, 1)$, axis $y = 1$, length of latus rectum 4, $p > 0$
12. Vertex (3, 2), axis $x = 3$, length of latus rectum 8, $p < 0$
13. Vertex (4, 3), passes through (5, 2), vertical axis
14. Vertex $(-7, -5)$, passes through (2, -1), horizontal axis
15. Focus (2, -6), $p = -2$, axis $x = 2$
16. Focus (3, 0), $p = 2$, vertical axis
17. Endpoints of latus rectum (0, 3) and (0, -3), $p < 0$
18. Endpoints of latus rectum (4, 0) and $(-4, 0)$, $p > 0$

Challenge Exercises

Answer each of the following. *(Hint: Determine D, E, and F in the general formula.)*

19. Write the equation of the parabola that has a horizontal axis and passes through the points (0, 0), $(-1, 2)$, and (3, -2).
20. Write the equation of the parabola that has a vertical axis and passes through the points (0, 0), $(-1, 2)$, and (3, -2).
21. The latus rectum of the parabola with equation $(x - 4)^2 = 8(y - 1)$ coincides with the diameter of a circle. Write the equation of the circle.
22. The latus rectum of the parabola with equation $(y - 2)^2 = 5(x - 4)$ coincides with the diameter of a circle. Write the equation of the circle.

Suppose an object is thrown vertically upward with an initial velocity v_O. Its distance, s, above the ground after t seconds (neglecting air resistance) is $s = v_O t - 16t^2$ where $v_O = 64$ ft/s.

23. Graph the function $s = v_O t - 16t^2$.

24. Name the coordinates of the vertex.

25. What is the significance of s at the vertex?

26. How many seconds will it take the object to hit the ground?

For the Scholar

Young John decided to raise chickens. By the end of the first year, the number of chickens had increased by 250. He had too many to care for and so decided to sell 28% of his chickens. He was then left with 68 more chickens than he had originally. How many chickens did John have originally?

12-3   Translation of Axes

The axes with respect to which a graph is drawn can be changed. In a **translation of axes** the new axes are parallel to the given axes.

Consider a point $P(x, y)$ in a coordinate plane with respect to a given x-axis and y-axis. Suppose you want to express P in coordinates with respect to new axes such that the x'-axis is parallel to the x-axis, and the y'-axis is parallel to the y-axis as shown.

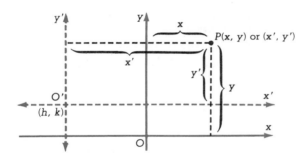

When $x' = y' = 0$,
$x = h$ *and* $y = k$.

Let the intersection of the new axes be the point (h, k). All points given with respect to the x'-axis and y'-axis will be designated by a prime ($'$) notation. Thus, the coordinates of P with respect to the new axes are (x', y'). In order to transform a point (x, y) into (x', y') the relation between the new and old coordinates is required. It can be seen from the figure that $x = x' + h$ and $y = y' + k$. These are called the **translation formulas.**

The translation formulas are

$$x = x' + h \quad \text{and} \quad y = y' + k$$

where (h, k) represents the origin of the coordinate system (x', y').

Translation Formulas

The shape of a graph is not affected by a translation of axes. Therefore, a translation can be used to obtain a simpler form of the equation of a parabola, circle, or other curve.

The new axes may intersect at any point, but a common and very useful translation for parabolas is to translate the origin to the vertex. For circles, it is often useful to translate the origin to the center.

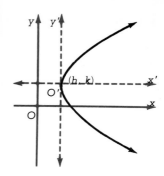

A parabola with vertex (h, k) is of the form $(y - k)^2 = 4p(x - h)$ or $(x - h)^2 = 4p(y - k)$. It is possible to translate the axes so that the y'-axis is the line $x = h$ and the x'-axis is the line $y = k$. The point of intersection of the axes is (h, k), the vertex of the parabola. Thus, in terms of coordinates of the new axes, the equation becomes $(y')^2 = 4px'$ or $(x')^2 = 4py'$.

Examples

1 **Express the equation of the parabola $(y - 1)^2 = 6(x + 4)$ with respect to new axes such that $x = x' - 4$ and $y = y' + 1$.**

$((y' + 1) - 1)^2 = 6((x' - 4) + 4)$ *Replace x by $x' - 4$ and y by $y' + 1$.*
$(y')^2 = 6x'$

Thus, $(y')^2 = 6x'$ is the equation of the parabola with respect to the x'-axis and the y'-axis. The new origin is at the vertex.

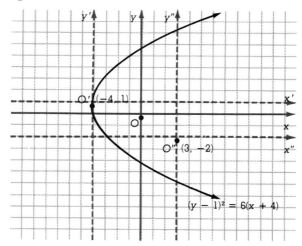

2 **Express the equation $(y - 1)^2 = 6(x + 4)$ in terms of a coordinate system (x'', y'') for which the origin is $(3, -2)$.**

$((y'' - 2) - 1)^2 = 6((x'' + 3) + 4)$ *Replace x by $x'' + 3$ and y by $y'' - 2$.*
$(y'' - 3)^2 = 6(x'' + 7)$

Thus, the equation with respect to axes that intersect at $(3, -2)$ is $(y'' - 3)^2 = 6(x'' + 7)$.

Exploratory Exercises

Find the center of each circle whose equation is given. Then, name the translation formulas that will translate the origin to the center of the circle.

1. $(x - 3)^2 + (y - 1)^2 = 4$

2. $(x + 4)^2 + (y - 6)^2 = 16$

3. $x^2 + y^2 + 2x = 0$

4. $x^2 + y^2 + 6x - 4y + 4 = 0$

Find the vertex of each parabola whose equation is given. Then, name the translation formulas that will translate the origin to the vertex.

5. $(y - 4)^2 = 2(x - 3)$

6. $(x + 5)^2 = 8(y - 1)$

7. $x^2 + 4x - 6y + 34 = 0$

8. $y^2 - 8x - 2y - 15 = 0$

Written Exercises

Solve each of the following.

1-8. Write the equation of each circle or parabola in the exploratory exercises with respect to axes translated so that the new origin is at the center or vertex.

9. Write the equation of the circle $(x - 8)^2 + (y + 3)^2 = 25$ with respect to axes translated so that the origin is $(8, -3)$.

10. Write the equation of the circle $x^2 + y^2 = 36$ with respect to axes translated so that the origin is $(0, -4)$.

11. Write the equation of the circle $x^2 + (y - a)^2 = c^2$ with respect to axes translated so that the origin is $(a, 0)$.

12. Write the equation of the circle $(x - h)^2 + (y - k)^2 = r^2$ with respect to axes translated so that the origin is $(0, k)$.

13. Write the equation of the parabola $(x - 3)^2 = 4(y + 5)$ with respect to axes translated so that the origin is $(3, -5)$.

14. Write the equation of the parabola $y^2 = 4px$ with respect to axes translated so that the origin is $(3, 0)$.

15. Write the equation of the parabola $x^2 = 4py$ with respect to axes translated so that the origin is $(0, 4)$.

16. Write the equation of the parabola $y^2 = 4px$ with respect to axes translated so that the origin is $(p, 0)$.

For the Scholar

In $\triangle XYZ$, M is the midpoint of $\overline{XY}$, N is the midpoint of $\overline{MY}$, and L is the midpoint of $\overline{YZ}$. Find the area of $\triangle XYZ$ when the area of $\triangle XNL$ is 123 square units.

12-4 The Ellipse

An **ellipse** is the set of all points in the plane such that the sum of the distances from two given points in the plane, called the **foci,** is constant. Thus, if F and F' are the foci and P and Q are any two points on an ellipse, $PF + PF' = QF + QF'$.

An ellipse has two axes of symmetry. The segments of these axes cut off by the ellipse are called the **major** (longer) and **minor** (shorter) axes. The endpoints of the major axis are called **vertices** and the intersection of the two axes is the **center** of the ellipse. In the figure on the next page, *a* and *b* represent the lengths of the **semi-major axis** and **semi-minor axis,** respectively. The distance from the center to a focus is *c.*

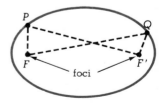

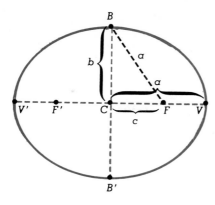

What are the lengths of the major axis $\overline{VV'}$ and the minor axis $\overline{BB'}$?

An important relationship exists between the lengths a, b, and c. Since $V'F' = VF$, then $VF + VF' = VV'$, or $2a$. Thus, the sum of the distances from the foci to any point on the ellipse is $2a$. Since $BF + BF' = 2a$ and $BF = BF'$, then $BF = a$. By the Pythagorean Theorem, $BF = \sqrt{b^2 + c^2}$. Therefore, $a = \sqrt{b^2 + c^2}$ or $a^2 = b^2 + c^2$.

Example

1 Name the coordinates of the foci of the ellipse shown below.

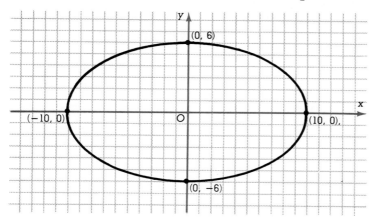

First, find the lengths of the semi-major axis and semi-minor axis.

$$a = 10 \qquad b = 6$$

Then, find the value of c using $a^2 = b^2 + c^2$.

$$100 = 36 + c^2$$
$$64 = c^2$$
$$8 = c$$

Since the center of the ellipse is at the origin, the coordinates of the foci are $(8, 0)$ and $(-8, 0)$.

The standard form of the equation of an ellipse can be derived from the definition and the distance formula. Consider the special case when the center is at the origin. Suppose the foci are $(c, 0)$ and $(-c, 0)$, and (x, y) is any point on the ellipse. Let $2a$ represent the sum of the distances from (x, y) to the foci.

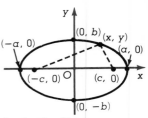

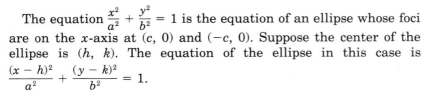

$$\sqrt{(x + c)^2 + y^2} + \sqrt{(x - c)^2 + y^2} = 2a$$

Apply the distance formula.

$$\sqrt{(x + c)^2 + y^2} = 2a - \sqrt{(x - c)^2 + y^2}$$

Rearrange terms.

$$(x + c)^2 + y^2 = 4a^2 + (x - c)^2 + y^2 - 4a\sqrt{(x - c)^2 + y^2}$$

Square each side.

$$a^2 - xc = a\sqrt{(x - c)^2 + y^2}$$

Simplify.

$$a^4 - 2a^2xc + x^2c^2 = a^2((x - c)^2 + y^2)$$

Square each side.

$$x^2(a^2 - c^2) + a^2y^2 = a^2(a^2 - c^2)$$

Simplify.

$$\frac{x^2}{a^2} + \frac{y^2}{a^2 - c^2} = 1$$

Divide by $a^2(a^2 - c^2)$.

$$\frac{x^2}{a^2} + \frac{y^2}{b^2} = 1$$

Substitute b^2 for $a^2 - c^2$.

The equation $\dfrac{x^2}{a^2} + \dfrac{y^2}{b^2} = 1$ is the equation of an ellipse whose foci are on the x-axis at $(c, 0)$ and $(-c, 0)$. Suppose the center of the ellipse is (h, k). The equation of the ellipse in this case is $\dfrac{(x - h)^2}{a^2} + \dfrac{(y - k)^2}{b^2} = 1$.

If the foci are on the y-axis at $(0, c)$ and $(0, -c)$, then the equation of the ellipse is $\dfrac{y^2}{a^2} + \dfrac{x^2}{b^2} = 1$. If the center is (h, k), then $\dfrac{(y - k)^2}{a^2} + \dfrac{(x - h)^2}{b^2} = 1$ is the equation of the ellipse.

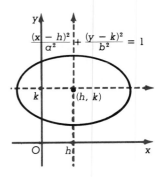

The standard form of the equation of an ellipse with center (h, k) and major axis of length $2a$ units, parallel to the x-axis, is

$$\frac{(x - h)^2}{a^2} + \frac{(y - k)^2}{b^2} = 1 \quad \text{where } b^2 = a^2 - c^2.$$

Standard Form of the Equation of an Ellipse

The standard form of the equation of an ellipse with center (h, k) and major axis of length $2a$ units, parallel to the y-axis, is

$$\frac{(y - k)^2}{a^2} + \frac{(x - h)^2}{b^2} = 1 \quad \text{where } b^2 = a^2 - c^2.$$

Example

2

Draw the ellipse that is given by the equation $\dfrac{(x-4)^2}{121} + \dfrac{(y+5)^2}{64} = 1$.

$a = \sqrt{121}$ or 11 $b = \sqrt{64}$ or 8

The center of the ellipse is $(4, -5)$. Thus, the vertices are $(15, -5)$ and $(-7, -5)$ and the endpoints of the minor axis are $(4, 3)$ and $(4, -13)$.

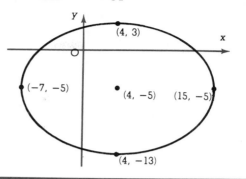

The general form of the equation of an ellipse is a second-degree equation of the form $Ax^2 + Cy^2 + Dx + Ey + F = 0$, where $A \neq 0$, $C \neq 0$, and A and C have the same sign. An equation in general form can be transformed into standard form to determine the center, (h, k), the semi-major axis, a, and the semi-minor axis, b.

If the major axis of the ellipse is <u>not</u> parallel to the x-axis or y-axis, the general equation has an additional term, Bxy.

Example

3

Find the coordinates of the center, the foci, and the vertices of the ellipse with equation $9x^2 + 4y^2 - 18x + 16y - 11 = 0$. Then, draw the graph.

Write the equation in standard form.

$(9x^2 - 18x + \quad) + (4y^2 + 16y + \quad) = 11$ *Group the terms.*

$9(x^2 - 2x + 1) + 4(y^2 + 4y + 4) = 11 + 9 + 16$ *Complete the square.*

$9(x - 1)^2 + 4(y + 2)^2 = 36$

$\dfrac{(y + 2)^2}{9} + \dfrac{(x - 1)^2}{4} = 1$ $h = 1, k = -2, a = 3, b = 2$

The coordinates of the center are $(1, -2)$.

To determine coordinates of the foci, first find c.

$a^2 = b^2 + c^2$

$9 = 4 + c^2$ *a is 3 and b is 2*

$5 = c^2$

$\pm\sqrt{5} = c$

The coordinates of the foci are $(1, -2 + \sqrt{5})$ and $(1, -2 - \sqrt{5})$. The coordinates of the vertices are $(1, 1)$ and $(1, -5)$. *Why?*

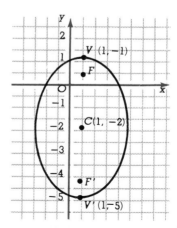

Exploratory Exercises

Write the equation of each ellipse described below.

1. Center $(0, 0)$, $a = 6$, $b = 4$, horizontal major axis

2. Center $(0, 0)$, $a = 8$, $b = 6$, vertical major axis

3. Center $(3, 5)$, $a = 4$, $b = 2$, vertical major axis

4. Center $(-3, -1)$, $a = 7$, $b = 5$, horizontal major axis

5. Foci $(-2, 0)$ and $(2, 0)$, $a = 7$

6. Foci $(2, 3)$ and $(2, -3)$, $a = 4$

Written Exercises

Name the center, the foci, and the vertices of each ellipse whose equation is given. Then, draw the graph.

1. $\dfrac{(x - 5)^2}{25} + \dfrac{y^2}{4} = 1$

2. $\dfrac{(y - 3)^2}{16} + \dfrac{x^2}{9} = 1$

3. $\dfrac{(x - 3)^2}{25} + \dfrac{(y - 4)^2}{16} = 1$

4. $\dfrac{(y + 2)^2}{25} + \dfrac{(x - 1)^2}{4} = 1$

5. $4y^2 + x^2 - 8y + 6x + 9 = 0$

6. $x^2 - 12x + 3y^2 + 12y + 39 = 0$

7. $4x^2 + 25y^2 + 250y + 525 = 0$

8. $x^2 - 2x + y^2 - 2y - 6 = 0$

9. $y^2 - 8y + 3x^2 + 30x + 85 = 0$

10. $9y^2 + 108y + 4x^2 - 56x = -484$

11. $4y^2 - 4y + 16x^2 + 16x - 11 = 0$

12. $12x^2 + 36x + 16y^2 + 32y - 5 = 0$

For the Scholar

The sum of the first six terms in a geometric sequence of real numbers is 252. Find the sum of the first four terms when the sum of the first two terms is 12.

12-5 More about the Ellipse

The shape of an ellipse is determined by its **eccentricity.** The eccentricity, **e**, of an ellipse is defined as $e = \dfrac{c}{a}$. Since $0 < c < a$, then $0 < e < 1$. If e is close to zero, the two foci are near the center of the ellipse. In this case, the ellipse looks nearly like a circle. If e is close to one, then the foci are near the ends of the major axis. In this case, the ellipse is very elongated.

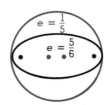

When $e = 0$, the ellipse is a circle.

Sometimes it is necessary to find the length of the semi-minor axis, b, when the length of the semi-major axis, a, and the eccentricity, e, are known. Since $a^2 = b^2 + c^2$, $c = ae$, and $c^2 = a^2e^2$, it can be shown that $b^2 = a^2(1 - e^2)$.

1 Write the equation of the ellipse with center $(-2, 3)$, semi-major axis of length 7 units, and eccentricity $\frac{1}{2}$. The major axis is parallel to the x-axis.

First, find b^2.

$b^2 = a^2(1 - e^2)$

$b^2 = 49\left(1 - \frac{1}{4}\right)$ $a = 7$ and $e = \frac{1}{2}$

$\quad = \dfrac{147}{4}$

Then, write the equation of the ellipse.

$\dfrac{(x - h)^2}{a^2} + \dfrac{(y - k)^2}{b^2} = 1$

$\dfrac{(x + 2)^2}{49} + \dfrac{(y - 3)^2}{\dfrac{147}{4}} = 1$ $h = -2, k = 3, a = 7,$ and $b^2 = \dfrac{147}{4}$

The equation of the ellipse is $\dfrac{(x + 2)^2}{49} + \dfrac{(y - 3)^2}{\dfrac{147}{4}} = 1$ or $\dfrac{(x + 2)^2}{49} + \dfrac{4(y - 3)^2}{147} = 1$.

A more accurate graph of an ellipse can be drawn, if the length of the **latus rectum** is known. The latus rectum of an ellipse is a chord perpendicular to the major axis through a focus. In the figure, $\overline{MN}$ is the latus rectum.

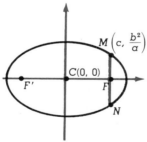

If the center of the ellipse is $(0, 0)$ and the ellipse has foci $(c, 0)$ and $(-c, 0)$, the equation has the form $\dfrac{x^2}{a^2} + \dfrac{y^2}{b^2} = 1$. If $x = c$ the value of y is $\pm\dfrac{b}{a}\sqrt{a^2 - c^2}$, or $\pm\dfrac{b^2}{a}$. Thus, the coordinates of point M shown in the figure are $\left(c, \dfrac{b^2}{a}\right)$ and therefore, $MN = \dfrac{2b^2}{a}$.

The length of a latus rectum of an ellipse is $\dfrac{2b^2}{a}$, where a is the length of the semi-major axis and b is the length of the semi-minor axis.	*Latus Rectum of an Ellipse*

Example

2 An ellipse has center $(0, 3)$, major axis of length 12 units parallel to the y-axis, and eccentricity $\frac{1}{2}$. Find the length of the latus rectum and determine a, b, and c. Then, draw the graph.

Use the formula $b^2 = a^2(1 - e^2)$ to determine b^2.

$b^2 = 36\left(1 - \frac{1}{4}\right)$ or 27 $a = 6$ and $e = \frac{1}{2}$.

$b = \sqrt{27}$ or $3\sqrt{3}$

Then, find the length of the latus rectum.

$\dfrac{2b^2}{a} = \dfrac{2(27)}{6}$ or 9

Use the formula $a^2 = b^2 + c^2$ to determine c.

$c^2 = a^2 - b^2$
$c^2 = 36 - 27$
$c^2 = 9$ so $c = 3$

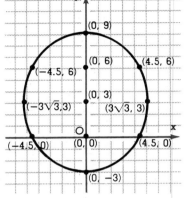

The length of the latus rectum is 9 units, a is 6 units, b is $3\sqrt{3}$ units, and c is 3 units.

Ellipses have many applications. An ellipse is the path of an object in orbit such as the planets around the sun and satellites around the planets. Elliptic gears have special uses where slow, powerful action is needed. Sometimes bridge arches are elliptic in shape. An ellipse has the property that light rays or other radiated energy emitted from one focus will be reflected to the other focus. This property of an ellipse is utilized in the construction of "whispering galleries" where walls and ceilings are roughly elliptical. Any sound emitted from a position at one focus is reflected from walls and ceiling to the other focus where even a whisper can be heard distinctly although other sounds may be in the room.

Exploratory Exercises

Name the coordinates of the foci of each ellipse described below. The major axis of each ellipse is horizontal.

1. Center $(0, 0)$, $a = 6$, $b = 4$
2. Center $(0, 0)$, $a = 5$, $b = 3$
3. Center $(3, 5)$, $a = 4$, $b = 1$
4. Center $(-3, 2)$, $a = 7$, $b = 2$

5-8. Find the eccentricity of each ellipse described in problems **1-4**.

9-12. Find the length of the latus rectum for each ellipse described in problems **1-4**.

Example

2 Write equations for the asymptotes of the hyperbola $\dfrac{(y-4)^2}{16} - \dfrac{(x+2)^2}{9} = 1$. Then, find the foci and vertices and draw the graph.

The hyperbola has a vertical transverse axis and center $(-2, 4)$. Since $a = 4$ and $b = 3$, the equations of the asymptotes are $y - 4 = \pm\dfrac{4}{3}(x + 2)$.

The vertices are $(-2, 8)$ and $(-2, 0)$. *Why?*

Also, $c^2 = a^2 + b^2$, so $c^2 = 25$ and $c = 5$.

Therefore, the foci are $(-2, 9)$ and $(-2, -1)$.

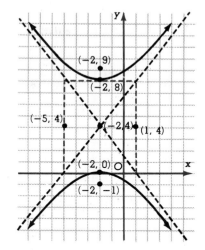

Exploratory Exercises

Write the equation of each hyperbola described below.

1. Center $(0, 0)$, $a = 8$, $b = 5$, horizontal transverse axis

2. Center $(0, 0)$, $a = 7$, $b = 4$, vertical transverse axis

3. Center $(6, -2)$, $a = 4$, $b = 5$, vertical transverse axis

4. Center $(-1, 4)$, $a = 2$, $b = 3$, horizontal transverse axis

5. Foci $(10, 0)$ and $(-10, 0)$, $2a = 16$

6. Foci $(0, 5)$ and $(0, -5)$, $2a = 8$

7. Vertices $(1, 2)$ and $(1, -2)$, $b = 2$

8. Vertices $(3, 4)$ and $(3, 0)$, $b = 3$

Written Exercises

Name the center, foci, vertices, and the equations of the asymptotes of each hyperbola whose equation is given. Then, draw the graph.

1. $\dfrac{y^2}{64} - \dfrac{x^2}{36} = 1$

2. $\dfrac{x^2}{9} - \dfrac{y^2}{10} = 1$

3. $\dfrac{x^2}{36} - \dfrac{y^2}{81} = 1$

4. $\dfrac{x^2}{25} - \dfrac{y^2}{16} = 1$

5. $\dfrac{(x+6)^2}{36} - \dfrac{(y+3)^2}{9} = 1$

6. $\dfrac{(y-3)^2}{25} - \dfrac{(x-2)^2}{16} = 1$

Write the equation of each hyperbola described below.

7. Center $(4, -2)$, focus $(7, -2)$, vertex $(6, -2)$

8. Center $(3, 3)$, focus $(8, 3)$, vertex $(6, 3)$

9. Center $(3, -1)$, vertex $(6, -1)$, equation of one asymptote $2x - 3y = 9$

10. Center $(4, 2)$, vertex $(4, 5)$, equation one asymptote $4y - 3x = -4$

For the Scholar

The square of Janet's age is 400 more than the square of the sum of Kim's and Sue's ages. Kim's and Sue's ages total 10 less than Janet's age. Find the square of the sum of the ages of Janet, Kim, and Sue.

12-7 More about the Hyperbola

The general form of the equation of a hyperbola that has axes parallel to the coordinate axes is $Ax^2 + Cy^2 + Dx + Ey + F = 0$, where $A \neq 0$, $C \neq 0$, and A and C have different signs. An equation in general form can be transformed into standard form by grouping and completing the square.

Example

1 **Find the coordinates of the center, the foci, and the vertices of the hyperbola with equation $25x^2 - 9y^2 - 100x - 72y - 269 = 0$. Then, draw the graph.**

Write the equation in standard form.

$(25x^2 - 100x + \quad) - (9y^2 + 72y + \quad) = 269$ *Group the terms.*

$25(x^2 - 4x + 4) - 9(x^2 + 8y + 16) = 269 + 100 - 144$ *Complete the square.*

$25(x - 2)^2 - 9(y + 4)^2 = 225$

$$\frac{(x - 2)^2}{9} - \frac{(y + 4)^2}{25} = 1$$

Thus, the center is $(2, -4)$, a is 3, b is 5, and c is $\sqrt{a^2 + b^2}$ or $\sqrt{34}$.

The foci are $(2 + \sqrt{34}, -4)$ and $(2 - \sqrt{34}, -4)$.

The vertices are $(5, -4)$ and $(-1, -4)$.

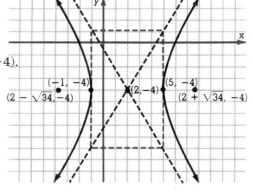

The shape of a hyperbola is determined by its eccentricity. As for the ellipse, the eccentricity, e, is defined as $e = \frac{c}{a}$. Since $c^2 = a^2 + b^2$ for a hyperbola, it can be shown that $b^2 = a^2(e^2 - 1)$.

$e > 1$ for a hyperbola

2 Write the equation of the hyperbola with center $(-3, 1)$, a focus $(2, 1)$, and eccentricity $\frac{5}{4}$.

This hyperbola has a horizontal transverse axis, so the equation has the form $\frac{(x - h)^2}{a^2} - \frac{(y - k)^2}{b^2} = 1$. Since the focus is 5 units to the right of center, c is 5. Also $e = \frac{c}{a}$ where $e = \frac{5}{4}$. Thus, $\frac{5}{4} = \frac{5}{a}$, so $a = 4$. Then, $b^2 = c^2 - a^2$, or 9.

Therefore, the equation is $\frac{(x + 3)^2}{16} - \frac{(y - 1)^2}{9} = 1$.

As in the other conics, the **latus rectum** of a hyperbola is a chord through a focus. The length of a latus rectum of a hyperbola is $\frac{2b^2}{a}$ units. The equation of the hyperbola at the right is $\frac{x^2}{4} - \frac{y^2}{9} = 1$ and the latera recta are $\overline{PQ}$ and $\overline{RS}$. Therefore, $PQ = RS = \frac{2(9)}{2}$ or 9.

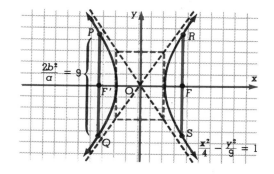

Two hyperbolas such that the transverse axis of one is the conjugate axis of the other, and conversely, are said to be **conjugate hyperbolas.** Conjugate hyperbolas share the same asymptotes. The equations of conjugate hyperbolas are closely related. If the equation of a hyperbola is in standard form, the equation of its conjugate can be written by reversing the x^2 and y^2 terms. For example, the equations $\frac{x^2}{9} - \frac{y^2}{4} = 1$ and $\frac{y^2}{4} - \frac{x^2}{9} = 1$ represent conjugate hyperbolas.

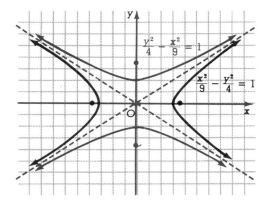

If $a = b$ is the standard form of a hyperbola, it is an **equilateral hyperbola** and the asymptotes are perpendicular. A special case of the equilateral hyperbola is when the coordinate axes are the asymptotes. The equation of such a hyperbola is $xy = k$, where k is a positive or negative constant. The branches of the equilateral hyperbola lie in the first and third quadrants if k is positive and in the second and fourth quadrants if k is negative.

Example

3 **Graph the hyperbola with equation $xy = 9$.**

The vertices of the hyperbola must lie along the line $y = x$, since the branches lie in the first and third quadrants. Thus, the vertices are $(3, 3)$ and $(-3, -3)$.

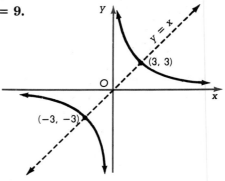

Exploratory Exercises

Write the standard form of each equation.

1. $5x^2 - 9y^2 = 45$

2. $25y^2 - 4x^2 - 100 = 0$

3. $4y^2 - x^2 + 4x - 8 = 0$

4. $x^2 - y^2 + 2y - 5 = 0$

5-8. Find the eccentricity of each hyperbola whose equation is given in problems **1-4**.

9-12. Find the length of the latus rectum of each hyperbola whose equation is given in problems **1-4**.

13-16. Write the equation of the conjugate of each hyperbola whose equation is given in problems **1-4**.

17-20. Graph each equation given in problems **1-4**.

Written Exercises

Graph each equation.

1. $xy = 25$

2. $xy = 12$

3. $xy = 8$

4. $xy = -16$

5. $4xy = -9$

6. $9xy = 25$

Name the center, foci, vertices, and the equations of the asymptotes of the hyperbola that has the given equation. Then, draw the graph.

7. $y^2 - 5x^2 + 20x = 50$

8. $9x^2 - 4y^2 - 54x - 40y - 55 = 0$

9. $9x^2 - 4y^2 - 90x - 24y = -153$

10. $49x^2 - 25y^2 + 294x + 200y = 1184$

Write the equation of each hyperbola described below.

11. Center $(3, -1)$, focus $(3, -4)$, $e = \frac{3}{2}$

12. Center $(0, 4)$, focus $(0, 9)$, $e = \frac{5}{4}$

13. Foci $(-5, 0)$ and $(5, 0)$, $e = \frac{5}{3}$

14. Foci $(0, 8)$ and $(0, -8)$, $e = \frac{4}{3}$

15. Foci $(4, 0)$ and $(-2, 0)$, slope of asymptotes $= \pm 4$

16. Foci $(1, 5)$ and $(1, -3)$, slope of asymptotes $= \pm 2$

17. Center $(-3, 1)$, $a = 4$, horizontal transverse axis, length of latus rectum $= 8$ units

18. Center $(0, 5)$, $b = 3$, vertical transverse axis, length of latus rectum $= 9$ units

19. Vertices $(5, -1)$ and $(5, 7)$, $e = 2$

20. Vertices $(-3, 1)$ and $(7, 1)$, $e = \frac{6}{5}$

Solve each of the following.

21. Write the equation of an equilateral hyperbola with foci (0, 5) and (0, −5).

22. Write the equation of an equilateral hyperbola with foci (8, 0) and (−8, 0).

Challenge Exercises _____

Solve each of the following.

23. Write the equation of the hyperbola that passes through (2, 0) and has asymptotes with equations $x - 2y = 0$ and $x + 2y = 0$.

24. Write the equation of the hyperbola that passes through (4, 2) and has asymptotes with equations $y = 2x$ and $y = -2x + 4$.

25. Find the eccentricity of the hyperbola that has foci (1, −4) and (1, 6) and passes through (1, 4).

26. Find the eccentricity of the hyperbola that has foci (0, 3) and (0, −3) and passes through (0, 2).

For the Scholar ▮▮▮▮▮▮▮▮▮▮▮

Circles *A*, *B*, and *C* are congruent. Points *M, A, N, B, O, C,* and *P* are collinear. If *CP* = 20 and $\overline{MH}$ is tangent to circle *C* at *H*, what is the sum of the lengths of chords *ML* and *KJ*?

12-8 Conic Sections

Parabolas, circles, ellipses, and hyperbolas can be formed by the intersection of a plane with a conical surface. Thus, these curves are called **conic sections**.

Each conical surface has two nappes, separated by a vertex.

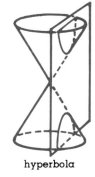

| circle | ellipse | parabola | hyperbola |

If the plane passes through the vertex of the conical surface, the intersection is a **degenerate case.** The degenerate cases are a point, a line, and two intersecting lines.

How can each degenerate case be formed?

The conic sections can also be defined using eccentricity. A conic section is a set of points in the plane such that for any point of the set the ratio of its distance from a fixed point to its distance from a fixed line is constant. The ratio is the eccentricity of the curve, denoted by *e*. When $e = 1$, the conic is a parabola. When $e < 1$, the conic is a circle or an ellipse, and when $e > 1$, the conic is a hyperbola.

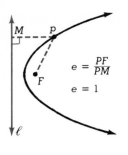

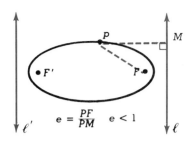

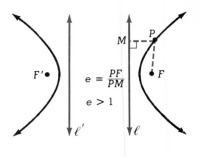

Parabola   Ellipse   Hyperbola

Notice that hyperbolas and ellipses have two directrices.

Each conic section can be described by a second-degree equation in two variables.

The equation of a conic section can be written in the form $Ax^2 + Bxy + Cy^2 + Dx + Ey + F = 0$ where A, B, and C are not all zero.	***General Equation for Conic Sections***

The graph of a second-degree equation in two variables always represents a conic or a degenerate case, unless the equation has no graph at all in the real number plane.

The equation $x^2 + y^2 = -8$ has no graph in the real number plane.

Most of the conic sections that have been studied have axes parallel to the x-axis and y-axis. The general equations of these conic sections have $B = 0$. To identify the conic section represented by a given equation, write the equation in standard form. The following table summarizes the standard forms of the conic sections.

Conic Section	Standard Form of Equation
circle	$(x - h)^2 + (y - k)^2 = r^2$
parabola	$(y - k)^2 = 4p(x - h)$ or $(x - h)^2 = 4p(y - k)$
ellipse	$\dfrac{(x - h)^2}{a^2} + \dfrac{(y - k)^2}{b^2} = 1$ or $\dfrac{(y - k)^2}{a^2} + \dfrac{(x - h)^2}{b^2} = 1$
hyperbola	$\dfrac{(x - h)^2}{a^2} - \dfrac{(y - k)^2}{b^2} = 1$ $\dfrac{(y - k)^2}{a^2} - \dfrac{(x - h)^2}{b^2} = 1$ or $xy = k$

If $A = C$, the equation represents a circle.

If either A or C is zero, the equation represents a parabola.

If A and C have the same sign and $A \neq C$, the equation represents an ellipse.

If A and C have opposite signs, the equation represents a hyperbola.

Examples

1 Identify and graph the conic section represented by the equation $x^2 + y^2 - 4x + 1 = 0$.

$$x^2 + y^2 - 4x + 1 = 0$$
$$x^2 - 4x + 4 + y^2 = -1 + 4 \quad \textit{Complete the square.}$$
$$(x - 2)^2 + y^2 = 3$$
$$(x - 2)^2 + (y - 0)^2 = (\sqrt{3})^2$$

The graph is a circle with center $(2, 0)$ and radius $\sqrt{3}$.

2 Write the standard form of the equation $x^2 - y^2 + 6y - 18 = 0$. Then, identify the conic section.

$$x^2 - y^2 + 6y - 18 = 0$$
$$x^2 - (y^2 - 6y + 9) = 18 - 9$$
$$x^2 - (y - 3)^2 = 9$$
$$\frac{x^2}{9} - \frac{(y - 3)^2}{9} = 1$$

The equation represents a hyperbola. *The hyperbola is equilateral. Why?*

Exploratory Exercises

Write the standard form of each equation.

1. $x^2 - 8x + y^2 = -11$
2. $x^2 - 6x - 4y + 9 = 0$
3. $9x^2 + 25y^2 - 54x - 50y = 119$
4. $x^2 + y^2 + 6y - 8x = -24$
5. $4y^2 + 4y + 8x - 15 = 0$
6. $x^2 - 4y^2 + 10x - 16y = -5$
7. $3y^2 + 24y - x^2 - 2x = -41$
8. $9y^2 + 27x^2 - 6y - 108x + 82 = 0$

9-16. State whether the graph of each equation in problems **1-8** is a circle, parabola, ellipse, or hyperbola. Then, draw the graph.

Written Exercises

Graph each equation. Some equations represent degenerate conics.

1. $x^2 = 5 - y^2$
2. $9xy = 4$
3. $y^2 + 8 = 8x$
4. $x^2 - 4y = 28$
5. $xy = 12$
6. $2x^2 + 5y^2 = 0$
7. $x^2 - 4x - y^2 = 5 + 4y$
8. $x^2 - 6x + y^2 - 12y = -41$
9. $3(x - 1)^2 + 4(y + 4)^2 = 0$
10. $(x + 1)^2 + 9(y - 6)^2 = 9$
11. $y^2 = 8x - 24$
12. $y^2 = 9x^2$
13. $(x - 2)^2 = -(y - 3)^2$
14. $(y + 5)^2 = 36 + 4(x + 1)^2$
15. $2(y - 3)^2 + 25(x + 1)^2 = 50$
16. $x^2 = y + 8x - 16$
17. $\dfrac{(y - 5)^2}{4} - (x + 1)^2 = 4$
18. $\dfrac{(x - 2)^2}{9} + \dfrac{y^2}{9} = 1$

For the Scholar

Find the least positive number n such that the product of the first n terms exceeds 390,625 when given the progression $5^{\frac{1}{7}}, 5^{\frac{2}{7}}, 5^{\frac{3}{7}}, \cdots, 5^{\frac{n}{7}}$.

Using Mathematics

Part of a solar-powered irrigation system is shown. Trough-shaped parabolic cylinders track the sun's movement to collect solar energy. The focus of each parabolic cylinder is a tube of water. Solar energy heats the water to provide input energy for turbine engines that power irrigation pumps.

The surface of each collector is covered with reflective material. The amount of reflective material needed for a collector like the one shown can be found by multiplying the length of $\overline{ST}$ by the length of the parabolic segment RVS.

The following formula can be used to find the length of the parabolic segment RVS, if the width of the collector, RS, and the focal length, FV, are known.

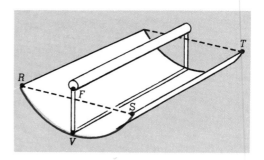

$$RVS = FV\left(\frac{x}{2}\sqrt{4 + x^2} + 2 \ln \left(\frac{x}{2} + \frac{1}{2}\sqrt{4 + x^2}\right)\right) \quad \text{where } x = \frac{RS}{2FV}$$

Example Find the surface area of the parabolic collector for which $FV = 1$, $RS = 4$, and $ST = 10$.

$x = \dfrac{4}{2}$ or 2   *Find x, then use the formula to find RVS.*

$$RVS = 1\left(\frac{2}{2}\sqrt{4 + 2^2} + 2 \ln \left(\frac{2}{2} + \frac{1}{2}\sqrt{4 + 2^2}\right)\right)$$
$$= 2\sqrt{2} + 2 \ln \left(1 + \sqrt{2}\right)$$
$$\approx 4.59$$

Therefore, the surface area is 4.59×10, or 45.9.

Exercises   **Find the surface area of each parabolic collector described below.**

1. $FV = 0.5$, $RS = 2$, $ST = 5$ **2.** $FV = 0.5$, $RS = 1.5$, $ST = 5$

3. $FV = 0.4$, $RS = 1.2$, $ST = 3$ **4.** $FV = 0.7$, $RS = 1.4$, $ST = 4$

12-9 Systems of Second-Degree Equations and Inequalities

To solve a system of two equations, you must find the ordered pairs that satisfy both equations. One way is to graph each equation and find the coordinates of the points of intersection of the two graphs. Sometimes algebra must be used to find the exact solutions.

Example

1 **Graph the following system. Then, state the solutions of the system of equations.**
$$x^2 + 4y^2 = 36$$
$$x^2 = -y + 3$$

The graph of $x^2 + 4y^2 = 36$ is an ellipse centered at the origin, with $a = 6$ and $b = 3$. The major axis is horizontal. The graph of $x^2 = -y + 3$ is a parabola with $p = -\frac{1}{4}$ and vertex $(0, 3)$. The parabola opens downward.

The graphs show that there are three solutions to the system.

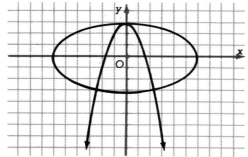

Use the substitution method to find the exact solutions.
$$x^2 + 4y^2 = 36$$
$$(-y + 3) + 4y^2 = 36$$
$$4y^2 - y - 33 = 0 \quad \textit{Use the quadratic formula.}$$
$$y = 3 \text{ or } -\frac{11}{4}.$$
$$x^2 = -y + 3$$

$$x^2 = -3 + 3 \quad \text{or} \quad x^2 = \frac{11}{4} + 3$$
$$x = 0 \qquad\qquad x = \pm\frac{\sqrt{23}}{2}$$

The solutions are $(0, 3)$, $\left(\frac{\sqrt{23}}{2}, -\frac{11}{4}\right)$, and $\left(-\frac{\sqrt{23}}{2}, -\frac{11}{4}\right)$.

Graphs also can be used to indicate the solutions of a system of inequalities.

2 Graph the solutions for the following system of inequalities.

$$x^2 + y^2 \leq 36$$
$$4x^2 - 9y^2 \geq 36$$

The graph of $x^2 + y^2 \leq 36$ consists of all points on or within the circle $x^2 + y^2 = 36$. The graph of $4x^2 - 9y^2 \geq 36$ consists of all points on or between the branches of the hyperbola $4x^2 - 9y^2 = 36$.

The intersection of these two graphs represents the solutions for the system of inequalities.

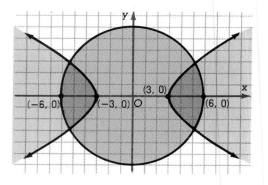

Written Exercises

Graph the following systems of equations. Then, state the solutions of the systems.

1. $x^2 + y^2 = 49$
$x = -1$

2. $y - 3 = 2x$
$y = x^2$

3. $x^2 + y^2 = 16$
$x^2 + y^2 = 9$

4. $y^2 = x^2 + 4$
$y = 5$

5. $x^2 = y^2 + 9$
$2y - x = -3$

6. $(x - 1)^2 + 4(y - 1)^2 = 20$
$x = y$

7. $x^2 - y^2 = 3$
$xy = 2$

8. $x^2 = -y$
$y = -x - 2$

9. $(x - 2)^2 - 9(y + 3)^2 = 36$
$y = x$

10. $x^2 + y^2 = 64$
$x^2 + 64y^2 = 64$

11. $x^2 - 4y = 0$
$y = 2x - 3$

12. $(y - 1)^2 = x + 4$
$y + x = -1$

Graph the solutions for the following systems of inequalities.

13. $x^2 < 9 - y^2$
$y < -x^2$

14. $x^2 \geq 16 + 16y^2$
$x^2 \geq 49 - y^2$

15. $4x^2 - 9(y - 1)^2 < 36$
$x^2 + y^2 < 25$

16. $(x + 1)^2 + (y + 1)^2 > 16$
$9x^2 + y^2 < 81$

17. $y \geq x^2 - 4$
$(y - 3)^2 \geq x + 2$

18. $(x + 3)^2 + (y + 2)^2 \leq 36$
$y = -4$

19. $xy < -3$
$(x - 1)^2 + (y - 2)^2 < 25$

20. $16x^2 - 25y^2 \geq 400$
$xy \geq 2$

21. $4(x - 2)^2 + (y - 3)^2 \leq 16$
$2y = x + 1$

22. $x^2 - 4y^2 < 16$
$x > (y - 1)^2$

23. $xy \geq 2$
$x - 3y = 2$

24. $9x^2 + 4y^2 \leq 36$
$4x^2 + 9y^2 \geq 36$

For the Scholar

Find the approximate value of $\log_{15} 10$ using $\log_{10} 2 = 0.301$ and $\log_{10} 3 = 0.477$.

12-10 Tangents and Normals to the Conic Sections

The tangent to a circle is perpendicular to the radius at the point of tangency. Since the slope of the radius to (x_1, y_1) on a circle with center $(0, 0)$ is $\dfrac{y_1}{x_1}$, the slope of the tangent is $-\dfrac{x_1}{y_1}$. Thus, if point $P_1(x_1, y_1)$ is on the circle, the point-slope form of the equation can be written.

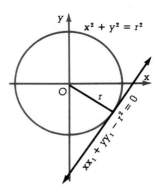

$$-\frac{x_1}{y_1} = \frac{y - y_1}{x - x_1}$$

$$xx_1 - x_1{}^2 = -yy_1 + y_1{}^2$$

$$xx_1 + yy_1 = x_1{}^2 + y_1{}^2 \qquad \textit{Since } (x_1, y_1) \textit{ is on the circle,}$$
$$\textit{x}_1{}^2 + y_1{}^2 = r^2.$$

$$xx_1 + yy_1 = r^2$$

The equation of the tangent to the circle $x^2 + y^2 = r^2$ at (x_1, y_1) is $xx_1 + yy_1 - r^2 = 0$.	*Equation of the Tangent to a Circle*

Equations for tangents to the graphs of other conic sections can also be found. The following chart lists formulas for the slope of tangents to the graphs of given equations. After the slope is found, the equation of the tangent can be written by applying the point-slope form of the equation of a line.

Conic Section	Standard Form of Equation	Slope of Tangent at (x, y)
circle	$(x - h)^2 + (y - k)^2 = r^2$	$-\dfrac{(x - h)}{(y - k)}$
parabola	$(y - k)^2 = 4p(x - h)$	$\dfrac{2p}{y - k}$
	$(x - h)^2 = 4p(y - k)$	$\dfrac{x - h}{2p}$
ellipse	$\dfrac{(x - h)^2}{a^2} + \dfrac{(y - k)^2}{b^2} = 1$	$-\dfrac{b^2(x - h)}{a^2(y - k)}$
	$\dfrac{(y - k)^2}{a^2} + \dfrac{(x - h)^2}{b^2} = 1$	$-\dfrac{a^2(x - h)}{b^2(y - k)}$
hyperbola	$\dfrac{(x - h)^2}{a^2} - \dfrac{(y - k)^2}{b^2} = 1$	$\dfrac{b^2(x - h)}{a^2(y - k)}$
	$\dfrac{(y - k)^2}{a^2} - \dfrac{(x - h)^2}{b^2} = 1$	$\dfrac{a^2(x - h)}{b^2(y - k)}$

1 Find the equation of the tangent to the circle with equation $x^2 + y^2 = 25$ at the point $(-3, 4)$ on the circle.

$$xx_1 + yy_1 - r^2 = 0$$
$$x(-3) + y(4) - 25 = 0 \qquad x_1 = -3 \text{ and } y_1 = 4$$
$$3x - 4y + 25 = 0$$

The equation of the tangent is $3x - 4y + 25 = 0$.

2 Find the equation of the tangent to the parabola with equation $2x^2 - 3x + 2y - 4 = 0$ at the point $(-2, -5)$.

First, write the equation in standard form.

$$2x^2 - 3x + 2y - 4 = 0$$
$$x^2 - \frac{3}{2}x + y - 2 = 0$$
$$x^2 - \frac{3}{2}x + \frac{9}{16} = -y + 2 + \frac{9}{16} \qquad \textit{Complete the square.}$$
$$\left(x - \frac{3}{4}\right)^2 = 4\left(-\frac{1}{4}\right)y + 2\frac{9}{16} \qquad h = \frac{3}{4} \text{ and } p = -\frac{1}{4}$$

Then, find the slope of the tangent at the point $(-2, -5)$.

$$\frac{x - h}{2p} = \frac{-2 - \frac{3}{4}}{2\left(-\frac{1}{4}\right)} = \frac{11}{2}$$

Finally, write the equation for the line through $(-2, -5)$ that has slope $\frac{11}{2}$.

$$\frac{11}{2} = \frac{y + 5}{x + 2}$$
$$11(x + 2) = 2(y + 5)$$
$$11x - 2y + 12 = 0$$

The equation of the tangent is $11x - 2y + 12 = 0$.

If $P(x_1, y_1)$ is a point and $(x - h)^2 + (y - k)^2 = r^2$ is the equation of a circle, then P lies outside the circle if $(x_1 - h)^2 + (y_1 - k)^2 > r^2$. In this case there are two tangents from P to the circle. It is sometimes necessary to find the length of a tangent segment, that is, the line segment joining a given point to a point of tangency on a circle.

The formula for the length of the tangent segment from an exterior point can be developed as follows. Let $C(h, k)$ be the center of the circle, $P(x_1, y_1)$ be the exterior point, and $T(x_2, y_2)$ be a point on the circle where a tangent from P touches the circle. Let $CT = r$, $PC = d$, and $PT = t$. The formula for t in terms of d and r is found using the Pythagorean Theorem.

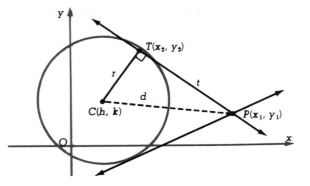

$$t = \sqrt{d^2 - r^2}$$

According to the distance formula, $d^2 = (x_1 - h)^2 + (y_1 - k)^2$. Thus, the formula for the length of the tangent segment can be expressed as follows.

The length of a tangent segment, t, from (x_1, y_1) to the circle $(x - h)^2 + (y - k)^2 = r^2$ can be found using the following formula. $$t = \sqrt{(x_1 - h)^2 + (y_1 - k)^2 - r^2}$$	*Length of a Tangent Segment to a Circle*

Example

3 **Find the length of the tangent segment from $(-1, 3)$ to the circle with equation $(x - 2)^2 + (y + 5)^2 = 16$.**

$$\begin{aligned} t &= \sqrt{(x_1 - h)^2 + (y_1 - k)^2 - r^2} \\ &= \sqrt{(-1 - 2)^2 + (3 + 5)^2 - 16} \qquad h = 2,\ k = -5,\ and\ r = 4 \\ &= \sqrt{9 + 64 - 16} \\ &= \sqrt{57} \end{aligned}$$

The length of the tangent segment is $\sqrt{57}$ units.

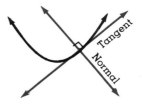

The **normal** to a curve at any point on the curve is the line perpendicular to the tangent at the point. Thus, the slope of the normal is the negative reciprocal of the slope of the tangent at any point.

Example

4 Find the equations of the tangent and the normal to the hyperbola with equation $\dfrac{x^2}{9} - \dfrac{y^2}{4} = 1$ at the point $(6, 2\sqrt{3})$.

Find the slope of the tangent.

$$\dfrac{b^2(x - h)}{a^2(y - k)} = \dfrac{4(6)}{9(2\sqrt{3})} \text{ or } \dfrac{4\sqrt{3}}{9} \quad h \text{ and } k \text{ are zero.}$$

Then find the equation of the tangent.

$$\dfrac{4\sqrt{3}}{9} = \dfrac{y - 2\sqrt{3}}{x - 6} \text{ or } 4x - 3\sqrt{3}y - 6 = 0$$

Since the slope of the tangent is $\dfrac{4\sqrt{3}}{9}$, the slope of the normal is $-\dfrac{9}{4\sqrt{3}}$ or $-\dfrac{3\sqrt{3}}{4}$.

Find the equation of the normal.

$$-\dfrac{3\sqrt{3}}{4} = \dfrac{y - 2\sqrt{3}}{x - 6} \text{ or } 9x + 4\sqrt{3}y - 78 = 0$$

The equation of the tangent is $4x - 3\sqrt{3}y - 6 = 0$ and the equation of the normal is $9x + 4\sqrt{3}y - 78 = 0$.

Exploratory Exercises

Given the slope of the tangent to a curve at a point, name the slope of the normal.

1. $\dfrac{3\sqrt{5}}{8}$ **2.** $-\dfrac{4}{5\sqrt{10}}$ **3.** $-\dfrac{25}{16}$ **4.** $\dfrac{7}{30}$

Find the equation of the tangent to the given circle at the given point.

5. $x^2 + y^2 = 25,\ (2, \sqrt{21})$ **6.** $x^2 + y^2 = 49,\ (\sqrt{13}, 6)$

7. $x^2 + y^2 = 145,\ (9, -8)$ **8.** $x^2 + y^2 = 116,\ (-10, -4)$

Find the slope of the tangent to the graph of the given equation at the given point.

9. $(x - 2)^2 + (y - 3)^2 = 10,\ (-1, 2)$ **10.** $(x + 4)^2 = 8(y + 3),\ (0, -1)$

11. $\dfrac{(x + 2)^2}{36} + \dfrac{(y - 3)^2}{9} = 1,\ (-2, 6)$ **12.** $\dfrac{(x - 3)^2}{4} + \dfrac{(y - 1)^2}{25} = 1,\ (3, -4)$

13. $(y + 2)^2 = 8(x - 3),\ (5, 2)$ **14.** $\dfrac{x^2}{8} - \dfrac{y^2}{9} = 1,\ (-4, -3)$

Written Exercises

Find the equations of the tangent and the normal to the given circle at the given point.

1. $x^2 + y^2 - 19 = 0,\ (-2, \sqrt{15})$ **2.** $3x^2 + 3y^2 - 5 = 0,\ \left(1, \dfrac{\sqrt{6}}{3}\right)$

3. $(x - 4)^2 + (y - 3)^2 - 16 = 0,\ (8, 3)$ **4.** $(x + 2)^2 + y^2 - 9 = 0,\ (-4, \sqrt{5})$

Find the equations of the tangent and the normal to the parabola at the given point.

5. $x^2 + 4x - y + 1 = 0$, $(0, 1)$

6. $y^2 - x + y - 5 = 0$, $(1, -3)$

7. $2x^2 - 7x + 5y - 11 = 0$, $\left(-1, \frac{2}{5}\right)$

8. $2y^2 + 4x - 3y - 11 = 0$, $\left(\frac{9}{4}, 2\right)$

Find the equations of the tangent and the normal to the ellipse at the given point.

9. $\frac{y^2}{64} + \frac{x^2}{49} = 1$, $\left(\frac{7\sqrt{3}}{2}, 4\right)$

10. $\frac{x^2}{25} + \frac{y^2}{9} = 1$, $\left(4, \frac{9}{5}\right)$

11. $\frac{(x-4)^2}{12} + \frac{y^2}{4} = 1$, $(7, 1)$

12. $\frac{(y-3)^2}{36} + \frac{x^2}{4} = 1$, $(\sqrt{3}, 6)$

Find the equations of the tangent and the normal to the hyperbola at the given point.

13. $\frac{x^2}{16} - \frac{y^2}{4} = 1$, $\left(5, \frac{3}{2}\right)$

14. $\frac{x^2}{4} - y^2 = 1$, $(2, 0)$

15. $\frac{(x-1)^2}{25} - \frac{(y+3)^2}{9} = 1$, $(-4, -3)$

16. $\frac{(x-2)^2}{18} - \frac{(y-1)^2}{64} = 1$, $(-4, -7)$

Find the length of the tangent segment from the given point to the given circle.

17. $(-4, 7)$, $x^2 + y^2 = 10$

18. $(9, 9)$, $x^2 + y^2 = 2$

19. $(6, 2)$, $x^2 + y^2 = 37$

20. $(10, 1)$, $x^2 + y^2 - 6x - 8y = 0$

21. $(4, -1)$, $(x + 3)^2 + y^2 - 4 = 0$

22. $(-7, 2)$, $(x + 3)^2 + (y - 2)^2 = 4$

Solve each of the following.

23. Find the equations of the horizontal tangents to the circle $x^2 + y^2 = 25$.

24. Find the equations of the vertical tangents to the circle $x^2 + y^2 = 49$.

25. Find the equations of the horizontal tangents to the ellipse $\frac{x^2}{25} + \frac{y^2}{64} = 1$.

26. Find the equations of the vertical tangents to the ellipse $\frac{x^2}{64} + \frac{y^2}{16} = 1$.

Challenge Exercises

Solve each of the following.

27. Find the point on the parabola $x^2 - 6x - 2y + 1 = 0$ at which the tangent makes a $45°$ angle with the positive x-axis.

28. The line $x + y = 4$ is tangent to an equilateral hyperbola $xy = k$, where $k > 0$. Determine the value of k.

29. Find the slopes of the tangents at the endpoints of the latus rectum of the parabola $y^2 - 4x - 2y + 9 = 0$. How are the tangents related?

30. Find the equations of the tangents at the endpoints of the latera recta of the hyperbola $\frac{x^2}{4} - \frac{y^2}{12} = 1$.

For the Scholar

The sides of a convex quadrilateral have lengths 24, 8, 6, and 26. If the two shorter sides are perpendicular to each other, what is the area of the quadrilateral?

12-11 Polar Equations of Conic Sections

Conic sections can be represented using polar equations. For example, if the center of a circle is at the pole and the radius is 5, then the polar equation of the circle is $r = 5$. In general, if any point $P(r, \theta)$ lies on a circle centered at the origin, the polar distance r is the radius of the circle.

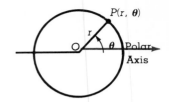

Example

1 If the equation of a circle in rectangular coordinates is $x^2 + y^2 = 12$, find the polar equation. Assume that the pole coincides with the origin and the polar axis coincides with the positive x-axis.

$$r = \sqrt{x^2 + y^2}$$
$$= \sqrt{12} \text{ or } 2\sqrt{3}$$

The polar equation is $r = 2\sqrt{3}$.

The simplest form of the polar equation of a parabola is obtained if the focus is taken as the pole and a line perpendicular to the directrix is taken as the polar axis. By definition, any point P on a parabola is equidistant from the focus, F, and a point on the directrix, M, as shown.

Therefore, $PF = PM$. Since $PM = ST$, the formula for PF can be derived as follows.

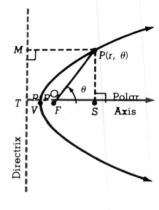

$$PF = SF + FV + VT$$
$$= r \cos \theta + p + p$$
$$= r \cos \theta + 2p$$

Replace PF by r and solve for r to obtain the polar equation.

$$r = \frac{2p}{1 - \cos \theta}$$

The parabola opens toward the polar axis, and its focus is at the pole.

The polar equation of a parabola that opens in the opposite direction has the form $r = \frac{2p}{1 + \cos \theta}$. Again, the polar axis is perpendicular to the directrix.

Example

2 Change the equation of the parabola $y^2 = 5x$ to the polar equation where the pole is at the focus and the polar axis coincides with the positive x-axis.

$$4p = 5 \qquad \textit{Why?}$$
$$p = \frac{5}{4} \text{ or } 1.25$$

The polar equation is $r = \frac{2.5}{1 - \cos \theta}$.

The simplest form of the polar equation of an ellipse is determined if a focus is at the pole and both foci are on the polar axis.

Let F be a focus, ℓ the corresponding directrix, and $P(r, \theta)$ a point on the ellipse. By definition, $\dfrac{PF}{PM} = e$ or $PF = e \cdot PM$ where $e < 1$. Also, $PM = SF + FT$ and $SF = r \cos \theta$. Let $FT = 2p$. Since $PF = r$, then $r = e(SF + FT)$ or $e(r \cos \theta + 2p)$. The following equation is obtained by solving for r.

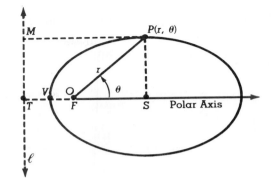

$$r = \frac{2ep}{1 - e \cos \theta} \quad (e < 1)$$

This is the polar equation of an ellipse when the pole coincides with one focus and the polar axis is directed toward the other focus. If the polar axis has the opposite direction the polar equation has the form $r = \dfrac{2ep}{1 + e \cos \theta}$. In either case, the polar axis is perpendicular to each directrix, and $2p = \dfrac{b^2}{c}$.

Example

3 **The equation of an ellipse in rectangular coordinates is $16x^2 + 49y^2 = 784$. Find the equation in polar coordinates if the pole is at the left focus and the polar axis is directed toward the right focus.**

The standard form of the equation is $\dfrac{x^2}{49} + \dfrac{y^2}{16} = 1$.

Thus, $a = 7$ and $b = 4$. Since $a^2 = b^2 + c^2$, $c = \sqrt{33}$. Also, $e = \dfrac{c}{a}$, or $\dfrac{\sqrt{33}}{7}$, and $2p = \dfrac{b^2}{c}$, or $\dfrac{16}{\sqrt{33}}$.

$$r = \frac{2ep}{1 - e \cos \theta}$$

$$r = \frac{\dfrac{\sqrt{33}}{7} \cdot \dfrac{16}{\sqrt{33}}}{1 - \dfrac{\sqrt{33}}{7} \cos \theta}$$

The origin of the rectangular coordinate system is at the center of the ellipse and the pole is at the left focus with the polar axis directed toward the positive x-axis.

$$r = \frac{16}{7 - \sqrt{33} \cos \theta}$$

The polar equation is $r = \dfrac{16}{7 - \sqrt{33} \cos \theta}$.

The polar equation of the hyperbola can be developed in the same manner as that of the parabola and ellipse. The polar equation is $r = \dfrac{2ep}{1 \pm e \cos \theta}$ where e is the eccentricity ($e > 1$) and $2p$ is the distance from the focus to the directrix. Again, the polar axis is perpendicular to the directrix and $2p = \dfrac{b^2}{c}$.

Note that for the parabola $e = 1$ and the equation reduces to $r = \dfrac{2p}{1 \pm \cos \theta}$.

Notice the similarity among the polar equations for conic sections.

The polar equation of any conic section where the pole is at a focus and the polar axis is perpendicular to the directrix can be written as follows, where e is the eccentricity and $2p$ is the distance from the focus to the directrix.

$$r = \frac{2ep}{1 \pm e \cos \theta}$$

Polar Equation of a Conic Section

If the polar axis is parallel to the directrix it can be shown that the polar equation of a conic section has the following form.

$$r = \frac{2ep}{1 \pm e \sin \theta}$$

Thus, if $e = 1$, the equation is a parabola. If $e < 1$, the equation is an ellipse. If $e > 1$, the equation is a hyperbola.

Exploratory Exercises

Identify the conic represented by each of the following polar equations.

1. $r = \dfrac{3.2}{1 - 0.6 \cos \theta}$

2. $r = \dfrac{1}{1 - \cos \theta}$

3. $r = 6\sqrt{5}$

4. $r = \dfrac{16}{5 + 3 \cos \theta}$

5. $r = \dfrac{6}{1 + \cos \theta}$

6. $r = 8$

7. $r = \dfrac{3}{1 - 2 \cos \theta}$

8. $r = \dfrac{6}{1 + 0.5 \cos \theta}$

9-16. Graph each equation in problems **1-8.**

Write a polar equation of each circle whose rectangular equation is given.

17. $x^2 + y^2 = 25$

18. $x^2 + y^2 = 49$

Written Exercises

Find the values of p and e for each of the following equations of conics.

1. $y^2 = 9x$

2. $y^2 = -7x$

3. $9x^2 + 16y^2 = 144$

4. $(y - 2)^2 = 3(x + 5)$

5. $x^2 - \dfrac{y^2}{4} = 1$

6. $\dfrac{x^2}{9} + \dfrac{y^2}{4} = 1$

7. $\dfrac{x^2}{16} + \dfrac{y^2}{36} = 1$

8. $3x^2 + 5y^2 = 15$

9. $9x^2 - 25y^2 = 225$

10. $\dfrac{x^2}{16} - \dfrac{y^2}{9} = 1$

11-20. Write a polar equation of each conic section in problems **1-10**.

For the Scholar

The area of $\triangle XYZ$ is 50 cm². L is the midpoint of $\overline{XZ}$, $\overline{LM} \perp \overline{YZ}$, and $\overline{KY} \parallel \overline{LM}$. Find the area of $\triangle ZLY$.

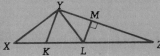

Chapter Summary

1. The standard form of the equation of a circle with radius r and center (h, k) is $(x - h)^2 + (y - k)^2 = r^2$. (345)

2. The standard form of the equation of a parabola with vertex (h, k) and directrix parallel to the y-axis, is

$$(y - k)^2 = 4p(x - h)$$

where p is the distance from the vertex to the focus.

The standard form of the equation of a parabola with vertex (h, k) and directrix parallel to the x-axis, is

$$(x - h)^2 = 4p(y - k)$$

where p is the distance from the vertex to the focus. (349)

3. The length of the latus rectum of a parabola is $4p$ units. (350)

4. The translation formulas are

$$x = x' + h \text{ and } y = y' + k$$

where (h, k) represents the origin of the coordinate system (x', y'). (352)

5. For an ellipse, $a^2 = b^2 + c^2$, where a is the length of the semi-major axis, b is the length of the semi-minor axis, and c is the distance from the center to a focus. (354)

6. The standard form of the equation of an ellipse with center (h, k) and major axis of length $2a$ units parallel to the x-axis, is
$$\frac{(x - h)^2}{a^2} + \frac{(y - k)^2}{b^2} = 1 \quad \text{where } b^2 = a^2 - c^2.$$

   The standard form of the equation of an ellipse with center (h, k) and major axis of length $2a$ units parallel to the y-axis, is
$$\frac{(y - k)^2}{a^2} + \frac{(x - h)^2}{b^2} = 1 \quad \text{where } b^2 = a^2 - c^2. \quad (356)$$

7. For an ellipse, the eccentricity $e = \frac{c}{a}$ and $e < 1$. Also, $b^2 = a^2(1 - e^2)$. (358)

8. The length of a latus rectum of an ellipse is $\frac{2b^2}{a}$. (359)

9. For a hyperbola, $a^2 + b^2 = c^2$, where $2a$ is the length of the transverse axis, $2b$ is the length of the conjugate axis, and c is the distance from the center to a focus. (362)

10. The standard form of the equation of a hyperbola with center (h, k) and transverse axis of length $2a$ units parallel to the x-axis, is
$$\frac{(x - h)^2}{a^2} - \frac{(y - k)^2}{b^2} = 1 \quad \text{where } b^2 = c^2 - a^2.$$

    The standard form of the equation of a hyperbola with center (h, k) and transverse axis of length $2a$ units parallel to the y-axis, is
$$\frac{(y - k)^2}{a^2} - \frac{(x - h)^2}{b^2} = 1 \quad \text{where } b^2 = c^2 - a^2. \quad (363)$$

11. The equations of the asymptotes of a hyperbola with a horizontal transverse axis are
$$y - k = \pm\frac{b}{a}(x - h).$$

    The equations of the asymptotes of a hyperbola with a vertical transverse axis are
$$y - k = \pm\frac{a}{b}(x - h). \quad (364)$$

12. For a hyperbola, $e = \frac{c}{a}$ and $e > 1$. Also, $b^2 = a^2(e^2 - 1)$. (366)

13. The length of a latus rectum of a hyperbola is $\frac{2b^2}{a}$. (367)

14. Two hyperbolas such that the transverse axis of one is the conjugate axis of the other, and conversely, are called conjugate hyperbolas. Conjugate hyperbolas share the same asymptotes. (367)

15. If $a = b$ in the standard form of a hyperbola, it is an equilateral hyperbola and the asymptotes are perpendicular. The equation of a special case of an equilateral hyperbola has the form $xy = k$. (367)

16. The equation of a conic section can be written in the form $Ax^2 + Bxy + Cy^2 + Dx + Ey + F = 0$ where $A, B,$ and C are not all zero. (370)

17. The equation of the tangent to the circle $x^2 + y^2 = r^2$ at (x_1, y_1) is $xx_1 + yy_1 - r^2 = 0$.   (375)

18. The slope of the tangent to the graph of any conic section can be found by using the formulas on page 375.

19. The length of the tangent segment, t, from (x_1, y_1) to the circle $(x - h)^2 + (y - k)^2 = r^2$ can be found using the formula

$$t = \sqrt{(x_1 - h)^2 + (y_1 - k)^2 - r^2}.   (377)$$

20. The normal to a curve at any point on the curve is the line perpendicular to the tangent at the point. The slope of the normal is the negative reciprocal of the slope of the tangent. (377)

21. The polar equation of any conic section where the pole is at a focus and the polar axis is perpendicular to the directrix can be written as follows, where e is the eccentricity and $2p$ is the distance from the focus to the directrix.

$$r = \frac{2ep}{1 \pm e \cos \theta}   (382)$$

Chapter Review

Write the equation of each circle described below.   (12-1)

1. Center $(3, -7)$, radius 3

2. Passes through $(-2, 1)$, $(5, 6)$, and $(-3, 6)$

Name the focus, vertex, directrix, and axis of each parabola whose equation is given. Then, draw the graph.   (12-2)

3. $(x - 7)^2 = 8(y - 3)$

4. $y^2 + 6y - 4x + 25 = 0$

Solve each of the following.   (12-3)

5. Write the equation of the circle with equation $x^2 - 6x + 9 + y^2 = 4$ with respect to axes translated so that the origin is $(3, 0)$.

6. Write the equation of the parabola with equation $y^2 = 4x + 4y - 4$ with respect to axes translated so that the origin is at the vertex.

Name the center, foci, and the vertices of each ellipse whose equation is given. Then, draw the graph.   (12-4)

7. $(x - 4)^2 + 4(y - 6)^2 = 36$

8. $3(x + 3)^2 + 2(y - 4)^2 = 12$

Write the equation of each ellipse described below.   (12-5)

9. Foci $(5, -1)$ and $(-1, -1)$, $2a = 10$

10. Foci $(3, 0)$ and $(3, 4)$, $e = 0.5$

Name the center, foci, vertices, and the equations of the asymptotes of each hyperbola whose equation is given. Then, draw the graph.   (12-6)

11. $9x^2 - 16y^2 - 36x + 96y + 36 = 0$

12. $2(x + 5)^2 - (y - 1)^2 = 8$

Solve each of the following. (12-7)

13. Write the equation of an equilateral hyperbola with foci $(0, 7)$ and $(0, -7)$.

14. Find the length of the latera recta of the hyperbola with equation $y^2 - 3x^2 - 8y - 6x + 4 = 0$.

15. Write the equation of a hyperbola that has $e = \frac{3}{2}$ and foci $(1, 4)$ and $(1, -2)$.

16. Write the equation of the conjugate of the hyperbola $9(x + 2)^2 - (y - 3)^2 = 9$.

Graph each equation. Some equations represent degenerate conics. (12-8)

17. $4x^2 - 8x + y^2 = 12$

18. $xy = 0$

19. $2(x - 4)^2 = -(y - 1)^2$

20. $x^2 - 6y - 8x + 16 = 0$

Graph each system. (12-9)

21. $x^2 - 4x - 4y - 4 = 0$
    $(x - 2)^2 = -4y$

22. $x^2 + (y - 2)^2 \geq 0$
    $x^2 + 9(y - 2)^2 \leq 9$

Solve each of the following. (12-10)

23. Find the length of the tangent segment from the point $(5, -1)$ to the circle with equation $x^2 + y^2 + 6x - 10y - 2 = 0$.

24. Write the equations of the tangent and normal to the hyperbola with equation $x^2 - 4y^2 + 2x + 8y - 7 = 0$ at $(1, 1)$.

Write a polar equation of each conic section whose equation is given. (12-11)

25. $x^2 - 4x + y^2 = 5$

26. $y^2 = 12x - 12$

Solve each of the following.

1. Write the equation of the circle with center $(-3, 7)$ that is tangent to the y-axis.

2. Write the equation of the circle with center $(-8, 3)$ that passes through the point $(-6, -4)$.

3. Name the focus, vertex, directrix, and axis of the parabola with equation $y^2 - 2x + 10y + 27 = 0$. Then, draw the graph.

4. Write the equation of the parabola that has a focus at $(3, -5)$ and whose directrix is $y = -2$.

5. Write the equation of the parabola with equation $y^2 = 8x - 4$ with respect to axes translated so that the origin is $(1, 0)$.

6. Find the length of the latus rectum of the parabola with equation $x^2 - 8x - 12y - 20 = 0$.

7. Name the center, foci, vertices, and find the length of the latus rectum for the ellipse with equation $x^2 + 2y^2 + 2x - 12y + 11 = 0$. Then, draw the graph.

8. Write the equation of an ellipse centered at the origin that has a horizontal major axis, $e = \frac{1}{2}$ and $2c = 1$.

9. Name the center, foci, vertices, and the equations of the asymptotes of the hyperbola with equation $(x - 4)^2 - 9(y - 5)^2 = 36$. Then, draw the graph.

10. Write the equation of the hyperbola that has eccentricity $\frac{3}{2}$ and foci $(-5, -2)$ and $(-5, 4)$.

11. Find the length of the tangent from the point $(5, 5)$ to the circle with equation $x^2 + y^2 = 9$.

12. Graph the following system.
$$x^2 + y^2 - 2x - 4y + 1 \geq 0$$
$$x^2 - 4y - 2x + 5 \geq 0$$

13. Write the equations of the tangent and normal to the hyperbola with equation $16x^2 - y^2 - 4y - 20 = 0$ at $(\sqrt{2}, 2)$.

14. Write a polar equation of the conic section that has the following rectangular equation. $4(x - 3)^2 + (y - 2)^2 = 4$

CHAPTER 13

Probability

When buying a new house, one has many choices such as style, exterior color, and number of bedrooms to consider. The probability of a certain kind of house being bought is related to the number of possible combinations of these choices.

13-1 Permutations

Suppose there are two tunnels under a river by which one can enter a city from the west and three highways by which one can leave the city going east. After entering the city by the first tunnel, one has the choice of leaving the city by three exits, and so there are three routes by way of the first tunnel. Likewise, there are three routes by way of the second tunnel. Altogether there are $2 \times 3 = 6$ possible routes through the city from west to east.

The choice of tunnels does *not* affect the choice of highways. Thus, these two choices are called **independent events**.

The example of choosing possible routes illustrates the use of the **Basic Counting Principle.**

Events that do not affect each other are independent events.

Events that do affect each other are dependent events.

Suppose an event can be chosen in p different ways. Another independent event can be chosen in q different ways. Then the two events can be chosen successively in $p \cdot q$ ways.	*Basic Counting Principle*

This principle can be extended to any number of independent events.

Examples

1   **On a trip a man took 3 suits, 2 ties, and 2 hats. How many different choices of these items of clothing are possible?**

There are $3 \cdot 2 \cdot 2 = 12$ different choices possible. The possible choices can be shown in a diagram.

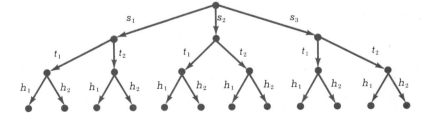

This diagram is called a tree diagram. Notice that there are 12 choices each of which differs from the other in some way.

2   **How many seven-digit phone numbers can begin with the prefix 364?**

Digit in phone number:	1st	2nd	3rd	4th	5th	6th	7th
Ways to choose:	1	1	1	10	10	10	10

There are $1 \cdot 1 \cdot 1 \cdot 10 \cdot 10 \cdot 10 \cdot 10 = 10^4$ or 10,000 numbers.

Suppose that seniors Pat, Corinne, and Wayne have been selected to be speakers at the graduation program. In how many different orders can they speak? If Pat speaks first, then either Corinne or Wayne can speak second and so on. The possible arrangements of speakers on the program are listed.

Pat	Pat	Corinne	Corinne	Wayne	Wayne
Corinne	Wayne	Pat	Wayne	Pat	Corinne
Wayne	Corinne	Wayne	Pat	Corinne	Pat

There are six distinct orders in which the speakers can be scheduled. This can also be confirmed by the Basic Counting Principle.

The arrangement of objects in a certain order is called a **permutation.** In a permutation, the order of the objects is very important.

Suppose that there is time for only two speakers on the program. How many ways can a program be arranged if two of the three persons are to be selected? There are three ways to choose the first speaker and two ways to choose the second speaker. Therefore, there are six ways to arrange the three speakers taken two at a time as can be verified by the Basic Counting Principle. The possible arrangements are listed.

$3 \cdot 2 = 6$

Pat	Pat	Corinne	Corinne	Wayne	Wayne
Corinne	Wayne	Pat	Wayne	Pat	Corinne

The symbol $P(n, n)$ denotes the number of permutations of n objects taken all at once. The symbol $P(n, r)$ denotes the number of permutations of n objects taken r at a time.

The number of permutations of n objects, taken n at a time, is defined as follows.

$$P(n, n) = n!$$

Recall $n! = n(n - 1)(n - 2) \cdots (1)$.

The number of permutations of n objects, taken r at a time, is defined as follows.

$$P(n, r) = \frac{n!}{(n - r)!}$$

Definition of $P(n, n)$ and $P(n, r)$

Examples

3 How many different three-letter patterns can be formed using the letters a, b, c, d, and e without repetition?

Find the number of permutations of 5 objects, taken 3 at a time.

$P(n, r) = \dfrac{n!}{(n - r)!}$

$P(5, 3) = \dfrac{5!}{(5 - 3)!}$

$\qquad = \dfrac{5 \cdot 4 \cdot 3 \cdot 2 \cdot 1}{2 \cdot 1}$ or 60

There are 60 ways to arrange the letters a, b, c, d, and e three at a time.

4 How many ways can five books be displayed from a group of eleven books?

$P(11, 5) = \dfrac{11!}{(11 - 5)!}$

$\qquad = \dfrac{11 \cdot 10 \cdot 9 \cdot 8 \cdot 7 \cdot 6 \cdot 5 \cdot 4 \cdot 3 \cdot 2 \cdot 1}{6 \cdot 5 \cdot 4 \cdot 3 \cdot 2 \cdot 1}$ or 55,440

There are 55,440 ways the books can be displayed.

Exploratory Exercises

State whether these events are independent or dependent.

1. choosing color and size when ordering an item of clothing

2. choosing a president, secretary, and treasurer for a club

3. choosing five numbers in a bingo game

4. throwing one die two times

5. tossing three coins at one time

6. each of four people writing down their guess of the total number of runs in a baseball game without telling what it is

State whether each statement is true or false.

7. $6! - 3! = 3!$

8. $5 \cdot 4! = 5!$

9. $\dfrac{8!}{4!} = 2!$

10. $(5 - 3)! = 5! - 3!$

11. $\dfrac{P(9, 9)}{9!} = 1$

12. $\dfrac{3!}{3} = \dfrac{2!}{2}$

Written Exercises

Find the value of each of the following.

1. $P(4, 3)$

2. $P(5, 2)$

3. $P(7, 1)$

4. $P(5, 3)$

5. $P(11, 10)$

6. $P(7, 4)$

7. $P(5, 5)$

8. $\dfrac{P(6, 4)}{P(5, 3)}$

9. $\dfrac{P(6, 3) \cdot P(4, 2)}{P(5, 2)}$

Find the value of n in each equation.

Examples

4 How many ways can 6 charms be placed on a bracelet that has no clasp?

This is a circular permutation. Because the bracelet can be turned over, it is also reflective.

$$\frac{(6-1)!}{2} = \frac{5 \cdot 4 \cdot 3 \cdot 2 \cdot 1}{2} \text{ or } 60$$

There are 60 ways to arrange the charms.

5 How many ways can 6 charms be placed on a bracelet that has a clasp?

This is no longer a circular permutation since objects are arranged with respect to a fixed point, the clasp. However, it is still reflective.

$$\frac{6!}{2} = \frac{6 \cdot 5 \cdot 4 \cdot 3 \cdot 2 \cdot 1}{2} \text{ or } 360$$

There are 360 ways to arrange the charms.

Exploratory Exercises

State whether each arrangement of objects is reflective or not.

1. a football huddle of 11 players
2. chairs arranged in a circle
3. beads on a necklace with no clasp
4. chairs arranged in a row
5. people seated around a square table relative to each other
6. people seated around a square table relative to one chair
7. a list of students in a given class
8. placing 6 coins in a circle on a table

9-16. State whether each arrangement of objects in problems **1-8** is circular or not.

Written Exercises

How many ways can the letters of each word be arranged?

1. FLOWER
2. ALGEBRA
3. PARALLEL
4. CANDIDATE
5. ARREARS
6. MONOPOLY
7. QUADRATIC
8. BASKETBALL
9. CLOCKMAKER

Solve each of the following.

10. How many different arrangements can be made with ten pieces of silverware laid in a row if three are spoons, four are forks, and three are knives?

11. How many different six-digit license plates of the same state can have the digits 3, 5, 5, 6, 2, and 6?

12. There are 3 identical red flags and 5 identical white flags that are used to send signals. All 8 flags must be used. How many signals can be given?

13. Five algebra and four geometry books are to be placed on a shelf. How many ways can they be arranged if all the algebra books must be together?

14. How many ways can 6 keys be arranged on a key ring?

15. How many ways can 6 people be seated around a campfire?

16. How many ways can 8 charms be arranged on a bracelet which has no clasp?

17. How many ways can 4 men and 4 women be seated alternately at a round table?

18. How many ways can 5 people be seated at a round table relative to each other?

19. How many ways can 5 people be seated at a round table relative to a door?

20. How many ways can 5 people be seated around a circular table if 2 of the people must be seated next to each other?

21. Twenty beads are strung in a circle. Fourteen are natural wood and six are red. How many ways can the red beads be strung in the circle?

Three men and three women are to be seated in a row containing six chairs. Find the number of ways each seating can be arranged.

22. The men and the women are to sit in alternate chairs.

23. The men are to sit in three adjoining chairs.

24. The men are to sit in three adjoining chairs and the women are to sit in three adjoining chairs.

For the Scholar

If the graph of the circle $x^2 + y^2 = k$ is tangent to the graph of the line $x + y = 2k$ where k is positive, find the value of k.

13-3 Combinations

Suppose 3 people are to be chosen from a group of 5 to work on a certain project. The first person can be selected in 5 ways, the second person in 4 ways, and the third person in 3 ways or a total of $5 \cdot 4 \cdot 3 = 60$ ways. But consider these 60 possible selections. The selections (A, B, C), (A, C, B), and (B, C, A) are considered the same. For each group of 3 there are 3! ways they can be arranged in order. Thus, if order of selection is disregarded, there are $\frac{60}{3!}$ or 10 different groups of 3 that can be selected from the 5 people.

$$\frac{60}{3!} = \frac{60}{3 \cdot 2 \cdot 1} \text{ or } 10$$

In this situation the order in which the people are chosen is *not* a consideration. The selection above is called a **combination** of 5 things taken 3 at a time. It is denoted by $C(5, 3)$.

The order of the arrangement is not important for a combination.

$$C(5, 3) = \frac{5!}{2!3!}$$

$$= \frac{5 \cdot 4 \cdot 3 \cdot 2 \cdot 1}{2 \cdot 1 \cdot 3 \cdot 2 \cdot 1} \text{ or } 10$$

> The number of combinations of n objects, taken r at a time, is written $C(n, r)$.
>
> $$C(n, r) = \frac{n!}{(n - r)!r!}$$
>
> **Definition of $C(n, r)$**

The main difference between a permutation and a combination is whether order is considered (permutation) or not (combination).

Examples

1 **From a list of 12 books, how many groups of 5 books can be selected?**

This selection is a combination of 12 things taken 5 at a time.

$$C(12, 5) = \frac{12!}{(12 - 5)!5!}$$
$$= \frac{12!}{7!5!}$$
$$= \frac{12 \cdot 11 \cdot 10 \cdot 9 \cdot 8}{5 \cdot 4 \cdot 3 \cdot 2 \cdot 1} \text{ or } 792$$

There are 792 groups.

2 **From a group of 4 men and 5 women, how many committees of 3 men and 2 women can be formed?**

Order is *not* considered. The questions are: How many ways can 3 men be chosen from 4? How many ways can 2 women be chosen from 5?

$$C(4, 3) \cdot C(5, 2) = \frac{4!}{(4 - 3)!3!} \cdot \frac{5!}{(5 - 2)!2!} \qquad \begin{array}{l} \textit{The combinations are} \\ \textit{multiplied to use the Basic} \\ \textit{Counting Principle.} \end{array}$$
$$= \frac{4!}{1!3!} \cdot \frac{5!}{3!2!}$$
$$= 4 \cdot 10 \text{ or } 40$$

There are 40 possible committees.

3 **A bag contains 3 red, 5 white, and 8 blue marbles. How many ways can 2 red, 1 white, and 2 blue marbles be chosen?**

$C(3, 2)$ Two of 3 red ones will be chosen.
$C(5, 1)$ One of 5 white ones will be chosen.
$C(8, 2)$ Two of 8 blue ones will be chosen.

$$C(3, 2) \cdot C(5, 1) \cdot C(8, 2) = \frac{3}{1} \cdot \frac{5}{1} \cdot \frac{8 \cdot 7}{2 \cdot 1} \text{ or } 420$$

There are 420 different ways.

Exploratory Exercises

State whether each arrangement represents a combination or a permutation.

1. seating students in a row
2. the answers on a true-false test
3. a committee of 4 men and 5 women chosen from 8 men and 7 women
4. the subsets of a given set
5. a team of 5 people chosen from a group of 12 people
6. three-letter patterns chosen from the letters of the word *algebra*
7. a hand of 5 cards
8. a batting order in baseball

Written Exercises

Find the value of each of the following.

1. $C(4, 2)$
2. $C(12, 7)$
3. $C(6, 6)$
4. $C(20, 15)$

Find the value of *n* in each of the following.

5. $C(n, 12) = C(30, 18)$
6. $C(14, 3) = C(n, 11)$
7. $C(n, 5) = C(n, 7)$

Solve each problem.

8. From a list of 10 books, how many groups of 4 books can be selected?
9. How many baseball teams of 9 members can be formed from 14 players?
10. How many ways can a club of 13 members choose 4 different officers?
11. How many ways can a club of 13 members choose a 4-person committee?
12. Suppose there are 9 points on a circle. How many different 4-sided closed figures can be formed by joining any 4 of these points?
13. Suppose there are 8 points in a plane, no 3 of which are collinear. How many distinct triangles could be formed with these points as vertices?
14. How many diagonals does a convex polygon that has 24 vertices have?
15. There are 85 telephones at Kennedy High School. How many 2-way connections can be made among the school telephones?
16. From a standard deck of cards, how many different 5-card hands can have 5 cards of the same suit?
17. From a standard deck of cards, how many different 4-card hands can have each card from a different suit?

A bag contains 4 red, 6 white, and 9 blue marbles. How many ways can 5 marbles be selected to meet each of the following conditions?

18. All the marbles are white.
19. All the marbles are blue.
20. Exactly two must be blue.
21. Two are 1 color and 3 are another color.

From a group of 8 men and 10 women, a committee of 5 is to be formed. How many committees can be formed if the committee is to be comprised as follows?

22. All are men.
23. There are 3 men and 2 women.
24. There is 1 man and 4 women.
25. All are women.
26. The cast of a school play that requires 4 girls and 3 boys is to be selected from 7 eligible girls and 9 eligible boys. How many ways can the cast be selected?
27. The Palace offers pepperoni, mushrooms, sausage, onions, anchovies, and peppers as toppings for their regular plain pizza. How many different pizzas can be made?

A student is to answer 10 out of 13 questions on an exam. How many ways can the questions be answered given the following conditions?

28. There are no restrictions.

29. The first two questions must be answered.

30. The first or the second question, but not both, must be answered.

31. Exactly three of the first five questions must be answered.

For the Scholar

$\overline{CD}$ is tangent to circle A at D and $\overline{BC}$ intersects circle A at E. If $AB = 4$, $CE = EB = 6$, and $CD = 2\sqrt{30}$, find the radius of circle A.

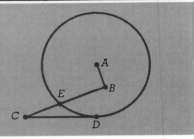

13-4 Probability

When a coin is tossed, only two outcomes are possible. The coin will show either a head or a tail. The desired outcome is called a **success**. Any other outcome is called a **failure**.

The probability of success for heads is $\frac{1}{2}$, as is the probability of success for tails.

If an event can succeed in s ways and fail in f ways, then the probability of success and the probability of failure are as follows.

$$P(s) = \frac{s}{s + f} \qquad P(f) = \frac{f}{s + f}$$

Probability of Success and of Failure

An event that cannot fail has a probability of 1. An event that cannot succeed has a probability of 0. Thus, the probability of success, $P(s)$, is always between 0 and 1 inclusive.

$$0 \le P(s) \le 1$$

The sum of the probability of success and the probability of failure for any event is always equal to 1.

$$P(s) + P(f) = \frac{s}{s + f} + \frac{f}{s + f}$$
$$= \frac{s + f}{s + f} \text{ or } 1$$

This property is often used in finding the probability of events. For example, if $P(s) = \frac{1}{4}$, then $P(f)$ is $1 - \frac{1}{4}$ or $\frac{3}{4}$. Because their sum is 1, $P(s)$ and $P(f)$ are called **complements**.

Examples

1

A box contains 3 baseballs, 7 softballs, and 11 tennis balls. What is the probability that a ball selected at random will be a tennis ball?

$$P(\text{tennis ball}) = \frac{s}{s + f}$$

$$= \frac{11}{11 + (3 + 7)} \text{ or } \frac{11}{21}$$

The probability of selecting a tennis ball is $\frac{11}{21}$.

2

Two cards are drawn at random from a standard deck of 52 cards. What is the probability that both are hearts?

$$P(\text{two hearts}) = \frac{C(13, 2)}{C(52, 2)}$$

There are C(13, 2) ways to select 2 of 13 hearts.
There are C(52, 2) ways to select 2 of 52 cards.

$$= \frac{\frac{13!}{11!2!}}{\frac{52!}{50!2!}}$$

$$= \frac{78}{1326} \text{ or } \frac{1}{17}$$

The probability of selecting two hearts is $\frac{1}{17}$.

3

A collection of 15 transistors contains 3 that are defective. If 2 transistors are selected at random, what is the probability that at least 1 of them is good?

The complement of selecting at least 1 good transistor is selecting 2 defective transistors.

$$P(\text{2 defective}) = \frac{C(3, 2)}{C(15, 2)}$$

$$= \frac{3}{105} \text{ or } \frac{1}{35}$$

Thus, the probability of selecting at least one good transistor is $1 - \frac{1}{35}$ or $\frac{34}{35}$.

The probability of the success of an event and its complement are used in computing the **odds** of an event.

The odds of the successful outcome of an event is the ratio of the probability of its success to the probability of its failure.

$$\textbf{Odds} = \frac{P(s)}{P(f)}$$

Definition of Odds

Example

4 **What are the odds of getting 2 ones in a single throw of a pair of dice?**

There are $6 \cdot 6$ or 36 possible outcomes when throwing two dice.

$$P(s) = \frac{1}{36} \qquad P(f) = 1 - \frac{1}{36} \text{ or } \frac{35}{36}$$

$$\text{Odds} = \frac{P(s)}{P(f)}$$

$$= \frac{\frac{1}{36}}{\frac{35}{36}} \text{ or } \frac{1}{35}$$

The odds of getting two ones is $\frac{1}{35}$. *This is read "one to thirty-five."*

Exploratory Exercises

State the odds of an event occurring given the probability that it occurs as follows.

1. $\frac{1}{2}$
2. $\frac{3}{4}$
3. $\frac{7}{15}$
4. $\frac{3}{20}$

State the probability of an event occurring given the following odds.

5. $\frac{3}{4}$
6. $\frac{6}{5}$
7. $\frac{4}{9}$
8. $\frac{1}{1}$

Solve each problem.

9. The odds are 6 to 1 *against* an event occurring. What is the probability that it will occur?

10. The probability of an event occurring is $\frac{3}{4}$. What are the odds that it will not occur?

A card is drawn at random from a standard deck of cards. Find the probability of each of the following.

11. heart
12. ace
13. ace of hearts

Written Exercises

Solve each problem.

1. Two dice are thrown. Find the probability that the same number will show on both dice.

2. Four coins are tossed at the same time. Find the probability that four heads will come up.

3. If the odds are 50 to 1 that it will rain today, find the probability that it will not rain.

4. Find the odds of getting a sum of 7 on a throw of a pair of dice.

5. A die is thrown two times. A 3 shows on the first throw. Find the probability that a 3 shows on the second throw.

6. A pair of dice are thrown and their sum is 6. Find the probability that each die shows a 3.

In a box are 4 black socks, 5 white socks, and 2 red socks. A sock is drawn at random.

7. Find the probability that it will not be red.

8. Find the probability that it will be white or red.

A number is picked at random from the integers 1 through 50. Find the probability of each of the following.

9. odd integer

10. multiple of 5

11. perfect square

In a bag are 5 red, 9 blue, and 6 white marbles. Two are selected at random. Find the probability of each of the following selections.

12. 2 red

13. 2 white

14. 2 blue

15. 1 red and 1 blue

16. 1 red and 1 white

Suppose you select 2 letters from the word *algebra*. What is the probability of selecting 2 letters and having the following occur?

17. 2 consonants

18. 1 vowel and 1 consonant

19. 2 vowels

A die is thrown two times. Find the odds of each of the following.

20. no fives

21. at least one five

22. both fives

Of ten students in a class, three have blue eyes. If two students are chosen at random, find the probability of each of the following.

23. Both have blue eyes.

24. Neither has blue eyes.

25. At least one has blue eyes.

The table gives the status of employment of 500 students at Hawkins College.

Employment	Class				
	Freshman	Sophomore	Junior	Senior	Totals
Unemployed	75	56	35	18	184
Part-time	55	46	45	45	191
Full-time	30	28	30	37	125
Totals	160	130	110	100	500

26. If a student is selected at random, find the probability that the student is unemployed.

27. If a student is selected at random, find the probability that the student is a freshman employed part-time.

28. If a sophomore is selected at random, find the probability that the student is employed full-time.

29. Find the probability that a student selected at random is a junior.

30. Find the probability that a senior selected at random is unemployed.

31. Find the probability that an unemployed student selected at random is a senior.

For the Scholar

For which positive values of x is the equation $(\log_5 2x)(\log_{2x} 7) = \log_5 7$ true?

The science that deals with the methods involved in encoding and decoding messages is called **cryptography.** This science plays a major role in governmental and military affairs of security.

Generally, codes involve substituting various letters, numbers, symbols, or a combination of these, for actual letters of the alphabet. To decipher a code, a pattern or sequence must be determined, then broken down.

Try to find the pattern for each of the following codes and finish the alphabet.

Caesar's Code	**Bacon's Alphabet**
A B C D E · · ·	A B C D E · · ·
D E F G H	11111 11112 11121 11122 11211

Sometimes codes are based on the idea of arranging the letters of the message into a geometric figure and then separating it by units of a fixed length. For example, the message "Meet me at noon," could be disguised as the following.

M E A N
E M T O   or   MEAN EMTO ETNO
E T N O

The message is read down the   *This is the same message*
first column and up the   *separated by units.*
second.

Exercises   **Find the next three elements in the following codes. Each has a pattern.**

1. A B C D E · · ·
   1 8 27 64 125 · · ·

2. I   J   K   L   M · · ·
   1881 1991 2002 2112 2222 · · ·

Transpose each message by deciphering the code.

3. V I
   A G
   C E N
   A B S I D A T R E
   T N F R A Y T H E
   I O

4. 992 071 113 221
   707 004 333 847
   923 320 010 756
   Hint: In each group,
   perform one of the basic
   operations and then
   substitute appropriate
   letters.
   (B = 101)

5. /\\\\\\\/\/\/\/\/\\\\\/////\/

   Hint: There are really only
   two different symbols in this
   message. Apply Bacon's
   alphabet.   *(B =*////\ *)*

6. 33 53 34 51
   23 11 54 51 34
   Hint: Each group of
   numbers can be written as
   an ordered pair. (B = (2, 1))

13-5 Probabilities of Independent and Dependent Events

Suppose a die is thrown twice. The second throw of the die is *not* affected by the first throw of the die. Thus, the events are **independent**. The probability of getting a 5 on each throw of the die is $\frac{6}{6} \cdot \frac{1}{6}$ or $\frac{1}{36}$.

If two events, **A** and **B**, are independent, then the probability of both events occurring is found as follows. $$P(A \text{ and } B) = P(A) \cdot P(B)$$	*Probability of Two Independent Events*

Examples

1 Find the probability of getting a sum of 7 on the first throw of two dice and a sum of 4 on the second throw.

Let A be a sum of 7 on the first throw. Let B be a sum of 4 on the second throw.

$$P(A) = \frac{6}{36} \qquad P(B) = \frac{3}{36} \qquad Why?$$

$$P(A \text{ and } B) = P(A) \cdot P(B)$$
$$= \frac{6}{36} \cdot \frac{3}{36} \text{ or } \frac{1}{72}$$

The probability is $\frac{1}{72}$.

2 A new phone is being installed. Find the probability that the final three digits in the telephone number will all be even.

$$P(\text{any digit being even}) = \frac{5}{10} \text{ or } \frac{1}{2}$$

$$P(\text{final three being even}) = \frac{1}{2} \cdot \frac{1}{2} \cdot \frac{1}{2} \text{ or } \frac{1}{8}$$

The probability that the final three digits will all be even is $\frac{1}{8}$.

Suppose two cards are drawn from a standard deck of cards. What is the probability that both cards are clubs? These events are **dependent** because the outcome of the first selection has an effect on the second selection.

$$P(\text{1st club}) = \frac{13}{52} \text{ or } \frac{1}{4} \qquad \textit{Thirteen of the 52 cards are clubs.}$$

$$P(\text{2nd club}) = \frac{12}{51} \text{ or } \frac{4}{17} \qquad \textit{Twelve of the remaining 51 cards are clubs.}$$

$$P(\text{both clubs}) = \frac{1}{4} \cdot \frac{4}{17} = \frac{1}{17}$$

If two events, *A* and *B*, are dependent, then the probability of both events occurring is found as follows. $P(A \text{ and } B) = P(A) \cdot P(B \text{ following } A)$	*Probability of Two Dependent Events*

Example

3 There are 5 red, 3 blue, and 7 black marbles in a bag. Three marbles are chosen without replacement. Find the probability of selecting a red one, then a blue one, and then a red one.

P(red, blue, and red)

$= P(\text{red}) \cdot P(\text{blue following red}) \cdot P(\text{red following red and blue})$

$= \dfrac{5}{15} \cdot \dfrac{3}{14} \cdot \dfrac{4}{13} \text{ or } \dfrac{2}{91}$

The probability is $\dfrac{2}{91}$.

Exploratory Exercises

Identify the events in each of the following problems as *independent* or *dependent*.

1. There are 2 cups of coffee and 4 cups of tea on the counter. Dave drinks two of them. What is the probability that he drinks 2 cups of coffee?

2. In a bag are 5 oranges and 4 tangerines. Noelle selects one, replaces it, and selects another. What is the probability that both selections are oranges?

3. A green die and a red die are thrown. What is the probability that a 4 shows on the green die and a 5 shows on the red die?

4. When Luis plays Jose in backgammon, the odds are 4 to 3 that Luis will win. What is the probability that Luis will win the next 4 games?

5. In a bag are 4 red, 4 green, and 7 blue marbles. Three are selected in sequence without replacement. What is the probability of selecting a red, green, and blue in that order?

6. Two cards are drawn from a standard deck of cards with replacement. What is the probability of drawing a heart and a spade in that order?

7-12. Solve problems **1-6.**

Written Exercises

Solve each problem.

1. Two dice are thrown. What is the probability that a 3 will show on each die?

2. A die is thrown three times. What is the probability that 6 will show all three times?

A bag contains 5 red, 4 white, and 7 blue marbles. If 3 marbles are selected in succession, what is the probability that they are red, white, and blue in that order given the following conditions?

3. No replacement occurs.

4. Replacement occurs each time.

Fifty tickets, numbered consecutively 1 to 50, are placed in a box. What is the probability that in 4 separate drawings, the following selections occur?

5. 4 odd numbers, if replacement occurs

6. 4 odd numbers, if no replacement occurs

7. 4 consecutive numbers in order if no replacement occurs

8. 4 consecutive numbers in order if replacement occurs

A red and a green die are thrown. What is the probability that each of the following occurs?

9. neither shows a 2

10. both show the same number

11. both show different numbers

12. the red shows a 2 and the green shows any other number

Diane's batting average is 0.300. That is, she gets an average of 3 hits for every 10 times at bat. What is the probability that the following occurs? Assume that she gets an out if she does not get a hit.

13. 3 hits for the next 3 times at bat

14. 3 outs for the next 3 times at bat

15. In one dresser drawer Kenneth has 6 pairs of black socks and 3 pairs of gray socks. In another drawer he has 11 white handkerchiefs and 6 colored handkerchiefs. In the dark he selects 2 pairs of socks and a handkerchief. What is the probability that he has a pair of black socks and a white handkerchief?

16. There are 100 clocks in a certain overseas shipment. Assume that there are 4 clocks damaged in shipment but the packaging gives no indication of such damage. If a dealer buys 6 clocks without examining the contents, what is the probability that he does not have a damaged clock?

A standard deck of cards contains 4 suits of 13 cards each.

17. What is the probability of drawing 13 diamonds without replacement?

18. What is the probability of drawing 13 cards of one suit without replacement?

19. What is the probability of drawing 13 red cards without replacement?

20. What is the probability of drawing 13 face cards without replacement?

21. Each member of a group of people were asked to choose their favorite letter. How many people would have to respond in order for the probability of two persons choosing the same letter to be greater than $\frac{1}{2}$?

22. How many people, selected at random, would have to be asked their birthdays, in order for the probability of any two of them having the same birthday to be greater than $\frac{1}{2}$? Assume 366 different birthdays are possible.

For the Scholar

All integers n, such that $n > 1$, are arranged in a five-column matrix as follows.

$$\begin{bmatrix} 0 & 2 & 3 & 4 & 5 \\ 9 & 8 & 7 & 6 & 0 \\ 0 & 10 & 11 & 12 & 13 \\ 17 & 16 & 15 & 14 & 0 \\ 0 & 18 & 19 & 20 & 21 \\ \cdot & \cdot & \cdot & \cdot & 0 \end{bmatrix}$$

In which column will the number 1992 be found?

13-6 Probability of Mutually Exclusive Events or Inclusive Events

Suppose a coin purse contains 5 nickels, 6 dimes, and 2 quarters. What is the probability of selecting a nickel or a dime? Since no coin is both a nickel and a dime the events are **mutually exclusive.** That is, if one event occurs, the other *cannot* occur. The probability of selecting a nickel or a dime is $\frac{5}{13} + \frac{6}{13}$ or $\frac{11}{13}$.

Mutually exclusive events cannot occur simultaneously.

If two events, *A* and *B*, are mutually exclusive, then the probability of both events occurring is found as follows. $$P(A \text{ or } B) = P(A) + P(B)$$	**Probability of Mutually Exclusive Events**

Example

1 **Find the probability of a sum of 6 or a sum of 9 on a single throw of two dice.**

$P(\text{sum of 6}) = \frac{5}{36}$ $P(\text{sum of 9}) = \frac{4}{36}$

$P(\text{sum of 6 or sum of 9}) = \frac{5}{36} + \frac{4}{36}$ or $\frac{9}{36}$

Since the sum cannot be both 6 and 9, these events are mutually exclusive.

The probability is $\frac{9}{36}$ or $\frac{1}{4}$.

What is the probability of drawing a king or a black card? It is possible to draw a card that is both a king and a black card. Therefore, these events are *not* mutually exclusive. They are called **inclusive.** The probability of selecting a king or a black card is as follows.

Inclusive events can occur simultaneously.

king		*black*		*black king*		*black or king*
$\frac{4}{52}$	$+$	$\frac{26}{52}$	$-$	$\frac{2}{52}$	$= \quad \frac{28}{52} \quad$ or	$\frac{7}{13}$

If two events, *A* and *B*, are inclusive, then the probability of either *A* or *B* occurring is found as follows. $$P(A \text{ or } B) = P(A) + P(B) - P(A \text{ and } B)$$	**Probability of Inclusive Events**

Examples

2 A letter is picked at random from the alphabet. Find the probability that the letter is contained in the word *house* or in the word *phone*.

Let event A be a letter from *house*. Let event B be a letter from *phone*.

$$P(A) = \frac{5}{26} \qquad P(B) = \frac{5}{26} \qquad P(A \text{ and } B) = \frac{3}{26} \qquad \textit{Why?}$$

$$P(A \text{ or } B) = \frac{5}{26} + \frac{5}{26} - \frac{3}{26} \text{ or } \frac{7}{26}$$

The probability is $\frac{7}{26}$.

3 A committee of 5 people is to be selected from a group of 6 men and 7 women. What is the probability that the committee will have at least 3 men?

$$\begin{aligned} P(\text{at least 3 men}) &= P(\text{3 men}) + P(\text{4 men}) + P(\text{5 men}) \qquad \substack{\textit{These events are mutually} \\ \textit{exclusive. Why?}} \\ &= \frac{C(6,3) \cdot C(7,2)}{C(13,5)} + \frac{C(6,4) \cdot C(7,1)}{C(13,5)} + \frac{C(6,5) \cdot C(7,0)}{C(13,5)} \\ &= \frac{140}{429} + \frac{35}{429} + \frac{2}{429} \text{ or } \frac{59}{143} \end{aligned}$$

The probability of at least 3 men on the committee is $\frac{59}{143}$.

Exploratory Exercises

Identify each of the following events as mutually exclusive or inclusive.

1. Ten slips of paper numbered from 1 to 10 are in a box. A slip of paper is drawn and a die is thrown. What is the probability of getting a 2 on only one of them?

2. A card is drawn from a standard deck of cards. What is the probability that the card is an ace or a red card?

3. The Ranger pitching staff has 5 left handers and 8 right-handers. If 2 are selected, what is the probability that at least one of them is a right-hander?

4. Five coins are tossed. What is the probability of getting at least 3 tails?

5. In a certain class, 5 of the 12 girls are blondes and 6 of the 15 boys are blondes. What is the probability of selecting a girl or a blonde?

6. A bag contains 7 red, 4 blue, and 14 black marbles. If 3 marbles are selected, what is the probability that all are red or all are blue?

7-12. Solve problems **1-6**.

Written Exercises

Two faces of a die are red, two are blue, and two are white. If the die is thrown, what is the probability that the following occurs?

1. The die shows either red or blue.

2. The die does not show red.

A bag contains 7 red and 4 white marbles. Three marbles are selected. What is the probability that the following occurs?

3. all 3 red or all 3 white

4. at least 2 red

5. at least 1 white

6. exactly 2 white

Two cards are drawn from a standard deck of cards. What is the probability that the following occurs?

7. both aces or both face cards

8. both aces or both black

9. both black or both face cards

10. both either red or an ace

Six coins are tossed. What is the probability that the following occurs?

11. 3 heads or 2 tails

12. at least 4 tails

13. 4 heads or 1 tail

14. all heads or all tails

A committee of 6 people is to be selected from a group of 7 men and 7 women. What is the probability of the following?

15. all men or all women

16. 5 men or 5 women

17. 3 men and 3 women

18. at least 4 women

Slips of paper numbered from 1 to 25 are in a box. A slip of paper is drawn at random. What is the probability that the following occurs?

19. The number is a multiple of 2 or 5.

20. The number is a multiple of 3 or is an odd number.

21. The number is a multiple of 3 or is a prime number.

22. The number is a multiple of 7 or is an even number.

For the Scholar

A magician cuts a rope in two parts at a point selected at random. What is the probability that the length of the longer rope is at least 8 times the length of the shorter rope?

13-7 Conditional Probability

Suppose Jack says, "If it rains, I will stay in and do my homework." While it is not certain that Jack will not do his homework if it does not rain, the occurrence of rain will have some effect on the completion of the homework.

The probability of an event given the occurrence of another event is called **conditional probability.** The conditional probability of A, given B, is denoted by $P(A/B)$.

The conditional probability of event A, given event B, is found as follows.

$$P(A/B) = \frac{P(A \text{ and } B)}{P(B)} \text{ where } P(B) \neq 0$$

Conditional Probability

Examples

1 **A pair of dice are thrown. Find the probability that the numbers of the dice match given that their sum is greater than 7.**

Let event A be that the numbers match. Let event B be that their sum is greater than 7.

$$P(B) = \frac{15}{36} \qquad P(A \text{ and } B) = \frac{3}{36} \qquad Why?$$

$$P(A/B) = \frac{P(A \text{ and } B)}{P(B)}$$

$$= \frac{\frac{3}{36}}{\frac{15}{36}} \text{ or } \frac{1}{5}$$

The probability is $\frac{1}{5}$.

2 **A pair of dice are thrown. Find the probability that their sum is greater than 7 given that the numbers match.**

Let event A be that the sum of the dice is greater than 7. Let event B be that the numbers match.

$$P(B) = \frac{6}{36} \qquad P(A \text{ and } B) = \frac{3}{36}$$

$$P(A/B) = \frac{P(A \text{ and } B)}{P(B)}$$

$$= \frac{\frac{3}{36}}{\frac{6}{36}} \text{ or } \frac{1}{2}$$

The probability is $\frac{1}{2}$.

Suppose a die is thrown twice. What is the probability of a 3 on the second throw given that a 3 occurred on the first throw?

$$P(A/B) = \frac{\frac{1}{36}}{\frac{6}{36}} \text{ or } \frac{1}{6}$$

But $P(A)$ is also $\frac{1}{6}$. Thus, in this case $P(A) = \frac{P(A \text{ and } B)}{P(B)}$ or $P(A \text{ and } B) = P(A) \cdot P(B)$. Therefore, events A and B are independent. The fact that a 3 occurred on the first throw does *not* affect the probability that a 3 will occur on the second throw.

Example

3 One card is drawn from a standard deck of 52 cards. What is the probability that it is a queen if it is known to be a face card?

$$P(B) = \frac{12}{52} \text{ or } \frac{3}{13} \qquad P(A \text{ and } B) = \frac{4}{52} \text{ or } \frac{1}{13} \qquad \begin{array}{l} \textit{event } A = \textit{queen} \\ \textit{event } B = \textit{face card} \end{array}$$

$$P(A/B) = \frac{\frac{1}{13}}{\frac{3}{13}} \text{ or } \frac{1}{3}$$

Exploratory Exercises

The conditional probability of *A* given *B* is represented as *P(A/B)*. Identify events *A* and *B* in each of the following problems.

1. A die is thrown three times. What is the probability that 4 shows on the third throw given that a 6 showed on the first two throws?

2. A coin is tossed three times. What is the probability that at the most 2 heads show given that at least one head shows?

3. Two coins are tossed. What is the probability that one coin shows tails if it is known that at least one coin shows heads?

4. Two boys and two girls are lined up at random. What is the probability that the girls are separated if a girl is on an end?

5. One bag contains 4 red marbles and 4 blue marbles. Another bag contains 2 red marbles and 6 blue marbles. A marble is drawn from one of the bags at random and found to be blue. What is the probability that the marble is from the first bag?

6. A city council consists of six Democrats, two of whom are women, and six Republicans, four of whom are men. A member is chosen at random. If the member is a man, what is the probability that he is a Democrat?

7-12. Solve problems **1-6.**

Written Exercises

Solve each problem.

1. One card is drawn from a standard deck of cards. What is the probability that it is a red king if it is known to be a face card?

2. A coin is tossed three times. What is the probability that the third toss shows heads given that the first two tosses showed heads?

A green die and a red die are thrown.

3. What is the probability that the sum of the dice is greater than 10 if the red die came up 6?

4. What is the probability that the sum of the dice is less than 6 if the red die came up 2?

5. What is the probability that the sum of the dice is 10 or greater if a 5 came up on at least one die?

6. What is the probability that the sum of the dice is 7 if the green die resulted in a number less than 4?

Three coins are tossed. What is the probability that they are all tails if the following events occur?

7. The first coin is a tail.

8. One of the coins is a head.

9. At least one of the coins is a tail.

10. At least two of the coins are tails.

Two dice are thrown. If the two numbers showing are different, what is the probability of each of the following?

11. Their sum is 5.

12. One of the dice shows a 1.

13. Their sum is greater than 9.

14. Their sum is 4 or less.

15. Five-digit numbers are formed from the numbers 7, 7, 7, 6, and 6. If a number is even, what is the probability that the 6's are together?

16. Two numbers are selected at random from the numbers 1 through 9. If their sum is even, what is the probability that both numbers are odd?

A committee of 3 is selected from Ron, Becky, Wes, Kay, Jo, and Rich.

17. If Becky is on the committee, what is the probability that Wes is also on it?

18. If Wes and Kay are on the committee, what is the probability that Jo is not on it?

19. If Ron was not selected, what is the probability that Becky and Kay were selected?

20. If neither Ron nor Rich were selected, what is the probability that Becky and Wes were selected?

21. One box contains 3 red balls and 4 white balls. A second box contains 5 red balls and 3 white balls. A box is selected at random and one ball is withdrawn. If the ball is white, what is the probability that it was taken from the second box?

22. A buyer for a department store will accept a carton containing 10 clocks if a sample of 2, chosen at random, is not defective. What is the probability that she will accept a carton of 10 if it contains 4 defective clocks?

In a game played with a standard deck of cards, each face card has a value of 10, each ace a value of 1, and each number card a value equal to the number. Two cards are drawn.

23. If one card is the queen of hearts, what is the probability that the sum of the cards is greater than 18?

24. If at least one card is an ace, what is the probability that the sum of the cards is 7 or less?

In a certain class, 40% of the students have brown hair, 25% have brown eyes, and 15% have both brown hair and brown eyes. A student is selected at random.

25. If the student has brown hair, what is the probability that the student also has brown eyes?

26. If the student has brown eyes, what is the probability that the student does not have brown hair?

For the Scholar

A chain is fitted without slack around two sprocket wheels on a custom-built racing bicycle. If the radii of the sprocket wheels are 5 inches and 3 inches, and the distance between contact points of the chain and the sprockets is 18 inches, find the distance between the centers of the sprocket wheels.

13-8 The Binomial Theorem and Probability

Suppose that 5 coins are tossed at the same time. What is the probability that exactly 2 coins will show heads? The number of ways this can happen is given by $C(5, 2)$ or 10.

The probability may be found by using the binomial expansion. Let p_h represent the probability that heads will show on one coin on one toss. Let p_t represent the probability that tails will show on one coin.

$$(p_h + p_t)^5 = 1p_h^5 + 5p_h^4p_t + 10p_h^3p_t^2 + 10p_h^2p_t^3 + 5p_hp_t^4 + 1p_t^5$$

coefficient	term	meaning	probability	
$C(5, 0)$	$1p_h^5$	1 way to get 5 heads	$1\left(\frac{1}{2}\right)^5$ or $\frac{1}{32}$	$p_h = p_t = \frac{1}{2}$
$C(5, 1)$	$5p_h^4p_t$	5 ways to get 4 heads and 1 tail	$5\left(\frac{1}{2}\right)^4\left(\frac{1}{2}\right)$ or $\frac{5}{32}$	
$C(5, 2)$	$10p_h^3p_t^2$	10 ways to get 3 heads and 2 tails	$10\left(\frac{1}{2}\right)^3\left(\frac{1}{2}\right)^2$ or $\frac{5}{16}$	
$C(5, 3)$	$10p_h^2p_t^3$	10 ways to get 2 heads and 3 tails	$10\left(\frac{1}{2}\right)^2\left(\frac{1}{2}\right)^3$ or $\frac{5}{16}$	
$C(5, 4)$	$5p_hp_t^4$	5 ways to get 1 head and 4 tails	$5\left(\frac{1}{2}\right)\left(\frac{1}{2}\right)^4$ or $\frac{5}{32}$	
$C(5, 5)$	$1p_t^5$	1 way to get 5 tails	$1\left(\frac{1}{2}\right)^5$ or $\frac{1}{32}$	

Thus, the probability that exactly two coins will show heads is $\frac{5}{16}$.

Other probabilities can be determined from the above expansion. For example, what is the probability of at least 2 heads showing if 5 coins are tossed simultaneously? The first, second, third, and fourth terms represent the condition that two or more heads show. Thus, the probability of this happening is as follows.

$$P(\text{at least 2 heads}) = \frac{1}{32} + \frac{5}{32} + \frac{5}{16} + \frac{5}{16}$$
$$= \frac{26}{32} \text{ or } \frac{13}{16}$$

Problems that can be solved using a binomial expansion are called **binomial experiments.**

A binomial experiment exists if and only if the following conditions occur.

1. **The experiment consists of *n* identical trials.**
2. **Each trial results in *one* of two outcomes.**
3. **The trials are independent.**

Binomial Experiments

Examples

1 **Suppose that three dice are thrown at the same time. Find the probability that at least one 4 will show.**

Let p_4 represent the probability that 4 shows on one throw of one die. Let q_4 represent the probability of failure of 4 to show on one throw of one die.

$$(p_4 + q_4)^3 = p_4{}^3 + 3p_4{}^2q_4 + 3p_4q_4{}^2 + q_4{}^3$$

$$P(\text{at least one 4}) = \left(\frac{1}{6}\right)^3 + 3\left(\frac{1}{6}\right)^2\left(\frac{5}{6}\right) + 3\left(\frac{1}{6}\right)\left(\frac{5}{6}\right)^2$$

$p_4 = \frac{1}{6}, q_4 = \frac{5}{6}$

$$= \frac{1}{216} + 3\left(\frac{1}{36}\right)\left(\frac{5}{6}\right) + 3\left(\frac{1}{6}\right)\left(\frac{25}{36}\right)$$

$$= \frac{1 + 15 + 75}{216} \text{ or } \frac{91}{216}$$

The probability is $\frac{91}{216}$.

2 **Peggy guesses on all 10 questions of a true-false quiz. What is the probability that exactly half of the answers are correct?**

There are only two outcomes on each question: true (T) or false (F). When $(T + F)^{10}$ is expanded, the term containing T^5F^5 will give the desired probability.

$$C(10, 5)T^5F^5 = \frac{10 \cdot 9 \cdot 8 \cdot 7 \cdot 6}{5 \cdot 4 \cdot 3 \cdot 2 \cdot 1} \cdot \left(\frac{1}{2}\right)^5\left(\frac{1}{2}\right)^5$$

Replace T by P(T) which is $\frac{1}{2}$ and F by P(F) which is $\frac{1}{2}$.

$$= 252\left(\frac{1}{32}\right)\left(\frac{1}{32}\right) \text{ or } \frac{63}{256}$$

The probability is $\frac{63}{256}$.

Exploratory Exercises

State whether each of the following situations represents a binomial experiment or not. Solve each that represents a binomial experiment.

1. A coin is tossed 4 times. What is the probability of 2 heads and 2 tails?

2. Five coins are tossed. What is the probability of at least 3 tails?

3. Bianca draws 4 cards from a standard deck of cards. What is the probability of drawing 4 kings if she replaces each card?

4. Randy draws 3 cards from a standard deck of cards. What is the probability of drawing 3 aces if he does not replace the cards?

5. On a shelf are 8 cans of vegetables and 4 cans of fruit. If 2 cans are selected and each is replaced, what is the probability that they both contain fruit?

6. A die is thrown 2 times. What is the probability that the die shows a 3 both times?

Written Exercises

Three coins are tossed. What is the probability of the following?

1. 3 heads
2. 3 tails
3. at least 2 heads
4. exactly 2 tails

A die is thrown 5 times. What is the probability of the following?

5. only one 4
6. at least three 4's
7. no more than two 4's
8. exactly five 4's

Connie has a bent coin. The probability of heads is $\frac{2}{3}$ with this coin. She tosses the coin 4 times. What is the probability of the following?

9. no heads
10. 4 heads
11. at least 3 heads

Maroa guesses on all 10 questions on a true-false test. What is the probability of the following?

12. 7 correct
13. at least 6 correct
14. all incorrect
15. at least half incorrect

A batter is now batting 0.200. In the next 5 at-bats, what is the probability of having the following?

16. exactly 1 hit
17. exactly 3 hits
18. at least 4 hits

If a tack is dropped, the probability that it will land point up is $\frac{2}{5}$. Six tacks are dropped. What is the probability of the following?

19. all point up
20. exactly 3 point up
21. exactly 5 point up
22. at least 6 point up

A "wheel of fortune" at a carnival has the numbers from 1 through 10.

23. What is the probability of 7 never coming up in 5 spins of the wheel?
24. What is the probability of 7 coming up exactly once in 5 spins of the wheel?
25. What is the probability of 7 coming up each time in 5 spins of the wheel?
26. What is the probability of 7 coming up at least once in 5 spins of the wheel?
27. The probability that Jeff wins a game of table tennis with John is $\frac{3}{5}$. Suppose they play 10 games. What is the probability that John will win 5 games?
28. A box contains 3 red and 3 white marbles. An experiment consists of selecting one marble at random, noting the color, and then replacing the marble in the box. What is the probability of selecting 5 white marbles in 8 trials?
29. The probability that the Mustang baseball team will win a home game is $\frac{3}{5}$. The team plays 10 home games before its next road trip. What is the probability that it will win 8 out of the 10 games?
30. The probability that a 55-year-old man will die before his next birthday is 0.02. What is the probability that no more than three 55-year-old men in a sample of 10 will die within a year?

For the Scholar

Let $p = q(0.96\overline{363})$ where p and q are relatively prime integers (no common divisor other than 1). Find the positive difference between p and q.

Chapter Summary

1. **Basic Counting Principle:** Suppose an event can be chosen in p different ways. Another independent event can be chosen in q different ways. Then the two events can be chosen successively in $p \cdot q$ ways. (389)

2. **Definition of $P(n, r)$:** The number of permutations of n objects, taken r at a time, is defined as follows. $P(n, r) = \dfrac{n!}{(n - r)!}$ (390)

3. **Permutations with Repetitions:** The number of permutations of n objects of which p are alike and q are alike is found by evaluating the following expression. $\dfrac{n!}{p!q!}$ (393)

4. **Circular Permutations:** If n objects are arranged in a circle, then there are $\dfrac{n!}{n}$ or $(n - 1)!$ permutations of the n objects. (394)

5. **Definition of $C(n, r)$:** The number of combinations of n objects, taken r at a time, is written $C(n, r)$. $C(n, r) = \dfrac{n!}{(n - r)!r!}$ (398)

6. **Probability of Success and of Failure:** If an event can succeed in s ways and fail in f ways, then the probability of success and the probability of failure are as follows.

$$P(s) = \frac{s}{s + f} \qquad P(f) = \frac{f}{s + f} \quad (400)$$

7. **Definition of Odds:** The odds of the successful outcome of an event is the ratio of the probability of its success to the probability of its failure. $\text{Odds} = \dfrac{P(s)}{P(f)}$ (401)

8. **Probability of Two Independent Events:** If two events, A and B, are independent, then the probability of both events occurring is found as follows. $P(A \text{ and } B) = P(A) \cdot P(B)$ (405)

9. **Probability of Two Dependent Events:** If two events, A and B, are dependent, then the probability of both events occurring is found as follows. $P(A \text{ and } B) = P(A) \cdot P(B \text{ following } A)$ (406)

10. **Probability of Mutually Exclusive Events:** If two events, A and B, are mutually exclusive, then the probability of both events occurring is found as follows. $P(A \text{ or } B) = P(A) + P(B)$ (408)

11. **Probability of Inclusive Events:** If two events, A and B, are inclusive, then the probability of either A or B occurring is found as follows. $P(A \text{ or } B) = P(A) + P(B) - P(A \text{ and } B)$ (408)

12. **Conditional Probability:** The conditional probability of event A, given event B, is found as follows. $P(A/B) = \dfrac{P(A \text{ and } B)}{P(B)}$ where $P(B) \neq 0$ (410)

13. **Binomial Experiments:** A binomial experiment exists if and only if the following conditions occur. The experiment consists of n identical trials. Each trial results in one of two outcomes. The trials are independent. (414)

Find the value of each of the following. (13-1)

1. $P(6, 3)$

2. $P(8, 6)$

3. $\dfrac{P(4, 2) - P(6, 3)}{P(5, 3)}$

4. How many different three-digit numbers can be formed using the digits 1, 2, 3, 4, 5, and 6 without repeating digits?

5. How many ways can six books be placed on a shelf if the only dictionary must be on an end?

How many ways can the letters of each word be arranged? (13-2)

6. LEVEL

7. CINCINNATI

8. How many ways can 8 people be seated at a round table?

9. How many ways can 5 keys be placed on a key ring?

Find the value of each of the following. (13-3)

10. $C(5, 3)$

11. $C(11, 8)$

12. $C(5, 5)$

13. From a standard deck of cards, how many different 4-card hands can have 4 cards of the same suit?

14. From a group of 3 men and 7 women, how many committees of 2 men and 2 women can be formed?

State the odds of an event occurring given the probability that it occurs as follows. (13-4)

15. $\dfrac{4}{9}$

16. $\dfrac{3}{5}$

17. $\dfrac{1}{12}$

A bag contains 7 pennies, 4 nickels, and 5 dimes. Three coins are selected at random with replacement. What is the probability of each of the following selections? (13-4)

18. all 3 pennies

19. all 3 dimes

20. 2 pennies, 1 nickel

A green die and a red die are thrown. What is the probability that the following occurs? (13-5)

21. The red die shows a 1 and the green die shows any other number.

22. Neither shows a 1.

Slips of paper numbered from 1 to 14 are in a box. A slip of paper is drawn at random. What is the probability that the following occurs? (13-6)

23. The number is a prime or is a multiple of 4.

24. The number is a multiple of 2 or a multiple of 3.

A green die and a red die are thrown. (13-7)

25. What is the probability that the sum of the dice is less than 5 if the green die shows a 1?

26. What is the probability that the sum of the dice is 9 if the two numbers showing are different?

A coin is tossed 4 times. What is the probability that the following occurs? (13-8)

27. exactly 1 head

28. no heads

29. 2 heads and 2 tails

30. at least 3 tails

Solve each problem.

1. The letters r, s, t, u, and v are to be used to form five-letter patterns. How many patterns can be formed if repetitions are not allowed?

2. There are 5 persons who are applicants for 3 different positions in a store, each person being qualified for each position. In how many ways is it possible to fill the positions?

3. How many ways can 6 charms be arranged on a charm bracelet that has no clasp?

4. How many ways can 7 people be seated at a round table relative to each other?

5. How many baseball teams can be formed from 15 players if only 3 pitch and the others play the remaining 8 positions?

6. A bag contains 4 red and 6 white marbles. How many ways can 5 marbles be selected if 2 must be red?

7. The probability that the Pirates will win a game against the Hornets is $\frac{4}{7}$. What are the odds that the Pirates will beat the Hornets?

8. Five cards are drawn from a standard deck of cards. What is the probability that they are all from one suit?

9. Find the probability of getting a sum of 8 on the first throw of two dice and a sum of 4 on the second throw.

10. A new phone is being installed at the Collier residence. What is the probability that the final 3 digits in the telephone number will be odd?

11. A bag contains 3 red, 4 white, and 5 blue marbles. If 3 marbles are selected at random, what is the probability that all are red or all are blue?

12. Two cards are drawn from a standard deck of cards. What is the probability of having drawn an ace or a black card?

13. Four-digit numbers are formed from the numbers 7, 3, 3, 2, and 2. If a number is odd, what is the probability that the 3's are together?

14. Two numbers are selected at random from the numbers 1 through 9. If their product is even, what is the probability that both numbers are even?

15. Five bent coins are tossed. The probability of heads is $\frac{2}{3}$ for each of them. What is the probability that no more than 2 will show heads?

16. While shooting arrows, Archie can hit the center of the target 4 out of 5 times. What is the probability that he will hit it exactly 4 out of the next 7 times?

CHAPTER 14

Descriptive Statistics

The advertising industry uses statistics to a great extent in making decisions. For example, an advertiser may collect data on costs, previous sales, consumer preference, and demand for a product. The techniques of collection, organization, analysis, and presentation of data are called descriptive statistics.

14-1 Measures of Central Tendency

A **measure of central tendency** is a number that represents a set of data. Measures of central tendency may be used to summarize a set of data. They also may be used to compare one set of data with another.

The **arithmetic mean** is a measure of central tendency that is found by adding the values in the set and dividing by the number of values in the set. For example, the arithmetic mean of 89, 73, and 92 is $\dfrac{89 + 73 + 92}{3}$ or $84\frac{2}{3}$. Frequently the arithmetic mean is referred to simply as the mean.

This is commonly called an average.

If X is a variable used to represent any value in a set of data, then the arithmetic mean, $\overline{X}$, of n values is given by the following formula.

$\overline{X}$ is read "X bar."

$$\overline{X} = \frac{X_1 + X_2 + X_3 + \cdots + X_n}{n}$$

The sum of the specified terms can be abbreviated using the summation symbol, Σ.

$$\sum_{i=1}^{n} X_i = X_1 + X_2 + X_3 + \cdots + X_n$$

The left member is read "the summation of X-sub-i from i equals 1 to n." The symbol X_i represents successive values of the set of data as i assumes successive integral values from 1 to n.

> If a set of data has n values, given by X_i such that $1 \leq i \leq n$, then the arithmetic mean, $\overline{X}$, can be found as follows.
>
> $$\overline{X} = \frac{1}{n} \sum_{i=1}^{n} X_i$$

The Arithmetic Mean

Example

1 Find the arithmetic mean of {24, 28, 21, 37, 31, 29, 23, 22, 34, 31}.

$n = 10$

$$\overline{X} = \frac{1}{10} \sum_{i=1}^{10} X_i$$

$$= \frac{1}{10}(24 + 28 + 21 + 37 + 31 + 29 + 23 + 22 + 34 + 31)$$

$$= 28$$

The value of every item in a set of data affects the value of the arithmetic mean. For example, the mean of 15, 16, 19, 16, and 14 is 16. But, 16 is also the mean of 1, 51, 5, and 7. When extreme values are included, the arithmetic mean may become less representative of the set.

The value of the mean can be considerably affected by extreme values.

The **median, M_d,** is another measure of central tendency. It is the mid-value of a set of data.

Before the median can be found, the data must be placed in an **array.** An array is formed by arranging the data into an ordered sequence. The **range** is the difference of the greatest and least values in the array.

The median of an odd number of data is the middle value of their array. The median of an even number of data is the arithmetic mean of the two middle values of their array.

The value of the median is affected very little by extreme values.

Example

2 **Find the median and range of each set of data.**

$$\{21, 19, 17, 19, 19\} \qquad \{4, 10, 1, 61\}$$

The array is $\{17, 19, 19, 19, 21\}$. There are five values. The middle value is 19. Thus, the median is 19. The range is $21 - 17$ or 4.

The array is $\{1, 4, 10, 61\}$. Since there are four values, the median is the mean of the two middle values. Thus, $M_d = \frac{4 + 10}{2}$ or 7. The range is $61 - 1$ or 60.

Compare the arithmetic means of these two sets of data.

The **mode** of a set of data is the value that appears more frequently than any other in the set. For example, the mode of $\{17, 19, 19, 19, 21\}$ is 19. Some sets of data have multiple modes. Data with two modes are said to be **bimodal.** Some sets have no mode. To have no mode, each item of the set has equal frequency. The mode is important in such data as sizes of shoes or clothing. *Why?*

The value of the mode is not affected by extreme values.

Example

3 Find the mean, median, and mode of the following set of data.

{64, 87, 62, 87, 63, 98, 76, 54, 87, 58, 70, 76}

$$\overline{X} = \frac{1}{n} \sum_{i=1}^{n} X_i$$

$$= \frac{1}{12} (64 + 87 + 62 + 87 + 63 + 98 + 76 + 54 + 87 + 58 + 70 + 76)$$

$$= 73.5$$

To find the median and mode, place the data in an array.

{54, 58, 62, 63, 64, 70, 76, 76, 87, 87, 87, 98}

There are two middle values, the 6th value, 70 and the 7th value, 76. Thus, $M_d = \frac{70 + 76}{2}$ or 73. The mode, the most frequently occurring value, is 87.

The mode, in this case, is not a representative value of central tendencies.

The mean is 73.5, the median is 73, and the mode is 87.

Exploratory Exercises

Find the median for each set of data.

1. {14, 15, 16, 17}
2. {3, 3, 6, 12, 3}
3. {10, 45, 58, 10}
4. {6, 10, 8, 5, 11, 6, 7, 12, 11, 11, 9, 6}

5-8. Find the mode or modes for each set of data in problems **1-4.**

9-12. Find the mean for each set of data in problems **1-4.**

Find a set of numbers that satisfies the conditions in each of the following.

13. The mean, median, and mode are all the same number.
14. The mean is greater than the median.
15. The mode is 10 and the median is greater than the mean.
16. The mean is 6, the median is $5\frac{1}{2}$, and the mode is 9.

Written Exercises

Answer each of the following.

1. Martin's scores on five tests were 84, 72, 91, 64, and 83. Find his mean score.
2. Find the mean of 5′7″, 4′8″, 6′1″, 5′4″, 8′0″, 6′7″, and 5′4″.

The weights in pounds of the members of the wrestling team at Allen East High School are 124, 155, 172, 117, 146, 138, 151, 160, and 142.

3. Find the difference between the arithmetic mean and the median of their weights.
4. If each member gains 5 lb, how are the mean and median affected?

Find the value of x so that the set of data given has the indicated arithmetic mean.

5. $\{2, 4, 6, 8, x\}$; $\overline{X} = 7\frac{1}{2}$

6. $\{x, 2x - 1, 2x, 3x + 1\}$; $\overline{X} = 6$

7. The mean height of five boys is 68 inches. If one boy is 5 feet tall and another is 6 feet tall, give possible heights for the other three boys.

8. Find possible values of x if the median of $\{11, 2, 3, 3.2, 13, 14, 8, x\}$ is 8.

The D & R Construction Company is owned by two partners and has eight employees. The partners are each taking salaries of $50,000 from the company. Of the eight employees, two earn $14,700 each, two earn $11,600 each, and four earn $10,700 each.

9. Make an array of the ten salaries.

10. Find the mean of the ten salaries.

11. Find the median of the ten salaries.

12. Find the mode of the ten salaries.

13. The company and the union representing its employees each give statements concerning "the average salaries of D & R employees." Which "average" might each side favor in its press release?

14. Which of the measures of central tendency best describes the salaries of D & R employees?

A math test is given to a large number of students.

15. Assume the test is very easy. Would the mode of the scores likely be higher or lower than the mean?

16. Assume the test is very difficult. Would the mode of the scores likely be higher or lower than the mean?

Statements such as the following are often made. "The average American family owns a car." "The average American woman wears a size 7 shoe."

17. What is meant by the word "average"?

18. Is the use of "average" closest to the mean, median, or mode?

The grade point averages for a random sample of thirty graduating seniors are listed.

3.4	2.4	2.6	3.6	3.8	3.4	2.0	3.0	2.8	2.6
3.2	2.4	4.0	2.8	3.6	3.2	2.8	2.2	2.6	3.6
2.0	2.2	2.4	3.2	3.6	2.6	2.2	4.0	2.2	2.6

19. Find the mean of the grade point averages.

20. Find the percentage of seniors in the sample who had a grade point average above the mean.

21. Since this is a random sample, estimate the number of seniors in the class of 472 who had a grade point average above the mean.

Challenge Exercises

A rod one meter long is suspended at the middle so that it balances. Suppose one-gram weights are hung on the rod at the following distances from one end: 5 cm, 20 cm, 37 cm, 44 cm, 52 cm, 68 cm, 71 cm, 85 cm. The rod does not balance at the 50 cm mark.

22. Where must one more 1-gram weight be hung so that the rod will balance at the 50 cm mark?

23. Where must a 2-gram weight be hung so that the rod will balance at the 50 cm mark?

For the Scholar

Find the points of intersection of the graphs of $(2x - 5y + 7)(2x + 2y - 4) = 0$ and $(6x + 2y - 8)(x - y + 2) = 0$.

14-2 Harmonic and Quadratic Means

In addition to the arithmetic mean there are other measures of central tendency of a set of data that may better describe the set.

The **harmonic mean,** *H*, is useful in special cases for averaging rates. It is given by this formula.

If a set of data has *n* values, given by X_i such that $1 \le i \le n$, then the harmonic mean, *H*, can be found as follows. $$H = \frac{n}{\dfrac{1}{X_1} + \dfrac{1}{X_2} + \cdots + \dfrac{1}{X_n}} = \frac{n}{\displaystyle\sum_{i=1}^{i} \frac{1}{X_i}}$$	*The Harmonic Mean*

Example 1 compares the use of the harmonic mean with the arithmetic mean.

Example

1 Jim Taulman travels two hours at a rate of 30 miles per hour and then on a freeway travels the next two hours at a rate of 55 miles per hour. What is his average speed?

Meiko King travels 100 miles at the rate of 30 miles per hour and then on a freeway travels the next 100 miles at the rate of 55 miles per hour. What is her average speed?

Jim's average speed is the arithmetic mean of 30 mph and 55 mph.

$$\overline{X} = \frac{30 + 55}{2} = 42.5 \text{ mph} \qquad \textit{The time travelled at each rate is the same.}$$

Meiko's average speed is the harmonic mean of 30 mph and 55 mph.

$$H = \frac{2}{\dfrac{1}{30} + \dfrac{1}{55}} = 38.8 \text{ mph} \qquad \textit{The distances travelled are equal.}$$

Check these averages. Jim travels a total distance of 170 miles in 4 hours or at an average speed of 42.5 miles per hour. Meiko travels a total distance of 200 miles in approximately 5.15 hours or at an average speed of 38.8 miles per hour.

Driving 100 miles at 30 mph takes 3.3 hours. Driving 100 miles at 55 mph takes 1.8 hours.

When equal *times* are involved the arithmetic mean of the rates is used. When equal *distances* are involved the harmonic mean is used.

Another measure of central tendency is the **quadratic mean.** It is the square root of the arithmetic mean of the squared values in a set of data.

> If a set of data has *n* values, given by X_i such that $1 \leq i \leq n$, then the quadratic mean, *Q*, can be found as follows.
>
> $$Q = \sqrt{\frac{X_1^2 + X_2^2 + X_3^2 + \cdots + X_n^2}{n}} = \sqrt{\frac{\sum_{i=1}^{n} X_i^2}{n}}$$

The Quadratic Mean

Example

2 Find the quadratic mean of {1.3, 1.5. 1.7, 1.0, 1.1}. Use a calculator.

$$Q = \sqrt{\frac{(1.3)^2 + (1.5)^2 + (1.7)^2 + (1.0)^2 + (1.1)^2}{5}}$$

$$= \sqrt{\frac{9.04}{5}}$$

$$\approx \sqrt{1.8} \text{ or } 1.34 \qquad \textit{After setting the calculator in statistic mode and inputting the data do the following.}$$

$\sqrt{x} \quad \Sigma_x^2$

ENTER: [2ndF] [x→M] [÷] 5 [=] [√]

DISPLAY: 9.04   1.808   1.3446

Exploratory Exercises

State whether the arithmetic mean or the harmonic mean is used to find the correct average.

1. A team of three students competed in a 375-mile relay race. Each student drove 125 miles. Assume their driving speeds are known. Find the average driving speed of the three students during the race.

2. A team of three students competed in a 375-mile relay race. Each student drove for 2.5 hours. Assume their driving speeds are known. Find the average driving speed of the team during the race.

3. Kathy Brauen purchased four different cuts of beef. Assume the price per pound of each cut of beef is known. If she purchased the same quantity of each cut, find the average price per pound.

4. Tony Rockey purchased three different cuts of pork. Assume the price per pound of each cut of pork is known. If he spent the same amount of money for each cut, find the average price per pound.

Written Exercises

Find the harmonic mean of each set of data.

1. {3, 4, 5, 6}

2. {5, 10, 15, 20, 25}

Find the quadratic mean of each set of data.

3. {6, 6, 7, 8, 8, 11, 11, 12}

4. {2.5, 2.5, 2.5, 3.5, 3.5, 3.8, 4.0, 4.2}

Find $\overline{X}$, M_d, H, and Q for each set of data.

5. {3, 2, 6, 8, 5}

6. {4, 8, 1, 15}

Solve each problem.

7. A team of three students competed in a 375-mile relay race. The driving speed of each student is as follows. Student A drives 40 mph. Student B drives 50 mph. Student C drives 60 mph. If each student drives 125 miles, find the average driving speed of the three students.

8. A team of three students competed in a 375-mile relay race. The driving speed of each student is as follows. Student A drives 45 mph. Student B drives 50 mph. Student C drives 55 mph. If each student drives for 2.5 hours, find the average driving speed of the three students.

9. At the Round-Up Butcher Shop the prices of each cut of beef are as follows. Chuck roast is \$1.80/lb, round steak is \$2.60/lb, T-bone steak is \$4.10/lb, and rib-eye steak is \$3.90/lb. If Ladene purchased 5 lb of each cut, find the average price per pound.

10. At the Sunset Drive Grocery, the prices of each cut of pork are as follows. Pork chops are \$2.00/lb, ham is \$2.30/lb, and pork roast is \$2.00/lb. If Benjamin purchased \$10 worth of each cut of pork, find the average price per pound.

11. A salesperson travels from Louisville to Chicago at an average speed of 36 mph and returns by the same route at an average speed of 55 mph. Find the average speed for the round trip.

12. Five employees punch IBM cards for a one hour period. The punching speeds of the five employees are 10, 20, 24, 30, and 40 seconds per card respectively. Find the average speed per card.

For the Scholar

Find the number of ways, n, that \$12 can be changed into dimes and quarters, assuming that at least one of each coin must be used.

14-3 Measures of Variability

The arithmetic mean and median are measures of central tendency and hence are statistics that describe a certain important characteristic of a set of data. However, they do *not* indicate anything about the variability of the data. For example, the mean of 35, 40, and 45 is 40, and the mean of 10, 40, and 70 is also 40. The variability is much greater in the second case than in the first, but this is *not* indicated by the mean.

One measure of variability is the **mean deviation.** If the deviations from the mean, $X_i - \overline{X}$, are found, it is evident that the sum of the deviations from the mean is zero. That is, $\sum_{i=1}^{n} (X_i - \overline{X}) = 0$. Thus, the average of the deviations can be found only if the absolute value of the deviations is considered. The arithmetic mean of the absolute value of the deviations from the mean of a set of data is called the mean deviation, *M.D.*

If a set of data has *n* values, given by X_i such that $1 \leq i \leq n$, with arithmetic mean, $\overline{X}$, then the mean deviation, *M.D.*, can be found as follows. $$M.D. = \frac{1}{n} \sum_{i=1}^{n} |X_i - \overline{X}|$$	*The Mean Deviation*

Example

1 Find the mean deviation for each of the following sets of data.

{35, 40, 45}

$$M.D. = \frac{1}{3} \sum_{i=1}^{3} |X_i - 40|$$

$$= \frac{1}{3} (|-5| + |0| + |5|)$$

$$= 3\frac{1}{3}$$

{10, 40, 70}

$$M.D. = \frac{1}{3} \sum_{i=1}^{3} |X_i - 40|$$

$$= \frac{1}{3} (|-30| + |0| + |30|)$$

$$= 20$$

Another measure of the variability is the **semi-interquartile range.** If the array of a set of data is separated into four parts having an equal number of data, each part is called a **quartile.** The median separates the data into two equal parts and thus is the second quartile point, Q_2. Each half can be separated into two equal parts to find the first and third quartile points. One-fourth of the data lies below the first quartile point, Q_1, and three-fourths of the data lies below the third quartile point, Q_3. The difference between the first quartile point and the third quartile point is called the **interquartile range.** When this difference is divided by 2, the quotient is the semi-interquartile range.

Q_1 and Q_3 are the medians of each half of the data.

If a set of data has first quartile point, Q_1, and third quartile point, Q_3, the semi-interquartile range, Q_R, can be found as follows. $$Q_R = \frac{Q_3 - Q_1}{2}$$	*The Semi-Interquartile Range*

Example

2 Find the semi-interquartile range of {38, 47, 18, 26, 41, 30, 27, 21, 35, 31, 29, 32, 25, 22}.

First make an array.   {18, 21, 22, 25, 26, 27, 29, 30, 31, 32, 35, 38, 41, 47}

The midpoint or median is $\dfrac{29 + 30}{2}$ or 29.5. Q_1 is 25 and Q_3 is 35.

The semi-interquartile range is $\dfrac{35 - 25}{2}$ or 5.

A measure of variability that is often associated with the arithmetic mean is the **standard deviation.** Like the mean deviation, the standard deviation is a measure of the average amounts by which individual items of data deviate from the arithmetic mean of all the data. The standard deviation of a set of data is the quadratic mean of the individual deviations from the arithmetic mean. Each individual deviation can be found by subtracting the arithmetic mean from each individual value, $X_i - \overline{X}$. Some of these differences will be negative, but since they are to be squared in computing their quadratic mean the results will be positive.

The square of the standard deviation, called the variance, often is used as a measure of variability.

If a set of data has n values, given by X_i such that $1 \le i \le n$, with arithmetic mean, $\overline{X}$, the standard deviation, σ, can be found as follows.

$$\sigma = \sqrt{\frac{1}{n} \sum_{i=1}^{n} (X_i - \overline{X})^2}$$

The Standard Deviation

When studying the standard deviation of a set of data, it is important to consider the mean. For example, compare a standard deviation of 50 with a mean of 100 to a standard deviation of 50 with a mean of 10,000. The latter indicates very little variation.

σ is the Greek lower case letter sigma.

Example

3 Compute the arithmetic mean and the standard deviation for {54, 57, 59, 59, 60, 61, 61, 62, 62, 62, 63, 64, 65, 65, 66, 66, 66, 66, 67, 67, 68, 68, 68, 68, 68, 69, 69, 69, 70, 71, 71, 72, 72, 73, 75, 75, 77, 79, 81, 83, 90}.

$\overline{X} = \dfrac{1}{41}(54 + 57 + \cdots + 90) = 68$

$\sigma = \sqrt{\dfrac{1}{41} \sum_{i=1}^{41} (X_i - 68)^2}$

$ = \sqrt{\dfrac{1}{41}[(54 - 68)^2 + (57 - 68)^2 + \cdots + (90 - 68)^2]}$ or about 7.1

The arithmetic mean is 68 and the standard deviation is 7.1.

Exploratory Exercises

An astronomer made ten measurements of the angular distance between two stars. The measurements were 11.20°, 11.17°, 10.92°, 11.06°, 11.19°, 10.97°, 11.09°, 11.05°, 11.22°, and 11.03°.

1. Find the mean of the measurements of the angular distance between the two stars.

2. Find the individual deviation of each value in the set of data.

3. Find the mean deviation of the measurements.

4. Find the values of Q_1, Q_2, and Q_3 for this set of data.

5. Find the interquartile range for this set of data.

6. Find the semi-interquartile range for this set of data.

7. Find the sum of the squares of the individual deviations for this set of data.

8. Find the standard deviation of the angular distance between the two stars.

Find the mean deviation of each set of data.

9. {2, 4, 3, 5, 2.9, 2.6, 3.0, 1.5}

10. {200, 476, 721, 579, 152, 158}

11-12. Find the semi-interquartile range for each set of data in problems **9-10.**

Written Exercises

The hourly wages of eight employees of the Ottawa Insurance Company are $3.35, $4.50, $4.50, $5.30, $6.80, $10.00, $11.20, and $16.20.

1. Find the mean of the hourly wages of Ottawa employees.

2. Find the mean deviation of the hourly wages of Ottawa employees.

3. Find the semi-interquartile range of the hourly wages of Ottawa employees.

4. Find the standard deviation of the hourly wages of Ottawa employees.

The number of students in each grade of two school systems is as follows.
  Governor Schools: 369, 398, 381, 392, 406, 413, 376, 454, 420, 385, 402, 446
  Wolf Local Schools: 360, 399, 413, 370, 431, 446, 427, 352, 493, 410, 363, 447

5. Find the range of grade size in the Governor School system.

6. Find the range of grade size in the Wolf Local School System.

7. Find the mean grade size in the Governor School System.

8. Find the mean grade size in the Wolf Local School System.

9. Find the mean deviation of grade size in the Governor School System.

10. Find the mean deviation of grade size in the Wolf Local School System.

11. Find the semi-interquartile range of the grade size in the Governor School System.

12. Find the semi-interquartile range of the grade size in the Wolf Local School System.

13. Find the standard deviation in grade size in the Governor School System.

14. Find the standard deviation in grade size in the Wolf Local School System.

At Funland Amusement Park, the ages of the riders on a ferris wheel in years are 38, 34, 12, 8, 64, 25, 32, 12, 10, 8, 5, 30, 28, 3, 17, 18, 31, 60, 13, and 12.

15. Find the mean age of the riders.

16. Find the mean deviation of age.

17. Find the semi-interquartile range of ages of the riders.

18. Find the standard deviation of the ages of the riders.

19. Compute the standard deviation and the mean deviation of the numbers 56, 83, 74, 50, 58, 66, 72, 41, 75, 64, 66, 57, 68, 54, and 61. Which measure of variability is greater?

20. Is it possible for the variance to be less than the standard deviation for a set of data? If so, explain when this could occur. When would the variance be equal to the standard deviation for a set of data?

For the Scholar

If $x^2 - 7x + 12 < 0$, find the largest integral value of m and the smallest integral value of n such that $m < x^2 + 7x + 12 < n$.

14-4   The Frequency Distribution

The number of values in a set of data is often too large for each value to be considered individually. In this case a **frequency distribution** is a convenient system of organizing the data. A number of classes are determined and all values in a class are tallied and grouped together.

Example

1   **Prepare a frequency distribution of the weights of 200 boys at a certain high school. Assume the smallest weight is 99 pounds and the largest is 203 pounds.**

First, copy the raw data from the school health records onto a data sheet. Next, make an array from the raw data and find the range. The range is $203 - 99 = 104$. Now group the data into classes. Eleven classes, each having a width of 10 pounds, are suitable. Let the lowest class be from 95 pounds to 105 pounds, the next class from 105 pounds to 115 pounds, and so on. The **class limits** are 95, 105, 115, $\cdots$, 205. If a given weight falls on one of these class limits, the weight is tallied in the higher class. For example, 115 is tallied in the 115-125 class rather than the 105-115 class. The frequency distribution is as follows.

Class Limits	Class Marks (X)	Tally	Frequency f
95 - 105	100	|||	3
105 - 115	110	₩ ||	7
115 - 125	120	₩ ₩ ₩	15
125 - 135	130	₩ ₩ ₩ ₩ ₩ ₩ ||||	34
135 - 145	140	₩ ₩ ₩ ₩ ₩ ₩ ₩ ₩ ||	42
145 - 155	150	₩ ₩ ₩ ₩ ₩ ₩ ₩ |||	38
155 - 165	160	₩ ₩ ₩ ₩ ||||	24
165 - 175	170	₩ ₩ ₩	15
175 - 185	180	₩ ₩		11
185 - 195	190	₩ ||	7
195 - 205	200	||||	4
		Total	200

The **class interval** is the range of each class. The class interval is 10 in example 1. For most purposes, all class intervals in a frequency distribution should be equal.

The averages of the class limits are called **class marks** and are represented by X. In example 1, the class marks are 100, 110, 120, $\cdots$, 200.

The *frequency,* f, is the sum of the tallies of a class.

The number of classes in a distribution usually varies from 5 to 20 depending upon various factors such as range, the number of values in the data, and the purpose of grouping. If fewer than 5 classes are recorded, the grouping is coarse. If more than 20 classes are recorded, the distribution is difficult to manage.

A single piece of data loses its identity in a frequency distribution. A weight of 138 tallied in the 135–145 class is grouped with all the others in the class. In working with such a distribution, it is assumed that the data in any class are uniformly distributed over the class. Usually, only a slight error is introduced by this assumption.

We assume that each class mark is the mean of the data tabulated in its class.

Example

2 **Make a frequency distribution of the following scores made by a class of freshmen students on an algebra test of 20 problems. The scores are 13, 19, 17, 15, 20, 9, 16, 15, 17, 14, 10, 16, 19, 20, 13, 17, 15, 18, 12, 16, 14, 18, 16, 7, 17, 19 and 15.**

First make an array.

{7, 9, 10, 12, 13, 13, 14, 14, 15, 15, 15, 15, 16, 16, 16, 16, 17, 17, 17, 17, 18, 18, 19, 19, 19, 20, 20}

The range is $20 - 7$ or 13. Form seven classes, each having a class interval of 2. The lowest class limit should be 6.5 so that the lowest score is included.

Class Limits	Class Marks (X)	Tally	Frequency (f)
6.5 - 8.5	7.5	|	1
8.5 - 10.5	9.5	||	2
10.5 - 12.5	11.5	|	1
12.5 - 14.5	13.5	||||	4
14.5 - 16.5	15.5	⊮ |||	8
16.5 - 18.5	17.5	⊮ |	6
18.5 - 20.5	19.5	⊮	5
		Total	27

Exploratory Exercises

The following distribution gives the annual salaries of a random sample of 100 U.S. citizens.

Annual Salary	Frequency
Under $6000	9
$6000 to $12,000	21
$12,000 to $18,000	31
$18,000 to $24,000	26
$24,000 to $30,000	13

1. State the class interval of the frequency distribution.
2. State the class limits of the frequency distribution.
3. State the class marks of the frequency distribution.
4. What percent of the 100 people earn $18,000 to $24,000?
5. What percent of the 100 people earn at least $18,000?

Find suitable class intervals, class limits, and class marks for each set of numbers. Assume that the two numbers given are the least and greatest values in a certain set of data.

6. {1, 7}
7. {2.1, 3.5}
8. {400, 1000}

Find the class interval and the class limits for each set of numbers. Assume that the numbers given are class marks of a frequency distribution.

9. {10, 20, 30, 40, 50}
10. {1.1, 1.2, 1.3, 1.4, 1.5, 1.6, 1.7}
11. {2.5, 5, 7.5, 10, 12.5}
12. {25, 26, 27, 28, 29, 30, 31, 32}

Written Exercises

The ages in years of a random sample of 60 patients admitted to City Memorial Hospital during October are given below.

```
45  70   8  68  53  28  95  39  77  21
20  62  38  57  38  31  43  29  61  63
21  63  49  65  89  80  76  49  43  35
57  54  63  57  49  40  31  18  13  28
27  37   1  34  47  16  57  76  79  48
75  46  72  59  32   3  81  41  66  50
```

1. Make a frequency distribution of the data using a class interval of ten.
2. Make a frequency distribution of the data using a class interval of eight.
3. Make a frequency distribution of the data with fourteen classes.
4. Make a frequency distribution of the data with eleven classes.

The weights in pounds of children in a certain fourth grade class are given below.

```
64  71  57  67  74  65  59  62  67
72  84  60  68  72  91  55  69  71
69  71  69  75  59  60  70  76  62
88  57  78  63  74  77  62  68  63
60  69  74  90  63  79  66  75  93
```

5. Make a frequency distribution using an appropriate class interval.

The IQ's of a random sample of 100 people in a certain population are given below.

84	120	78	89	107	116	73	88	106	117
144	92	100	124	84	100	115	76	93	112
89	109	110	128	101	109	135	100	112	81
99	119	88	117	110	81	103	127	97	120
93	115	92	116	68	97	66	102	84	108
95	72	104	95	80	85	106	99	87	115
104	100	95	85	121	112	97	106	113	82
104	102	111	103	125	95	102	88	102	97
99	100	103	78	99	99	91	97	99	103
102	110	88	100	90	100	103	92	103	100

6. Make a frequency distribution of the data using a class interval of ten.

7. Make a frequency distribution of the data using a class interval of twelve.

8. Make a frequency distribution of the data with sixteen classes.

9. Make a frequency distribution of the data with ten classes.

Independent measurements of the length in meters of a college campus taken by twenty-four students in a civil engineering class are given below.

2013.3	2012.8	2013.4	2012.2	2012.0	2012.2	2011.8	2011.7
2012.6	2013.5	2012.4	2012.1	2012.6	2013.9	2013.7	2012.8
2012.3	2011.4	2012.3	2011.6	2012.2	2012.7	2012.4	2012.7

10. Make a frequency distribution of the data using an appropriate class interval.

11. How should the data be handled if the last measurement was reported as 2112.7 m rather than 2012.7 m?

12. Think of a situation from which a frequency distribution could be made. Collect the data and make the frequency distribution.

For the Scholar

The figure shows ⊙P and equilateral triangle ACT. The radius of ⊙P is equal to the altitude of △ACT, and ⊙P is always tangent to AC at some point M as it rolls back and forth from A to C. If m is the measure of ∠XPY where X and Y are variable points on AT and CT respectively, find the maximum and minimum values of m as ⊙P moves from A to C.

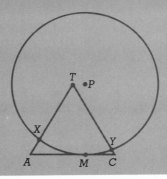

14-5 Graphical Representation of Data

Graphs often are used to represent the data in a frequency distribution. Two ways of representing the data in the following frequency distribution are shown below.

Test Scores on a History Test

Score	6.5–8.5	8.5–10.5	10.5–12.5	12.5–14.5	14.5–16.5	16.5–18.5	18.5–20.5
Frequency	1	2	1	4	8	6	5

The **bar graph** consists of parallel bars, either vertical or horizontal. Each bar represents the frequency, f, of the values in a class.

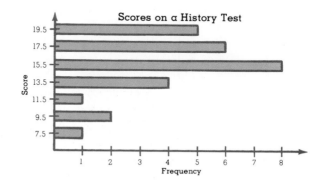

The **histogram** is a vertical bar graph whose bars are next to each other. The class marks, X, are measured on the horizontal axis and the frequency, f, is measured on the vertical axis. Bar graphs and histograms are used to compare frequencies.

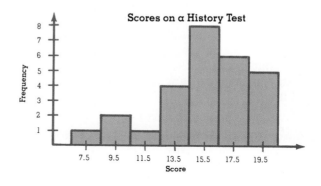

The **broken line graph** is useful in showing changing conditions over a period of time. For example, this graph shows the median family income in the United States from 1974 to 1982.

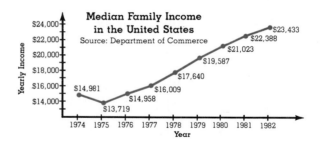

Example

1 Draw a histogram and a broken line graph to present the following data.

Number of Immigrants to U.S.
(in thousands of persons)
Source: Department of Justice

Year	1900	1910	1920	1930	1940	1950	1960	1970	1980
Immigrants	449	1042	430	242	71	249	265	373	531

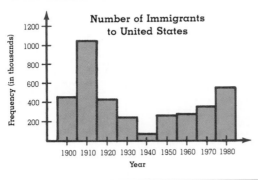

The **circle graph** shows the relationship between the parts and the whole. The circle is separated into proportional parts called **sectors.** For example, 7% of the expenditures for recreation in 1982 were for commercial amusements. Thus, the sector that represents commercial amusements has a central angle of 7% of 360° or 25.2°.

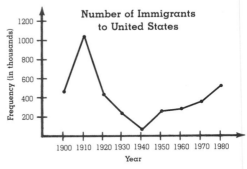

Personal Expenditures for Recreation—1982
Source: U.S. Bureau of Census

Example

2 Draw a circle graph for the following data.

Oil Production by States - 1982
(in millions of 42-gallon barrels)
Source: Department of the Interior

State	Oil
Texas	925
Alaska	619
Louisiana	458
California	402
Oklahoma	159
Other States	602

First, find the percent of the circle area represented by each state. Then, figure the number of degrees of the central angle to obtain the sector having that percent of the area.

State	Percent of Circle Area	Approximate Degrees of Central Angle
Texas	$\frac{925}{3165}$ or 29%	$360° \times 29\%$ or 104.4°
Alaska	$\frac{619}{3165}$ or 20%	$360° \times 20\%$ or 72°
Louisiana	$\frac{458}{3165}$ or 14%	$360° \times 14\%$ or 50.4°
California	$\frac{402}{3165}$ or 13%	$360° \times 13\%$ or 46.8°
Oklahoma	$\frac{159}{3165}$ or 5%	$360° \times 5\%$ or 18°
Other States	$\frac{602}{3165}$ or 19%	$360° \times 19\%$ or 68.4°

Oil Production by States—1982

Exploratory Exercises

Use the histogram to solve each of the following.

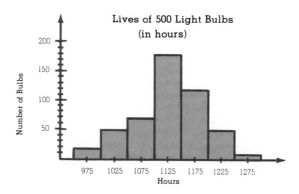

Lives of 500 Light Bulbs (in hours)

1. Find the class limits.

2. Find the class interval.

3. Find the number of light bulbs that had lives between 1000 and 1050 hours.

4. Find the number of light bulbs that had lives over 1250 hours.

5. Find the number of light bulbs that had lives over 1100 hours.

6. Find the number of light bulbs that had lives less than 1150 hours.

7. Find the percent of light bulbs that had lives less than 1100 hours.

8. Find the percent of light bulbs that had lives less than 1200 hours.

9. Make a horizontal bar graph of the data from the histogram above.

10. Make a broken line graph of the data from the histogram above.

Written Exercises

Draw bar graphs for the data in each of the following frequency distributions.

1. Number of hours of daily TV viewing

Hours	0-1	1-2	2-3	3-4	4-5	5-6	6-7	7-8
Frequency	8	6	38	72	61	44	20	4

2. U.S. Population by Age, 1977 (in millions of persons)

Source: Department of Commerce

Ages	0-10	10-20	20-30	30-40	40-50	50-60	60-70	70-80	over 80
Population	32	40	38	28	23	23	18	10	5

3. Birth Rates (per 1000 population)

Source: Department of Commerce

Year	1915	1935	1955	1975
Rate	29.5	25.1	25.0	14.8

4. Institutions of Higher Education

Source: Department of Health, Education, & Welfare

Year	1940	1950	1960	1970	1980
Number	1708	1863	1959	2525	3231

5. College Graduates in U.S. (in thousands)

Source: Department of Health, Education and Welfare

Year	1900	1910	1920	1930	1940	1950	1960	1970	1980
Graduates	27	37	49	122	187	432	392	827	999

6-10. Draw histograms for the frequency distributions in problems 1-5.

11-13. Draw broken line graphs for the frequency distributions in problems 3-5.

The following table gives the percents of sea areas in the world.

Sea Area	Pacific	Atlantic	Indian	Arctic	Other Seas
Percentage	46%	23%	20%	4%	7%

14. Draw a circle graph to show the percents of sea area in the world.

The following frequency distribution gives a breakdown of the civilian labor force in the United States from 1979-1982 in millions of persons.

Source: Department of Labor

Employment Status	1979	1980	1981	1982
Employed in Nonagricultural Industries	95.5	96.0	97.0	96.1
Employed in Agriculture	3.3	3.4	3.4	3.4
Unemployed	6.1	7.6	8.3	10.7

15-18. For each year 1979-1982, draw a circle graph to show the breakdown of the civilian labor force.

Find a statistical graph in a newspaper or magazine.

19. Does the graph accurately represent the data?

20. Could the data have been presented as effectively without the graph?

For the Scholar

If $(\log_5 n)(\log_{11} n) = \log_5 11$, which real values of n satisfy the given equation?

Sometimes it is necessary to estimate points on an empirical line graph of a set of data at locations not coincident with obtained points. If the desired point is between obtained points, the process is called **interpolation**. Interpolation of logarithms or trigonometric values are examples of such interpretation. If the desired point is beyond obtained points, the process is called **extrapolation**. Extrapolation of data makes the assumption that the plotted graph continues to behave outside the range of data in a manner similar to the obtained range.

Extrapolation can be used to predict trends. If the data can be graphed as a line, equations can be used to estimate the results of values at a certain point. These types of equations can be called regression equations.

Example   Given the following data, graph the points. Then, predict the results if $x = 27$.

x	3	5	6	9	12	15
y	11	17	20	29	38	47

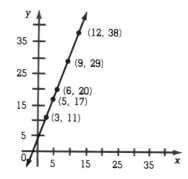

An equation that will fit the line seems to be $y = 3x + 2$.

From the equation, it can be estimated that, if $x = 27$, then y is predicted to be 83.

Exercises   For each of the following, construct a line graph for the given data. Then, predict the value of y for the desired values of x.

1.

x	10	20	30	40
y	50	65	80	95

Find y, if $x = 60$ and $x = 5$.

2.

A	3	4	5	6
B	90	74	49	13

Find B, if $A = 1$ and $A = 8$.

3.

R	20	30	40	50
S	30	70	130	210

Find S, if $R = 60$ and $R = 90$.

4.

a	1	2	4	7	9
b	12	19	33	54	68

Find y, if $a = 11$ and $a = 14$.

14-6 Using the Frequency Distribution

In a frequency distribution, each individual value in the data loses its identity. The data in each class are assumed to be uniformly distributed over the class. Thus, the class mark is assumed to be the mean of the data tallied in its class. For example, the mean of the data in a class with limits 22.5–27.5 is assumed to be 25, the class mark.

In a frequency distribution the sum of the values in a class is found by multiplying the class mark, X, by the frequency, f, of that class. The sum of the values in a class can be represented by $f \cdot X$. The sum of all the values in a given set of data is found by adding the sums of the values of each class in the frequency distribution.

The sum of all values in the set can be represented by $\sum\limits_{i=1}^{k} (f_i \cdot X_i)$

where k is the number of classes in the frequency distribution. Thus, the arithmetic mean of n values in a frequency distribution is found by dividing the sum of the values in the set by n or $\sum\limits_{i=1}^{k} f_i$.

$\sum\limits_{i=1}^{k} f_i$ *is the sum of the class frequencies.*

If X_1, X_2, $\cdots$, X_k are the class marks in a frequency distribution with k classes and f_1, f_2, $\cdots$, f_k are the corresponding frequencies, then the arithmetic mean, $\overline{X}$, is approximated by the following. $$\overline{X} \approx \frac{\sum\limits_{i=1}^{k} f_i \cdot X_i}{\sum\limits_{i=1}^{k} f_i}$$	***The Mean of the Data in a Frequency Distribution***

Example

1 **Find the arithmetic mean of the scores of 90 students on a mathematics test given in the following frequency distribution.**

Class Limits	Class Marks (X)	Frequency (f)	$f \cdot X$
93 - 101	97	12	1164
85 - 93	89	19	1691
77 - 85	81	38	3078
69 - 77	73	11	803
61 - 69	65	7	455
53 - 61	57	3	171
		$\sum\limits_{i=1}^{6} f_i = 90$	$\sum\limits_{i=1}^{6} f_i \cdot X_i = 7362$

$$\overline{X} \approx \frac{7362}{90} \text{ or } 81.8$$

The median, M_d, of the data in a frequency distribution is found from a cumulative frequency distribution. The cumulative frequency of each class is the sum of the frequency of the class and the frequencies of the previous classes. The two columns show the frequency, f, and the cumulative frequency of the frequency distribution in Example 1. Since the median is the value below which 50% of the data lie, the class in which the median lies can be located. This class is called the **median class.** Now the median can be found by using linear interpolation. This method can also be used to find any percentile value other than 50%.

What is linear interpolation?

Frequency f	Cumulative Frequency
12	90
19	78
38	59
11	21
7	10
3	3

Notice the cumulative frequency column is read bottom to top.

Example

2 **Find the median of the data in the frequency distribution in Example 1.**

Repeat the Class Limits and Frequency columns of the frequency distribution. Then, find the Cumulative Frequency.

Class Limits	Frequency (f)	Cumulative Frequency
93 - 101	12	90
85 - 93	19	78
77 - 85	38	59
69 - 77	11	21
61 - 69	7	10
53 - 61	3	3

$$\sum_{i=1}^{6} f_i = 90$$

Since there are 90 scores in this frequency distribution, 45 scores are below the median. From the cumulative frequency column, it is apparent that the median class is the class $77 - 85$. The cumulative frequency column also shows that 21 scores fall below point 77. Thus, by subtracting 21 from 45, it is found that 24 scores above the point 77 are required to reach the median of the frequency distribution. Since there are 38 scores in the median class, $\frac{24}{38}$ of 8, the class interval, must be added to the lower limit of that class to reach the median.

$$M_d = 77 + \left(\frac{24}{38} \times 8\right)$$
$$\approx 82.1$$

Linear interpolation is used to estimate the value of the median within the class interval.

In a frequency distribution, deviations from the mean are found for a given class by subtracting the mean from the class mark and multiplying this result by the frequency of the class. Then, the standard deviation can be found by computing the quadratic mean of these deviations.

If X_1, X_2, ... , X_k are the class marks in a frequency distribution with k classes, and f_1, f_2, ... , f_k are the corresponding frequencies, then the standard deviation, σ, of the data in the frequency distribution is approximated by the following.

$$\sigma \approx \sqrt{\frac{\sum\limits_{i=1}^{k} (X_i - \overline{X})^2 f_i}{\sum\limits_{i=1}^{k} f_i}}$$

The Standard Deviation of the Data in a Frequency Distribution

Example

3 Find the standard deviation of the data in the frequency distribution in Example 1.

Repeat the X and f columns of the frequency distribution. Then find $(X - \overline{X})$, and $(X - \overline{X})^2 f$. The results are shown below.

X	f	$(X - \overline{X})$	$(X - \overline{X})^2 f$
97	12	15.2	2772.48
89	19	7.2	984.96
81	38	−0.8	24.32
73	11	−8.8	851.84
65	7	−16.8	1975.68
57	3	−24.8	1845.12

$$\sum_{i=1}^{6} f_i = 90 \qquad\qquad \sum_{i=1}^{6} (X_i - \overline{X})^2 f_i = 8454.40$$

$$\sigma = \sqrt{\frac{8454.40}{90}} \quad \text{or } 9.69$$

Exploratory Exercises

Solve each problem using the following frequency distribution.

Weekly Wages	$130–140	$140–150	$150–160	$160–170	$170–180	$180–190	$190–200
Frequency	11	24	30	10	13	8	4

1-7. Find the sum of the values in each class.

8. Find the sum of the values in the frequency distribution.

9. Find the number of values in the frequency distribution.

10. Find the arithmetic mean of the data in the frequency distribution.

11. Make a column showing the cumulative frequency of the classes.

12. Find the median class of the frequency distribution.

13. Find the median of the data in the frequency distribution.

Written Exercises

Solve each problem using the following frequency distribution.

Class	1 - 5	5 - 9	9 - 13	13 - 17	17 - 21	21 - 25	25 - 29	29 - 33
Frequency	2	8	15	6	38	31	13	7

1. Find the arithmetic mean of the data in the frequency distribution.

2. Find the median class of the frequency distribution.

3. Find the median of the data in the frequency distribution.

4. Find the standard deviation of the data in the frequency distribution.

The sales made by 200 stores in Lafayette during September are given in the following frequency distribution.

Sales	Frequency
Less than $10,000	15
$10,000 – $20,000	30
$20,000 – $30,000	50
$30,000 – $40,000	60
$40,000 – $50,000	30
$50,000 and over	15

5. Is it possible to find the arithmetic mean? Why or why not?

6. Make a column showing the cumulative frequency of the classes.

7. Find the median class of the frequency distribution.

8. Find the median of the data in the frequency distribution.

The following data is a random sample of the amounts in dollars and cents spent on purchases at the Super Saver Market on a certain day.

$24.60	34.56	53.62	24.52	54.28	20.53	13.19	32.54
51.83	8.68	34.23	20.72	32.03	32.35	33.20	43.90
31.97	2.80	14.53	12.00	14.09	14.10	22.75	23.24
41.09	40.70	10.10	44.73	21.60	62.95	53.30	12.98
32.78	14.45	32.43	14.98	23.60	9.90	7.41	30.81
4.36	8.88	24.54	32.85	47.40	21.64	18.18	45.49

9. Make a frequency distribution of the data using $8.00 as the class interval.

10. Find the arithmetic mean of the data in the frequency distribution.

11. Make a column showing the cumulative frequency of the classes.

12. Find the median class of the frequency distribution.

13. Find the median of the data in the frequency distribution.

14. Find the standard deviation of the data in the frequency distribution.

Challenge Exercise

15. Using problem 9, find the point below which 70% of the values lie.

For the Scholar

How many positive integers less than 1,000,000 are not divisible by either 3 or 7?

14-7 The Normal Distribution Curve

A frequency distribution that often occurs when there is a large number of values in a set of data is called the **normal distribution.** In a normal distribution small deviations are much more frequent than large ones. Negative deviations and positive deviations usually occur with about the same frequency.

When a normal distribution is shown graphically, the curve representing the distribution, called the **normal curve,** is symmetrical or bell-shaped. The points on the x-axis represent values that are a certain number of standard deviations from the mean. The total area under the normal curve and above the x-axis represents the total probability of the distribution, which is 1.

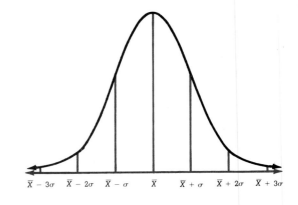

The following table gives the fractional parts of a normally distributed set of data for selected ranges about the mean. The expression, $\overline{X} \pm t\sigma$, indicates the upper and lower limits of the range of numbers in the data for any selected value of t. The fractional part of the data, P, is also the probability that a randomly selected value will lie in the interval $\overline{X} \pm t\sigma$. For example, the fractional part of normally distributed data that is within one standard deviation is 0.683. Thus, if the mean of the data is 60 and the standard deviation is 6, then 68.3% of the data are within the limits $60 \pm (1)(6)$ or 54 and 66.

The percentage of the data that is within these limits is $100 \cdot P$.

t	P		t	P		t	P
0.0	0.000		1.2	0.770		2.2	0.972
0.1	0.080		1.3	0.807		2.3	0.979
0.2	0.159		1.4	0.838		2.4	0.984
0.3	0.236		1.5	0.866		2.5	0.988
0.4	0.311		1.6	0.891		2.58	0.990
0.5	0.383		1.65	0.900		2.6	0.991
0.6	0.451		1.7	0.911		2.7	0.993
0.7	0.516		1.8	0.928		2.8	0.995
0.8	0.576		1.9	0.943		2.9	0.996
0.9	0.632		1.96	0.950		3.0	0.997
1.0	0.683		2.0	0.955		3.5	0.9995
1.1	0.729		2.1	0.964		4.0	0.9999

Thus, normal distributions have the following properties.

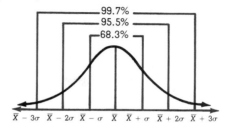

1. The maximum point of the curve is at the mean.

2. About 68.3% of the data are within one standard deviation from the mean.

3. About 95.5% of the data are within two standard deviations from the mean.

4. About 99.7% of the data are within three standard deviations from the mean.

A sample of 600 young people are weighed at a clinic. Suppose the mean weight is 100 pounds, the standard deviation is 20 pounds, and the data is normally distributed.

As the graph of the distribution shows the mean, 100 pounds, is the most frequent weight. Out of 600 young people, about 409 have weights between 80 pounds and 120 pounds. About 573 have weights between 60 pounds and 140 pounds. And about 598 have weights between 40 pounds and 160 pounds.

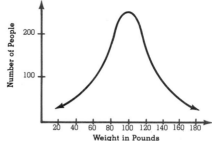

$$68.3\% \times 600 \approx 409$$
$$95.5\% \times 600 \approx 573$$
$$99.7\% \times 600 \approx 598$$

Examples

1 **Find the upper and lower limits within which 80% of the values of a set of normally distributed data are found. Suppose the mean, $\overline{X}$, is 65 and the standard deviation, σ, is 6.**

Find t in the table when P = 0.80.	$t = 1.3$
Find the limits.	$\overline{X} \pm t\sigma = 65 \pm (1.3)(6)$
	$= 72.8 \text{ and } 57.2$

Thus, 80% of the values lie between 57.2 and 72.8.

2 **A value is selected at random from a normally distributed set of data. Suppose the mean $\overline{X}$ is 65 and the standard deviation σ is 5. What is the probability that the selected value lies within the limits 61 and 69?**

Express the limits using the mean.	$61 = 65 - 4 \text{ and } 69 \text{ or } 65 + 4$
	$\overline{X} \pm t\sigma = 65 \pm 4$
Solve for t.	$t\sigma = 4$
	$t \cdot 5 = 4$
	$t = 0.8$
Find P in the table when t = 0.8	$P = 0.576$

Thus, the probability is 0.576 that a value selected at random from the data will lie within 4 units of the mean, that is, between 61 and 69.

Example

3

The grades on a standardized college entrance examination are assumed to form a normal distribution with a mean score of 80 and a standard deviation of 12. What is the probability that an entering student will score between 86 and 100 on the examination?

First, find the probability that the score is between the mean and the upper limit.

$$\overline{X} + t\sigma = 100$$
$$80 + t \cdot 12 = 100$$

Find P in the table
when t = 1.7.
$$t = 1.7$$
$$P = 0.911$$

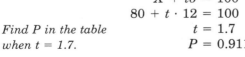

The probability that a student's score is between 80 and 100 is $\frac{1}{2}(0.911)$ or 0.456. One-half of the P value in the table must be taken since only the values above the mean are being considered.

Next, find the probability that the score is between the mean and the lower limit.

$$\overline{X} + t\sigma = 86$$
$$80 + t \cdot 12 = 86$$

Find P in the table
when t = 0.5.
$$t = 0.5$$
$$P = 0.383$$

The probability that a student's score is between 80 and 86 is $\frac{1}{2}(0.383)$ or 0.192.

Therefore, the probability that an entering student will score between 86 and 100 is $0.456 - 0.192$ or 0.264.

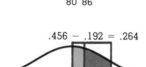

Exploratory Exercises

Suppose 200 values in a set of data have a normal distribution.

1. How many values are within one standard deviation from the mean?

2. How many values are within two standard deviations from the mean?

3. How many values are within one standard deviation greater than the mean?

4. How many values are between two and three standard deviations less than the mean?

5-8. Answer problems **1-4** for a normal distribution of 5000 values.

9-12. Answer problems **1-4** for a normal distribution of 100,000 values.

A teacher decides to grade a certain test by marking "on the curve." The teacher determines that the A grades will fall in the range above $\overline{X} + 1.5\sigma$, the B grades from $\overline{X} + 0.5\sigma$ to $\overline{X} + 1.5\sigma$, the C grades from $\overline{X} + 0.5\sigma$ to $\overline{X} - 0.5\sigma$, the D grades from $\overline{X} - 0.5\sigma$ to $\overline{X} - 1.5\sigma$, and the F grades below $\overline{X} - 1.5\sigma$.

13-17. What percent of the class will receive each letter grade?

Written Exercises

A set of 500 values has a normal distribution. The mean of the data is 24 and the standard deviation is 2.

1. What percent of the data is in the range 22 to 26?

2. What percent of the data is in the range 20.5 to 27.5?

3. Find the range about the mean that includes 95% of the data.

4. Find the range about the mean that includes 50% of the data.

The mean of a set of normally distributed data is 140 and the standard deviation is 20.

5. What percent of the data is in the range 120 to 160?

6. What percent of the data is in the range 130 to 150?

7. Find the probability that a value selected at random from the data will be within the limits 110 and 170.

8. Find the probability that a value selected at random from the data will be less than 100.

9. Find the probability that a value selected at random from the data will be greater than 160.

10. Find the probability that a value selected at random from the data will be within the limits 110 and 200.

11. Find the range about the mean that includes 90% of the data.

12. Find the point below which 90% of the data lie.

The lengths of 2400 babies born at Valley Hospital in the past year were normally distributed. The mean length was 50.5 cm and the standard deviation was 3.6 cm.

13. Find the range about the mean that includes 80% of the babies' lengths.

14. Find the range about the mean that includes 50% of the babies' lengths.

15. Find the probability that a baby's length selected at random from this set of data is within the limits 49 cm and 52 cm.

16. Find the probability that a baby's length selected at random from this set of data is within the limits 45 cm and 56 cm.

17. Find the probability that a baby's length selected at random from this set of data is greater than 50.5 cm.

18. Find the probability that a baby's length selected at random from this set of data is less than 45 cm.

19. What percent of babies' lengths were between 48 cm and 50.5 cm?

20. What percent of babies' lengths were between 52 and 55 cm?

For the Scholar

A bag contains 15 billiard balls, numbered 1, 2, 3, $\cdots$, 15. If 6 are selected randomly at the same time, what is the probability that the sum of the numbers on the billiard balls will be odd?

14-8 Sample Sets of Data

The population or universe in a statistical study is all of the items or individuals in the group being considered. It rarely happens that 100% of a population is accessible as a source of data. Therefore, a random sample of the population must be selected. The sample should be representative of the population. The various characteristics of the population pertinent to the study should be found in the sample in about the same ratio as they exist in the population. Then, based upon this sample, certain inferences can be made about the population from which the sample was selected.

This area of statistics is known as inferential statistics.

Suppose, for example, that you need to know the mean height of 1031 high school senior boys in a certain city. It is impractical to measure all of them. However, 100 senior boys in the city are organized into an all-city boys' chorus in which all high schools are represented in proportion to their enrollment of boys. It is assumed that musical talent has no relationship to height. Hence, this sample of 100 boys is assumed to be random with respect to height.

At a practice session of the chorus, actual measurements of the heights of the 100 boys correct to the nearest tenth of an inch are made. After tabulating the data, the arithmetic mean and the standard deviation are computed. $\overline{X}$ is 67.6 in. and σ is 2.7 in. Now the mean of the heights of the entire population, that is, of all 1031 senior boys in the city can be estimated.

With nearly complete certainty, it can be said that the true mean of all 1031 boys, represented by $\widetilde{X}$, lies somewhere within a large range of the sample mean 67.6 (for example, 47.6 to 87.6). However, this range is so broad that it is of little value. On the other hand, if a narrow range around 67.6 (for example, 67.5 to 67.7) is given, it is not possible to predict with any great degree of certainty or confidence that $\widetilde{X}$ is in this range.

$\widetilde{X}$ is read "X tilde."

Some level of confidence is needed. A statistic called the **standard error of the mean** is used to give a level of confidence about the sample mean.

> **If a sample set of data has N values and σ is the standard deviation, then the standard error of the mean, $\sigma_{\bar{x}}$, can be found as follows.**
>
> $$\sigma_{\bar{x}} = \frac{\sigma}{\sqrt{N}}$$
>
> *The symbol $\sigma_{\bar{x}}$ is read "sigma sub-x bar."*

The Standard Error of the Mean

Sample means of various random samples of the same population are normally distributed about the true mean with the standard error of the mean as a measure of their variability. Thus, the standard error of the mean behaves like the standard deviation. Probabilities of the occurrence of sample means and true means may be determined by referring to the table on page 444. For example, there is a 68.3% chance that the true mean, $\widetilde{X}$, of a population lies within one standard error of the mean, or $\overline{X} \pm \sigma_{\bar{x}}$. Likewise, there is a 0.90 probability that the true mean lies in the range $\overline{X} \pm 1.65\,\sigma_{\bar{x}}$.

Example

1   The mean height of a random sample of 100 senior boys in a certain city is 67.6 inches and the standard deviation is 2.7 inches. Find the range of heights such that the probability is 0.90 that the mean height of the entire population of senior boys lies within it.

Find t when P = 0.90. $t = 1.65$

Find $\sigma_{\bar{x}}$. $\sigma_{\bar{x}} = \dfrac{2.7}{\sqrt{100}}$ or 0.27

Find the range. $\overline{X} \pm t\sigma_{\bar{x}} = 67.6 \pm (1.65)(0.27)$
$$= 67.6 \pm 0.4$$

The probability is 0.90 that the true mean, $\widetilde{X}$, is within the range 67.2 to 68.0.

If a higher level of confidence is desired for the same number of values, accuracy must be sacrificed by giving a wider range. However, if the number of values in the sample is larger, the range for a given probability or level of confidence is smaller.

The larger the sample the more accurately it represents the population.

The most commonly used levels of confidence are the 1% and the 5% levels. A 1% level of confidence means that there is less than a 1% chance that the true mean differs from the sample mean by a certain amount. That is, the probability that the true mean is within a certain range of the sample mean is 0.99. A 5% level of confidence means that the probability of the true mean being within a certain range of the sample mean is 0.95.

Example

2   The mean height of a random sample of 144 senior boys in a certain city is 68.5 inches and the standard deviation is 2.8 inches. Find the range of the sample mean that has a 1% level of confidence.

A 1% level of confidence is given when $P = 0.99$.

Find t when P = 0.99. $t = 2.58$

Find $\sigma_{\bar{x}}$. $\sigma_{\bar{x}} = \dfrac{2.8}{\sqrt{144}}$ or 0.23

Find the range. $\overline{X} \pm t\sigma_{\bar{x}} = 68.5 \pm (2.58)(0.23)$
$$= 68.5 \pm 0.6$$

Thus, the range that has a 1% level of confidence is 67.9 inches to 69.1 inches.

Exploratory Exercises

Find the probabilities of each of the following.

1. The true mean of a set of data is within 2 standard errors from the sample mean.

2. The true mean of a set of data is within 1.5 standard errors from the sample mean.

Find the standard error of the mean $\sigma_{\bar{x}}$, for each of the following.

3. $\sigma = 40, N = 64, \overline{X} = 200$ **4.** $\sigma = 5, N = 36, \overline{X} = 45$

5. $\sigma = 2.4, N = 100, \overline{X} = 24$ **6.** $\sigma = 12, N = 200, \overline{X} = 80$

7-10. Find the range that has a 1% level of confidence for problems **3-6.**

11-14. Find the range that has a 5% level of confidence for problems **3-6.**

Written Exercises

In Middletown a random sample of 100 families showed that the mean number of hours the television set was turned on was 4.6 hours. The standard deviation was 1.4 hours.

1. Find the standard error of the mean.

2. Find the range about the sample mean that has a 1% level of confidence.

3. Find the range about the sample mean that gives a 50% chance that the true mean lies within it.

4. Find the range about the sample mean such that the probability is 0.90 that the true mean lies within it.

A random sample of 50 acorns from an oak tree reveals a mean diameter of 16.2 mm and a standard deviation of 1.4 mm.

5. Find the standard error of the mean.

6. Find the range about the sample mean that has a 5% level of confidence.

7. Find the range about the sample mean that gives a 99% chance that the true mean lies within it.

8. Find the range about the sample mean such that the probability is 0.80 that the true mean lies within it.

The following is a frequency distribution of the time in minutes required for registration. The distribution is a random sample from a total population of 2361 students.

Class Marks	4	6	8	10	12	14	16	18	20
Frequency	1	3	5	12	17	13	7	4	2

9. Find the standard deviation of the data in the frequency distribution.

10. Find the standard error of the mean.

11. Find the range about the sample mean such that the probability is 0.95 that the true mean lies within it.

12. Find the probability that the mean of the population will be less than one point from the mean of the sample.

Solve each problem.

13. The standard deviation of the weights of 36 seven-year olds in the United States is 8 pounds. What is the probability that the mean weight of the random sample will differ by more than one pound from the mean weight of all seven-year olds?

14. Eighty-one beef cattle were fed a special diet for six weeks. The mean gain in weight was 40 lb with a standard deviation of 5 lb. With what level of confidence can it be said that the diet will cause an average gain in weight of between 30 to 50 lb in a similar group of cattle?

For the Scholar

In rectangle $ABCD$, diagonal $\overline{AC}$ is trisected by points U and N. If $AD = 12$ and $CD = 8$, find the area of quadrilateral $BNDU$.

Chapter Summary

1. If a set of data has n values, given by X_i such that $1 \le i \le n$, then the arithmetic mean, $\overline{X}$, is $\dfrac{1}{n} \sum\limits_{i=1}^{n} X_i$.   (421)

2. The median, M_d of a set of data is the mid-value. If there are two mid-values, it is the arithmetic mean of these values.   (422)

3. The mode of a set of data is the most frequently occurring value.   (422)

4. A set of data has n values, given by X_i such that $1 \le i \le n$, with arithmetic mean, $\overline{X}$.

   a. The harmonic mean, H, is $\dfrac{n}{\sum\limits_{i=1}^{n} \dfrac{1}{X_i}}$.   (425)

   b. The quadratic mean, Q, is $\sqrt{\dfrac{\sum\limits_{i=1}^{n} X_i^2}{n}}$.   (426)

   c. The mean deviation, $M.\,D.$, is $\dfrac{1}{n} \sum\limits_{i=1}^{n} |X_i - \overline{X}|$.   (428)

   d. The standard deviation, σ, is $\sqrt{\dfrac{1}{n} \sum\limits_{i=1}^{n} (X_i - \overline{X})^2}$.   (429)

5. If a set of data has first quartile point, Q_1, and third quartile point, Q_3, the semi-interquartile range, Q_R, is $\dfrac{Q_3 - Q_1}{2}$.   (428)

6. A frequency distribution organizes a large number of data into classes.   (431)

7. Graphs can be used to represent the data in a frequency distribution. Bar graphs and histograms are used to compare frequencies. Broken line graphs show trends. Circle graphs show the relationship between the parts and the whole.   (435)

8. A frequency distribution has k classes where X_i are class marks, such that $1 \le i \le k$, and f_i are the corresponding frequencies of each class.

   a. The arithmetic mean, $\overline{X}$, of the data is approximated by

   $$\dfrac{\sum\limits_{i=1}^{k} f_i \cdot X_i}{\sum\limits_{i=1}^{k} f_i}.   \quad (440)$$

   b. The standard deviation, σ, of the data is approximated

   by $\sqrt{\dfrac{\sum\limits_{i=1}^{k} (X_i - \overline{X})^2 f_i}{\sum\limits_{i=1}^{k} f_i}}$.   (442)

9. The median of the data in a frequency distribution is in the median class of the cumulative frequency distribution.   (441)

10. The normal distribution often occurs when there is a large number of values in the frequency distribution. (444)

11. If a sample set of data has N values and σ is the standard deviation, then the standard error of the mean, $\sigma_{\bar{x}}$, is $\dfrac{\sigma}{\sqrt{N}}$. (448)

12. A 1% level of confidence means that the probability of the true mean being within a certain range of the sample mean is 0.99. A 5% level of confidence means that the probability of the true mean being within a certain range of the sample mean is 0.95. (449)

Chapter Review

A die was tossed 10 times with these results. (14-1, 14-2, 14-3)

$$5 \quad 1 \quad 5 \quad 4 \quad 2 \quad 3 \quad 6 \quad 2 \quad 5 \quad 1$$

1. Find the range of the data.
2. Find the arithmetic mean of the data.
3. Find the median of the data.
4. Find the mode of the data.
5. Find the harmonic mean of the data.
6. Find the quadratic mean of the data.
7. Find the mean deviation of the data.
8. Find the semi-interquartile range of the data.
9. Find the standard deviation of the data.

At Founder's University the achievement of students is reported as a number from 0 to 5, where 5 is the highest rating. The point averages for a random sample of 500 freshmen are summarized in the following frequency distribution. (14-4, 14-5, 14-6)

Point Average	below 1.0	1.0 - 2.0	2.0 - 3.0	3.0 - 4.0	4.0 - 5.0
Frequency	54	92	124	145	85

10. What are the class marks?
11. Find the class interval.
12. Make a bar graph of the data.
13. Make a broken line graph of the data in the frequency distribution.
14. Find the arithmetic mean of the data in the frequency distribution.
15. Find the median of the data in the frequency distribution.
16. Find the standard deviation of the data in the frequency distribution.

Assume the data in the frequency distribution given above is normally distributed. (14-7, 14-8)

17. Find the range about the mean that includes 80% of the data.
18. Find the probability that a student selected at random will have a point average of 4.0 or higher.
19. Find the standard error of the mean.
20. Find the range about the sample mean that has a 1% level of confidence.

A small metal object is weighed on a laboratory balance by each of 15 pupils in a class. The weight of the object in grams is reported as 2.341, 2.347, 2.338, 2.350, 2.344, 2.342, 2.345, 2.348, 2.340, 2.345, 2.343, 2.344, 2.347, 2.341, and 2.344.

1. Make an array of the data.
2. Find the range of the data.
3. Find the arithmetic mean of the data.
4. Find the median of the data.
5. Find the mode of the data.
6. Find the mean deviation of the data.
7. Find the semi-interquartile range of the data.
8. Find the standard deviation of the data.

A fruit stand owner mixed four different grades of apples into one pile for resale. His costs for the different grades are as follows.

Grades	Costs
A	20¢ per pound
B	24¢ per pound
C	16¢ per pound
D	30¢ per pound

9. Assume the owner purchased the same quantity of apples for each grade. Find the average cost per pound of the mixed grade.

10. Assume that the owner spent the same amount of money for each grade. Find the average cost per pound of the mixed grade.

The days missed for a random sample of 80 high school students at Main High School in a certain school year are given.

```
 6  16  12   7   7   9  13  12   7   7
 4  11  13  10  16  20  10  17  11  12
 3   8   8  12  13   8   8  11  12   1
16  13   5  10   1  10   8  15  10  13
 9  15  11  18  12  14  10  16   8  10
10  12  17  14   6   9  12  10  14   8
19   4   9   6   9  10  11   5  11   9
20   5   2  11  19   9   7   9   6  14
```

11. Make a frequency distribution of the data using a class interval of three.
12. Draw a histogram for the data in the frequency distribution.
13. Draw a circle graph for the data in the frequency distribution.
14. Find the mean of the data in the frequency distribution.
15. Find the median of the data in the frequency distribution.
16. Find the standard deviation of the data in the frequency distribution.

Assume the data given for problems 11-16 is normally distributed.

17. Find the lower and upper limits within which 90% of the data lie.
18. Find the probability that a value selected at random from the data will be between 8 and 12.
19. Find the standard error of the mean.
20. Find the range about the sample mean that has a 5% level of confidence.

CHAPTER 15

Limits, Derivatives, and Integrals

Rectangles can be used to approximate the area under a curve by a process called integration. If the width of each rectangle is decreased and the number of rectangles is increased, their total area approaches the actual area under the curve. The windows under the curving roof of this building architecturally illustrate how integration using trapezoids finds the area under a curve.

15-1   Concept of Limit

Consider the sequence, $\frac{1}{2}, \frac{1}{4}, \frac{1}{8}, \cdots, \frac{1}{2^n}$ as n increases without limit.

From the graph, the sequence seems to converge to zero.

As n increases, the denominator of $\frac{1}{2^n}$ increases, and the value of the fraction approaches zero. The limit of this sequence is represented as follows.

$$\lim_{n \to \infty} \frac{1}{2^n} = 0$$

Consider the sum $\frac{1}{2} + \frac{1}{4} + \frac{1}{8} + \cdots + \frac{1}{2^n}$ as n increases without limit. This sum approaches a limit if it becomes and remains close to some constant for large values of n. The limit of the sum itself is the constant being approached as n increases indefinitely. The sum of n terms can be represented by the length of the line segment from zero to the nth point as shown below.

As n increases without limit, the points representing the sum cluster closer and closer to 1, but always remain less than 1. Thus, the limit of the sum $\frac{1}{2} + \frac{1}{4} + \frac{1}{8} + \cdots + \frac{1}{2^n}$ as n increases indefinitely is 1.

The concept of a limit may be extended to a function. What is the limit of $2x + 3$ as x approaches 0? What is the limit as x approaches 4? As would be expected, the answers to these questions are 3 and 11, respectively.

Example

1   Show that $\lim\limits_{x \to 4} (x^2 - 4) = 12$ by selecting replacements for **x** near 4.

x	3.8	3.9	3.99	3.999
$x^2 - 4$	10.44	11.21	11.9201	11.992001

x	4.1	4.01	4.001	4.0001
$x^2 - 4$	12.81	12.0801	12.008001	12.00080001

Thus, the limit of $x^2 - 4$ as x approaches 4 is 12.

Consider any polynomial function with real coefficients of the form $P(x) = a_0x^n + a_1x^{n-1} + a_2x^{n-2} + \cdots + a_{n-1}x + a_n$. Let the domain of P be the set of all real numbers. Then, for any real number r, there exists a real number $P(r)$. The limit of such a polynomial function as x approaches r is $P(r)$. For example, the limit of $x^2 - x + 3$ as x approaches 2 is $2^2 - 2 + 3$ or 5.

The limit of a polynomial function, $P(x)$, as x approaches r, is $P(r)$. $$\lim_{x \to r} P(x) = P(r)$$	Limit of a Polynomial Function

Now consider the rational function $f(x) = \dfrac{x^3}{x}$. What value of x is *not* in the domain? Suppose it is necessary to find the limit of $\dfrac{x^3}{x}$ as x approaches 2. Let $r = 2$.

$$\lim_{x \to r} f(x) = f(r)$$

$$\lim_{x \to 2} \frac{x^3}{x} = f(2)$$

$$= \frac{8}{2} \text{ or } 4$$

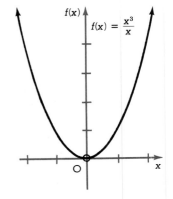

$f(x)$

$f(x) = \dfrac{x^3}{x}$

What is $\lim\limits_{x \to 0} \dfrac{x^3}{x}$? Let $r = 0$. In this case, $f(r)$ is undefined. *Why?*

Replace x by values close to zero to obtain values close to $\dfrac{x^3}{x}$ at zero.

x	1	0.1	0.01	0.001	0.0001
$\dfrac{x^3}{x}$	1	0.01	0.0001	0.000001	0.00000001

It appears that $\lim\limits_{x \to 0} \dfrac{x^3}{x} = 0$. Although the function is undefined at zero, the limit of the function exists as x approaches zero. The limit is 0.

An alternate way of showing that $\lim\limits_{x \to 0} \dfrac{x^3}{x} = 0$ is to transform $\dfrac{x^3}{x}$ into x^2 since the two functions are equal for all values of x except $x = 0$. Because x^2 is a polynomial, $\lim\limits_{x \to 0} x^2 = 0$. This method succeeds whenever a transformation is possible, even if the given function is *not* defined at that point.

Change rational functions to polynomial functions whenever possible.

Example

2 Find $\lim\limits_{x \to 2} \dfrac{x^2 - 4}{x - 2}$.

$$\lim_{x \to 2} \frac{(x^2 - 4)}{x - 2} = \lim_{x \to 2} \frac{(x + 2)(x - 2)}{(x - 2)}$$ *Factor.*

$$= \lim_{x \to 2} (x + 2)$$ *Note that $\dfrac{x^2 - 4}{x - 2} = x + 2$ for all real values of x*

$$= 4$$ *except 2. However, this fact does <u>not</u> affect the value of the limit as x <u>approaches</u> 2.*

The limit of $\dfrac{x^2 - 4}{x - 2}$ as x approaches 2 is 4.

Sometimes the limit of a function that involves the function $f(x) = \dfrac{1}{x}$ is needed. From the graph of $y = \dfrac{1}{x}$ shown at the right, notice $\dfrac{1}{x}$ approaches zero as x increases in value. Thus, $\lim\limits_{x \to \infty} \dfrac{1}{x} = 0$.

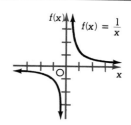

Example

3 Find $\lim\limits_{n \to \infty} \dfrac{7n^2}{n^2 + 3n + 1}$.

Recall from Chapter 8 that an expression can be altered to make the limit easier to find.

$$\lim_{n \to \infty} \frac{7n^2}{n^2 + 3n + 1} = \lim_{n \to \infty} \frac{7n^2 \cdot \dfrac{1}{n^2}}{(n^2 + 3n + 1)\dfrac{1}{n^2}}$$

$$= \lim_{n \to \infty} \frac{7}{1 + \dfrac{3}{n} + \dfrac{1}{n^2}}$$ *The values of $\dfrac{3}{n}$ and $\dfrac{1}{n^2}$ both approach zero as n increases.*

$$= 7$$

Thus, $\lim\limits_{n \to \infty} \dfrac{7n^2}{n^2 + 3n + 1} = 7$.

Exploratory Exercises

Show that the limit of each function, $F(x)$, as x approaches r, is $F(r)$ by selecting four successive replacements for x near r.

1. $\lim\limits_{x \to 2} 5x$

2. $\lim\limits_{x \to 2} (x^2 + 3x + 2)$

3. $\lim\limits_{x \to 1} \dfrac{x - 2}{x + 2}$

4. $\lim\limits_{x \to 3} x^2$

5. $\lim\limits_{x \to -2} (x^2 - 4)$

6. $\lim\limits_{x \to 5} \sqrt{25 - x^2}$

7. $\lim\limits_{x \to 4} (3x + 2)$

8. $\lim\limits_{x \to 0} (4x + 1)$

9. $\lim\limits_{x \to -3} (2x - 5)$

10. $\lim\limits_{x \to 2} (x^2 - 4x + 1)$

11. $\lim\limits_{x \to 3} \dfrac{x - 2}{x + 2}$

12. $\lim\limits_{x \to -2} \dfrac{x^2 - 4}{x^2 + 4}$

Written Exercises

Find each limit.

1. $\lim\limits_{x \to 2} x^2$

2. $\lim\limits_{x \to 1} (x^2 + 4x + 3)$

3. $\lim\limits_{x \to 1} \dfrac{x + 1}{x + 2}$

4. $\lim\limits_{n \to 0} \left(5^n + \dfrac{1}{5^n}\right)$

5. $\lim\limits_{x \to 5} (3x - 8)$

6. $\lim\limits_{x \to 3} \dfrac{x^2 - 9}{x + 3}$

7. $\lim\limits_{x \to 3} \dfrac{x^2 - 9}{x - 3}$

8. $\lim\limits_{x \to -3} \dfrac{x^2 - 9}{x + 3}$

9. $\lim\limits_{x \to 2} \dfrac{x^2 - 4}{x^3 - 8}$

10. $\lim\limits_{x \to 3} \dfrac{x - 3}{x^2 - 9}$

11. $\lim\limits_{x \to -2} (x^4 - x^2 + x - 2)$

12. $\lim\limits_{x \to 2} \dfrac{x^3 - 8}{x - 2}$

13. $\lim\limits_{x \to -1} \dfrac{x^3 + 1}{x + 1}$

14. $\lim\limits_{n \to -2} \dfrac{n^3 - 8}{n - 2}$

15. $\lim\limits_{x \to 2} \dfrac{x^2 - x - 2}{x^2 - 4}$

16. $\lim\limits_{x \to \infty} \dfrac{x + 1}{x}$

17. $\lim\limits_{x \to \infty} \dfrac{2x - 5}{x}$

18. $\lim\limits_{n \to \infty} \dfrac{n^2 + n - 6}{n^2}$

19. $\lim\limits_{n \to 0} \dfrac{(1 + n)^2 - 1}{n}$

20. $\lim\limits_{x \to \infty} \dfrac{\sqrt{x + 4} - 2}{x}$

21. $\lim\limits_{n \to \infty} \dfrac{(n - 2)(n + 1)}{n^2}$

For the Scholar

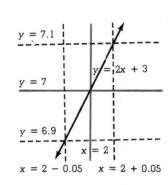

The above map shows the area in which Andy, Betty, and Carol live. Every day Andy walks to Carol's always walking either south or west. At each intersection where he has a choice, he chooses randomly with probability $\frac{1}{2}$ whether to go south or west. Find the probability that on any given day, he walks through the intersection right in front of Betty's house on his way to Carol's.

15-2 Formal Definition of a Limit

Consider the function $y = 2x + 3$. Suppose it is required that the value of $2x + 3$ be within 0.1 of 7. That is, $6.9 < 2x + 3 < 7.1$. Can an interval of values of x around 2 be found so that this condition is met? Will $1.9 < x < 2.1$ satisfy the requirement? Replacing x by 1.9 and 2.1 in $y = 2x + 3$ yields $6.8 < 2x + 3 < 7.2$. Thus, this interval of values of x around 2 is not close enough for $2x + 3$ to be within 0.1 of 7. Will $1.95 < x < 2.05$ satisfy the requirement that $6.9 < 2x + 3 < 7.1$? This gives $6.9 < 2x + 3 < 7.1$. Thus, an interval of values of x around 2 such that the value of $2x + 3$ is within 0.1 of 7 has been found. This interval is $2 - 0.05 < x < 2 + 0.05$.
Will any range less than 0.05 around 2 also be acceptable?

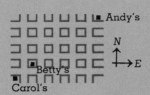

To generalize the preceding example, substitute the symbol ϵ for the specified value 0.1. Thus, $7 - \epsilon < 2x + 3 < 7 + \epsilon$. This inequality can be solved for x.

The symbol ϵ, lower case Greek letter epsilon, is usually used when referring to closeness in the range. ϵ is a positive real number.

$$7 - \epsilon < 2x + 3 < 7 + \epsilon$$
$$(7 - \epsilon) - 3 < 2x < (7 + \epsilon) - 3$$
$$4 - \epsilon < 2x < 4 + \epsilon$$
$$\frac{4 - \epsilon}{2} < x < \frac{4 + \epsilon}{2}$$
$$2 - \frac{\epsilon}{2} < x < 2 + \frac{\epsilon}{2}$$

Thus, if $2 - \frac{\epsilon}{2} < x < 2 + \frac{\epsilon}{2}$, then $7 - \epsilon < 2x + 3 < 7 + \epsilon$.

So an interval of the domain around 2, $\left|\frac{\epsilon}{2}\right|$, can be found for any value of ϵ.

$7 \pm \epsilon$ is sometimes referred to as a neighborhood around 7.

Example

1 **How close to 2 must x be chosen so that $5x - 1$ is within 0.01 of 9?**

$$9 - 0.01 < 5x - 1 < 9 + 0.01$$
$$-0.01 < (5x - 1) - 9 < 0.01$$
$$-0.01 < 5x - 10 < 0.01$$
$$-0.002 < x - 2 < 0.002$$
$$2 - 0.002 < x < 2 + 0.002$$
$$1.998 < x < 2.002$$

Thus, if values of x are within 0.002 of 2, then $5x - 1$ is within 0.01 of 9.

Consider the general function $y = mx + b$. The concept of finding values of x close to a such that $mx + b$ is within a certain interval of $ma + b$ is illustrated at the right. Let $L = ma + b$. Consider the neighborhood of L between $L - \epsilon$ and $L + \epsilon$ where ϵ is a positive real number. How close to a must the value of x be selected in order to insure that $L - \epsilon < mx + b < L + \epsilon$? Let the values of x be limited by the interval $a - \delta < x < a + \delta$ where δ is a positive real number. Can a value of δ be found that will insure that the value of $mx + b$ falls within the interval from $L - \epsilon$ to $L + \epsilon$

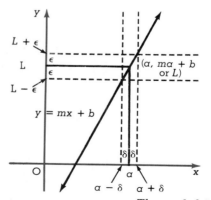

no matter how small ϵ is chosen? If such a value of δ can be found, regardless of the choice of ϵ, then the limit of $mx + b$ as x approaches a is L or $\lim\limits_{x \to a} (mx + b) = L$.

The symbol δ, delta, is usually used when referring to closeness in the domain.

To prove that $\lim\limits_{x \to a} (mx + b) = ma + b$ it must be shown that for any choice of $\epsilon > 0$, there is a $\delta > 0$ such that whenever $a - \delta < x < a + \delta$, the following double inequality is satisfied.

$a \pm \delta$ is a neighborhood around a.

$$(ma + b) - \epsilon < mx + b < (ma + b) + \epsilon$$
$$-\epsilon < (mx + b) - (ma + b) < \epsilon$$
$$-\epsilon < m(x - a) < \epsilon$$
$$\frac{-\epsilon}{m} < x - a < \frac{\epsilon}{m}$$

If m is less than zero, the inequality is reversed.

$$a - \frac{\epsilon}{m} < x < a + \frac{\epsilon}{m}$$

Thus, if δ is equal to $\dfrac{\epsilon}{|m|}$ or any smaller positive number, the required inequality will be satisfied when $a - \delta < x < a + \delta$. Therefore, a value of δ can be found for any given value of ϵ which will insure that $(mx + b)$ is in the desired range whenever x is within δ units of a.

Absolute value notation can be used to represent a double inequality. Recall that $|x| = x$ if $x \geq 0$ or $|x| = -x$ if $x < 0$. So, $|x| < 5$ expresses the same relationship as $-5 < x < 5$.

Example

2 **Express $-\delta < x - a < \delta$ as a single inequality using absolute value notation.**

The expression $-\delta < x - a < \delta$ is equivalent to $|x - a| < \delta$.
This is true because $|x - a| < \delta$ means that $x - a < \delta$ if $x \geq a$, but $x - a > -\delta$ if $x < a$.

The absolute value notation is used in the formal definition of the limit of a function.

The limit of a function $f(x)$ as x approaches a is L, written $\lim\limits_{x \to a} f(x) = L$, if, for every real number $\epsilon > 0$, there exists a real number $\delta > 0$ such that $|f(x) - L| < \epsilon$ when $0 < |x - a| < \delta$.

Limit of a Function

For the limit of $f(x)$ to be L, when values of x are selected in the neighborhood of a for any $f(x)$, values of $f(x)$ must be in the neighborhood of L. If it is required that $f(x)$ be arbitrarily close to L, say within ϵ units of L, then it must be possible to meet this requirement by selecting values of x sufficiently close to a, that is, within δ units of a. If this is satisfied, it is said that $f(x)$ approaches the limit L as x approaches a. The inequality $0 < |x - a|$ in the last line of the definition means that $x \neq a$. Thus, it is *not* required that a be in the domain of $f(x)$. *Why?*

Examples

3 **Prove $\lim\limits_{x \to 2} (3x + 7) = 13$.**

To prove $\lim\limits_{x \to 2} (3x + 7) = 13$, for each $\epsilon > 0$, it is
necessary to find a $\delta > 0$ such that $|f(x) - L|$ or
$|(3x + 7) - 13| < \epsilon$ when $0 < |x - 2| < \delta$.

$$\begin{aligned} |f(x) - L| &= |(3x + 7) - 13| \\ &= |3x - 6| \\ &= 3|x - 2| \end{aligned}$$

Thus, $|(3x + 7) - 13|$ or $3|x - 2|$ will be less than ϵ
when $|x - 2| < \dfrac{\epsilon}{3}$.

Therefore, if you choose $\delta \leq \dfrac{\epsilon}{3}$, the conditions of the
definition are satisfied and $\lim\limits_{x \to 2} (3x + 7) = 13$.

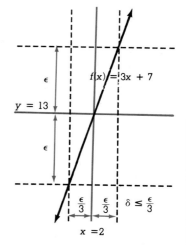

4 **Prove that $\lim\limits_{x \to 2} x^2 = 4$.**

To prove $\lim\limits_{x \to 2} x^2 = 4$, for each $\epsilon > 0$, it is necessary to
find a $\delta > 0$ such that $|f(x) - L|$ or $|x^2 - 4| < \epsilon$ when
$0 < |x - 2| < \delta$. But $|x^2 - 4|$ or $|x - 2| \cdot |x + 2| < \epsilon$
only if $|x - 2| < \dfrac{\epsilon}{|x + 2|}$. If you choose $\delta = 0.5$, then
$0 < |x - 2| < 0.5$ and $1.5 < x < 2.5$. This means
$|x + 2| < |2.5 + 2|$ or $|x + 2| < 4.5$. Therefore, to
have $|x^2 - 4| < \epsilon$ and $1.5 < x < 2.5$, you must have
$|x - 2| < \dfrac{\epsilon}{4.5}$.   *Remember $|x - 2| < \dfrac{\epsilon}{|x + 2|}$.*

So for each $\epsilon > 0$, choose δ to be smaller than either
0.5 or $\dfrac{\epsilon}{4.5}$.

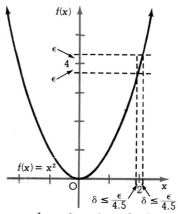

Thus, the $\lim\limits_{x \to 2} x^2 = 4$ because for each $\epsilon > 0$ there corresponds a $\delta > 0$ such that
$|x^2 - 4| < \epsilon$ when $0 < |x - 2| < \delta$.

There are many functions for
which $\lim\limits_{x \to a} f(x)$ does *not* exist. For
example, $\lim\limits_{x \to 0} \dfrac{1}{x}$ and $\lim\limits_{x \to 2} [x]$ do *not*
exist, as indicated by their graphs.

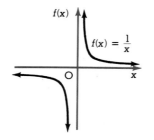

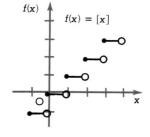

Exploratory Exercises

Express each inequality as a single inequality using absolute value notation.

1. $-0.1 < x - 2 < 0.1$
2. $-0.002 < x - 5 < 0.002$
3. $-\delta < x - 8 < \delta$
4. $-\delta < x - 1 < \delta$
5. $-0.001 < x - 8 < 0.001$
6. $-\delta < x - 2 < \delta$

State each inequality without using absolute value notation.

7. $|x - 4| < 0.001$
8. $|x - 3| < 0.2$
9. $|x - 7| < \delta$
10. $|x - 2| < 0.1$
11. $|x - 8| < 0.00003$
12. $|x - 1| < \delta$

Describe each shaded area with double inequalities.

13.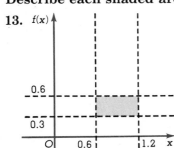

14.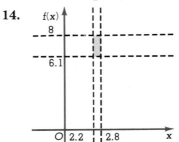

15.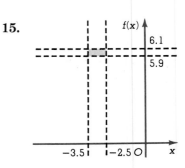

16-18. Describe each shaded area in problems **13-15** using absolute value notation.

Written Exercises

Find the interval that x must be within so that each inequality is satisfied.

1. $-0.01 < 4 - 2x < 0.01$
2. $7.8 < 5x + 3 < 8.2$
3. $2.9 < x - 2 < 3.1$
4. $6.8 < 2x + 3 < 7.2$
5. $|6 - 3x| < 0.01$
6. $15.99 < 15x + 1 < 16.01$
7. $3.7 < \dfrac{3x - 2}{4} < 4.3$
8. $\left|\dfrac{x + 1}{2}\right| < 0.01$

Find the smallest interval that $f(x)$ will be within if x is within each given interval.

9. $f(x) = 3x - 8;\ 3 < x < 5$
10. $f(x) = 2x - 1;\ 2.9 < x < 3.1$
11. $f(x) = x^2;\ 6.5 < x < 7.5$
12. $f(x) = 3x + 1;\ 1.6 < x < 1.7$
13. $f(x) = \dfrac{x}{2};\ -1.7 < x < -1.3$
14. $f(x) = x^2 - 2x;\ -0.1 < x < 0.1$
15. $f(x) = 6 - x;\ a > 0;\ 2 - a < x < 2 + a$
16. $f(x) = 2x;\ a > 0;\ -a < x - 3 < a$

Solve each of the following.

17. Show that the limit of $2x - 6$ as x approaches 4 is 2 by finding a value $\delta > 0$ for any $\epsilon > 0$ so that $2 - \epsilon < 2x - 6 < 2 + \epsilon$ whenever $4 - \delta < x < 4 + \delta$.

18. Graph the function $f(x) = 3x - 5$. Show the relationship between ϵ and δ on the graph by finding values of δ corresponding to ϵ values of 0.1 and 0.01 as x approaches 2.

Given that $\epsilon = 0.01$, find a δ such that the following limits are verified using the definition.

19. $\lim\limits_{x \to -1} (x + 3) = 2$

20. $\lim\limits_{x \to 1} \dfrac{x - 1}{3} = 0$

21. $\lim\limits_{x \to 3} \dfrac{2x - 5}{2} = \dfrac{1}{2}$

22. $\lim\limits_{x \to 0} (4x + 5) = 5$

23. $\lim\limits_{x \to 0} x = 0$

24. $\lim\limits_{x \to \frac{1}{2}} (2x - 1) = 0$

25. $\lim\limits_{x \to 2} \dfrac{x^2 - 4}{x - 2} = 4$

26. $\lim\limits_{x \to 2} \dfrac{1}{x} = \dfrac{1}{2}$

For the Scholar

If 110111011110111110 is a base two number, find the second digit on the left of the base eight representation.

15-3 Continuity

A function is **continuous** if there are no "breaks" in the graph of the function. That is, the graph of a continuous function may be drawn completely without lifting the pencil.

There are three conditions that must be met for a function to be **continuous at a point.** The function must be defined at that point. It must have a limit for the x-value of the point. And, the value of the function must be equal to the limit of the function at that point.

A function which is not continuous at a point is said to be discontinuous at that point.

A function f is continuous at $x = a$ if $f(a)$ exists and if $\lim\limits_{x \to a} f(x) = f(a)$.	*Continuity of a Function at a Point*

Examples

1 **Show that $f(x) = x^2 + 2x$ is continuous at $x = 2$.**

Show that $f(2)$ exists. $\qquad$ $f(2) = 2^2 + 2 \cdot 2$ or 8

Show that $\lim\limits_{x \to 2} f(x) = f(2)$. $\qquad$ Since $f(x)$ is a polynomial, the limit of $f(x)$ as x approaches 2 is $f(2)$.

Thus, the function is continuous at 2.

2 **State whether the function, $f(x) = \dfrac{x - 1}{x}$ is continuous or discontinuous at $x = 0$.**

First, determine if $f(x)$ exists.

$$f(x) = \frac{x - 1}{x}$$
$$f(0) = \frac{0 - 1}{0}$$

Therefore, since $f(x)$ at $x = 0$ is undefined, the function is discontinuous at 0.

Example

3 Show that $\lim_{x \to 2} \dfrac{x^2 - 4}{x - 2} = 4$. Then, state whether the function, $f(x) = \dfrac{x^2 - 4}{x - 2}$, is continuous or discontinuous at $x = 2$.

Find a value of δ such that if $0 < |x - 2| < \delta$, then $\left| \dfrac{x^2 - 4}{x - 2} - 4 \right| < \epsilon$ for any choice of ϵ.

$$\left| \frac{x^2 - 4}{x - 2} - 4 \right| < \epsilon$$

$$-\epsilon < \frac{x^2 - 4}{x - 2} - 4 < \epsilon$$

$$4 - \epsilon < \frac{(x - 2)(x + 2)}{(x - 2)} < 4 + \epsilon$$

$$4 - \epsilon < x + 2 < 4 + \epsilon$$

$$-\epsilon < x - 2 < \epsilon$$

$$0 < |x - 2| < \epsilon$$

Thus, if $0 < |x - 2| < \delta$, you must choose $\delta \le \epsilon$. Therefore, the conditions of the definition of a limit are satisfied and $\lim_{x \to 2} \dfrac{x^2 - 4}{x - 2} = 4$. However, the function $f(x) = \dfrac{x^2 - 4}{x - 2}$, is *not* continuous at $x = 2$ because $f(2)$ is undefined.

The concept of continuity may be extended from a point to an interval and then to the whole domain of a function.

A function f is continuous on an interval if it is continuous at each point of the interval.	*Continuity of a Function on an Interval*
A function f is continuous if it is continuous at each point of its domain.	*Continuous Function*

It is obvious that any polynomial function, $P(x)$, is continuous since for any value r, there exists $P(r)$ and $\lim_{x \to r} P(x) = P(r)$.

The graphs of some discontinuous functions are shown below.

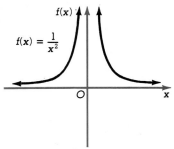

$f(x) = \dfrac{1}{x^2}$

Infinite Discontinuity

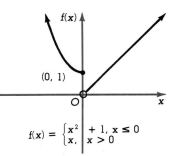

$f(x) = \begin{cases} x^2 + 1, & x \le 0 \\ x, & x > 0 \end{cases}$

Jump Discontinuity

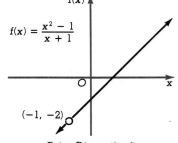

$f(x) = \dfrac{x^2 - 1}{x + 1}$

Point Discontinuity

The function, $f(x) = \begin{cases} 1, & x \text{ rational} \\ 0, & x \text{ irrational} \end{cases}$, is an example of a discontinuous function that is everywhere discontinuous.

It is impossible to graph this function.

Example

4 Determine if $f(x) = \dfrac{|x|}{x}$ is continuous or discontinuous. If it is discontinuous, state the type of discontinuity indicated by its graph.

Graph the function.

The graph indicates that $f(x)$ is discontinuous. The function $f(x) = \dfrac{|x|}{x}$ has jump discontinuity at $x = 0$.

Exploratory Exercises

Identify a point(s) at which each function is discontinuous.

1. $f(x) = \dfrac{8}{x}$

2. $f(x) = 1 - \dfrac{1}{x}$

3. $f(x) = \dfrac{1}{(x-3)^2}$

4. $f(x) = \dfrac{x-2}{x^2 - 3x + 2}$

5. $f(x) = [x]$

6. $f(x) = \begin{cases} 1, & x > 0 \\ 0, & x = 0 \\ -1, & x < 0 \end{cases}$

Each of the following functions has point discontinuity. Assign values to $f(x)$ that remove the discontinuity.

7. $f(x) = \dfrac{x^2 - 1}{x - 1}$

8. $f(x) = \dfrac{x^2 - 5x + 6}{x - 2}$

9. $f(x) = \dfrac{x^2 - 5}{x + \sqrt{5}}$

10. $f(x) = \dfrac{x^3 + 8}{x + 2}$

Written Exercises

State whether each function is continuous or discontinuous. If it is discontinuous, identify the discontinuity as infinite, jump, or point.

1. $f(x) = x^2 + 2$

2. $f(x) = \dfrac{x(x-1)}{x-1}$

3. $f(x) = \dfrac{1}{x}$

4. $f(x) = \begin{cases} x, & x \le 0 \\ x^2 + 1, & x > 0 \end{cases}$

5. $f(x) = \begin{cases} |x| + x + 1, & x < 0 \\ |x| - x + 1, & x \ge 0 \end{cases}$

6. $f(x) = \begin{cases} x, & x > 0 \\ -x, & x < 0 \end{cases}$

7. $f(x) = \dfrac{x^2 - 1}{x - 1}$

8. $f(x) = x + \dfrac{1}{x}$

9. $f(x) = \begin{cases} \dfrac{x^2 - 1}{x - 1}, & x \ne 1 \\ 2, & x = 1 \end{cases}$

10. $f(x) = x + [x]$

11. $f(x) = |x - 1|$

12. $x^2 y = 1$

Write an example of a function that satisfies each condition.

13. everywhere continuous

14. discontinuous only at $x = 0$

15. discontinuous only at $x = 2$

16. discontinuous at odd multiples of π

Show that each of the following functions is either continuous or discontinuous at the given value of x.

17. $f(x) = x + 5$ at $x = 1$

18. $f(x) = x^2 + 2x - 1$ at $x = 0$

19. $f(x) = \dfrac{x^2 - 16}{x + 4}$ at $x = 4$

20. $f(x) = \dfrac{x^2 - 16}{x - 4}$ at $x = 4$

For the Scholar

Two bugs start at the origin, one traveling along the positive half of the *x*-axis and the other traveling along the positive half of the *y*-axis. If each bug moves 1 unit on the first move, $\frac{1}{2}$ unit on the second move, and so on where on any subsequent move the bug moves only half as far as the immediately preceding move, how far will the bugs be apart assuming their moves are frequent and over an infinite amount of time?

15-4   Theorems about Limits

It is useful to have principles that define operations involving limits when attempting to find the limits of some functions. These operations include addition, subtraction, multiplication, and division as well as using powers and roots. The principles are stated as theorems without proofs.

The following theorems are given for $\lim\limits_{x \to a} f(x) = F$ and $\lim\limits_{x \to a} g(x) = G$ and real numbers a and c, and n a positive integer.		
Limit of a Constant Function	If $f(x) = c$, then $\lim\limits_{x \to a} f(x) = c$.	*Theorem 1*
Addition	$\lim\limits_{x \to a} [f(x) + g(x)] = \lim\limits_{x \to a} f(x) + \lim\limits_{x \to a} g(x) = F + G$	*Theorem 2*
Subtraction	$\lim\limits_{x \to a} [f(x) - g(x)] = \lim\limits_{x \to a} f(x) - \lim\limits_{x \to a} g(x) = F - G$	*Theorem 3*
Multiplication	$\lim\limits_{x \to a} [f(x) \cdot g(x)] = \left[\lim\limits_{x \to a} f(x)\right]\left[\lim\limits_{x \to a} g(x)\right] = F \cdot G$	*Theorem 4*
Division	$\lim\limits_{x \to a} \dfrac{f(x)}{g(x)} = \dfrac{\lim\limits_{x \to a} f(x)}{\lim\limits_{x \to a} g(x)} = \dfrac{F}{G}(G \neq 0)$	*Theorem 5*
Product of a Constant and a Limit	$\lim\limits_{x \to a} [c \cdot g(x)] = c \lim\limits_{x \to a} g(x) = cG$	*Theorem 6*
Powers	$\lim\limits_{x \to a} [f(x)^n] = \left[\lim\limits_{x \to a} f(x)\right]^n = F^n$	*Theorem 7*
Roots	$\lim\limits_{x \to a} \sqrt[n]{f(x)} = \sqrt[n]{\lim\limits_{x \to a} f(x)} = \sqrt[n]{F}$	*Theorem 8*

Examples

1 Use the limit theorems to evaluate $\lim\limits_{x \to 1} \dfrac{x^2 + x - 5}{3x^2 + 2}$.

$$\lim_{x \to 1} \frac{x^2 + x - 5}{3x^2 + 2} = \frac{\lim\limits_{x \to 1} (x^2 + x - 5)}{\lim\limits_{x \to 1} (3x^2 + 2)} \qquad \textit{Theorem 5}$$

$$= \frac{1 + 1 - 5}{3 + 2} \text{ or } \frac{-3}{5}$$

2 Find $\lim\limits_{x \to 0} \dfrac{\sqrt{3x^2 + x + 1}}{\sqrt[3]{x^3 - x + 8}}$.

$$\lim_{x \to 0} \frac{\sqrt{3x^2 + x + 1}}{\sqrt[3]{x^3 - x + 8}} = \frac{\lim\limits_{x \to 0} \sqrt{3x^2 + x + 1}}{\lim\limits_{x \to 0} \sqrt[3]{x^3 - x + 8}} \qquad \textit{Theorem 5}$$

$$= \frac{\sqrt{\lim\limits_{x \to 0} (3x^2 + x + 1)}}{\sqrt[3]{\lim\limits_{x \to 0} (x^3 - x + 8)}} \qquad \textit{Theorem 8}$$

$$= \frac{1}{\sqrt[3]{8}} \text{ or } \frac{1}{2}$$

If $f(x)$ and $g(x)$ are two functions of x, the composite of f and g is defined to be $f[g(x)]$. For example, if $f(x) = x^2$ and $g(x) = x + 2$, $f[g(x)] = f(x + 2)$ or $(x + 2)^2$. In general, composition of functions is *not* a commutative operation. In other words, the value of $f[g(x)]$ is usually not the same as the value of $g[f(x)]$.

In general,
$f(g(x)) \neq g(f(x))$.

> Given functions $f(x)$ and $g(x)$, $\lim\limits_{x \to a} g(x) = G$, and any real number a, the limit of the composite of functions $f(x)$ and $g(x)$ is as follows.
> $$\lim_{x \to a} f[g(x)] = f\left[\lim_{x \to a} g(x)\right] = f(G)$$

Theorem 9

Example

3 Find $\lim\limits_{x \to 2} f[g(x)]$ if $f(x) = x^2$ and $g(x) = x + 2$.

$$\lim_{x \to 2} f[g(x)] = f\left[\lim_{x \to 2} g(x)\right]$$

$$= f\left[\lim_{x \to 2} (x + 2)\right]$$

$$= f(4)$$

$$= 4^2 \text{ or } 16 \qquad f(x) = x^2$$

The following theorem is used to find the limits of trigonometric functions.

The limit of $\frac{\sin x}{x}$ is equal to 1 as x approaches 0 where x is the radian measure of an angle. $\lim\limits_{x\to 0} \frac{\sin x}{x} = 1$	*Theorem 10*

This can be shown as follows. Suppose that $0 < x < \frac{\pi}{2}$. Arc AB is part of a circle with center O and radius 1 unit. As x approaches 0, the length of $\overline{AD}$ approaches the length of $\overset{\frown}{AB}$. Thus, $\dfrac{\overline{AD}}{\text{measure of } \overset{\frown}{AB}}$ approaches 1 as x approaches 0. But, $\overline{AD} = \sin x$ and the measure of $\overset{\frown}{AB} = x$, so $\lim\limits_{x\to 0} \frac{\sin x}{x} = 1$.

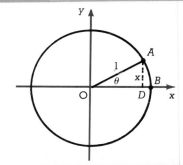

Example

4 Find $\lim\limits_{x\to 0} \frac{\sin 2x}{x}$.

$$\lim_{x\to 0} \frac{\sin 2x}{x} = \lim_{x\to 0} \frac{2 \cdot \sin 2x}{2x}$$ *Multiply numerator and denominator by 2.*

$$= 2 \cdot \lim_{x\to 0} \frac{\sin 2x}{2x}$$ $\lim\limits_{x\to 0} \frac{\sin nx}{nx} = \lim\limits_{x\to 0} \frac{\sin x}{x}$

$$= 2 \cdot 1 \text{ or } 2$$

Exploratory Exercises

Evaluate each limit.

1. $\lim\limits_{x\to 4} 6(x - 5)$

2. $\lim\limits_{x\to 1} (x + 2)(x - 3)$

3. $\lim\limits_{x\to 0} [(x^2 + 3x) - (2x + 5)]$

4. $\lim\limits_{x\to 2} \frac{x + 1}{x}$

5. $\lim\limits_{x\to 0} \frac{x^2 + 5x}{x + 4}$

6. $\lim\limits_{x\to 3} (x + 2)^4$

Find $f[g(2)]$ and $g[f(2)]$ given each $f(x)$ and $g(x)$.

7. $f(x) = x^2 + 2$
$g(x) = x - 3$

8. $f(x) = x^2 + 2x + 1$
$g(x) = x^2 - 1$

9. $f(x) = |x + 1|$
$g(x) = 2|x - 3|$

10-12. Find $g[f(2)]$ given each $f(x)$ and $g(x)$ in problems **7-9.**

Written Exercises

Solve each of the following.

1. Show that $\lim\limits_{x\to 2} (x^2 - 5x + 6) =$ $\lim\limits_{x\to 2} (x - 2) \cdot \lim\limits_{x\to 2} (x - 3) = 0.$

2. Show that $\lim\limits_{x\to 0} x^2 = 0$ by using the fact that $x \cdot x = x^2$.

3. Express $\lim\limits_{x\to a} (px^2 + qx + r)$ as the product of the limits of two linear functions.

4. Find $\lim\limits_{x\to 3} (x - 1)^3$ in two ways.

Use the limit theorems to evaluate each limit.

5. $\lim\limits_{x\to 3} \dfrac{x^2 - 2x + 1}{x^3}$

6. $\lim\limits_{x\to 1} \dfrac{x^2 + 2}{x}$

7. $\lim\limits_{x\to 1} \dfrac{x - 3}{2x - 4}$

8. $\lim\limits_{x\to 3} (2x^2 + 3x + 4)$

9. $\lim\limits_{x\to -1} \sqrt{x^2 - 1}$

10. $\lim\limits_{x\to 3} (x^3 - 5x^2 + 2x - 1)$

11. $\lim\limits_{x\to 2} \dfrac{x^2 - 4}{x - 2}$

12. $\lim\limits_{x\to -1} \dfrac{2x^2 + 3x - 5}{5x^3 - 2}$

13. $\lim\limits_{x\to 1} \dfrac{x - 1}{x^3 - 1}$

Find the limit of $f[g(x)]$ as x approaches 1 for each $f(x)$ and $g(x)$.

14. $f(x) = 2x + 1$
$g(x) = x - 3$

15. $f(x) = 3x - 4$
$g(x) = 2x + 5$

16. $f(x) = x^2 + 3$
$g(x) = 2x - 1$

Use Theorem 10 to evaluate each limit.

17. $\lim\limits_{x\to 0} \dfrac{\sin^2 x}{x}$

18. $\lim\limits_{x\to 0} \dfrac{\sin 3x}{5x}$

19. $\lim\limits_{x\to 0} \dfrac{1 - \cos x}{x^2}$

For the Scholar

The wire structure shown in the figure represents the edges of a regular tetrahedron. Each edge has a length of 2 meters. If a spider, S, moves up and down wire $\overline{OR}$, while fly, F, moves back and forth on wire $\overline{PQ}$, what is the shortest possible distance between the spider and the fly at any time during their movement?

15-5 Derivatives

The concept of the limit is used in the definition of the **derivative** of a function f. Consider the function $f(x)$ at the values a and $(a + h)$. The slope of the secant line intersecting the graph of f at $(a, f(a))$ and $(a + h, f(a + h))$ is given by $\dfrac{f(a + h) - f(a)}{(a + h) - a}$ or $\dfrac{f(a + h) - f(a)}{h}$. This ratio is called the **difference quotient**. The limit of the difference quotient as h approaches zero is the **derivative** of f at $x = a$ and is denoted by $f'(a)$. Thus, $f'(a)$ is actually the slope of the tangent to the graph of f at $(a, f(a))$.

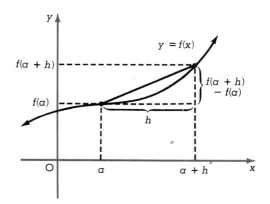

For a function f, the derivative of f at $x = a$, $f'(a)$, is defined as follows.

$$f'(a) = \lim_{h\to 0} \frac{f(a + h) - f(a)}{h}$$

Derivative of a Function

The process of finding derivatives, which are defined as limits of difference quotients, is called **differentiation**. A function is **differentiable** at a if the derivative of the function exists at a and is finite.

Recall in Chapter 2, a derivative was defined as the slope of the tangent.

Examples

1 Find the derivative of $f(x) = x^2$.

Find the difference quotient and simplify.

$$\frac{f(x + h) - f(x)}{h} = \frac{(x + h)^2 - x^2}{h}$$

$$= \frac{x^2 + 2hx + h^2 - x^2}{h}$$

$$= \frac{2hx + h^2}{h}$$

$$= 2x + h$$

Find the limit of the difference quotient as h approaches 0.

$$\lim_{h \to 0} (2x + h) = 2x$$

Thus, $f'(x) = 2x$.

2 Find the slope of the tangent and the equation of the tangent to the curve $y = 2x^2 + 3$ at the point (2, 11).

Find the slope of the tangent using the definition of the derivative.

$$\lim_{h \to 0} \frac{f(x + h) - f(x)}{h} = \lim_{h \to 0} \frac{[2(x + h)^2 + 3] - (2x^2 + 3)}{h}$$

$$= \lim_{h \to 0} \frac{2(x^2 + 2hx + h^2) + 3 - 2x^2 - 3}{h}$$

$$= \lim_{h \to 0} \frac{2x^2 + 4hx + 2h^2 + 3 - 2x^2 - 3}{h}$$

$$= \lim_{h \to 0} \frac{4hx + 2h^2}{h}$$

$$= \lim_{h \to 0} (4x + 2h)$$

$$= 4x$$

So the slope of the tangent is $4x$ at any point on the curve.

Next, find the slope of the tangent at the point (2, 11) by substituting 2 for x.

$$\text{Slope of tangent} = 4(2) \text{ or } 8$$

Use the point-slope form to find the equation of the tangent.

$y - y_1 = m(x - x_1)$
$y - 11 = 8(x - 2)$
$\quad\quad y = 8x - 5$

Thus, the slope of the tangent at the point (2, 11) is 8 and the equation of the tangent at the point (2, 11) is $y = 8x - 5$.

The symbol h often is replaced by Δx to show the change in x. Then, the difference quotient is $\dfrac{f(x + \Delta x) - f(x)}{\Delta x}$. But $f(x + \Delta x) - f(x)$ can be denoted as Δy since it is actually the change in y. Thus, the derivative of $f(x)$ may be written with the delta notation as follows.

Δx is read "delta X."

$$f'(x) = \lim_{\Delta x \to 0} \frac{f(x + \Delta x) - f(x)}{\Delta x} \text{ or } \lim_{\Delta x \to 0} \frac{\Delta y}{\Delta x}$$

When the function is written in the form $y = f(x)$, the derivative is sometimes written as $\dfrac{dy}{dx}$. Thus, $\dfrac{dy}{dx} = \lim\limits_{\Delta x \to 0} \dfrac{f(x + \Delta x) - f(x)}{\Delta x}$ or $\lim\limits_{\Delta x \to 0} \dfrac{\Delta y}{\Delta x}$. The notation, $\dfrac{dy}{dx}$, is called **derivative notation** and is read "the derivative of y with respect to x."

$f'(x) = \dfrac{dy}{dx} = \lim\limits_{\Delta x \to 0} \dfrac{\Delta y}{\Delta x}$

Example

3 If $y = 2x^2 + 1$, find $\dfrac{dy}{dx}$ at $x = 2$.

$$\frac{\Delta y}{\Delta x} = \frac{f(x + \Delta x) - f(x)}{\Delta x}$$

First, find $\dfrac{\Delta y}{\Delta x}$.

$$= \frac{[2(x + \Delta x)^2 + 1] - [2(x)^2 + 1]}{\Delta x}$$

$$= \frac{2(x^2 + 2x\,\Delta x + \Delta x^2) + 1 - 2x^2 - 1}{\Delta x}$$

$$= \frac{4x\Delta x + 2\Delta x^2}{\Delta x}$$

$$= 4x + 2\Delta x$$

$$\frac{dy}{dx} = \lim_{\Delta x \to 0} \frac{\Delta y}{\Delta x}$$

Now, find $\dfrac{dy}{dx}$.

$$= \lim_{\Delta x \to 0} (4x + 2\Delta x)$$

$$= 4x$$

Thus, $\dfrac{dy}{dx}$ at $x = 2$ is 8. *The slope of the tangent to $y = 2x^2 + 1$ at $x = 2$ is 8.*

Exploratory Exercises

Find the difference quotient of each function and simplify.

1. $f(x) = x$
2. $f(x) = 3x + 2$
3. $f(x) = -2x - 4$
4. $f(x) = -x$
5. $f(x) = 2x^2$
6. $f(x) = -2x^2$
7. $f(x) = x^3$
8. $f(x) = 2x^3$
9. $f(x) = 5x - 9$
10. $f(x) = 4x^2$
11. $f(x) = x^2 + 1$
12. $f(x) = x^2 + x$

Written Exercises

Solve each problem.

1-12. Find the derivative of each function in problems **1-12** of the exploratory exercises.

Find the slope and the equation of the tangent to each of the following at the given point.

13. $y = x^2$ at $(0, 0)$

14. $y = 2x^2$ at $(3, 18)$

15. $y = x^2 + 2x + 1$ at $(-2, 1)$

16. $y = x^3$ at $(-1, -1)$

17. $y = 3x^2 + 5$ at $(1, 8)$

18. $y = x^3 + x^2 + x + 1$ at $(-2, -5)$

19. $y = \dfrac{1}{x}$ at $\left(3, \dfrac{1}{3}\right)$

20. $y = \dfrac{1}{x - 3}$ at $(4, 1)$

21. $y = \dfrac{x}{x - 1}$ at $(2, 2)$

22. $y = \dfrac{1}{x^2}$ at $\left(-2, \dfrac{1}{4}\right)$

23-32. Find the point(s) on each curve in problems **13-22** where the slope of the tangent to the curve is 2. If no such point exists, write *none*.

For the Scholar

A positive integer $n \leq 120$ is chosen in such a way that if $n \leq 80$, then the probability of choosing n is p, and if $n > 80$, then the probability of choosing n is $2p$. What is the probability that a perfect square is chosen?

15-6   Differentiation Techniques

The process of finding a derivative by setting up a difference quotient and then finding its limit can become rather involved. To shorten this process, formulas can be used to find derivatives of functions.

Consider the function $f(x) = c$, where c is a constant.

$$f'(x) = \lim_{h \to 0} \frac{f(x + h) - f(x)}{h}$$

$$= \lim_{h \to 0} \frac{c - c}{h} \text{ or } 0$$

Thus, the derivative of a constant function, $f(x) = c$, is zero. For example, if $f(x) = 5$, then $f'(x) = 0$.

One of the most important differentiation formulas is the power formula.

If $f(x) = cx^n$ and n is a real number and c is a constant, then $f'(x) = cnx^{n-1}$.	*Power Formula*

Examples

1 Find $f'(x)$ if $f(x) = x^2$.

Use the power formula.

$f(x) = x^2$
$f'(x) = 2x^{2-1}$ or $2x$

2 Find $f'(x)$ if $f(x) = 5x^8$.

$f(x) = 5x^8$
$f'(x) = 5 \cdot 8x^{8-1}$
$\qquad = 40x^7$

The notation $\dfrac{dy}{dx}$ is used in the statement of the following theorems. This notation can be used with other functions of x. For example, $\dfrac{du}{dx}$ is the derivative of the function u with respect to x.

The derivative of y with respect to x is $\dfrac{dy}{dx}$.

If $u = f(x)$ and $v = g(x)$ are differentiable functions of x, then $\dfrac{d(u + v)}{dx} = \dfrac{du}{dx} + \dfrac{dv}{dx}$.	*Theorem 11*

Example

3 Find the derivative of $x^3 + (x^2 + 2)$.

Use $\dfrac{d(u + v)}{dx} = \dfrac{du}{dx} + \dfrac{dv}{dx}$.

$\dfrac{d[x^3 + (x^2 + 2)]}{dx} = \dfrac{d(x^3)}{dx} + \dfrac{d(x^2 + 2)}{dx}$ $\quad u = x^3$ and $v = x^2 + 2$

$\qquad\qquad\qquad = (3x^2) + (2x + 0)$
$\qquad\qquad\qquad = 3x^2 + 2x$

If $u = f(x)$ is a differentiable function of x and c is a constant, then $\dfrac{d(cu)}{dx} = c\dfrac{du}{dx}$.	*Theorem 12*

Example

4 Find the derivative of $3(x^2 + 2x + 1)$.

Use $\dfrac{d(cu)}{dx} = c\dfrac{du}{dx}$.

$\dfrac{d[3(x^2 + 2x + 1)]}{dx} = 3\dfrac{d(x^2 + 2x + 1)}{dx}$ $\quad c = 3$ and $u = x^2 + 2x + 1$

$\qquad\qquad\qquad\qquad = 3(2x + 2)$
$\qquad\qquad\qquad\qquad = 6x + 6$

If $u = f(x)$ and $v = g(x)$ are differentiable functions of x, then $\dfrac{d(uv)}{dx} = u\dfrac{dv}{dx} + v\dfrac{du}{dx}$.	**Theorem 13**

Example

5 Find the derivative of $(x^2 + 2x)(x^3)$.

Use $\dfrac{d(uv)}{dx} = u\dfrac{dv}{dx} + v\dfrac{du}{dx}$.

$$\frac{d[(x^2 + 2x)(x^3)]}{dx} = (x^2 + 2x)(3x^2) + (x^3)(2x + 2) \qquad u = x^2 + 2x$$
$$v = x^3$$
$$= 3x^4 + 6x^3 + 2x^4 + 2x^3$$
$$= 5x^4 + 8x^3$$

If $u = f(x)$ is a differentiable function of x and n is a nonzero rational number, then $\dfrac{d(u^n)}{dx} = nu^{n-1}\dfrac{du}{dx}$.	**Theorem 14**

Examples

6 Find the derivative of $\sqrt{x^2 - 1}$.

Use $\dfrac{d(u^n)}{dx} = nu^{n-1}\dfrac{du}{dx}$.

$$\frac{d(\sqrt{x^2 - 1})}{dx} = \frac{1}{2}(x^2 - 1)^{-\frac{1}{2}}(2x) \qquad u = x^2 - 1;\ n = \tfrac{1}{2};\ \sqrt{x^2 - 1} = (x^2 - 1)^{\frac{1}{2}}$$

$$= \frac{2x}{2\sqrt{x^2 - 1}} \quad \textit{Remember not to forget } \tfrac{du}{dx}, \textit{ which}$$
$$= \frac{x}{\sqrt{x^2 - 1}} \qquad \textit{in this example is } 2x.$$

7 Find the derivative of $x^2(x^2 + 1)^{-3}$.

Use $\dfrac{d(uv)}{dx} = u\dfrac{dv}{dx} + v\dfrac{du}{dx}$ and $\dfrac{d(u^n)}{dx} = nu^{n-1}\dfrac{du}{dy}$.

$u = x^2,\ \dfrac{du}{dx} = 2x$

$v = (x^2 + 1)^{-3},\ \dfrac{dv}{dx} = -3(x^2 + 1)^{-4}(2x)$

$$\frac{d[x^2(x^2 + 1)^{-3}]}{dx} = x^2(-3)(x^2 + 1)^{-4}(2x) + (x^2 + 1)^{-3}(2x)$$
$$= -6x^3(x^2 + 1)^{-4} + 2x(x^2 + 1)^{-3}$$
$$= \frac{-6x^3}{(x^2 + 1)^4} + \frac{2x}{(x^2 + 1)^3}$$
$$= \frac{-6x^3 + 2x(x^2 + 1)}{(x^2 + 1)^4}$$
$$= \frac{-4x^3 + 2x}{(x^2 + 1)^4}$$
$$= -2x(2x^2 - 1)(x^2 + 1)^{-4}$$

Mastery of this theorem will be very helpful.

Examples

8 Find the derivative of $\dfrac{x^2 - 2x + 1}{x + 1}$.

Use $\dfrac{d\left(\frac{u}{v}\right)}{dx} = \dfrac{v\frac{du}{dx} - u\frac{dv}{dx}}{v^2}$.

$u = x^2 - 2x + 1, \dfrac{du}{dx} = 2x - 2$

$v = x + 1, \dfrac{dv}{dx} = 1$

$$\dfrac{d\left(\frac{x^2 - 2x + 1}{x + 1}\right)}{dx} = \dfrac{(x + 1)(2x - 2) - (x^2 - 2x + 1)(1)}{(x + 1)^2}$$

$$= \dfrac{(2x^2 - 2) - (x^2 - 2x + 1)}{x^2 + 2x + 1}$$

$$= \dfrac{x^2 + 2x - 3}{x^2 + 2x + 1}$$

9 Find the derivative of $\dfrac{(x + 1)^2}{(x - 1)^2}$.

Use Theorem 15 and Theorem 14.

$u = (x + 1)^2, \dfrac{du}{dx} = 2(x + 1)(1)$

$v = (x - 1)^2, \dfrac{dv}{dx} = 2(x - 1)(1)$

$$\dfrac{d\frac{(x + 1)^2}{(x - 1)^2}}{dx} = (x - 1)^2 2(x + 1) - (x + 1)^2(2)(x - 1)$$

$$= \dfrac{(x^2 - 2x + 1)(2x + 2) - (x^2 + 2x + 1)(2x - 2)}{(x - 1)^4}$$

$$= \dfrac{-4(x^2 - 1)}{(x - 1)^4} \text{ or } \dfrac{-4(x + 1)}{(x - 1)^3}$$

Exploratory Exercises

Name the theorem(s) that would be used to find the derivative of each function.

1. $f(x) = 8x^4 - 10x^3$

2. $f(x) = x^{\frac{1}{2}}$

3. $f(x) = \sqrt[3]{x}$

4. $f(x) = x^2(x^2 - 3)$

5. $f(x) = (x^3 - 2x)(3x^2)$

6. $f(x) = (x^2 + 4)^3$

7. $f(x) = (x^3 - 2x + 1)^4$

8. $f(x) = \sqrt{x^2 + 2x - 1}$

9. $f(x) = (x^2 - 4)^{-\frac{1}{2}}$

10. $f(x) = \dfrac{x + 1}{x^2 - 4}$

11. $f(x) = \left(\dfrac{x + 1}{x - 1}\right)^2$

12. $f(x) = \dfrac{1}{\sqrt{x + 1}}$

13. $f(x) = x^5 + 3x^3 - 4x^2 + 3$

14. $f(x) = \dfrac{1}{4}x^4 - \dfrac{1}{3}x^3 + \dfrac{1}{2}x^2 - x$

Written Exercises

Solve each problem.

1-14. Find the derivative of each function in problems **1-14** of the exploratory exercises.

Find $f'(2)$ for each of the following functions.

15. $f(x) = \dfrac{x^2}{2}$ **16.** $f(x) = 6x$ **17.** $f(x) = x^2 + 2x + 5$

18. $f(x) = (x + 3)(2x - 1)$ **19.** $f(x) = (x^2 - 3x)^2$ **20.** $f(x) = 1 + 2x - 3x^2 + 4x^3$

Find the derivative of each function.

21. $f(x) = x^2(x + 1)^{-1}$ **22.** $f(x) = (x + x^{-1})^2$ **23.** $f(x) = (x^2 - x)^{-2}$

24. $f(x) = \dfrac{3x}{1 + x^3}$ **25.** $f(x) = x\sqrt{1 - x^3}$ **26.** $f(x) = 2x^3 + \dfrac{2}{x^3}$

27. $f(x) = x^4(x - 5)^6$ **28.** $f(x) = \sqrt{2x} - \sqrt{2}x$ **29.** $f(x) = \dfrac{x - 1}{x + 1}$

For the Scholar

In the figure, $\overline{AB}$ and $\overline{CD}$ are externally tangent to both circles at points A, B, C, and D. $\overline{EF}$ is internally tangent to both circles at E and F. Extend $\overline{EF}$ to intersect the external tangents at points G and H. If $DH = 16$ and $HC = 4$, find GH.

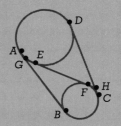

15-7   Applying the Derivative

The derivative of a function can be used in sketching the graph of the function in a certain interval. For example, the sign of the derivative indicates whether the function is increasing or decreasing at a point.

Remember that the derivative of the function at a point is the slope of the tangent line at that point.

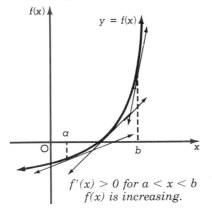

$f'(x) > 0$ for $a < x < b$
$f(x)$ is increasing.

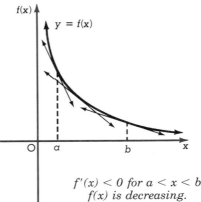

$f'(x) < 0$ for $a < x < b$
$f(x)$ is decreasing.

If $f'(x) > 0$ for all values of x in the interval, $a < x < b$, then the function is increasing in the interval. If $f'(x) < 0$ for all values of x in the interval, $a < x < b$, then the function is decreasing in the interval.	*Increasing and Decreasing Functions*

Example

1 Find the values of x for which the function $f(x) = x^2 + 6x - 6$ is increasing.

$f(x) = x^2 + 6x - 6$
$f'(x) = 2x + 6$

The function $f(x)$ is increasing when $f'(x) > 0$.

$2x + 6 > 0$
$2x > -6$
$x > -3$

Thus, the function is increasing when $x > -3$.

If the derivative of a function at a certain point is zero, the point is a **critical point.** At these points the function is neither increasing nor decreasing and is said to have **stationary values.** For example, the function $f(x) = 5x^3 - 3x^5$ shown on the graph has stationary values at $x = -1$, 0, and 1. Since $f'(x)$ changes sign from positive through zero to negative at $x = 1$, $f(1)$ or 2 is a **maximum value.** Since $f'(x)$ changes from negative through zero to positive at $x = -1$, $f(-1)$ or -2 is a **minimum value.** However, notice that at $x = 0$, $f'(x)$ does not change sign through zero and $f'(x) = 0$ at $x = 0$. The point $(0, f(0))$ or $(0, 0)$ is a **point of inflection** on the graph of $f(x) = 5x^3 - 3x^5$.

Suppose $f'(a) = 0$ and $f'(x)$ exists at every point near a. Then at $x = a$ there are four possibilities for the graph of f.

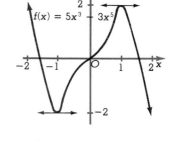

$f'(x) = 15x^2 - 15x^4$ or
$15x^2(1 - x^2)$

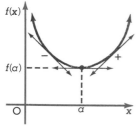

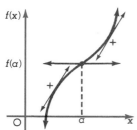

$f(a)$ is a
minimum value

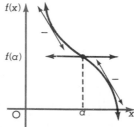

$f(a)$ is a
maximum value

Points of inflection occur whenever a function has a change in concavity. That is, it goes from concave up to concave down or vice versa.

Point $(a, f(a))$ is a point of inflection.

Example

2 **Find the stationary values of $f(x) = x^3(4 - x)$. Determine whether each is a maximum, minimum, or a point of inflection.**

$f(x) = x^3(4 - x)$
$\qquad = 4x^3 - x^4$
$f'(x) = 12x^2 - 4x^3$
$\qquad = 4x^2(3 - x)$

To find the stationary values, let $f'(x) = 0$.

$4x^2(3 - x) = 0$
$\qquad\qquad x = 0 \text{ or } x = 3$

Thus, f has stationary values at $x = 0$ and at $x = 3$.

Determine values of $f'(x)$ near 0.

$f'(-0.1) = 4(-0.1)^2(3 + 0.1)$ or 0.124 *$f(x)$ is increasing*
$\ f'(0.1) = 4(0.1)^2(3 - 0.1)$ or 0.116 *$f(x)$ is increasing*

Since $f'(x)$ does not change sign through zero at $x = 0$, the point $(0, f(0))$ or $(0, 0)$ is a point of inflection.

Determine values of x near 3.

$f'(2.9) = 4(2.9)^2(3 - 2.9)$ or 3.364 *$f(x)$ is increasing*
$f'(3.1) = 4(3.1)^2(3 - 3.1)$ or -3.844 *$f(x)$ is decreasing*

Since $f'(x)$ changes sign from positive through zero to negative at $x = 3$, $f(3)$ is a maximum value.

Maximum or minimum values can be **relative maximum values** or **relative minimum values.** These are local properties of a function. They refer only to the behavior of a function in the neighborhood of a critical point. The terms **absolute maximum** and **absolute minimum** refer to the greatest or least value assumed by a function throughout its domain of definition.

Since the derivative of a polynomial function, $f(x)$, also is a polynomial function, $f'(x)$, the derivative of $f'(x)$ can be found. It is called the **second derivative** of $f(x)$ and is written $f''(x)$. The value of the second derivative indicates whether the derivative, $f'(x)$, is increasing or decreasing at a point. A second derivative test can be used to find relative maximum and relative minimum values.

If $f''(x)$ changes sign at a given point, then that point is a point of inflection.

If $f'(x) = 0$ at x, then $f(x)$ is one of the following stationary values.

1. **If $f''(x) > 0$, then $f(x)$ is a relative minimum.**
2. **If $f''(x) < 0$, then $f(x)$ is a relative maximum.**
3. **If $f''(x) = 0$ or does not exist, then the test fails.**

Second Derivative Test

Example

3 Find the stationary values of $f(x) = x^3 - 3x$. Determine whether each is a relative maximum, relative minimum, or neither. Then, graph the function.

$f(x) = x^3 - 3x$
$f'(x) = 3x^2 - 3$
$3x^2 - 3 = 0$ *Let $f'(x) = 0$ to find the stationary values.*
$3(x + 1)(x - 1) = 0$
$x = -1$ or $x = 1$

The stationary values occur at $x = \pm 1$.
Find $f''(x)$ and use the second derivative test.

$f''(x) = 6x$
$f''(-1) = -6$ and $f''(1) = 6$

Since $f''(-1) < 0$, $f(x)$ has a relative maximum at $x = -1$.
Since $f''(1) > 0$, $f(x)$ has a relative minimum at $x = 1$.

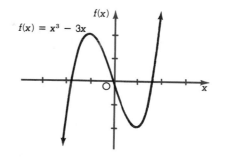

Exploratory Exercises

Find $f'(x)$ for each of the following functions.

1. $f(x) = x^2 + 6x - 27$
2. $f(x) = -x^2 - 8x - 15$
3. $f(x) = x^2 - 2x$
4. $f(x) = x^3$
5. $f(x) = x^3 - 3x$
6. $f(x) = 2x^3 - 9x^2 + 12x$
7. $f(x) = x^3(4 - x)$
8. $f(x) = x^3 - 12x + 3$
9. $f(x) = 2x^4 - 2x^2$
10. $f(x) = x(x - 2)^2$

11-20. Find $f''(x)$ for each function in problems **1-10**.

Written Exercises

Find the values of x for which each of the following functions is increasing.

1. $f(x) = x^2$
2. $f(x) = x^2 - 2x$
3. $f(x) = x^2 + 6x - 6$
4. $f(x) = x^3 - 3x$
5. $f(x) = 2x^3 - 9x^2 + 12x$
6. $f(x) = x(x - 2)^2$
7. $f(x) = \frac{1}{4}x^4 - \frac{9}{2}x^2$
8. $f(x) = x^3(4 - x)$
9. $f(x) = x + \frac{1}{x}$

10-18. Find the values of x for which each function in problems **1-9** is decreasing.

Find the stationary values of each of the following functions. State whether each is a maximum, minimum, or neither. Then, graph the function.

19. $f(x) = x - x^2$
20. $f(x) = x^3$
21. $f(x) = 2x^3 - 9x^2 + 12x$
22. $f(x) = \frac{1}{2}x^4 - \frac{9}{2}x^2$
23. $f(x) = x^3(4 - x)$
24. $f(x) = 2x^4 - 2x^2$

For the Scholar

Assume $a_1, a_2, a_3, \cdots$ and $b_1, b_2, b_3, \cdots$ are arithmetic sequences such that $a_1 = 30$, $b_1 = 70$, and $a_{50} + b_{50} = 100$. Find the sum of the first fifty terms of the sequence $a_1 + b_1, a_2 + b_2, a_3 + b_3, \cdots$.

Using Mathematics

Differentiation techniques may be used to solve problems in which maximum or minimum solutions are necessary. Consider the following example.

Example Suppose a rectangular field along a straight river is to be fenced. There are 300 m of fencing available. What is the greatest area that can be enclosed?

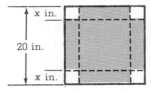

Let the width of the field be x meters. Then, the length is $300 - 2x$ meters. The area in square meters is $A = x(300 - 2x)$ or $300x - 2x^2$. This defines a function f for which $f(x) = 300x - 2x^2$. Since $x \geq 0$ and $300 - 2x \geq 0$, the maximum value must be in the interval $0 \leq x \leq 150$.

$$f(x) = 300x - 2x^2$$
$$f'(x) = 300 - 4x$$

Let $f'(x) = 0$ to find relative minima or maxima.

$$300 - 4x = 0$$
$$x = 75$$

Find the second derivative of f to determine if 75 is a minimum or maximum.

$$f''(x) = -4$$

Since $f''(x) < 0$, $f(0) = 0$, and $f(150) = 0$, $x = 75$ gives a maximum stationary value $f(75) = 11{,}250$. Thus, the required maximum area is 11,250 sq m. This occurs when the width is 75 m and the length is 150 m.

Exercises Solve each of the following.

1. An area of farmland along a stone wall is to be fenced. There are 500 m of fencing available. What is the maximum rectangular area that can be fenced?

2. The perimeter of a field must be 600 m. Find the dimensions of the maximum rectangular area of the field.

3. The sum of two positive integers is 36. Find the maximum value of the product of the integers and also the integers.

4. The sum of two positive integers is 120. Find the maximum value of the product of one integer and the square of the other and also the integers.

5. An open pan is to be made from a 20 inch square piece of metal by cutting four equal square pieces from each corner and turning up the sides. What size pieces should be cut out so that the pan will have maximum volume?

15-8 Area Under a Curve

Consider the area between a function $f(x)$ and the x-axis for an interval from $x = a$ to $x = b$. Suppose that the interval is separated into n subintervals of equal width and vertical lines are drawn at each interval to form rectangles.

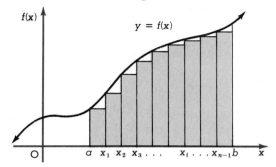

The area of the rectangles under the curve and above the x-axis is given by A_u.

The area of the first rectangle is $f(a)(x_1 - a)$.

The area of the second rectangle is $f(x_1)(x_2 - x_1)$.

The area of the third rectangle is $f(x_2)(x_3 - x_2)$.

$\vdots$

The area of the $(i + 1)$th rectangle is $f(x_i)(x_{i+1} - x_i)$.

$\vdots$

The area of the nth rectangle is $f(x_{n-1})(b - x_{n-1})$.
The total area, A_u, is the sum of the areas of these rectangles.

$$A_u = f(a)(x_1 - a) + f(x_1)(x_2 - x_1) + f(x_2)(x_3 - x_2) +$$
$$\cdots + f(x_i)(x_{i+1} - x_i) + \cdots + f(x_{n-1})(b - x_{n-1})$$

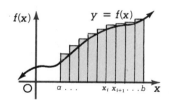

The area of the rectangles above the curve and the x-axis is given by A_a. It is found in a similar manner as A_u.

$$A_a = f(x_1)(x_1 - a) + f(x_2)(x_2 - x_1) + f(x_3)(x_3 - x_2) +$$
$$\cdots + f(x_i + 1)(x_{i+1} - x_i) + \cdots + f(b)(b - x_{n-1})$$

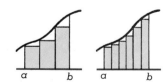

Thus, the actual area, A, is between A_u and A_a. Therefore, $A_u \leq A \leq A_a$. As the number of subintervals, n, is increased, the areas A_u and A_a approach the actual area A. So, A is the limit of A_u as n increases without limit. The area A_u may be written using summation notation.

$$A_u = \sum_{i=1}^{n} f(x_i)(x_{i+1} - x_i)$$

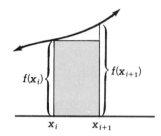

Example

1   **Find the area of the region between $y = x^3$ and the x-axis from $x = 0$ to $x = 1$.**

Form n equal intervals on the x-axis such that

$$0 < \frac{1}{n} < \frac{2}{n} < \frac{3}{n} < \cdots < \frac{i}{n} < \cdots < \frac{n-1}{n} < 1.$$

The area of each rectangle can be represented by

$$f\left(\frac{i}{n}\right)(x_{i+1} - x_i) \text{ or } \left(\frac{i}{n}\right)^3\left(\frac{1}{n}\right).$$

Why is $(x_{i+1} - x_i) = \frac{1}{n}$?

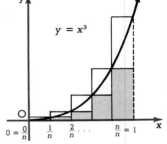

Use the definition of the area under a curve, $A = \lim_{n \to \infty} \sum_{i=1}^{n} f(x_i)(x_{i+1} - x_i)$.

$$A = \lim_{n \to \infty} \sum_{i=1}^{n} \left(\frac{i}{n}\right)^3\left(\frac{1}{n}\right)$$

$$= \lim_{n \to \infty} \frac{1}{n^4}(1^3 + 2^3 + \cdots + n^3)$$

$$= \lim_{n \to \infty} \frac{1}{n^4} \cdot \left(\frac{n^2(n+1)^2}{4}\right) \quad \text{Recall that } 1^3 + 2^3 + \cdots + n^3 = \frac{n^2(n+1)^2}{4}.$$

$$= \lim_{n \to \infty} \frac{(n+1)^2}{4n^2}$$

$$= \lim_{n \to \infty} \frac{1}{4}\left(\frac{n^2 + 2n + 1}{n^2}\right)$$

$$= \lim_{n \to \infty} \frac{1}{4}\left(1 + \frac{2}{n} + \frac{1}{n^2}\right)$$

$$= \frac{1}{4}$$

Thus, the area is $\frac{1}{4}$ sq units.

Sometimes it is necessary to find the area under a curve from $x = a$ to $x = b$. This can be determined by finding the area from $x = 0$ to $x = b$ and then subtracting the area from $x = 0$ to $x = a$.

Example

2 **Find the area of the region between $y = x^2$ and the x-axis from $x = 1$ to $x = 4$.**

First find the area under the curve from $x = 0$ to $x = 4$. Form n equal intervals on the x-axis such that

$$0 < \frac{4 \cdot 1}{n} < \frac{4 \cdot 2}{n} < \frac{4 \cdot 3}{n} < \cdots < \frac{4 \cdot i}{n} <$$
$$\cdots < \frac{4(n - 1)}{n} < \frac{4n}{n} \text{ or } 4.$$

The area of each rectangle can be represented as follows.

$$f\left(\frac{4 \cdot i}{n}\right)(x_{i+1} - x_i) \text{ or } \left(\frac{4i}{n}\right)^2\left(\frac{4}{n}\right)$$

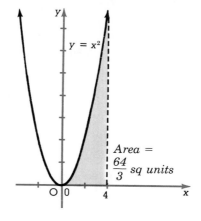

Area =
$\frac{64}{3}$ *sq units*

$$A = \lim_{n \to \infty} \sum_{i=1}^{n} \left(\frac{4i}{n}\right)^2\left(\frac{4}{n}\right)$$

$$= \lim_{n \to \infty} \frac{64}{n^3}(1^2 + 2^2 + 3^2 + \cdots + n^2)$$

$$= \lim_{n \to \infty} \frac{64}{n^3}\left(\frac{n(n + 1)(2n + 1)}{6}\right) \quad \textit{Recall that } 1^2 + 2^2 + 3^2 + \cdots + n^2 = \frac{n(n + 1)(2n + 1)}{6}.$$

$$= \lim_{n \to \infty} \frac{64}{6}\left(\frac{2n^3 + 3n^2 + n}{n^3}\right)$$

$$= \lim_{n \to \infty} \frac{64}{6}\left(2 + \frac{3}{n} + \frac{1}{n^2}\right)$$

$$= \frac{64}{6} \cdot 2 \text{ or } \frac{64}{3}$$

Then, find the area under the curve from $x = 0$ to $x = 1$.

$$A = \lim_{n \to \infty} \sum_{i=1}^{n} \left(\frac{i}{n}\right)^2\left(\frac{1}{n}\right)$$

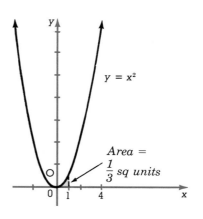

Area =
$\frac{1}{3}$ *sq units*

$$= \lim_{n \to \infty} \frac{1}{n^3}(1^2 + 2^2 + 3^2 + \cdots + n^2)$$

$$= \lim_{n \to \infty} \frac{1}{n^3}\left(\frac{n(n + 1)(2n + 1)}{6}\right)$$

$$= \lim_{n \to \infty} \frac{1}{6}\left(2 + \frac{3}{n} + \frac{1}{n^2}\right)$$

$$= \frac{1}{6} \cdot 2 \text{ or } \frac{1}{3}$$

Thus, the area of the region between $y = x^2$ and the x-axis from $x = 1$ to $x = 4$ is $\frac{64}{3} - \frac{1}{3}$ or 21 sq units.

The following list of formulas are the sums of series that may be needed to solve problems in this section.

Mathematical induction can be used to prove these formulas as was done in Chapter 8.

$$1 + 2 + 3 + \cdots + n = \frac{n(n + 1)}{2}$$

$$1^2 + 2^2 + 3^2 + \cdots + n^2 = \frac{n(n + 1)(2n + 1)}{6}$$

$$1^3 + 2^3 + 3^3 + \cdots + n^3 = \frac{n^2(n + 1)^2}{4}$$

$$1^4 + 2^4 + 3^4 + \cdots + n^4 = \frac{6n^5 + 15n^4 + 10n^3 - n}{30}$$

$$1^5 + 2^5 + 3^5 + \cdots + n^5 = \frac{2n^6 + 6n^5 + 5n^4 - n^2}{12}$$

Exploratory Exercises

Write a limit to find the area between each curve and the x-axis for the given interval. Do *not* find the area.

1. $y = x^2$ from $x = 0$ to $x = 1$ **2.** $y = x$ from $x = 0$ to $x = 1$

3. $y = x^5$ from $x = 0$ to $x = 1$ **4.** $y = x^2$ from $x = 0$ to $x = a, a > 0$

5. $y = x^3$ from $x = 0$ to $x = a, a > 0$ **6.** $y = x^2$ from $x = a$ to $x = b, 0 < a < b$

7. $y = x$ from $x = 2$ to $x = 5$ **8.** $y = x^4$ from $x = 4$ to $x = 7$

9-12. Sketch a graph of the indicated regions in problems **1-4.**

Written Exercises

Find the area between each curve and the x-axis for the given interval.

1. $y = x^2$ from $x = 0$ to $x = 1$ **2.** $y = x$ from $x = 0$ to $x = 1$

3. $y = x^5$ from $x = 0$ to $x = 1$ **4.** $y = x^2$ from $x = 0$ to $x = a, a > 0$

5. $y = x^3$ from $x = 0$ to $x = a, a > 0$ **6.** $y = x^2$ from $x = a$ to $x = b, 0 < a < b$

7. $y = x$ from $x = 2$ to $x = 5$ **8.** $y = x^4$ from $x = 4$ to $x = 7$

9. $y = x^2$ from $x = -3$ to $x = 2$ **10.** $y = |x|$ from $x = -2$ to $x = 4$

Find the area for each shaded region.

11.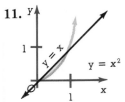

12.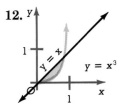

Write a formula for the areas between each curve and the x-axis for the given interval. Assume that $0 < a < b$.

13. $y = x$ from $x = a$ to $x = b$ **14.** $y = x^2$ from $x = a$ to $x = b$

For the Scholar

If $f(g(x)) = \dfrac{x^4 + x^2}{1 + x^2}$ when $x^2 \neq -1$ and $g(x) = 1 - x^2$, find $f\left(\frac{1}{2}\right)$.

15-9　Integration

The formal notation for the area, A, under a curve from $x = a$ to $x = b$ is as follows.

$$A = \int_a^b f(x)\,dx$$

It is read "the integral of f, with respect to x, from a to b." By definition $\int_a^b f(x)\,dx$ is equal to $\lim\limits_{n \to \infty} \sum\limits_{i=1}^{n} f(x_i)(x_{i+1} - x_i)$.

To understand the concept of an integral, consider the function $f(x)$ in the following equation.

$$\frac{dy}{dx} = f(x) \text{ with } a < x < b$$

Is it possible to find a function $y = F(x)$ for which $f(x)$ is the derivative? This is the "anti" or "inverse" problem of finding the derivative. Thus, the function $F(x)$ is called an **antiderivative** of $f(x)$ if and only if $F'(x) = f(x)$.

$F(x)$ and $f(x)$ represent different functions.

Is it possible to find an antiderivative of $f(x)$, represented by $F(x)$, if $f(x) = 3x^2$? Several possibilities are $y = x^3 + 3$, $y = x^3 + \pi$, and $y = x^3 - 5$. These are all valid answers and can be summarized as $y = x^3 + C$ where C is a constant.

The following theorem gives the connection between the antiderivative and the integral.

The function $F(x)$ is an integral of $f(x)$ with respect to x if and only if $F(x)$ is an antiderivative of $f(x)$. That is,

$$F(x) = \int f(x)\,dx \text{ if and only if } F'(x) = f(x).$$

Definition of an Integral

Thus, in the previous example, $\int 3x^2\,dx = x^3 + C$ since $F'(x^3 + C) = 3x^2$.

Examples

1 Find $\int 1\,dx$.

Since $F'(x) = 1$ when $F(x) = x + C$, then $\int 1\,dx = x + C$.

2 Find $\int x^2\,dx$.

Since $F'(x) = x^2$ when $F(x) = \dfrac{x^3}{3} + C$, then $\int x^2\,dx = \dfrac{x^3}{3} + C$.

Several formulas that are useful in finding integrals are listed below.

1. If h is a constant, $\int h\,dx = hx + C.$

2. If $n \neq -1$, $\int u^n du = \dfrac{u^{n+1}}{n+1} + C$ where u is a differentiable function.

Note by definition,
$$\int x^{-1}\,dx = \ln x + c.$$

3. The integral of a sum of functions is the sum of the integrals of the functions.
$$\int (f(x) + g(x))\,dx = \int f(x)\,dx + \int g(x)\,dx$$

4. The integral of the product of a constant, a, and a function, $f(x)$, is the product of the constant and the integral of the function.
$$\int a f(x)\,dx = a \int f(x)\,dx$$

Examples

3 **Find $\int (2x + 5)\,dx.$**

$$\int (2x + 5)\,dx = \int 2x\,dx + \int 5\,dx \qquad \text{Use the third formula.}$$
$$= 2\int x\,dx + \int 5\,dx \qquad \text{Use the fourth formula.}$$
$$= 2\left(\frac{x^2}{2}\right) + C_1 + 5x + C_2 \qquad \begin{array}{l}\text{Use the second and first}\\ \text{formulas, respectively.}\end{array}$$
$$= x^2 + 5x + C \qquad \text{Let } C = C_1 + C_2.$$

Thus, $\int (2x + 5)\,dx = x^2 + 5x + C.$

4 **Find $\int (3x^2 + 2x + 4)\,dx.$**

$$\int (3x^2 + 2x + 4)\,dx = \int 3x^2 dx + \int 2x\,dx + \int 4\,dx$$
$$= 3\int x^2 dx + 2\int x\,dx + \int 4\,dx$$
$$= 3\left(\frac{x^3}{3} + C_1\right) + 2\left(\frac{x^2}{2} + C_2\right) + (4x + C_3)$$
$$= x^3 + x^2 + 4x + C$$

Thus, $\int (3x^2 + 2x + 4)\,dx = x^3 + x^2 + 4x + C.$

Sometimes it is possible to rewrite the integral by using u and $\dfrac{du}{dv}$.
$$\int f(x)\,dx = \int u\frac{du}{dx} \cdot dx = \int u\,du$$

Example

5 Find $\int (x^2 + 1)2x\ dx$.

Use the formula $\int u^n du = \dfrac{u^{n+1}}{n+1} + C$.

If $u = x^2 + 1$, then $\dfrac{du}{dx} = \dfrac{d(x^2 + 1)}{dx} = 2x$.

$$\int (x^2 + 1)2x\ dx = \int u \cdot \dfrac{du}{dx} \cdot dx \qquad \text{Substitute.}$$

$$= \int u\,du \qquad\qquad \text{Simplify.}$$

$$= \dfrac{u^2}{2} + C \qquad\qquad \text{Use the second formula.}$$

$$= \dfrac{(x^2 + 1)^2}{2} + C \qquad \text{Substitute.}$$

Thus, $\int (x^2 + 1)2x\ dx = \dfrac{(x^2 + 1)^2}{2} + C$.

Exploratory Exercises

Find two functions, $F(x)$ and $G(x)$, such that $F'(x) = f(x)$ and $G'(x) = f(x)$ for each function.

1. $f(x) = 2x$

2. $f(x) = 3x^2$

3. $f(x) = 2x + 1$

4. $f(x) = 2x - 3$

5. $f(x) = 4x^3$

6. $f(x) = 8x^7 + 2x$

Written Exercises

Find each integral.

1. $\int 2x\ dx$

2. $\int 3x^2 dx$

3. $\int (8x^7 + 2x)dx$

4. $\int (\pi x + \sqrt{x})dx$

5. $\int (x + 5)^{20}dx$

6. $\int \sqrt{1 + x}\ dx$

7. $\int (-2x + 3)dx$

8. $\int \dfrac{-2x}{\sqrt{1 - x^2}}dx$

9. $\int \dfrac{(x + 1)dx}{\sqrt[3]{x^2 + 2x + 2}}$

Find the antiderivative of each function.

10. $f(x) = 5x^3$

11. $f(x) = 4\sqrt[3]{x}$

12. $f(x) = \sqrt{2x}$

13. $f(x) = \dfrac{2}{x^3}$

14. $f(x) = \dfrac{4}{x^2}$

15. $f(x) = \dfrac{2}{\sqrt{x}}$

For the Scholar

If the area of $\triangle ABC$ is 80 sq units and the geometric mean between sides $\overline{AB}$ and $\overline{AC}$ is 16 units, find $\sin A$.

15-10 The Fundamental Theorem of Calculus

The derivative has been defined as the limit of the difference quotients.

$$f'(x) = \lim_{h \to 0} \frac{f(x + h) - f(x)}{h}$$

The integral has been defined as the limit of the sum of areas.

$$A = \lim_{n \to \infty} \sum_{i=1}^{n} f(x_i)(x_{i+1} - x_i) \text{ where } (x_{i+1} - x_i) \text{ approaches zero}$$

The **Fundamental Theorem of Calculus** formally states that these limiting processes are inverse operations.

If the function $f(x)$ is continuous and $F(x)$ is such that $F'(x) = f(x)$, **then** $\int_a^b f(x)dx = F(b) - F(a)$.	*Fundamental Theorem of Calculus*

The Fundamental Theorem of Calculus provides a way to evaluate the **definite integral** $\int_a^b f(x)dx$ if an antiderivative $F(x)$ can be found. A square bracket on the right side is used to abbreviate $F(b) - F(a)$. Thus, the principal statement of the theorem may be written as follows.

a and b are called the lower and upper limits or bounds of the integration.

$$\int_a^b f(x)dx = F(x)\Big]_a^b$$

Example

1 Evaluate $\int_1^2 (1 - 2x)^2 dx$.

$$\int_1^2 (1 - 2x)^2 dx = \int_1^2 (1 - 4x + 4x^2)dx$$

$$= x - 2x^2 + \frac{4}{3}x^3\Big]_1^2$$

$$= \left(2 - 2 \cdot 2^2 + \frac{4}{3} \cdot 2^3\right) - \left(1 - 2 \cdot 1^2 + \frac{4}{3} \cdot 1^3\right) \qquad F(x)\Big]_a^b = F(b) - F(a)$$

$$= 4\frac{1}{3}$$

Since $F(x)$ is any antiderivative of $f(x)$, the constant C is omitted when using the integration formulas to find a definite integral.

2 Evaluate $\int_1^4 \left(\sqrt{x} + \dfrac{1}{\sqrt{x}} \right) dx.$

$$\int_1^4 \left(\sqrt{x} + \dfrac{1}{\sqrt{x}} \right) dx = \int_1^4 \left(x^{\frac{1}{2}} + x^{-\frac{1}{2}} \right) dx$$

$$= \dfrac{x^{\frac{3}{2}}}{\frac{3}{2}} + \dfrac{x^{\frac{1}{2}}}{\frac{1}{2}} \Bigg]_1^4$$

$$= \left[\dfrac{(4)^{\frac{3}{2}}}{\frac{3}{2}} + \dfrac{(4)^{\frac{1}{2}}}{\frac{1}{2}} \right] - \left[\dfrac{(1)^{\frac{3}{2}}}{\frac{3}{2}} + \dfrac{(1)^{\frac{1}{2}}}{\frac{1}{2}} \right]$$

$$= \left(\dfrac{16}{3} + 4 \right) - \left(\dfrac{2}{3} + 2 \right) \text{ or } \dfrac{20}{3}$$

The definite integral will produce a negative value if $f(x) < 0$ in the interval from $x = a$ to $x = b$. It will produce a positive value if $f(x) > 0$ in the same interval. Therefore, if the integral is being used to find the area between a curve and the x-axis, the absolute value of the integral is used.

3 Find the area between the x-axis and the function $f(x) = x^2 - 9$ from $x = -3$ to $x = 3$.

$A = \left| \int_{-3}^{3} (x^2 - 9) dx \right|$ *The absolute value is used since area is being found.*

$f(x) = x^2 - 9$

$$= \left| \dfrac{x^3}{3} - 9x \Bigg]_{-3}^{3} \right|$$

$$= \left| \left[\dfrac{27}{3} - 9(3) \right] - \left[\dfrac{-27}{3} - 9(-3) \right] \right|$$

$$= |-36|$$

The area is 36 sq units.

When a function $f(x)$ is both positive and negative in the interval from $x = a$ to $x = b$, and the area is to be found, the limits of integration must be split at the zeros of the function.

Example

4 Find the total area between $f(x) = x^3 - x$ and the x-axis from $x = -1$ to $x = 1$.

The area is the sum of the areas of A_1 and A_2.

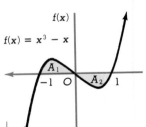

$$A_1 = \left| \int_{-1}^{0} (x^3 - x)\,dx \right|$$

$$= \left| \frac{x^4 - 2x^2}{4} \right]_{-1}^{0} \right|$$

$$= \left| \frac{(0)^4 - 2(0)^2}{4} - \frac{(-1)^4 - 2(-1)^2}{4} \right|$$

$$= \left| \frac{1}{4} \right|$$

$$A_2 = \left| \int_{0}^{1} (x^3 - x)\,dx \right|$$

$$= \left| \frac{x^4 - 2x^2}{4} \right]_{0}^{1} \right|$$

$$= \left| \frac{(1)^4 - 2(1)^2}{4} - \frac{(0)^4 - 2(0)^2}{4} \right|$$

$$= \left| -\frac{1}{4} \right|$$

$$A = A_1 + A_2$$

$$= \left| \frac{1}{4} \right| + \left| -\frac{1}{4} \right|$$

Thus, the area is $\frac{1}{2}$ sq units.

Exploratory Exercises

Use integration to find the area of each shaded region. Verify your answers by finding the area geometrically.

1.
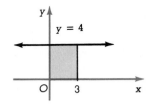

2.
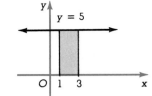

3.
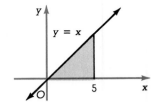

4.
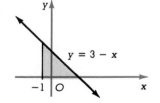

5.
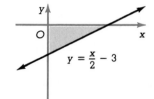

6.
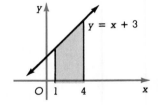

Written Exercises

Use integration to find the area of each shaded region.

1.

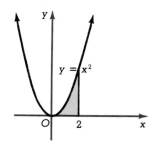

$y = x^2$

2.

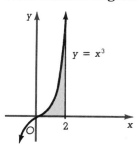

$y = x^3$

3.

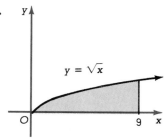

$y = \sqrt{x}$

4.

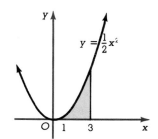

$y = \frac{1}{2}x^2$

5.

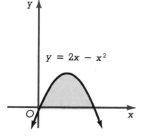

$y = 2x - x^2$

6.

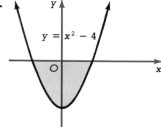

$y = x^2 - 4$

Graph each of the following functions. Then, find the area between the function and the x-axis for the given interval using integration.

7. $f(x) = 2x + 3$ for $x = 1$ to $x = 4$

8. $f(x) = -x$ for $x = 1$ to $x = 4$

9. $f(x) = x^2$ for $x = -2$ to $x = 2$

10. $f(x) = x^3$ for $x = -1$ to $x = 2$

11. $f(x) = -x^2$ for $x = 0$ to $x = 5$

12. $f(x) = -x^3$ for $x = -4$ to $x = 0$

13. $f(x) = x^3 - 4x$ for $x = -2$ to $x = 2$

14. $f(x) = x^3 - 4x$ for $x = -3$ to $x = 3$

15. $f(x) = \dfrac{3x^2 - 18x + 15}{5}$ for $x = 0$ to $x = 6$

16. $f(x) = 9 - 3x^2$ for $x = 0$ to $x = 3$

Evaluate each definite integral.

17. $\displaystyle\int_0^1 (2x + 3)\,dx$

18. $\displaystyle\int_0^1 (3x^2 + 6x + 1)\,dx$

19. $\displaystyle\int_{-1}^1 (x + 1)^2\,dx$

20. $\displaystyle\int_{-1}^1 (4x^3 + 3x^2)\,dx$

21. $\displaystyle\int_1^4 \left(x^2 + \frac{2}{x^2}\right)dx$

22. $\displaystyle\int_{-1}^1 12u(u + 1)(u - 1)\,du$

23. $\displaystyle\int_0^2 (x - 4x^2)\,dx$

24. $\displaystyle\int_4^5 (x^2 + 6x - 7)\,dx$

25. $\displaystyle\int_{-1}^0 (1 - x^2)\,dx$

26. $\displaystyle\int_1^4 (3x^2 - 6x)\,dx$

27. $\displaystyle\int_{-2}^{-1} (2x^2 - 3x + 4)\,dx$

28. $\displaystyle\int_{-2}^3 (x + 2)(x - 3)\,dx$

For the Scholar

If $\log_4 (\log_5 (\log_6 x)) = \log_5 (\log_6 (\log_4 y)) = \log_6 (\log_4 (\log_5 z)) = 0$, find the value of the sum of $x + y + z$.

1. **Limit of a Polynomial Function:** The limit of a polynomial function, $P(x)$, as x approaches r, is $P(r)$. (456)

$$\lim_{x \to r} P(x) = P(r)$$

2. **Limit of a Function:** The limit of a function, $f(x)$, as x approaches a is L, written $\lim_{x \to a} f(x) = L$, if, for every real number $\epsilon > 0$, there exists a real number $\delta > 0$ such that $|f(x) - L| < \epsilon$ when $0 < |x - a| < \delta$. (460)

3. **Continuity of a Function at a Point:** A function f is continuous at $x = a$ if $f(a)$ exists and if $\lim_{x \to a} f(x) = f(a)$. (463)

4. **Continuity of a Function on an Interval:** A function f is continuous on an interval if it is continuous at each point of the interval. (464)

5. **Continuous Function:** A function f is continuous if it is continuous at each point of its domain. (464)

6. The following theorems are given for $\lim_{x \to a} f(x) = F$ and $\lim_{x \to a} g(x) = G$ and real numbers a and c, and n a positive integer. (466)

Theorem 1	Limit of a Constant Function	If $f(x) = c$, then $\lim_{x \to a} f(x) = c$.
Theorem 2	Addition	$\lim_{x \to a} [f(x) + g(x)] = \lim_{x \to a} f(x) + \lim_{x \to a} g(x) = F + G$
Theorem 3	Subtraction	$\lim_{x \to a} [f(x) - g(x)] = \lim_{x \to a} f(x) - \lim_{x \to a} g(x) = F - G$
Theorem 4	Multiplication	$\lim_{x \to a} [f(x) \cdot g(x)] = \left[\lim_{x \to a} f(x)\right]\left[\lim_{x \to a} g(x)\right] = F \cdot G$
Theorem 5	Division	$\lim_{x \to a} \dfrac{f(x)}{g(x)} = \dfrac{\lim_{x \to a} f(x)}{\lim_{x \to a} g(x)} = \dfrac{F}{G} \quad (G \neq 0)$
Theorem 6	Product of a Constant and a Limit	$\lim_{x \to a} [c \cdot g(x)] = c \lim_{x \to a} g(x) = cG$
Theorem 7	Powers	$\lim_{x \to a} [f(x)^n] = \left[\lim_{x \to a} f(x)\right]^n = F^n$
Theorem 8	Roots	$\lim_{x \to a} \sqrt[n]{f(x)} = \sqrt[n]{\lim_{x \to a} f(x)} = \sqrt[n]{F}$

7. **Theorem 9:** Given functions $f(x)$ and $g(x)$, $\lim_{x \to a} g(x) = G$, and any real number a, the limit of the composite of the functions $f(x)$ and $g(x)$ is as follows.

$$\lim_{x \to a} f[g(x)] = f\left[\lim_{x \to a} g(x)\right] = f(G) \quad (467)$$

8. **Theorem 10:** The limit of $\dfrac{\sin x}{x}$ is equal to 1 as x approaches 0 where x is the radian measure of an angle. $\lim_{x \to 0} \dfrac{\sin x}{x} = 1$ (468)

9. **Derivative of a Function:** For a function f, the derivative of f at $x = a$, $f'(a)$, is defined as follows. (469)

$$f'(a) = \lim_{h \to 0} \frac{f(a + h) - f(a)}{h}$$

10. **Power Formula:** If $f(x) = cx^n$ and n is a real number and c is a constant, then $f'(x) = cnx^{n-1}$. (472)

11. **Theorem 11:** If $u = f(x)$ and $v = g(x)$ are differentiable functions of x, then $\dfrac{d(u + v)}{dx} = \dfrac{du}{dx} + \dfrac{dv}{dx}$. (473)

12. **Theorem 12:** If $u = f(x)$ is a differentiable function of x and c is a constant, then $\dfrac{d(cu)}{dx} = c\dfrac{du}{dx}$. (473)

13. **Theorem 13:** If $u = f(x)$ and $v = g(x)$ are differentiable functions of x, then $\dfrac{d(uv)}{dx} = u\dfrac{dv}{dx} + v\dfrac{du}{dx}$. (474)

14. **Theorem 14:** If $u = f(x)$ is a differentiable function of x and n is a nonzero rational number, then $\dfrac{d(u^n)}{dx} = nu^{n-1}\dfrac{du}{dx}$. (474)

15. **Theorem 15:** If $u = f(x)$ and $v = g(x)$ are differentiable functions of x at a point where $v \neq 0$, then $\dfrac{d\frac{u}{v}}{dx} = \dfrac{v\frac{du}{dx} - u\frac{dv}{dx}}{v^2}$. (475)

16. **Increasing and Decreasing Functions:** If $f'(x) > 0$ for all values of x in the interval, $a < x < b$, then the function is increasing in the interval. If $f'(x) < 0$ for all values of x in the interval, $a < x < b$, then the function is decreasing in the interval. (476)

17. **Second Derivative Test:** If $f'(x) = 0$ at x, then $f(x)$ is one of the following stationary values. (478)
    1. If $f''(x) > 0$, then $f(x)$ is a relative minimum.
    2. If $f''(x) < 0$, then $f(x)$ is a relative maximum.
    3. If $f''(x) = 0$ or does not exist, then $(x, f(x))$ is a point of inflection.

18. **Area Under a Curve:** The area A between the curve $y = f(x)$ and the x-axis from $x = a$ to $x = b$ is as follows. (482)

$$A = \lim_{n \to \infty} \sum_{i=1}^{n} f(x_i)(x_{i+1} - x_i)$$

where the width of each rectangle, $x_{i+1} - x_i$, approaches zero.

19. **Definition of an Integral:** The function, $F(x)$, is an integral of $f(x)$ with respect to x if and only if $F(x)$ is an antiderivative of $f(x)$. That is, $F(x) = \int f(x)dx$ if and only if $F'(x) = f(x)$. (485)

20. **Fundamental Theorem of Calculus:** If the function $f(x)$ is continuous and $F(x)$ is such that $F'(x) = f(x)$, then $\int_a^b f(x)dx = F(b) - F(a)$. (488)

Find each limit or state that the limit does not exist. (15-1)

1. $\lim\limits_{x\to a} (x^2 + 3x + 2)$

2. $\lim\limits_{x\to 0} \left(4^x + \dfrac{1}{4^x}\right)$

3. $\lim\limits_{x\to 3} \dfrac{x^2 - 9}{x + 3}$

Find the interval that x must be within so that each inequality is satisfied. (15-2)

4. $-0.05 < x - 2 < 0.05$

5. $\left|\dfrac{x + 1}{2} - 3\right| < 0.01$

Given that $\epsilon = 0.01$, find a δ such that the following limits are verified using the formal definition of a limit. (15-2)

6. $\lim\limits_{x\to 2} \dfrac{x - 2}{3} = 0$

7. $\lim\limits_{x\to 3} \dfrac{x^2 - 9}{x - 3} = 6$

State whether each function is continuous or discontinuous. If it is discontinuous, identify the discontinuity as infinite, jump, or point. (15-3)

8. $f(x) = x^3 + 1$

9. $f(x) = \dfrac{x - 3}{x^2 + x - 6}$

10. $f(x) = \left|\dfrac{1}{x}\right|$

Use the limit theorems to evaluate each limit. (15-4)

11. $\lim\limits_{x\to -1} (x^2 - 1)$

12. $\lim\limits_{x\to 0} \dfrac{3x^3 - 2x}{2x^2 - 3x}$

13. $\lim\limits_{x\to 0} \dfrac{\sqrt{3x^2 + x + 1}}{\sqrt[3]{3x^3 - x + 8}}$

Find the slope and equation of the tangent to each of the following curves at the given point. (15-5)

14. $y = 1 - x^2$ at $(0, 1)$

15. $y = 2x^4$ at $(-1, 2)$

Find the derivative of each function. (15-6)

16. $f(x) = x^6$

17. $f(x) = 4x^3$

18. $f(x) = 3x + 4x^2$

Find the values of x for which each of the following functions is increasing. (15-7)

19. $f(x) = x^2 - 2x$

20. $f(x) = \dfrac{1}{x} + x$

Find the stationary values of each function. State whether each is a maximum, minimum, or a point of inflection. (15-7)

21. $f(x) = x^3 - 2x$

22. $f(x) = x + \dfrac{4}{x}$

Find the area between each curve and the x-axis for the given interval using the limit of the area of rectangles. (15-8)

23. $y = 2x$ from $x = 0$ to $x = 2$

24. $y = x^3$ from $x = 0$ to $x = 1$

Find each integral. (15-9)

25. $\displaystyle\int \dfrac{4}{x^2}\, dx$

26. $\displaystyle\int 5x^3\, dx$

27. $\displaystyle\int (1 - x)\, dx$

28. Find the area between $f(x) = 3x^2$ and the x-axis from $x = 1$ to $x = 3$. (15-10)

Evaluate each integral. (15-10)

29. $\displaystyle\int_2^4 6x\, dx$

30. $\displaystyle\int_{-3}^2 3x^2\, dx$

31. $\displaystyle\int_{-2}^2 (3x^2 - x + 5)\, dx$

Chapter Test

Find each limit or state that the limit does not exist.

1. $\lim\limits_{x \to 2} \dfrac{x^2 - 4}{x - 2}$

2. $\lim\limits_{x \to 3} \dfrac{x^2 - 9}{x^3 - 27}$

Given that $\epsilon = 0.1$, find a δ such that the following limits are verified using the formal definition of a limit.

3. $\lim\limits_{x \to 0} (3x + 4) = 4$

4. $\lim\limits_{x \to -2} \dfrac{x^2 - 4}{x + 2} = -4$

5. Find the points at which the function $f(x) = \dfrac{x - 2}{x^2 + 2x - 8}$ is discontinuous.

Use the limit theorems to evaluate each limit.

6. $\lim\limits_{x \to 2} \dfrac{x^2 - 1}{x^2 + 1}$

7. $\lim\limits_{x \to 1} \dfrac{x^2 - 2x + 3}{3x^2 - 5}$

8. $\lim\limits_{x \to -1} (x^2 - 3x + 4)$

Find the slope and the equation of the tangent to each of the following curves at the given point.

9. $y = x^2 - 3x + 2$ at $(1, 0)$

10. $y = 2x^2 - 3$ at $(2, 5)$

Find the derivative of each function.

11. $f(x) = 3x + 4x^2$

12. $f(x) = (x + 3)^2$

13. $f(x) = \dfrac{2x}{1 + x^2}$

Find the values of x for which each of the following functions is decreasing.

14. $f(x) = x^3 - 3x$

15. $f(x) = \dfrac{1}{4}x^4 - \dfrac{9}{2}x^2$

Find the stationary values of each function. State whether each is a maximum, minimum, or a point of inflection.

16. $f(x) = \dfrac{1}{3}x^2$

17. $f(x) = x^4 - 2x^2 + 2$

18. Find the area between $y = x^2$ and the x-axis from $x = 0$ to $x = 2$ using the limit of the area of rectangles.

Find each integral.

19. $\displaystyle\int (1 - x)\, dx$

20. $\displaystyle\int (3x^2 + 4x + 7)\, dx$

Evaluate each integral.

21. $\displaystyle\int_0^1 (2x + 3)\, dx$

22. $\displaystyle\int_1^4 \left(x^2 + \dfrac{2}{x^2}\right) dx$

Pascal

Computers are now an essential part of our society. We use many languages to communicate through the computer. One of these languages is the language of Pascal.

A-1 The Pascal Language

Pascal is a high level programming language. The instructions to the computer programs are very structural and easily read. As a result, more than one programmer can work on a complete program and new programmers can take up where others stop.

In Pascal, programs are written in blocks. Within these blocks variables can be words descriptive of their replacements. The format of a basic program includes the title, a begin statement, the body, and an end statement.

PROGRAM (*Name of program*) (INPUT, OUTPUT);

BEGIN

———
——— (*program statements*)
———

END.

The name of a Pascal program can contain no spaces. For example, SQUAREROOT is acceptable but SQUARE ROOT is not.

The following program calculates the area of a rectangle. The lines are numbered for reference and are not part of the program.

1. PROGRAM RECTANGLE(INPUT, OUTPUT);

2. VAR LENGTH, WIDTH:INTEGER;

3. BEGIN

4. READ (LENGTH, WIDTH);

5. WRITELN('AREA EQUALS ', LENGTH * WIDTH)

END.

In the first line, the word PROGRAM alerts the computer to expect a Pascal program. The name chosen for the program is RECTANGLE. The words INPUT and OUTPUT in parentheses and separated by a comma tell the computer that there will be data input and also an output from the program. Nearly all programs will have output, but it may happen that input data is not required, in which case the word INPUT is omitted. A semicolon follows the line.

In line 2, two variables have been identified, LENGTH and WIDTH. All variables used in a program must be identified. The variables in this program will accept only integers as input. If real numbers are to be entered, then REAL would replace INTEGER. In some systems, real numbers *must* contain a decimal point, for example, use 25.0 not 25. If single letters are to be entered, then CHAR would replace INTEGER. A word or a phrase is just a string of letters and spaces, so if words or phrases are to be entered, use STRING instead of INTEGER. Notice the use of the comma, colon, and semicolon punctuation.

The BEGIN in the next line identifies the actual starting point of the program called RECTANGLE. There is no punctuation.

The **READ statement** indicates that values for the variables LENGTH and WIDTH will be input during the running of the program. In some Pascal systems, there will appear a prompt signal such as a question mark to indicate there is input to be entered for variables. The values entered are assigned to the variables in parentheses sequentially. In line 5, **WRITELN** calls for output on the current line followed by an advance to the next line. The statement **WRITE** is used when a continuation of the same line is desired. The words in single quotes will be printed on the screen or the printer as typed. Then, the calculation of the product of the replacements of the variables is performed and printed.

Punctuation is very critical in Pascal. Semicolons are used to separate statements and periods are used to indicate the end of a program. Notice there is no semicolon at the end of Line 5 since it is the last statement and semicolons *separate* Pascal statements. In line 6, the END of the program is indicated.

Run the program. The replacements for the variables are typed. These replacements must be integers. For example, if 9 and 5 had been entered as replacements for the variables LENGTH and WIDTH, the following would be the printout.

Check the manual for a specific system to determine what procedures need to be followed to run a program. How could units and a period be included in the printout?

AREA EQUALS 45

At any line in the program a remark may be inserted using the format (*the remark*). The computer ignores the remark, but clarifications and explanations of features or procedures of the program are often included for readers of the program.

The order of operations is the same in Pascal as in algebra.

The symbols for the basic arithmetic operations are as follows.

Addition	+
Subtraction	−
Multiplication	*
Division of Reals	/
Division of Integers	DIV using MOD to find the remainder.

There is no special symbol for exponentiation (powers) in Pascal.

Example

1 **Write a program to find the average of the following test scores.**
      89   75   84   62   91

```
PROGRAM AVERAGE (INPUT, OUTPUT);

VAR T1, T2, T3, T4, T5: REAL;

BEGIN (*THIS PROGRAM FINDS AVERAGES FOR 5 TESTS*)
   WRITELN ('LIST THE TEST SCORES TO BE AVERAGED.');
   READLN (T1, T2, T3, T4, T5);
   WRITELN ('THE AVERAGE IS ',(T1 + T2 + T3 + T4 + T5)/5)
END.
```

Exploratory Exercises

Write appropriate names in Pascal for programs to find each of the following.

1. area of a circle

2. average age of a group of people

3. price of an item after discount

4. ending checkbook balance

Write each of the following expressions in Pascal.

5. $6(9 + 4)$

6. $\dfrac{5^2 - 1}{2}$

7. $\dfrac{4}{3}\pi 8^3$

8. $\dfrac{(6(-1) + 8)^2}{-2(5)}$

9. $\dfrac{(3.0 - 1.5)}{7.3}$

10. $[2.0(2.1 + 3.0) + 4]9$

Written Exercises

Answer the following.

1-6. Evaluate each expression in problems **5-10** of the exploratory exercises.

Name the variables and the type of variables (integer or real) to be used in a program to find each of the following.

7. area of a circle

8. volume of a rectangular prism

9. number of factors of 36

10. simple interest on a sum of money invested

11. distance traveled on a trip

12. number of multiples of 7 less than 1000

13. surface area of a cube

14. how many ways 6 people can be formed into committees of four

Use the given program to solve each of the following. The program finds the commission at a given rate.

```
PROGRAM COMMISSION(INPUT, OUTPUT);

VAR AMOUNT, RATE:REAL;

BEGIN
    READ (AMOUNT, RATE);
    WRITELN ('COMMISSION ON ',AMOUNT, ' AT ', RATE,' PERCENT');
    WRITELN ('IS ',AMOUNT*RATE/100)
END.
```

15. What is the name of the program?

16. What type of variables are being used?

17. What input is needed?

18. Why is there no punctuation at the end of the sixth line?

19. Given the amount of sales to be $100 and the rate to be 12%, show the output of the program.

20. Given the amount of sales to be $450 and the rate to be 15%, show the output of the program.

Write a Pascal program using READLN and WRITELN statements for each of the following.

21. Find the sum and product of 13, 41, and 26.

22. Find the circumference and area of a circle. Use 3.1416 for π.

A-2 Assignment Statement

Specific values can be assigned to a variable by using an **assignment statement.** Consider the following statements.

X := 5	*Assigns the number 5 to the variable X.*
AREA := LENGTH * WIDTH	*Assigns the product of the length and the width to the variable AREA.*
ANSWER := 'N'	*Assigns the character N to the variable ANSWER.*
NAME := 'SMITH'	*Assigns the string SMITH to the string variable NAME.*
VECTOR [2] := 10.4	*Assigns the value 10.4 to the second entry of a one-dimensional array VECTOR.*

In the second statement, the right side is calculated and the resulting value is assigned to the variable on the left side. The variables on the right side need to have values assigned to them prior to this statement. Note in the third and fourth statements, string and character expressions must be enclosed in single quotes.

The fifth statement assigns a value to a place in a one-dimensional array. The variable VECTOR must have been declared previously in a VAR statement like the following.

VAR VECTOR: ARRAY [1 . . 5] OF REAL

In the statement above, **VECTOR** is declared to be a one-dimensional array that can hold up to five real numbers. Multidimensional arrays are also possible.

VAR MATRIX : ARRAY [1 . . 10, 1 . . 20] OF INTEGER

The VAR statement above declares **MATRIX** to be a 10 × 20 array of integers.

Example

1   Write a program to find the total surface area of a cylinder.

```
PROGRAM CYLINDERAREA (INPUT, OUTPUT);

CONST PI = 3.14159;
VAR RADIUS, HEIGHT, BASAREA, LATAREA, TOTAREA: REAL;

BEGIN
   READ (RADIUS, HEIGHT);
   BASAREA := PI * RADIUS * RADIUS ;
   LATAREA := 2 * PI * RADIUS * HEIGHT;
   TOTAREA := 2 * BASAREA + LATAREA ;
   WRITELN('THE TOTAL AREA OF A CYLINDER');
   WRITELN('WITH RADIUS ', RADIUS,'AND HEIGHT ', HEIGHT);
   WRITE('IS ', TOTAREA)
END.
```

The constant PI is declared by using CONST before the variables are listed with their types.

Notice the variable names. Remember there are to be no spaces in a variable name.

The WRITE statement in a program is used so that the output will not advance to the next line.

Exploratory Exercises

State whether each of the following is an acceptable Pascal assignment statement. Write yes or no, and be able to justify.

1. X := 17.04

2. Y = 9

3. TOP := X + 2

4. BOTTOM := 8R

5. HYP := X ↑ 2 + Y ↑ 2

6. 3 * X := 5/9

Find the value assigned to X by each assignment statement, if A = 2, B = 4, and C = 3.

7. X := A + B/C

8. X := (A + B)/C

9. X := A/B*C

10. X := A/(B * C)

11. X := A + B/A + C

12. X := (A + B)/(A + C)

Written Exercises

Show the output of each of the following Pascal programs.

1.
```
PROGRAM SQUARES (OUTPUT);
CONST A = 5, B = 12;
VAR C : INTEGER ;
BEGIN
   C := A * A + B * B ;
   WRITELN (A, ' ' , B, ' ' , C)
END.
```

2.
```
PROGRAM CHANGE (INPUT, OUTPUT);
VAR COST, TENDERED, CHANGE: REAL;
(*THIS PROGRAM FINDS CHANGE*)
BEGIN
   READ (COST, TENDERED);
   CHANGE := TENDERED − COST;
   WRITELN ('THE CHANGE FROM ', TENDERED,
      'FOR');
   WRITE('A PURCHASE OF ', COST, ' IS ',
      CHANGE,'.')
END.
```
For input use: 7.46, 10.00.

3.
```
PROGRAM AVERAGE (INPUT, OUTPUT);
VAR A, B, C : INTEGER ;
BEGIN
   READ (A, B, C);
   WRITELN ('AVERAGE=', (A + B + C)/3)
END.
```
For input use: 73, 87, 64.

4. Modify program AVERAGE in problem 3 as follows.
```
VAR A, B, C: INTEGER;
    MEAN: REAL;
BEGIN
   READ (A, B, C);
   MEAN := (A + B + C)/3
```
What would the WRITELN statement be?

5.
```
PROGRAM INVEST (OUTPUT);
VAR AMOUNT, RATE, INTEREST : REAL ;
BEGIN
   AMOUNT := 5000.00;
   RATE := 12.5;
   INTEREST := AMOUNT * RATE / 100;
   WRITELN('AMOUNT', 'RATE', 'INTEREST');
   WRITELN(AMOUNT, RATE, INTEREST)
END.
```

6.
```
PROGRAM TEMPCONV(INPUT,OUTPUT);
VAR FDEG, CDEG: REAL;
BEGIN
   READ(FDEG);
   CDEG := (FDEG − 32)*5/9;
   WRITELN('A TEMPERATURE OF ', FDEG,
      ' FAHRENHEIT');
   WRITELN('IS EQUIVALENT TO ', CDEG,
      ' CELSIUS.')
END.
```
For input use: 41, 68, 77, 104.

In Pascal, SQR (number) determines the square of a number and SQRT(number) determines the square root of a nonnegative number. When using SQRT the statement, USES TRANSCEND;, must be included immediately after the program name in some Pascal systems. Use these functions if needed to write programs in Pascal for each of the following.

7. Convert 1°C, 17°C, −6°C, and 0°C to Fahrenheit.

8. Find the diagonal of a rectangle given the length is 10 m and the width is 5 m.

9. Find the fourth root of 1296, 20,736, and 3.8416.

A-3 Program Loops

There are three statements in Pascal that generate a repetition, or loop, of program statements. The first of these statements to consider is the **FOR statement.** The FOR statement is used to repeat a sequence of steps a specified number of times. The main structure of the FOR statement is as follows.

FOR (assignment statement) TO (value of an assignment statement) DO

```
BEGIN
 _____ ;        a subprogram
 _____
END;
```

There is a main program and a subprogram. In the main program a variable is given a lower and upper limit on its value. Then, the FOR statement tells the computer to DO the following subprogram as long as the variable is less than or equal to the second value. Each time after the first that the FOR statement is executed, the variable is incremented by one.

Example

1 Write a program to add four integers.

```
PROGRAM ADDFOUR (INPUT, OUTPUT);
(*THIS PROGRAM ADDS ANY FOUR INTEGERS*)

VAR SUM, NUMBER, NEXT : INTEGER;

BEGIN
   WRITELN ('ENTER FOUR NUMBERS');
   SUM := 0;
   FOR NUMBER := 1 TO 4 DO          How many times will the subprogram
   BEGIN                            be executed?
     READ(NEXT);                    What is the input?
     SUM := SUM + NEXT
   END; (*END OF THE FOR LOOP*)
   WRITELN('THE SUM IS ', SUM)      What is the output?
END.
```

Suppose it is necessary to make the computer print out the integers from 1 to 10 in a column. Study the following FOR loop.

FOR N := 1 TO 10 DO WRITELN(N)

When there is only a single step in the loop it may be written on one line. Otherwise, several steps require a BEGIN-END statement as in the program in example 1.

If no new line is needed, use WRITE(N) and the printout would be on a single line. Study the following FOR loop.

FOR N := 1 TO 10 DO WRITE(N)

To improve the format of the output, it is possible to modify the information in parentheses. WRITELN(48:5) will print the numeral 48 preceeded by 3 spaces for a total of 5 character positions. WRITE(N:8) will print the numeral for N so that the last digit is in the eighth position. To write the first ten positive integers on a single line with appropriate spacing the following Pascal statement could be used.

FOR N := 1 TO 10 DO WRITE(N:4)

A WRITELN statement can be used to move to a new line without printing anything. Then, a WRITE statement can print the information.

This formatting capability can be used to create tabular printouts such as tables of squares and square roots.

To print integers from 10 to 1 in a column use:
FOR NUMBER := 10 DOWNTO 1 DO WRITELN (NUMBER).

Example

2 Write a program to find the squares and square roots for integers from A to B.

```
PROGRAM TABLEPOWERSROOTS(INPUT,OUTPUT);

USES TRANSCEND;
VAR NUMBER, SQUARE, A, B: INTEGER;
    SQUAREROOT: REAL;

BEGIN
  WRITE ('ENTER A AND B: ');
  READ(A,B);
  WRITELN('NUMBER':6,'SQUARE':15,'SQUAREROOT': 30);   This line prints the heading.
  WRITELN;   This line provides a blank line under the heading.
  FOR NUMBER := A TO B DO
  BEGIN
    WRITE (NUMBER:6);
    WRITE(SQR(NUMBER): 15);      The numbers after the colons give
    WRITELN(SQRT(NUMBER):30:3)   position of the table entries as well
  END                            as the number of decimal places.
END.
```

The SQRT function contains formatting instructions. The 30 means that the last digit will occur in the 30th space. The 3 means that three digits will follow the decimal point. In summary, the output will appear in columns under the appropriate headings. The number (integer) will end in the 6th position, its square will end in the 15th position and the square root will end in the 30th position with the result containing three decimal places (thousandths).

Exploratory Exercises

State what is wrong with each of the following Pascal statements. Then, write a correct Pascal statement.

1. FOR X = 1 TO 5 DO

2. FOR NUMBER := 10 TO 5 DO

3. FOR Y := 1 TO N DO;

4. FOR Z := 1 TO Z DO

5. FOR LARGE := 1 TO 100

6. FOR X = 7 TO 10 DO;

State the values the variable X will have as the loop is performed.

7. FOR X := 1 TO 10 DO

8. FOR X := 0 TO 1 DO

9. FOR X := 1 TO N DO
$\quad$ (N > 1)

10. FOR X := −N TO 5 DO
$\quad$ (N is positive.)

11. FOR X := Y TO Z DO
$\quad$ (Y < Z)

12. FOR X := 1 TO Y DO
$\quad$ (Y = X)

Written Exercises

Write a Pascal statement for each of the following.

1. Assign to the variable NUMBER the integer values from 1 to 10.

2. Assign to the variable X the integer values from −9 to A (A > −9).

3. Assign to the variable X five consecutive integers starting at 0.

4. Assign to the variable Y the integers from 90 to 100.

5. Assign to the variable Z the integers from A to B (A < B).

6. Assign to the variable C the even integers from 2 to 20.

Solve each of the following using the Pascal statement given.

FOR NUMBER := A TO X DO

7. What values of X would make the statement invalid?

8. Should A be a real number or an integer?

9. How many values can NUMBER obtain?

10. What values can NUMBER obtain?

11. If NUMBER obtains the values −1, 0, 1, 2, 3, and 4, what are the values of A and X?

12. If NUMBER obtains the values 10, 11, 12, 13, 14, 15, 16, 17, and 18, what are the values of A and X?

Show the output of each of the following programs.

13. PROGRAM SUMS (OUTPUT);

VAR X, Y, Z, S: INTEGER;

```
BEGIN
  X := 5;
  Y := X + 5;
  S := 0;
  FOR Z := X TO Y DO
     BEGIN
        S := S + Z;
        WRITELN(Z)
     END;
  WRITELN(S)
END.
```

14. PROGRAM SOLUTION (OUTPUT);

VAR X, Y: INTEGER;

```
BEGIN
  FOR X := −5 TO 5 DO
     BEGIN
        Y := X * X + 5 * X + 6;
        WRITELN ( '( ',X,',',Y,')')
     END
END.
```

Write a Pascal program for each of the following using the FOR statement.

15. Print the integers from 1 to 10 with their squares.

16. Add the integers from 1 to 20 and print the result.

17. Enter two integers and add the numbers between them and print the result.

18. Determine the factorial value for $n!$ and print the result. Enter the value for n.

19. Write a program that will determine the average of the integers from 15 to 220.

20. Write a program to find the least integral value of x such that $3^x \geq 15,000$.

A-4 Other Loops

Many times during a Pascal program it is required that a set of statements be repeated until some condition is satisfied. One way of accomplishing this is the **REPEAT—UNTIL** statement.

```
REPEAT
  X := X + 1
UNTIL X > 10
```

During the running of this loop the steps between REPEAT and UNTIL are performed over and over again until the condition following UNTIL is reached. A test occurs at the end of the loop. This means the list of statements will be performed at least once. When the test is passed, that is, the condition is true, the program ends the loop and proceeds with the next statement.

Example

1 Write a program that adds integers and counts them until the sum of 100 is exceeded. Then, write the output.

```
PROGRAM HUNDREDSUM(INPUT, OUTPUT);

CONST MAX = 100;
VAR NEXT, TOTAL, COUNT : INTEGER;

BEGIN
    COUNT := 0; TOTAL := 0;   Two statements can be on the same line.
    WRITELN ('ENTER A SEQUENCE OF NUMBERS TO BE ADDED');
    REPEAT
        COUNT := COUNT + 1;
        READ(NEXT);
        TOTAL := TOTAL + NEXT
    UNTIL TOTAL > MAX;
    WRITELN;
    WRITELN('THE SUM HAS EXCEEDED ', MAX);
    WRITELN('AFTER ', COUNT, ' NUMBERS WERE ADDED.')
END.
```

In the program in example 1, whole numbers are entered in any sequence by the READ statement. On the first pass through the REPEAT—UNTIL loop, COUNT is increased to 1, and the entered number is added to zero. This becomes TOTAL. Then, TOTAL is tested to see if it exceeds 100. If the test is false and TOTAL <= MAX after the first pass, the loop will be repeated. Thus, COUNT is increased to 2 and a new number is entered, which is added to the first. The new value for TOTAL is tested, and the loop is repeated until the value of TOTAL is greater than MAX, which is 100. The computer will then print out the following output.

```
THE SUM HAS EXCEEDED 100
AFTER ___ NUMBERS WERE ADDED.
```

In the blank the last value of COUNT, the number of numbers added, will appear.

Another means of repeating a sequence of steps until a condition is satisfied is accomplished by the Pascal statement **WHILE-DO**.

WHILE (**statement**) DO

A subprogram is generated by this statement as shown in example 2.

Example

2

Write a program to add whole numbers until a sum of 100 is exceeded using a WHILE-DO statement. Then, write the output.

```
PROGRAM HUNDREDSUM(INPUT, OUTPUT);

CONST MAX = 100;
VAR NEXT, TOTAL, COUNT: INTEGER;

BEGIN
   TOTAL := 0;
   COUNT := 0;
   WRITELN (' ENTER A SEQUENCE OF NUMBERS TO BE ADDED');
   WHILE TOTAL <= MAX DO         TOTAL is used as a
   BEGIN                         loop control variable.
      READ (NEXT);
      COUNT := COUNT + 1;
      TOTAL := TOTAL + NEXT
   END;
   WRITELN;
   WRITELN('THE SUM HAS EXCEEDED ',MAX);
   WRITELN(AFTER ', COUNT + 1, ' NUMBERS WERE ADDED.')
END.
```

In the program in example 2, the test is made at the beginning of the WHILE-DO statement. If the test is true, the steps in the loop are performed. If the test is false, the program proceeds to the step following the first END.

Although both of these loops provide a way of repeating a process, there are some differences between the REPEAT-UNTIL loop and the WHILE-DO loop. A comparison of these loops is as follows.

REPEAT-UNTIL	WHILE-DO
1. The program stops the loop when the loop test is true.	1. The program stops the loop when the loop test is false.
2. The loop is performed at least once.	2. The loop may not be processed at all.
3. Many statements may occur between REPEAT and UNTIL.	3. BEGIN and END are used when more than one statement occurs in the WHILE-DO sequence.

Exploratory Exercises

State whether each of the following Pascal statements are valid or invalid. If they are not valid, tell why.

1. WHILE X > 0 DO
    X := X − 1;

2. REPEAT UNTIL X = 5
    X := X + 1;

3. WHILE X > 3 DO
    Y := Y + 1;

4. REPEAT
    X := X + 5
    UNTIL X > 15;

5. WHILE X > 5 DO;
    X := X − 1;

6. REPEAT
    X = X + 1
    UNTIL X > 15;

Write a Pascal statement for each of the following.

7. Increment the variable COUNTER until COUNTER > 100. Remember COUNTER could have been used before.

8. Read the variable PRESSURE until it exceeds 1000 using a REPEAT-UNTIL loop.

9. Read the variable VOLUME until it exceeds 5000 using a WHILE-DO loop.

10. Increment the variable COUNTER by twos until COUNTER exceeds 500.

Written Exercises

State whether each of the following is true or false.

1. The main difference between the REPEAT-UNTIL loop and the WHILE-DO loop is that the REPEAT-UNTIL is tested before the loop and the WHILE-DO is tested after the loop.

2. The REPEAT-UNTIL loop is processed at least once.

3. A BEGIN-END pair is needed for the REPEAT-UNTIL loop.

4. The REPEAT-UNTIL loop is processed until the loop test is FALSE.

5. There is no maximum number of statements that may occur in a REPEAT-UNTIL loop or a WHILE-DO loop.

6. The WHILE-DO loop is always processed at least once.

Write a Pascal program with output for each of the following.

7. Read the variable NUMBER and add it to the variable SUM that starts at zero until SUM exceeds 100.

8. Use a REPEAT-UNTIL loop to read A, B, and C until their sum is less than 10.

9. Use a WHILE-DO loop to read and calculate the SUM of ten integers. The loop control variable should be the number of variables to be read.

10. Read the variable PRESSURE until the variable exceeds 1000.

11. Read in grades of a class calculating the class average until a grade of more than 100 is read.

12. Find all solutions to the equation $3x^2 + 20x - 7 = 0$ that are between 0 and 5.

A-5 Branching (IF-THEN-ELSE)

The **IF-THEN statement** makes a comparison of two numbers. It tells the computer what to do based on the results of the comparison. The general form of the statement is as follows.

IF   _condition_   THEN   _statement_

The program performs the statement if the condition is true, that is N < 100, but skips it if the condition is false.

The following relational operators are permitted in Pascal.

Operator	Meaning
=	is equal to
<	is less than
<=	is less than or equal to
>	is greater than
>=	is greater than or equal to
<>	is not equal to

Another form of the conditional statement is IF-THEN-ELSE. In this case, the program branches to the THEN statement when the condition is true and to the ELSE statement if it is false.

Examples

1 **Write a program to find the square root of a real number, if it exists.**

```
PROGRAM REALROOTS(INPUT, OUTPUT);
USES TRANSCEND;
VAR A: REAL;
BEGIN
    WRITELN('ENTER ANY REAL NUMBER');
    READ(A);
    IF A >= 0 THEN WRITELN('THE SQUARE ROOT OF ',A,' IS ',SQRT(A))
    ELSE WRITELN('NO REAL SQUARE ROOT.')
END.
```

2 **Write a program to arrange two integers in order with the lesser number first.**

```
PROGRAM NUMBERORDER(INPUT,OUTPUT);
VAR FIRST, SECOND, TEMP : INTEGER;
BEGIN
    WRITELN('ENTER TWO INTEGERS');
    READ(FIRST, SECOND);
    IF FIRST > SECOND THEN        The statement following a
    BEGIN                          THEN or an ELSE can be a
        TEMP := FIRST;             BEGIN-END block.
        FIRST := SECOND;
        SECOND := TEMP
    END; (*IF-THEN*)
    WRITELN(FIRST,',',SECOND)
END.
```

Exploratory Exercises

Write Pascal statements for each of the following.

1. Print DANGER if the variable VOLTS is greater than 1000.

2. Increment X by 1 if X > 10 otherwise decrement X by 1.

3. Print "They are equal." if the variable COUNTER equals the variable SUM.

4. Print "Positive" if X = 0 otherwise print "Negative".

5. If the variable STUDENTS is less than 50 then increment it and print "Not enough students".

6. Print "Correct" and increment SCORE if X = 100 otherwise print "Wrong" and decrement SCORE.

Written Exercises

Rewrite the following program correcting the invalid statements.

1.
```
PROGRAM TEST1(INPUT, OUTPUT)
VAR X, Y, Z, A: INTEGERS;
BEGIN
    READ (B):
    X := 5;
    Y := 7;
    Z = X * Y:
    A := 0;
    IF B > 30 THEN DO
        BEGIN;
            A := A + 1;
            Writeln ('TEST COMPLETE Z = 'Z);
        END:
END.
```

Write Pascal statements for each of the following.

2. Check if the variable SALES exceeds 1000. If so set it to zero and increment the variable THOUSAND by 1.

3. Print ONE if the variable X is one otherwise print NOT ONE.

4. Print "John" if the variable STUDENT is one and "Mary" if STUDENT is two.

5. Check if the variable PRICE is greater than the variable MONEY. If so print "Too much" otherwise print "Buy it".

Write a Pascal program with output for each of the following.

6. Read a number and tell if it is negative.

7. Read in two numbers and tell which is larger.

8. Read 100 integers and count how many times the number 5 is read.

9. Read 100 numbers in the range of 0 to 50 and print the largest and smallest numbers.

10. Read 1000 grades and keep the number of students that are failing (GRADE < 60), passing ($60 \leq$ GRADE ≤ 100), and exceptional (GRADE > 100).

11. Read 50 temperatures and determine which is the coldest and which is the hottest.

A-6 Special Functions

There are a number of special functions incorporated in Pascal. Two functions that have already been used are SQR and SQRT for square and square root, respectively. The form is SQR(N) and SQRT(N) where N may not be negative for SQRT.

Two Pascal special functions operate only on integers. Consider the following example.

$$\begin{array}{r} 6 \\ 3\overline{)20} \\ 18 \\ \hline 2 \end{array}$$

A DIV B   The DIV function divides A by B and gives only the integer part of the quotient.

A MOD B   The MOD function divides A by B and gives only the remainder.

For 20 ÷ 3 the statements would be used as shown.

20 DIV 3 gives the value 6.

20 MOD 3 gives the value 2.

The functions TRUNC(N) and ROUND(N) operate on real numbers to truncate or to round the number respectively.

ROUND(N) rounds N to an integer.

TRUNC(N) truncates N to an integer.

ROUND(13.72) gives the value 14.

TRUNC(13.72) gives the value 13.

To raise a number to an integral power the SQR function may be used repeatedly. SQR(SQR(N)) yields the fourth power of N. N*SQR(SQR(SQR(N))) gives the ninth power, and N^{15} is given by SQR(SQR(SQR(SQR(N))))/N.

The EXP and LN functions relate to exponents and logarithms. In combination they can give real powers of positive numbers. For example, EXP(7.5*LN(N)) gives $N^{7.5}$.

The absolute value function ABS(N) gives the absolute value of N.

ABS(8 − 15) gives 7.

Other functions available in Pascal include three from trigonometry.

SIN(X) gives the value of the Sine function for X radians.

COS(X) gives the value of the Cosine function for X radians.

ARCTAN(X) (in some Pascal systems, ATAN(X)) gives the value of the Arctan function in radians for the real number X.

Before using the functions LOG, EXP, LN, SIN, COS, ARCTAN (or ATAN), and SQRT in some Pascal systems, it is necessary to state USES TRANSCEND; before the variable listing.

1 Write a program to convert a number of minutes into hours and minutes.

```
PROGRAM HOURMINUTES(INPUT, OUTPUT);

VAR MINUTES, HOURS: INTEGER;

BEGIN
   WRITELN('INPUT TIME IN MINUTES');
   READ(MINUTES);
   HOURS := MINUTES DIV 60;
   MINUTES := MINUTES MOD 60;
   WRITELN(HOURS, ' HOURS ' , MINUTES, ' MINUTES')
END.
```

If 400 is entered in the READ statement, the output would be "6 HOURS 40 MINUTES."

2 Write a program to find the cube and cube root of a given number.

```
PROGRAM ROOT(INPUT. OUTPUT);

USES TRANSCEND;
VAR NUMBER, CUBE, CUBEROOT: REAL;

BEGIN
   WRITELN('INPUT NUMBER');
   READ(NUMBER);
   CUBE := NUMBER * SQR(NUMBER);
   CUBEROOT := EXP(LN(NUMBER)/3);
   WRITELN('FOR THE NUMBER ',NUMBER:10:2);
   WRITE('THE CUBE IS ',CUBE:10:2,'AND THE ');
   WRITE(' CUBEROOT IS ',CUBEROOT:10:2)
END.
```

Exploratory Exercises

Find the value for each of the following functions.

1. TRUNC(23.97)

2. ROUND(23.97)

3. ABS(−49)

4. SQR(16)

5. SQRT(16)

6. 46 DIV 9

7. 46 MOD 9

8. EXP(3*LN(5))

Written Exercises

Find the value of each function.

1. 8 MOD 7

2. 10 MOD 11

3. 5 MOD 5

4. 0 MOD 15

5. 7 DIV 5

6. 5 DIV 7

7. 10 DIV 0

8. 0 DIV 6

9. ROUND (7.5)

10. ROUND (−6.3)

11. TRUNC (0.9)

12. TRUNC (−5.3)

13. SQR(SQR(3))

14. SQR(SQRT(SQR(SQRT(4))))

15. SIN(3.14159265)

16. COS(−3.14159265)

Write a Pascal program with output for each of the following.

17. Read ten integers and count how many are evenly divisible by four.

18. Enter a number of radians and calculate its X and Y coordinates on a circle of radius 1.

19. Enter A and B then calculate (using the EXP and LN functions) and print A raised to the B power.

20. Enter the radius of a sphere and calculate its volume and its surface area.

A-7 Boolean Variables

So far only variables with numerical replacements, either INTEGER or REAL, have been emphasized. In Pascal it is possible to declare a variable to be of the type **BOOLEAN**. For a Boolean variable, only two values are possible. The variable can be either true or false. The following is an example of a variable declaration for a Boolean variable.

TRUE and FALSE are reserved words.

```
VAR TALL : BOOLEAN;
```

At any stage in the program the variable TALL may be either true or false.

Boolean variables can be assigned a value also.

```
TALL := TRUE
```

Example

1 Write a program to determine whether the given height of a man classifies him as tall or not. Assume the requirement for a man to be called tall is that he is over 2 meters in height.

```
PROGRAM HEISTALL(INPUT, OUTPUT);

VAR HEIGHT: REAL:
    TALL : BOOLEAN;
(*HEIGHT REFERS TO HEIGHT IN CENTIMETERS*);

BEGIN
  WRITELN('ENTER HEIGHT IN CENTIMETERS');
  READ(HEIGHT);
  TALL := HEIGHT >= 200;
  IF TALL THEN WRITELN('HE IS TALL.')
  ELSE WRITELN('HE IS NOT TALL.')
END.
```

In the program in example 1, after a height has been entered, the IF statement tests the value of TALL to determine if it is 200 or more centimeters. If the condition is true, the output is HE IS TALL. If the condition is false, the output is HE IS NOT TALL.

Compound sentences may also be written having Boolean variables. The words AND, OR, and NOT can be used.

A AND B   *Both A and B must be true for the composite to be true.*

A OR B   *Both A and B must be false for the composite to be false.*

NOT A   *This has the opposite value of A.*

Example

2 Write a program to determine if a number is divisible by both 2 and 3.

```
PROGRAM DIVISIBLE(INPUT, OUTPUT);

VAR NUMBER : INTEGER;
    A, B : BOOLEAN;

BEGIN
  WRITELN('ENTER A NUMBER');
  READ (NUMBER);
  A := NUMBER MOD 2 = 0;
  B := NUMBER MOD 3 = 0;
  IF A AND B THEN WRITELN(NUMBER,' IS DIVISIBLE BY 2 AND 3,')
  ELSE WRITELN('NOT DIVISIBLE.')
END.
```

Example

3 Write a program to determine if a weekend can be classified as nice.

```
PROGRAM NICEWEEKEND(INPUT,OUTPUT);

VAR DAY, WEATHER : INTEGER;
    WEEKEND, NORAIN : BOOLEAN;

BEGIN
  WRITELN('ENTER A NUMBER 1 TO 7 TO REPRESENT THE DAYS OF');
  WRITELN('THE WEEK WITH 1 BEING MONDAY. THEN ENTER 1 FOR RAIN');
  WRITELN('OR 0 FOR NO RAIN');
  READ (DAY, WEATHER);
  WEEKEND := DAY >= 6;
  NORAIN := WEATHER = 0;
  IF ((DAY <= 7) AND (DAY >= 1)) AND ((WEATHER = 1) OR (WEATHER = 0)) THEN
    BEGIN
      IF WEEKEND AND NORAIN
      THEN WRITELN ('IT IS A NICE WEEKEND')
      ELSE
        IF WEEKEND AND NOT NORAIN
      THEN WRITELN('HAVE A PLEASANT DAY ANYWAY')
      ELSE WRITELN('HOPE FOR THE BEST')
    END
    ELSE WRITELN('INPUT UNACCEPTABLE')
END.
```

THEN statements can be written on a separate line in a program without affecting any result.

Exploratory Exercises

Write a Pascal statement for each of the following.

1. Assign False to the Boolean variable POWER.

2. Assign True to the Boolean variable NEGATIVE.

3. Assign True to the Boolean variable FRACTION.

4. Assign True to the Boolean variable POSITIVE if $X > 0$.

5. Assign False to the Boolean variable SALES if $X = 0$.

6. Print "True" if the Boolean variable CHECK = True.

7. Print "Not True" if the Boolean variable CHECK <> True.

8. Print "Good Choice" if the Boolean variable SNACK = True.

Written Exercises

Write a Pascal statement for each of the following using an increment or decrement of one.

1. Increment the variable COUNTER if the Boolean variable PLUS = True.

2. Increment the variable COUNTER if the Boolean variable PLUS <> True.

3. Assign to the Boolean variable ADD the value True.

4. Decrement the variable COUNTER if X = 3 and Y = 4.

5. Decrement the variable X if X > 10 and X < 20.

6. If Y = 10 and the Boolean variable SUM = False then increment Y.

7. Increment the variable BOOK if the Boolean variables SALES and CREDIT are both True.

8. Increment the variable BOOK if either of the Boolean variables SALE or CREDIT is True.

9. If the Boolean variable SIGN is False change it to True or if it is True change it to False.

10. If the Boolean variable SIGN is True and the Boolean variable THOUSAND is False then increment the variable SUM.

Write a Pascal program with output for each of the following.

11. Read integers until a negative is read. Use the Boolean variable NEGATIVE as the loop control variable.

12. Read integers until a 0 is read or 100 numbers are read whichever comes first. Use only Boolean variables to control the loop.

13. Set the Boolean variable DANGER to True and stop reading data if PRESSURE, a real variable being read, exceeds 100.0. Use DANGER as the loop control variable.

14. Enter 30 grades of an 11th grade math class. Determine the mean. Use a Boolean variable to stop the input at 30.

A-8 Function Definitions

In Pascal it is possible to define functions of special significance to the program. These special functions are used in the same way as the predefined functions. The result of the application of both predefined and defined functions must be a single value.

A **user-defined function** is first *declared* and then *called* in the Pascal program. The types of variables in a function must be specified as well as the type of the function value.

```
FUNCTION POWER (BASE : REAL; EXPONENT : INTEGER) : REAL;
```

Since there is no special function in Pascal for the general power of a base, it is possible to write a subprogram to declare POWER as a user-defined function.

Example

1 Write a user-defined function to find integral powers of a real number.

```
FUNCTION POWER(BASE:REAL; EXPONENT: INTEGER): REAL;
(*NOTE THE BASE IS A REAL NUMBER, THE EXPONENT AN INTEGER, AND THE
RESULTING POWER IS A REAL NUMBER*)

VAR COUNT: INTEGER;
    TEMP: REAL;

BEGIN
   IF EXPONENT = 0 THEN POWER := 1
   ELSE
      BEGIN
         TEMP := BASE;
         FOR COUNT := 2 TO ABS(EXPONENT) DO
            TEMP := TEMP * BASE;
         IF EXPONENT < 0 THEN
            POWER := 1/TEMP
         ELSE
            POWER := TEMP
      END
END;   This end has a semicolon since the function will always
       need to be in a program.
```

In example 1, the function subprogram raises BASE to the appropriate power designated by ABS(EXPONENT), unless it is zero. The result, **POWER**, is expressed properly according to whether **EXPONENT** is positive or negative.

Now, the **POWER** function can be called in a program in the following form.

POWER(BASE, EXPONENT)

The value assigned to the function name is the value passed back to the program. For example, WRITELN(POWER(3.2,5)) would printout the value of 3.2^5, or 335.54432.

Functions are declared before the main program and after CONST and VAR declarations. A function can be called several times in a program by statements in the main program.

A variable declared for the main program is called a **global variable** and may be used anywhere in the program. A variable declared in a function is a **local variable** and is restricted to the function. A variable name cannot be used for both a local variable and a global variable.

Example

2 Write a program to multiply the numbers of greater value of two ordered pairs.

```
PROGRAM MULTGREATER(INPUT,OUTPUT);

VAR M,N,P,Q : REAL;

FUNCTION GREATER(FIRSTNUMBER, SECONDNUMBER: REAL):REAL;
BEGIN
   IF FIRSTNUMBER > SECONDNUMBER THEN GREATER := FIRSTNUMBER
   ELSE GREATER := SECONDNUMBER
END;

BEGIN
   WRITELN('INPUT TWO ORDERED PAIRS.');
   READ(M,N,P,Q);
   WRITELN(GREATER(M,N)*GREATER(P,Q):10:2)
END.
```

Exploratory Exercises

State whether each of the following is True or False.

1. The declaration of a function can appear anywhere in a program.

2. The type of value to be returned from a function must be stated.

3. A user-defined function must always end with a period.

4. A function may return any type of variable.

5. A function is called by stating the function name in an expression.

6. The function value is returned by using the function name.

Write a function for each of the following.

7. To return the largest of three integers.

8. To return the opposite value of any integer.

Written Exercises

Use the function USABLE to answer each of the following.

```
FUNCTION USABLE(NUMBER:INTEGER):BOOLEAN;

VAR X,Y:REAL;

BEGIN
   X := SQRT(NUMBER);
   Y := SQR(NUMBER);
   IF (X <= 4) AND (Y > 120) THEN USABLE := TRUE
      ELSE USABLE := FALSE
END;
```

1. What type of variable will be returned?

2. What value would the function return if the value 16 is used in the function?

3. What value would be returned if 9 were used?

4. What values could be used in the function to return the value True?

5. If Z were defined to be real, would IF USABLE(Z) THEN WRITE ('YES'); be a valid statement?

Write a Pascal program with output using functions for each of the following.

6. Return the factorial of any positive integer. If the integer is negative, indicate this by printing "NO FACTORIAL".

7. Return the Boolean function SAFE as True if the value of PRESSURE, a real variable, is less than 1000.

8. Return the fifth power of a real number.

9. Return the fourth root of a real number.

A-9 Procedures

A subprogram called a **procedure** may be declared and called in Pascal. It is similar to a function subprogram but more general in nature. A procedure is not limited to a numerical or character value, as is a function, but is designated to accomplish a specific task. Often the task will be repeatedly called in the main program or subsequent procedures.

In a procedure, the values passed to the procedure need to be defined as part of the declaration. For example, to order numbers, the following procedure can be used as a declaration.

PROCEDURE ORDER (VAR A,B : REAL);

In the main program, the procedure would be called by the following statement.

ORDER (FIRST,SECOND);

Example

1 **Write a program to arrange any three real numbers in increasing order.**

```
PROGRAM ORDERNUMBERS(INPUT, OUTPUT);

VAR FIRST, SECOND, THIRD : REAL;

PROCEDURE ORDER (VAR A,B: REAL);
VAR TEMP: REAL;
BEGIN
   IF A > B THEN
     BEGIN
        TEMP := A;
        A := B;
        B := TEMP
     END (* IF-THEN*)
END; (*ORDER*)
```

```
BEGIN (*MAIN PROGRAM*)
   READ(FIRST, SECOND, THIRD);
   ORDER(FIRST, SECOND);
   ORDER(FIRST, THIRD);
   ORDER(SECOND, THIRD);
   (*THE ORDER PROCEDURE HAS BEEN CALLED THREE TIMES*)
   WRITELN(FIRST:10:2, SECOND:10:2, THIRD:10:2)
END.
```

This program examines a set of any three real numbers that are input by the READ statement. The first and second numbers are compared and switched if necessary to obtain increasing order. Then the new first is compared with the third and the same procedure applied. Finally the new second and new third are compared and the procedure applied. This guarantees that the three numbers have been arranged in increasing order and the program directs their printout. There are other "sorting" programs using nested loops that also accomplish this.

The use of functions and procedures allows for great simplification and logical order of Pascal programs. An outline of a program to find the Mean, Median, and Mode of a set is shown as follows.

```
PROGRAM STATISTICS(INPUT, OUTPUT);

CONST  _____

VAR  _____

PROCEDURE READATA
      _____
      _____
      _____

FUNCTION MEAN
      _____
      _____
      _____

PROCEDURE MEDIAN
      _____
      _____

PROCEDURE MODE
      _____
      _____

BEGIN (*MAIN PROGRAM*)
   READATA(DATA);
   MEAN(DATA);
   MEDIAN(DATA);
   MODE(DATA);
      _____
END.
```

Exploratory Exercises

Use the previous outline of the program to find mean, median, and mode to solve each of the following.

1. Why is MEAN called by a function?

2. Why is MEDIAN a procedure?

3. Why can a main program be short compared to the total program or even a procedure?

4. Can words be arranged in alphabetical order using a program similar to ordering numbers?

Written Exercises

Write a procedure to do each of the following.

1. Order words in alphabetical order.

2. Underline certain words in the output.

3. Reverse digits in a number.

4. Calculate the coordinates for the graph of a function.

5. Compute the mean of a set of numbers.

6. Determine the number of words in a sentence.

7. Determine the number of letters in a word.

8. Determine if a number is a palindrome. A palindrome is a number that reads the same forwards and backwards such as 747.

Answer each of the following.

9. How do functions and procedures allow programs to be planned and written in modular format?

10. What are the advantages of modular, or structured, programming?

Lists for Pascal

A. RESERVED WORDS: AND, ARRAY, BEGIN, CASE, CONST, DIV, DO, DOWNTO, ELSE, END, FALSE, FILE, FOR, FUNCTION, GOTO, IF, IN, LABEL, MOD, NIL, NOT, OF, OR, PACKED, PROCEDURE, PROGRAM, RECORD, REPEAT, SET, THEN, TO, TRUE, TYPE, UNTIL, VAR, WHILE, WITH

B. OPERATIONS: AND, OR, IN, NOT, DIV, MOD, $+$, $-$, $*$, $/$, $=$, $>$, $<$, $>=$, $<=$, $<>$

C. FUNCTIONS: ABS, ARCTAN, CHR, COS, EOF, EOLN, EXP, LN, ODD, ORD, PRED, ROUND, SIN, SQR, SQRT, SUCC, TRUNC

D. PROCEDURES: DISPOSE, GET, NEW, PACK, PAGE, PUT, READ, READLN, RESET, REWRITE, UNPACK, WRITE, WRITELN

Computer Programming Exercises

The following section provides a variety of problems that are to be solved by computer programs. The Pascal programming techniques in the previous lessons are to be used when writing the computer programs. The problems are listed by chapter for easy reference.

Most of the problems do not have specific data. In these problems a READ statement must be inserted in the program. When the program is run, data must be entered. If specific data is given, the problem is to be solved using this data only.

All programs must label the output with appropriate headings.

Chapter 1   Linear Relations and Functions

1. Find the zero of the function, $f(x) = mx + b$, given values of m and b.

2. Find the values of x for which $ax + b < c$ given values of a, b, and c.

3. Given two points, P and Q, in the coordinate plane, find the slope of the line through the two points, if defined, or state that the slope is undefined.

4. Find the perimeter of a triangle that has vertices (a, b), (c, d), and (e, f).

A linear equation of the form $ax + by + c = 0$ is given. Assume that a and b are rational numbers that are not both zero.

5. Find the slope of the graph of the equation if it exists.

6. Determine whether a given point $P(r, s)$ lies on the graph of the equation.

7. Given the coordinates of a point (a, b) determine whether the point lies in the solution set of the following system of inequalities.
$$x + y \le 5$$
$$y - x \le 5$$
$$y \ge -10$$

8. Find the minimum and maximum values of the function $f(x, y) = \frac{1}{2}x + 3y$ defined for the polygonal convex set having vertices (a, b), (c, d), (e, f), and (g, h).

Chapter 2   Theory of Equations

1. Evaluate $f(x) = x^4 - x^3 + x^2 - x + 1$ for integral values of x from -6 to 6 inclusive.

2. Find the discriminant of $ax^2 + bx + c = 0$ given a, b, and c.

3. Find the square roots, real or imaginary, of any real number R.

4. A quadratic equation of the form $ax^2 + bx + c = 0$ is given. Determine if r is a root by using substitution for integral values of r from -20 to 20 inclusive.

5. Determine if an equation of the form $ax^2 + bx + c = 0$ has real roots.

6. Use the Factor Theorem to find factors of the polynomial $p(x) = ax^3 + bx^2 + cx + d$.

7. Find the integers that are factors of x given that x is an integer.

8. Use the Rational Root Theorem to find all possible rational roots of the equation $ax^3 + bx^2 + cx + d = 0$ given that a, b, c, and d are integers.

9. Given the degree and coefficients of a polynomial, use Descarte's Rule of Signs to find the number of possible positive real zeros and negative real zeros.

10. Approximate to the nearest hundredth the positive real zero(s) of the function $f(x) = 2x^3 - 4x^2 - 3$.

Chapter 3   Matrices and Vectors

1. Evaluate the determinant of a third order matrix.

2. Given a third order matrix, find its additive inverse.

3. Use Cramer's rule to solve the following system of equations.
$$3x - y = 3$$
$$6x + 5y = -1$$

4. Given a second order matrix, find its multiplicative inverse if it exists.

5. Find the ordered pair that represents $\overrightarrow{AB}$ given $A(p, q)$ and $B(r, s)$.

6. Find the magnitude of the vector from $A(p, q)$ to $B(r, s)$.

7. Find the inner product of $\vec{a}$ and $\vec{b}$ if $\vec{a} = (p, q)$ and $\vec{b} = (r, s)$.

8. Find the cross product of $\vec{a}$ and $\vec{b}$ if $\vec{a} = (l, m, n)$ and $\vec{b} = (r, s, t)$.

Chapter 4   The Circular Functions

1. A real number s is given. Determine in which quadrant or on which axis the arc measured by s on the unit circle terminates.

2. Given $\sin x$, find $\cos x$, $\tan x$, $\cot x$, $\sec x$, and $\csc x$. Assume that the arc measured by x on the unit circle terminates in the third quadrant.

Use the double and half number formulas to solve each of the following.

3. Given $\cos s = 0.6$ and the arc measured by s terminates in the first quadrant, find $\sin 2s$.

4. Given $\sin s = 0.8$ and the arc measured by s terminates in the second quadrant, find $\cos 2s$.

5. Given $\cos s = 0.2$ and the arc measured by s terminates in the fourth quadrant, find $\sin \frac{s}{2}$.

6. Given $\cos s = -0.333$ and the arc measured by s terminates in the third quadrant, find $\cos \frac{s}{2}$.

Chapter 5 The Trigonometric Functions

1. Given the lengths of the hypotenuse and one leg of a right triangle, find the values of the six trigonometric functions of each acute angle of the triangle.

2. Given the degree measure of an angle in standard position, determine the quadrant in which the terminal side of the angle lies or if the terminal side lies on an axis, which part of which axis.

3. Given x and y, find the values of the six trigonometric functions of α if the point (x, y) lies on the terminal side of an angle with measure α.

4. Given $\tan \theta = x$, find the values of the other trigonometric functions of θ. Assume θ is between $0°$ and $90°$.

5. Make a table of the degree measures of angles given their radian measures in increments of 0.01 from 0 to 2.

6. Given the degree measure of an angle, find the measure of its reference angle. (Include angles whose terminal side coincides with one of the axes.)

Chapter 6 Graphs and Inverses of the Trigonometric Functions

1. Find the amplitude of the function $y = A \cos \theta$ for integer values of A from -4 to 4 inclusive.

2. Find the period of the function $y = \sin k\theta$ for integer values of k from 1 to 5 inclusive.

3. Find the phase shift of the function $y = \tan (k\theta + c)$ given the values of k and c. Determine if the shift is to the left or right.

4. Find the amplitude, period, and phase shift of the function $y = A \sin (k\theta + c)$ given values of A, k, and c.

The Arctangent of an angle may be found in Pascal using the internal function, ARCTAN(X). The answer is in radians. Use this function to evaluate each of the following.

5. $\sin [\arctan (-\sqrt{3})]$

6. $\cos \left(2 \tan^{-1} \dfrac{3}{5}\right)$

Chapter 7 Applications of Trigonometry

Use the ARCTAN function as described for problems 5-6 of Chapter 6 to solve each equation for principal values of x.

1. $\tan^2 x - 1 = 0$

2. $\tan^2 x - 3 \tan x + 2 = 0$

Suppose $\triangle ABC$ is a right triangle. Let A and B be the acute angles, and a and b be the measures of the sides opposite these angles. The measure of the hypotenuse is c. Solve the triangle given each of the following.

3. the measures of b and angle A

4. the measures of a and angle B

5. the measures of a and c

6. the measures of c and angle A

7. Given the measures of two sides of a triangle and an angle not included between them, determine the number of possible triangles.

8. If the information in problem **7** determines at least one triangle, solve the triangle(s).

Given each of the following parts of a nonright triangle, solve each triangle. Use the Law of Sines and/or Law of Cosines.

9. the measures of two angles and their included side

10. the measures of two angles and a side not included between them

11. the measures of the triangle(s) sides

12. the measures of two sides and their included angle

Find the area of triangle given each of the following.

13. the measures of two sides and the included angle

14. the measures of the sides (Use Hero's formula.)

An airplane is heading due west at a given speed.

15. The wind blows from the north at a given speed. Find the ground speed and direction of the plane.

16. The wind blows from the southwest at a given speed. Find the ground speed and direction of the plane.

Chapter 8   Sequences and Series

Let a be the first term of an arithmetic sequence, d be the common difference, and n be a positive integer.

1. Find the nth term of the sequence.

2. Find the sum of the first n terms of the sequence.

3. Given two real numbers, a and b, find three arithmetic means between a and b.

4. Given two real numbers, a and b, find three geometric means between a and b.

Let a be the first term of a geometric sequence, r the common ratio, and n a positive integer.

5. Find the nth term of the sequence.

6. Find the sum of the first n terms of the sequence.

7. Find the least integral value of n such that $1 + \frac{1}{2} + \frac{1}{3} + \frac{1}{4} + \cdots \frac{1}{n} > 4$.

8. Find the sum of the series $1 + 2 + 4 + 8 + \cdots + 2^n$ for any positive integer, n.

9. Generate the numbers in Pascal's triangle up to row 10.

10. Find the sum of the first ten terms of $1 - \frac{1}{2!} + \frac{1}{4!} - \frac{1}{6!} + \cdots$.

11. Estimate $\sin x$ for 2 to 14 terms in steps of 2 using the following series.
$$\sin x = x - \frac{x^3}{3!} + \frac{x^5}{5!} - \frac{x^7}{7!} + \cdots + \frac{x^n}{n!}$$
(x is in radians)

12. Estimate $\cos x$ for 2 to 14 terms in steps of 2 using the following series.
$$\cos x = 1 - \frac{x^2}{2!} + \frac{x^4}{4!} - \frac{x^6}{6!} + \cdots + \frac{x^n}{n!}$$
(x is in radians)

Chapter 9   Polar Coordinates and Complex Numbers

1. Given the polar coordinates of a point, find its rectangular coordinates.

2. Given the rectangular coordinates of a point, find its polar coordinates. (Use the ARCTAN (X) function as described for problems **5–6** of Chapter 6.)

3. Change the polar equation $r = \sin\theta + \cos\theta$ to an equation in rectangular coordinates.

4. Change the equation $x^2 + y^2 = r^2$ into an equation in polar coordinates.

5. Given two complex numbers $a + bi$ and $c + di$, find their sum.

6. Given two complex numbers $a + bi$ and $c + di$, find their product.

Given a complex number $a + bi$ find each of the following.

7. conjugate of $a + bi$

8. amplitude of $a + bi$

9. modulus of $a + bi$

10. polar form of $a + bi$

11. Given two complex numbers in polar form, find their product.

12. Use De Moivre's Theorem to find the nth roots of a complex number.

Chapter 10   Exponential and Logarithmic Functions

1. Find logarithms of n to the base eight for $n = 1, 2, 3, \cdots, 50$.

2. Given a real number x such that $1 < x < 10^9$, print x and the characteristic of its common logarithm.

3. Estimate the value of e by evaluating $(1 + x)^{\frac{1}{x}}$ for values of x close to 0. Let $x = 1, 0.1, 0.01, 0.001, 0.0001,$ and 0.00001.

4. Find which value is larger, e^π or π^e.

5. The formula for the amount of money accumulated, A, on an investment, P, deposited for t years at $r\%$ interest rate, and compounded n times annually is $A = P\left(1 + \frac{r}{n}\right)^{nt}$. Find the amount of interest earned on $2500 for 5 years at interest rates of 5.5%, 5.75%, 6.00%, $\cdots$, 12% compounded quarterly.

6. When the interest is compounded continuously, the formula in problem **5** becomes $A = Pe^{rt}$ where e is approximately 2.718. If $1000 is deposited in a savings account at an interest rate of 6% compounded continuously, when will the money be double the original amount?

7. A radioactive substance decays according to the equation, $A = A_0 \times 10^{-0.024t}$ where t is in hours. Find the half-life of the substance when $A = 0.5A_0$.

8. A piece of machinery valued at $50,000 depreciates 10% per year. The value at the end of n years is $V(n) = 50,000 \times 0.9^n$. Make a table that shows the value of the machine after each year for 1 to 20 years.

Chapter 11   The Straight Line

A linear equation of the form $Ax + By + C = 0$ is given. Assume that A and B are rational numbers that are not both zero.

1. Find the slope of the graph of the equation.

2. Find the y-intercept of the graph of the equation.

Two linear equations, $ax + by = c$ and $dx + ey = f$, are given.

3. Determine if the graphs of the equations are parallel.

4. Determine if the graphs of the equations are perpendicular.

5. Find the angle from the first line to the second line.

6. Make a table of ordered pairs of $ax + by = c$ if a, b, and c are constant and c is an integer varying from -20 to 20.

7. Find the distance d from a point $P(r, s)$ to a line $Ax + By + C = 0$.

Chapter 12   Conics

1. Find the center and radius of a circle given by the equation $Ax^2 + Cy^2 + Dx + Ey + F = 0$.

2. Find the center and radius of a circle given by the equation $Ax^2 + Cy^2 + F = 0$.

3. The equation of a parabola with directrix parallel to the x-axis is $(x - h)^2 = 4p(y - k)$. Find the coordinates of the vertex and focus of the parabola.

4. The standard form of the equation of a hyperbola with center (h, k) and transverse axis of length $2a$, parallel to the x-axis, is $\frac{(x - h)^2}{a^2} - \frac{(y - k)^2}{b^2} = 1$. Find the coordinates of the foci and the length of the latus rectum.

Find the point(s) of intersection of each of the following conic sections and the circle $x^2 + y^2 = r^2$.

5. $ax^2 + bx + c = y$

6. $\frac{x^2}{a^2} - \frac{y^2}{b^2} = 1$

7. $(x - h)^2 + (y - k)^2 = s^2$

Chapter 13   Probability

1. How many different ways can n charms be put on a charm bracelet with no clasp?

2. How many different 13-card hands can be dealt from a standard deck of cards?

3. Simulate the tossing of six coins 1000 times and count the number of heads and tails for each coin.

4. Simulate the throwing of a die 1000 times. Count the number of times each number shows.

5. Simulate the throwing of 2 dice for 1000 times. Count the number of times that the sum is 7 or 11.

6. Find the probability of a number between 2 and 100 being a prime number.

7. Suppose n persons are chosen at random from a certain population. Find the probability that two of them have the same birthday if n varies from 10 to 30.

8. Simulate the dealing of four five-card hands from a standard deck of cards.

Chapter 14   Statistics

Andy bowls three games every Tuesday for 10 weeks. Given his scores of the three games each Tuesday, solve each problem.

1. Find the arithmetic mean of his scores each Tuesday.

2. Find the arithmetic mean of all thirty scores.

3. Make an array of the thirty scores from lowest to highest.

4. Find the mode(s) (if any) of the thirty scores.

5. Find the harmonic mean of the thirty scores.

6. Find the quadratic mean of the thirty scores.

7. Find the mean deviation of the thirty scores.

8. Find the median of the thirty scores.

9. Find the semi-interquartile range of the thirty scores.

10. Find the standard deviation of the thirty scores.

11. Print a frequency distribution of the thirty scores. Use an appropriate class width.

Chapter 15   Limits, Derivatives, and Integrals

1. Determine the limit of $\dfrac{x^2 - 4}{x - 2}$ as x approaches 2 by finding $\dfrac{x^2 - 4}{x - 2}$ for $x = 1, 1.5,$ 1.75, 1.875, $\cdots$ until the difference between successive values is less than 0.0001.

2. Determine the limit of $\dfrac{\sin x}{x}$ as x approaches zero by finding $\dfrac{\sin x}{x}$ for $x = 1,$ 0.5, 0.25, $\cdots$ until the difference between successive values is less than 0.0005.

3. Given a polynomial P, find the first derivative of the function determined by P.

4. Find the slope of the secant line intersecting the graph of $f(x) = x^2 + 2x + 1$ at $(a, f(a))$ and $(a + h, f(a + h))$ as h varies from 3 to 0 in steps of 0.1.

5. Given a polynomial of the form $ax^3 + bx^2 + cx + d$ where $a \neq 0$ find the critical point(s) (if any) and determine whether each is a maximum or minimum.

6. Find the area under the curve $y = x^2$ from $x = 0$ to $x = 1$ by finding the limit of the area of N rectangles under the curve.

Symbols

$=$	is equal to
$\neq$	is not equal to
$<$	is less than
$\leq$	is less than or equal to
$>$	is greater than
$\geq$	is greater than or equal to
$\approx$	is approximately equal to
$\{\ \}$	set notation
$\pm$	plus or minus
$\mp$	minus or plus
$f(x)$	f of x or the value of function f at x
$f'(x)$	f prime of x or the derivative of f at x
$f''(x)$	the second derivative of $f(x)$
$f \circ g$ or $f(g(x))$	composite of functions f and g
$\lim\limits_{x \to a}$	the limit as x approaches a
$\triangle ABC$	triangle ABC
$\overset{\frown}{RTS}$	arc RTS
$\angle ABC$	angle ABC
$m\angle ABC$	measure of angle ABC
AB	measure of line segment AB
$\overline{AB}$	line segment AB
$|n|$	the absolute value of n
x^n	the nth power of x
$\sqrt{x}$	the square root of x
$\sqrt[n]{x}$ or $x^{\frac{1}{n}}$	the nth root of x
$[x]$	greatest integer not greater than x
A^{-1}	inverse of A
a_{ij}	the element of the ith row and the jth column
$\begin{vmatrix} a_1 & b_1 \\ a_2 & b_2 \end{vmatrix}$	the determinant $a_1 b_2 - a_2 b_1$
$\vec{v}$ or $\overrightarrow{AB}$	a vector or directed line segment
$|\vec{v}|$	magnitude of the vector $\mathbf{v}$
$\vec{a} \cdot \vec{b}$	inner product or dot product of vectors a and b
$\vec{a} \times \vec{b}$	cross product of vectors a and b
$\sin^{-1} x$	arcsin x
∞	infinity
i	$\sqrt{-1}$
e	base of natural logarithms; ≈ 2.718
$n!$	n factorial
$\ln x$	logarithm of x to the base e; natural logarithm
$\log_a x$	logarithm of x to the base a
$\log x$	logarithm of x to the base 10
$P(n, r)$	permutation of n objects, taken r at a time
$C(n, r)$	combination of n objects, taken r at a time
$\overline{X}$	X bar or arithmetic mean
M_d	median
σ_X	standard error of the mean
$\widetilde{X}$	X tilde
$\dfrac{dy}{dx}$	the derivative of y with respect to x
$\int$	integral
α	alpha
β	beta
$\triangle$ or δ	delta
ϵ	epsilon
θ	theta
λ	lambda
π	pi
σ	sigma; standard deviation
Σ	sigma; summation symbol
ϕ	phi

Squares and Square Roots

n	n^2	$\sqrt{n}$	$\sqrt{10n}$	n	n^2	$\sqrt{n}$	$\sqrt{10n}$
1.0	1.00	1.000	3.162	5.5	30.25	2.345	7.416
1.1	1.21	1.049	3.317	5.6	31.36	2.366	7.483
1.2	1.44	1.095	3.464	5.7	32.49	2.387	7.550
1.3	1.69	1.140	3.606	5.8	33.64	2.408	7.616
1.4	1.96	1.183	3.742	5.9	34.81	2.429	7.681
1.5	2.25	1.225	3.873	6.0	36.00	2.449	7.746
1.6	2.56	1.265	4.000	6.1	37.21	2.470	7.810
1.7	2.89	1.304	4.123	6.2	38.44	2.490	7.874
1.8	3.24	1.342	4.243	6.3	39.69	2.510	7.937
1.9	3.61	1.378	4.359	6.4	40.96	2.530	8.000
2.0	4.00	1.414	4.472	6.5	42.25	2.550	8.062
2.1	4.41	1.449	4.583	6.6	43.56	2.569	8.124
2.2	4.84	1.483	4.690	6.7	44.89	2.588	8.185
2.3	5.29	1.517	4.796	6.8	46.24	2.608	8.246
2.4	5.76	1.549	4.899	6.9	47.61	2.627	8.307
2.5	6.25	1.581	5.000	7.0	49.00	2.646	8.367
2.6	6.76	1.612	5.099	7.1	50.41	2.665	8.426
2.7	7.29	1.643	5.196	7.2	51.84	2.683	8.485
2.8	7.84	1.673	5.292	7.3	53.29	2.702	8.544
2.9	8.41	1.703	5.385	7.4	54.76	2.720	8.602
3.0	9.00	1.732	5.477	7.5	56.25	2.739	8.660
3.1	9.61	1.761	5.568	7.6	57.76	2.757	8.718
3.2	10.24	1.789	5.657	7.7	59.29	2.775	8.775
3.3	10.89	1.817	5.745	7.8	60.84	2.793	8.832
3.4	11.56	1.844	5.831	7.9	62.41	2.811	8.888
3.5	12.25	1.871	5.916	8.0	64.00	2.828	8.944
3.6	12.96	1.897	6.000	8.1	65.61	2.846	9.000
3.7	13.69	1.924	6.083	8.2	67.24	2.864	9.055
3.8	14.44	1.949	6.164	8.3	68.89	2.881	9.110
3.9	15.21	1.975	6.245	8.4	70.56	2.898	9.165
4.0	16.00	2.000	6.325	8.5	72.25	2.915	9.220
4.1	16.81	2.025	6.403	8.6	73.96	2.933	9.274
4.2	17.64	2.049	6.481	8.7	75.69	2.950	9.327
4.3	18.49	2.074	6.557	8.8	77.44	2.966	9.381
4.4	19.36	2.098	6.633	8.9	79.21	2.983	9.434
4.5	20.25	2.121	6.708	9.0	81.00	3.000	9.487
4.6	21.16	2.145	6.782	9.1	82.81	3.017	9.539
4.7	22.09	2.168	6.856	9.2	84.64	3.033	9.592
4.8	23.04	2.191	6.928	9.3	86.49	3.050	9.644
4.9	24.01	2.214	7.000	9.4	88.36	3.066	9.695
5.0	25.00	2.236	7.071	9.5	90.25	3.082	9.747
5.1	26.01	2.258	7.141	9.6	92.16	3.098	9.798
5.2	27.04	2.280	7.211	9.7	94.09	3.114	9.849
5.3	28.09	2.302	7.280	9.8	96.04	3.130	9.899
5.4	29.16	2.324	7.348	9.9	98.01	3.146	9.950

Values of Trigonometric Functions

∠ is measured in degrees and minutes 60' = 1°

Angle	Radians	Sin	Cos	Tan	Cot	Sec	Csc	Radians	Angle
0°00'	0.0000	0.0000	1.0000	0.0000	—	1.000	—	1.5708	90°00'
10'	0.0029	0.0029	1.0000	0.0029	343.8	1.000	343.8	1.5679	50'
20'	0.0058	0.0058	1.0000	0.0058	171.9	1.000	171.9	1.5650	40'
30'	0.0087	0.0087	1.0000	0.0087	114.6	1.000	114.6	1.5621	30'
40'	0.0116	0.0116	0.9999	0.0116	85.94	1.000	85.95	1.5592	20'
50'	0.0145	0.0145	0.9999	0.0145	68.75	1.000	68.76	1.5563	10'
1°00'	0.0175	0.0175	0.9998	0.0175	57.29	1.000	57.30	1.5533	89°00'
10'	0.0204	0.0204	0.9998	0.0204	49.10	1.000	49.11	1.5504	50'
20'	0.0233	0.0233	0.9997	0.0233	42.96	1.000	42.98	1.5475	40'
30'	0.0262	0.0262	0.9997	0.0262	38.19	1.000	38.20	1.5446	30'
40'	0.0291	0.0291	0.9996	0.0291	34.37	1.000	34.38	1.5417	20'
50'	0.0320	0.0320	0.9995	0.0320	31.24	1.001	31.26	1.5388	10'
2°00'	0.0349	0.0349	0.9994	0.0349	28.64	1.001	28.65	1.5359	88°00'
10'	0.0378	0.0378	0.9993	0.0378	26.43	1.001	26.45	1.5330	50'
20'	0.0407	0.0407	0.9992	0.0407	24.54	1.001	24.56	1.5301	40'
30'	0.0436	0.0436	0.9990	0.0437	22.90	1.001	22.93	1.5272	30'
40'	0.0465	0.0465	0.9989	0.0466	21.47	1.001	21.49	1.5243	20'
50'	0.0495	0.0494	0.9988	0.0495	20.21	1.001	20.23	1.5213	10'
3°00'	0.0524	0.0523	0.9986	0.0524	19.08	1.001	19.11	1.5184	87°00'
10'	0.0553	0.0552	0.9985	0.0553	18.07	1.002	18.10	1.5155	50'
20'	0.0582	0.0581	0.9983	0.0582	17.17	1.002	17.20	1.5126	40'
30'	0.0611	0.0610	0.9981	0.0612	16.35	1.002	16.38	1.5097	30'
40'	0.0640	0.0640	0.9980	0.0641	15.60	1.002	15.64	1.5068	20'
50'	0.0669	0.0669	0.9978	0.0670	14.92	1.002	14.96	1.5039	10'
4°00'	0.0698	0.0698	0.9976	0.0699	14.30	1.002	14.34	1.5010	86°00'
10'	0.0727	0.0727	0.9974	0.0729	13.73	1.003	13.76	1.4981	50'
20'	0.0756	0.0756	0.9971	0.0758	13.20	1.003	13.23	1.4952	40'
30'	0.0785	0.0785	0.9969	0.0787	12.71	1.003	12.75	1.4923	30'
40'	0.0814	0.0814	0.9967	0.0816	12.25	1.003	12.29	1.4893	20'
50'	0.0844	0.0843	0.9964	0.0846	11.83	1.004	11.87	1.4864	10'
5°00'	0.0873	0.0872	0.9962	0.0875	11.43	1.004	11.47	1.4835	85°00'
10'	0.0902	0.0901	0.9959	0.0904	11.06	1.004	11.10	1.4806	50'
20'	0.0931	0.0929	0.9957	0.0934	10.71	1.004	10.76	1.4777	40'
30'	0.0960	0.0958	0.9954	0.0963	10.39	1.005	10.43	1.4748	30'
40'	0.0989	0.0987	0.9951	0.0992	10.08	1.005	10.13	1.4719	20'
50'	0.1018	0.1016	0.9948	0.1022	9.788	1.005	9.839	1.4690	10'
6°00'	0.1047	0.1045	0.9945	0.1051	9.514	1.006	9.567	1.4661	84°00'
10'	0.1076	0.1074	0.9942	0.1080	9.255	1.006	9.309	1.4632	50'
20'	0.1105	0.1103	0.9939	0.1110	9.010	1.006	9.065	1.4603	40'
30'	0.1134	0.1132	0.9936	0.1139	8.777	1.006	8.834	1.4573	30'
40'	0.1164	0.1161	0.9932	0.1169	8.556	1.007	8.614	1.4544	20'
50'	0.1193	0.1190	0.9929	0.1198	8.345	1.007	8.405	1.4515	10'
7°00'	0.1222	0.1219	0.9925	0.1228	8.144	1.008	8.206	1.4486	83°00'
10'	0.1251	0.1248	0.9922	0.1257	7.953	1.008	8.016	1.4457	50'
20'	0.1280	0.1276	0.9918	0.1287	7.770	1.008	7.834	1.4428	40'
30'	0.1309	0.1305	0.9914	0.1317	7.596	1.009	7.661	1.4399	30'
40'	0.1338	0.1334	0.9911	0.1346	7.429	1.009	7.496	1.4370	20'
50'	0.1367	0.1363	0.9907	0.1376	7.269	1.009	7.337	1.4341	10'
8°00'	0.1396	0.1392	0.9903	0.1405	7.115	1.010	7.185	1.4312	82°00'
10'	0.1425	0.1421	0.9899	0.1435	6.968	1.010	7.040	1.4283	50'
20'	0.1454	0.1449	0.9894	0.1465	6.827	1.011	6.900	1.4254	40'
30'	0.1484	0.1478	0.9890	0.1495	6.691	1.011	6.765	1.4224	30'
40'	0.1513	0.1507	0.9886	0.1524	6.561	1.012	6.636	1.4195	20'
50'	0.1542	0.1536	0.9881	0.1554	6.435	1.012	6.512	1.4166	10'
9°00'	0.1571	0.1564	0.9877	0.1584	6.314	1.012	6.392	1.4137	81°00'
		Cos	Sin	Cot	Tan	Csc	Sec	Radians	Angle

Values of Trigonometric Functions

Angle	Radians	Sin	Cos	Tan	Cot	Sec	Csc		
9°00'	0.1571	0.1564	0.9877	0.1584	6.314	1.012	6.392	1.4137	81°00'
10'	0.1600	0.1593	0.9872	0.1614	6.197	1.013	6.277	1.4108	50'
20'	0.1629	0.1622	0.9868	0.1644	6.084	1.013	6.166	1.4079	40'
30'	0.1658	0.1650	0.9863	0.1673	5.976	1.014	6.059	1.4050	30'
40'	0.1687	0.1679	0.9858	0.1703	5.871	1.014	5.955	1.4021	20'
50'	0.1716	0.1708	0.9853	0.1733	5.769	1.015	5.855	1.3992	10'
10°00'	0.1745	0.1736	0.9848	0.1763	5.671	1.015	5.759	1.3963	80°00'
10'	0.1774	0.1765	0.9843	0.1793	5.576	1.016	5.665	1.3934	50'
20'	0.1804	0.1794	0.9838	0.1823	5.485	1.016	5.575	1.3904	40'
30'	0.1833	0.1822	0.9833	0.1853	5.396	1.017	5.487	1.3875	30'
40'	0.1862	0.1851	0.9827	0.1883	5.309	1.018	5.403	1.3846	20'
50'	0.1891	0.1880	0.9822	0.1914	5.226	1.018	5.320	1.3817	10'
11°00'	0.1920	0.1908	0.9816	0.1944	5.145	1.019	5.241	1.3788	79°00'
10'	0.1949	0.1937	0.9811	0.1974	5.066	1.019	5.164	1.3759	50'
20'	0.1978	0.1965	0.9805	0.2004	4.989	1.020	5.089	1.3730	40'
30'	0.2007	0.1994	0.9799	0.2035	4.915	1.020	5.016	1.3701	30'
40'	0.2036	0.2022	0.9793	0.2065	4.843	1.021	4.945	1.3672	20'
50'	0.2065	0.2051	0.9787	0.2095	4.773	1.022	4.876	1.3643	10'
12°00'	0.2094	0.2079	0.9781	0.2126	4.705	1.022	4.810	1.3614	78°00'
10'	0.2123	0.2108	0.9775	0.2156	4.638	1.023	4.745	1.3584	50'
20'	0.2153	0.2136	0.9769	0.2186	4.574	1.024	4.682	1.3555	40'
30'	0.2182	0.2164	0.9763	0.2217	4.511	1.024	4.620	1.3526	30'
40'	0.2211	0.2193	0.9757	0.2247	4.449	1.025	4.560	1.3497	20'
50'	0.2240	0.2221	0.9750	0.2278	4.390	1.026	4.502	1.3468	10'
13°00'	0.2269	0.2250	0.9744	0.2309	4.331	1.026	4.445	1.3439	77°00'
10'	0.2298	0.2278	0.9737	0.2339	4.275	1.027	4.390	1.3410	50'
20'	0.2327	0.2306	0.9730	0.2370	4.219	1.028	4.336	1.3381	40'
30'	0.2356	0.2334	0.9724	0.2401	4.165	1.028	4.284	1.3352	30'
40'	0.2385	0.2363	0.9717	0.2432	4.113	1.029	4.232	1.3323	20'
50'	0.2414	0.2391	0.9710	0.2462	4.061	1.030	4.182	1.3294	10'
14°00'	0.2443	0.2419	0.9703	0.2493	4.011	1.031	4.134	1.3265	76°00'
10'	0.2473	0.2447	0.9696	0.2524	3.962	1.031	4.086	1.3235	50'
20'	0.2502	0.2476	0.9689	0.2555	3.914	1.032	4.039	1.3206	40'
30'	0.2531	0.2504	0.9681	0.2586	3.867	1.033	3.994	1.3177	30'
40'	0.2560	0.2532	0.9674	0.2617	3.821	1.034	3.950	1.3148	20'
50'	0.2589	0.2560	0.9667	0.2648	3.776	1.034	3.906	1.3119	10'
15°00'	0.2618	0.2588	0.9659	0.2679	3.732	1.035	3.864	1.3090	75°00'
10'	0.2647	0.2616	0.9652	0.2711	3.689	1.036	3.822	1.3061	50'
20'	0.2676	0.2644	0.9644	0.2742	3.647	1.037	3.782	1.3032	40'
30'	0.2705	0.2672	0.9636	0.2773	3.606	1.038	3.742	1.3003	30'
40'	0.2734	0.2700	0.9628	0.2805	3.566	1.039	3.703	1.2974	20'
50'	0.2763	0.2728	0.9621	0.2836	3.526	1.039	3.665	1.2945	10'
16°00'	0.2793	0.2756	0.9613	0.2867	3.487	1.040	3.628	1.2915	74°00'
10'	0.2822	0.2784	0.9605	0.2899	3.450	1.041	3.592	1.2886	50'
20'	0.2851	0.2812	0.9596	0.2931	3.412	1.042	3.556	1.2857	40'
30'	0.2880	0.2840	0.9588	0.2962	3.376	1.043	3.521	1.2828	30'
40'	0.2909	0.2868	0.9580	0.2994	3.340	1.044	3.487	1.2799	20'
50'	0.2938	0.2896	0.9572	0.3026	3.305	1.045	3.453	1.2770	10'
17°00'	0.2967	0.2924	0.9563	0.3057	3.271	1.046	3.420	1.2741	73°00'
10'	0.2996	0.2952	0.9555	0.3089	3.237	1.047	3.388	1.2712	50'
20'	0.3025	0.2979	0.9546	0.3121	3.204	1.048	3.356	1.2683	40'
30'	0.3054	0.3007	0.9537	0.3153	3.172	1.049	3.326	1.2654	30'
40'	0.3083	0.3035	0.9528	0.3185	3.140	1.049	3.295	1.2625	20'
50'	0.3113	0.3062	0.9520	0.3217	3.108	1.050	3.265	1.2595	10'
18°00'	0.3142	0.3090	0.9511	0.3249	3.078	1.051	3.236	1.2566	72°00'
		Cos	Sin	Cot	Tan	Csc	Sec	Radians	Angle

Values of Trigonometric Functions

Angle	Radians	Sin	Cos	Tan	Cot	Sec	Csc		
18°00'	0.3142	0.3090	0.9511	0.3249	3.078	1.051	3.236	1.2566	72°00'
10'	0.3171	0.3118	0.9502	0.3281	3.047	1.052	3.207	1.2537	50'
20'	0.3200	0.3145	0.9492	0.3314	3.018	1.053	3.179	1.2508	40'
30'	0.3229	0.3173	0.9483	0.3346	2.989	1.054	3.152	1.2479	30'
40'	0.3258	0.3201	0.9474	0.3378	2.960	1.056	3.124	1.2450	20'
50'	0.3287	0.3228	0.9465	0.3411	2.932	1.057	3.098	1.2421	10'
19°00'	0.3316	0.3256	0.9455	0.3443	2.904	1.058	3.072	1.2392	71°00'
10'	0.3345	0.3283	0.9446	0.3476	2.877	1.059	3.046	1.2363	50'
20'	0.3374	0.3311	0.9436	0.3508	2.850	1.060	3.021	1.2334	40'
30'	0.3403	0.3338	0.9426	0.3541	2.824	1.061	2.996	1.2305	30'
40'	0.3432	0.3365	0.9417	0.3574	2.798	1.062	2.971	1.2275	20'
50'	0.3462	0.3393	0.9407	0.3607	2.773	1.063	2.947	1.2246	10'
20°00'	0.3491	0.3420	0.9397	0.3640	2.747	1.064	2.924	1.2217	70°00'
10'	0.3520	0.3448	0.9387	0.3673	2.723	1.065	2.901	1.2188	50'
20'	0.3549	0.3475	0.9377	0.3706	2.699	1.066	2.878	1.2159	40'
30'	0.3578	0.3502	0.9367	0.3739	2.675	1.068	2.855	1.2130	30'
40'	0.3607	0.3529	0.9356	0.3772	2.651	1.069	2.833	1.2101	20'
50'	0.3636	0.3557	0.9346	0.3805	2.628	1.070	2.812	1.2072	10'
21°00'	0.3665	0.3584	0.9336	0.3839	2.605	1.071	2.790	1.2043	69°00'
10'	0.3694	0.3611	0.9325	0.3872	2.583	1.072	2.769	1.2014	50'
20'	0.3723	0.3638	0.9315	0.3906	2.560	1.074	2.749	1.1985	40'
30'	0.3752	0.3665	0.9304	0.3939	2.539	1.075	2.729	1.1956	30'
40'	0.3782	0.3692	0.9293	0.3973	2.517	1.076	2.709	1.1926	20'
50'	0.3811	0.3719	0.9283	0.4006	2.496	1.077	2.689	1.1897	10'
22°00'	0.3840	0.3746	0.9272	0.4040	2.475	1.079	2.669	1.1868	68°00'
10'	0.3869	0.3773	0.9261	0.4074	2.455	1.080	2.650	1.1839	50'
20'	0.3898	0.3800	0.9250	0.4108	2.434	1.081	2.632	1.1810	40'
30'	0.3927	0.3827	0.9239	0.4142	2.414	1.082	2.613	1.1781	30'
40'	0.3956	0.3854	0.9228	0.4176	2.394	1.084	2.595	1.1752	20'
50'	0.3985	0.3881	0.9216	0.4210	2.375	1.085	2.577	1.1723	10'
23°00'	0.4014	0.3907	0.9205	0.4245	2.356	1.086	2.559	1.1694	67°00'
10'	0.4043	0.3934	0.9194	0.4279	2.337	1.088	2.542	1.1665	50'
20'	0.4072	0.3961	0.9182	0.4314	2.318	1.089	2.525	1.1636	40'
30'	0.4102	0.3987	0.9171	0.4348	2.300	1.090	2.508	1.1606	30'
40'	0.4131	0.4014	0.9159	0.4383	2.282	1.092	2.491	1.1577	20'
50'	0.4160	0.4041	0.9147	0.4417	2.264	1.093	2.475	1.1548	10'
24°00'	0.4189	0.4067	0.9135	0.4452	2.246	1.095	2.459	1.1519	66°00'
10'	0.4218	0.4094	0.9124	0.4487	2.229	1.096	2.443	1.1490	50'
20'	0.4247	0.4120	0.9112	0.4522	2.211	1.097	2.427	1.1461	40'
30'	0.4276	0.4147	0.9100	0.4557	2.194	1.099	2.411	1.1432	30'
40'	0.4305	0.4173	0.9088	0.4592	2.177	1.100	2.396	1.1403	20'
50'	0.4334	0.4200	0.9075	0.4628	2.161	1.102	2.381	1.1374	10'
25°00'	0.4363	0.4226	0.9063	0.4663	2.145	1.103	2.366	1.1345	65°00'
10'	0.4392	0.4253	0.9051	0.4699	2.128	1.105	2.352	1.1316	50'
20'	0.4422	0.4279	0.9038	0.4734	2.112	1.106	2.337	1.1286	40'
30'	0.4451	0.4305	0.9026	0.4770	2.097	1.108	2.323	1.1257	30'
40'	0.4480	0.4331	0.9013	0.4806	2.081	1.109	2.309	1.1228	20'
50'	0.4509	0.4358	0.9001	0.4841	2.066	1.111	2.295	1.1199	10'
26°00'	0.4538	0.4384	0.8988	0.4877	2.050	1.113	2.281	1.1170	64°00'
10'	0.4567	0.4410	0.8975	0.4913	2.035	1.114	2.268	1.1141	50'
20'	0.4596	0.4436	0.8962	0.4950	2.020	1.116	2.254	1.1112	40'
30'	0.4625	0.4462	0.8949	0.4986	2.006	1.117	2.241	1.1083	30'
40'	0.4654	0.4488	0.8936	0.5022	1.991	1.119	2.228	1.1054	20'
50'	0.4683	0.4514	0.8923	0.5059	1.977	1.121	2.215	1.1025	10'
27°00'	0.4712	0.4540	0.8910	0.5095	1.963	1.122	2.203	1.0996	63°00'
		Cos	Sin	Cot	Tan	Csc	Sec	Radians	Angle

Values of Trigonometric Functions

Angle	Radians	Sin	Cos	Tan	Cot	Sec	Csc		
27°00'	0.4712	0.4540	0.8910	0.5095	1.963	1.122	2.203	1.0996	63°00'
10'	0.4741	0.4566	0.8897	0.5132	1.949	1.124	2.190	1.0966	50'
20'	0.4771	0.4592	0.8884	0.5169	1.935	1.126	2.178	1.0937	40'
30'	0.4800	0.4617	0.8870	0.5206	1.921	1.127	2.166	1.0908	30'
40'	0.4829	0.4643	0.8857	0.5243	1.907	1.129	2.154	1.0879	20'
50'	0.4858	0.4669	0.8843	0.5280	1.894	1.131	2.142	1.0850	10'
28°00'	0.4887	0.4695	0.8829	0.5317	1.881	1.133	2.130	1.0821	62°00'
10'	0.4916	0.4720	0.8816	0.5354	1.868	1.134	2.118	1.0792	50'
20'	0.4945	0.4746	0.8802	0.5392	1.855	1.136	2.107	1.0763	40'
30'	0.4974	0.4772	0.8788	0.5430	1.842	1.138	2.096	1.0734	30'
40'	0.5003	0.4797	0.8774	0.5467	1.829	1.140	2.085	1.0705	20'
50'	0.5032	0.4823	0.8760	0.5505	1.816	1.142	2.074	1.0676	10'
29°00'	0.5061	0.4848	0.8746	0.5543	1.804	1.143	2.063	1.0647	61°00'
10'	0.5091	0.4874	0.8732	0.5581	1.792	1.145	2.052	1.0617	50'
20'	0.5120	0.4899	0.8718	0.5619	1.780	1.147	2.041	1.0588	40'
30'	0.5149	0.4924	0.8704	0.5658	1.767	1.149	2.031	1.0559	30'
40'	0.5178	0.4950	0.8689	0.5696	1.756	1.151	2.020	1.0530	20'
50'	0.5207	0.4975	0.8675	0.5735	1.744	1.153	2.010	1.0501	10'
30°00'	0.5236	0.5000	0.8660	0.5774	1.732	1.155	2.000	1.0472	60°00'
10'	0.5265	0.5025	0.8646	0.5812	1.720	1.157	1.990	1.0443	50'
20'	0.5294	0.5050	0.8631	0.5851	1.709	1.159	1.980	1.0414	40'
30'	0.5323	0.5075	0.8616	0.5890	1.698	1.161	1.970	1.0385	30'
40'	0.5352	0.5100	0.8601	0.5930	1.686	1.163	1.961	1.0356	20'
50'	0.5381	0.5125	0.8587	0.5969	1.675	1.165	1.951	1.0327	10'
31°00'	0.5411	0.5150	0.8572	0.6009	1.664	1.167	1.942	1.0297	59°00'
10'	0.5440	0.5175	0.8557	0.6048	1.653	1.169	1.932	1.0268	50'
20'	0.5469	0.5200	0.8542	0.6088	1.643	1.171	1.923	1.0239	40'
30'	0.5498	0.5225	0.8526	0.6128	1.632	1.173	1.914	1.0210	30'
40'	0.5527	0.5250	0.8511	0.6168	1.621	1.175	1.905	1.0181	20'
50'	0.5556	0.5275	0.8496	0.6208	1.611	1.177	1.896	1.0152	10'
32°00'	0.5585	0.5299	0.8480	0.6249	1.600	1.179	1.887	1.0123	58°00'
10'	0.5614	0.5324	0.8465	0.6289	1.590	1.181	1.878	1.0094	50'
20'	0.5643	0.5348	0.8450	0.6330	1.580	1.184	1.870	1.0065	40'
30'	0.5672	0.5373	0.8434	0.6371	1.570	1.186	1.861	1.0036	30'
40'	0.5701	0.5398	0.8418	0.6412	1.560	1.188	1.853	1.0007	20'
50'	0.5730	0.5422	0.8403	0.6453	1.550	1.190	1.844	0.9977	10'
33°00'	0.5760	0.5446	0.8387	0.6494	1.540	1.192	1.836	0.9948	57°00'
10'	0.5789	0.5471	0.8371	0.6536	1.530	1.195	1.828	0.9919	50'
20'	0.5818	0.5495	0.8355	0.6577	1.520	1.197	1.820	0.9890	40'
30'	0.5847	0.5519	0.8339	0.6619	1.511	1.199	1.812	0.9861	30'
40'	0.5876	0.5544	0.8323	0.6661	1.501	1.202	1.804	0.9832	20'
50'	0.5905	0.5568	0.8307	0.6703	1.492	1.204	1.796	0.9803	10'
34°00'	0.5934	0.5592	0.8290	0.6745	1.483	1.206	1.788	0.9774	56°00'
10'	0.5963	0.5616	0.8274	0.6787	1.473	1.209	1.781	0.9745	50'
20'	0.5992	0.5640	0.8258	0.6830	1.464	1.211	1.773	0.9716	40'
30'	0.6021	0.5664	0.8241	0.6873	1.455	1.213	1.766	0.9687	30'
40'	0.6050	0.5688	0.8225	0.6916	1.446	1.216	1.758	0.9657	20'
50'	0.6080	0.5712	0.8208	0.6959	1.437	1.218	1.751	0.9628	10'
35°00'	0.6109	0.5736	0.8192	0.7002	1.428	1.221	1.743	0.9599	55°00'
10'	0.6138	0.5760	0.8175	0.7046	1.419	1.223	1.736	0.9570	50'
20'	0.6167	0.5783	0.8158	0.7089	1.411	1.226	1.729	0.9541	40'
30'	0.6196	0.5807	0.8141	0.7133	1.402	1.228	1.722	0.9512	30'
40'	0.6225	0.5831	0.8124	0.7177	1.393	1.231	1.715	0.9483	20'
50'	0.6254	0.5854	0.8107	0.7221	1.385	1.233	1.708	0.9454	10'
36°00'	0.6283	0.5878	0.8090	0.7265	1.376	1.236	1.701	0.9425	54°00'
		Cos	Sin	Cot	Tan	Csc	Sec	Radians	Angle

Values of Trigonometric Functions

Angle	Radians	Sin	Cos	Tan	Cot	Sec	Csc		
36°00'	0.6283	0.5878	0.8090	0.7265	1.376	1.236	1.701	0.9425	54°00'
10'	0.6312	0.5901	0.8073	0.7310	1.368	1.239	1.695	0.9396	50'
20'	0.6341	0.5925	0.8056	0.7355	1.360	1.241	1.688	0.9367	40'
30'	0.6370	0.5948	0.8039	0.7400	1.351	1.244	1.681	0.9338	30'
40'	0.6400	0.5972	0.8021	0.7445	1.343	1.247	1.675	0.9308	20'
50'	0.6429	0.5995	0.8004	0.7490	1.335	1.249	1.668	0.9279	10'
37°00'	0.6458	0.6018	0.7986	0.7536	1.327	1.252	1.662	0.9250	53°00'
10'	0.6487	0.6041	0.7969	0.7581	1.319	1.255	1.655	0.9221	50'
20'	0.6516	0.6065	0.7951	0.7627	1.311	1.258	1.649	0.9192	40'
30'	0.6545	0.6088	0.7934	0.7673	1.303	1.260	1.643	0.9163	30'
40'	0.6574	0.6111	0.7916	0.7720	1.295	1.263	1.636	0.9134	20'
50'	0.6603	0.6134	0.7898	0.7766	1.288	1.266	1.630	0.9105	10'
38°00'	0.6632	0.6157	0.7880	0.7813	1.280	1.269	1.624	0.9076	52°00'
10'	0.6661	0.6180	0.7862	0.7860	1.272	1.272	1.618	0.9047	50'
20'	0.6690	0.6202	0.7844	0.7907	1.265	1.275	1.612	0.9018	40'
30'	0.6720	0.6225	0.7826	0.7954	1.257	1.278	1.606	0.8988	30'
40'	0.6749	0.6248	0.7808	0.8002	1.250	1.281	1.601	0.8959	20'
50'	0.6778	0.6271	0.7790	0.8050	1.242	1.284	1.595	0.8930	10'
39°00'	0.6807	0.6293	0.7771	0.8098	1.235	1.287	1.589	0.8901	51°00'
10'	0.6836	0.6316	0.7753	0.8146	1.228	1.290	1.583	0.8872	50'
20'	0.6865	0.6338	0.7735	0.8195	1.220	1.293	1.578	0.8843	40'
30'	0.6894	0.6361	0.7716	0.8243	1.213	1.296	1.572	0.8814	30'
40'	0.6923	0.6383	0.7698	0.8292	1.206	1.299	1.567	0.8785	20'
50'	0.6952	0.6406	0.7679	0.8342	1.199	1.302	1.561	0.8756	10'
40°00'	0.6981	0.6428	0.7660	0.8391	1.192	1.305	1.556	0.8727	50°00'
10'	0.7010	0.6450	0.7642	0.8441	1.185	1.309	1.550	0.8698	50'
20'	0.7039	0.6472	0.7623	0.8491	1.178	1.312	1.545	0.8668	40'
30'	0.7069	0.6494	0.7604	0.8541	1.171	1.315	1.540	0.8639	30'
40'	0.7098	0.6517	0.7585	0.8591	1.164	1.318	1.535	0.8610	20'
50'	0.7127	0.6539	0.7566	0.8642	1.157	1.322	1.529	0.8581	10'
41°00'	0.7156	0.6561	0.7547	0.8693	1.150	1.325	1.524	0.8552	49°00'
10'	0.7185	0.6583	0.7528	0.8744	1.144	1.328	1.519	0.8523	50'
20'	0.7214	0.6604	0.7509	0.8796	1.137	1.332	1.514	0.8494	40'
30'	0.7243	0.6626	0.7490	0.8847	1.130	1.335	1.509	0.8465	30'
40'	0.7272	0.6648	0.7470	0.8899	1.124	1.339	1.504	0.8436	20'
50'	0.7301	0.6670	0.7451	0.8952	1.117	1.342	1.499	0.8407	10'
42°00'	0.7330	0.6691	0.7431	0.9004	1.111	1.346	1.494	0.8378	48°00'
10'	0.7359	0.6713	0.7412	0.9057	1.104	1.349	1.490	0.8348	50'
20'	0.7389	0.6734	0.7392	0.9110	1.098	1.353	1.485	0.8319	40'
30'	0.7418	0.6756	0.7373	0.9163	1.091	1.356	1.480	0.8290	30'
40'	0.7447	0.6777	0.7353	0.9217	1.085	1.360	1.476	0.8261	20'
50'	0.7476	0.6799	0.7333	0.9271	1.079	1.364	1.471	0.8232	10'
43°00'	0.7505	0.6820	0.7314	0.9325	1.072	1.367	1.466	0.8203	47°00'
10'	0.7534	0.6841	0.7294	0.9380	1.066	1.371	1.462	0.8174	50'
20'	0.7563	0.6862	0.7274	0.9435	1.060	1.375	1.457	0.8145	40'
30'	0.7592	0.6884	0.7254	0.9490	1.054	1.379	1.453	0.8116	30'
40'	0.7621	0.6905	0.7234	0.9545	1.048	1.382	1.448	0.8087	20'
50'	0.7650	0.6926	0.7214	0.9601	1.042	1.386	1.444	0.8058	10'
44°00'	0.7679	0.6947	0.7193	0.9657	1.036	1.390	1.440	0.8029	46°00'
10'	0.7709	0.6967	0.7173	0.9713	1.030	1.394	1.435	0.7999	50'
20'	0.7738	0.6988	0.7153	0.9770	1.024	1.398	1.431	0.7970	40'
30'	0.7767	0.7009	0.7133	0.9827	1.018	1.402	1.427	0.7941	30'
40'	0.7796	0.7030	0.7112	0.9884	1.012	1.406	1.423	0.7912	20'
50'	0.7825	0.7050	0.7092	0.9942	1.006	1.410	1.418	0.7883	10'
45°00'	0.7854	0.7071	0.7071	1.000	1.000	1.414	1.414	0.7854	45°00'
		Cos	Sin	Cot	Tan	Csc	Sec	Radians	Angle

Common Logarithms of Numbers

n	0	1	2	3	4	5	6	7	8	9
10	0000	0043	0086	0128	0170	0212	0253	0294	0334	0374
11	0414	0453	0492	0531	0569	0607	0645	0682	0719	0755
12	0792	0828	0864	0899	0934	0969	1004	1038	1072	1106
13	1139	1173	1206	1239	1271	1303	1335	1367	1399	1430
14	1461	1492	1523	1553	1584	1614	1644	1673	1703	1732
15	1761	1790	1818	1847	1875	1903	1931	1959	1987	2014
16	2041	2068	2095	2122	2148	2175	2201	2227	2253	2279
17	2304	2330	2355	2380	2405	2430	2455	2480	2504	2529
18	2553	2577	2601	2625	2648	2672	2695	2718	2742	2765
19	2788	2810	2833	2856	2878	2900	2923	2945	2967	2989
20	3010	3032	3054	3075	3096	3118	3139	3160	3181	3201
21	3222	3243	3263	3284	3304	3324	3345	3365	3385	3404
22	3424	3444	3464	3483	3502	3522	3541	3560	3579	3598
23	3617	3636	3655	3674	3692	3711	3729	3747	3766	3784
24	3802	3820	3838	3856	3874	3892	3909	3927	3945	3962
25	3979	3997	4014	4031	4048	4065	4082	4099	4116	4133
26	4150	4166	4183	4200	4216	4232	4249	4265	4281	4298
27	4314	4330	4346	4362	4378	4393	4409	4425	4440	4456
28	4472	4487	4502	4518	4533	4548	4564	4579	4594	4609
29	4624	4639	4654	4669	4683	4698	4713	4728	4742	4757
30	4771	4786	4800	4814	4829	4843	4857	4871	4886	4900
31	4914	4928	4942	4955	4969	4983	4997	5011	5024	5038
32	5051	5065	5079	5092	5105	5119	5132	5145	5159	5172
33	5185	5198	5211	5224	5237	5250	5263	5276	5289	5302
34	5315	5328	5340	5353	5366	5378	5391	5403	5416	5428
35	5441	5453	5465	5478	5490	5502	5514	5527	5539	5551
36	5563	5575	5587	5599	5611	5623	5635	5647	5658	5670
37	5682	5694	5705	5717	5729	5740	5752	5763	5775	5786
38	5798	5809	5821	5832	5843	5855	5866	5877	5888	5899
39	5911	5922	5933	5944	5955	5966	5977	5988	5999	6010
40	6021	6031	6042	6053	6064	6075	6085	6096	6107	6117
41	6128	6138	6149	6160	6170	6180	6191	6201	6212	6222
42	6232	6243	6253	6263	6274	6284	6294	6304	6314	6325
43	6335	6345	6355	6365	6375	6385	6395	6405	6415	6425
44	6435	6444	6454	6464	6474	6484	6493	6503	6513	6522
45	6532	6542	6551	6561	6571	6580	6590	6599	6609	6618
46	6628	6637	6646	6656	6665	6675	6684	6693	6702	6712
47	6721	6730	6739	6749	6758	6767	6776	6785	6794	6803
48	6812	6821	6830	6839	6848	6857	6866	6875	6884	6893
49	6902	6911	6920	6928	6937	6946	6955	6964	6972	6981
50	6990	6998	7007	7016	7024	7033	7042	7050	7059	7067
51	7076	7084	7093	7101	7110	7118	7126	7135	7143	7152
52	7160	7168	7177	7185	7193	7202	7210	7218	7226	7235
53	7243	7251	7259	7267	7275	7284	7292	7300	7308	7316
54	7324	7332	7340	7348	7356	7364	7372	7380	7388	7396

Common Logarithms of Numbers

n	0	1	2	3	4	5	6	7	8	9
55	7404	7412	7419	7427	7435	7443	7451	7459	7466	7474
56	7482	7490	7497	7505	7513	7520	7528	7536	7543	7551
57	7559	7566	7574	7582	7589	7597	7604	7612	7619	7627
58	7634	7642	7649	7657	7664	7672	7679	7686	7694	7701
59	7709	7716	7723	7731	7738	7745	7752	7760	7767	7774
60	7782	7789	7796	7803	7810	7818	7825	7832	7839	7846
61	7853	7860	7868	7875	7882	7889	7896	7903	7910	7917
62	7924	7931	7938	7945	7952	7959	7966	7973	7980	7987
63	7993	8000	8007	8014	8021	8028	8035	8041	8048	8055
64	8062	8069	8075	8082	8089	8096	8102	8109	8116	8122
65	8129	8136	8142	8149	8156	8162	8169	8176	8182	8189
66	8195	8202	8209	8215	8222	8228	8235	8241	8248	8254
67	8261	8267	8274	8280	8287	8293	8299	8306	8312	8319
68	8325	8331	8338	8344	8351	8357	8363	8370	8376	8382
69	8388	8395	8401	8407	8414	8420	8426	8432	8439	8445
70	8451	8457	8463	8470	8476	8482	8488	8494	8500	8506
71	8513	8519	8525	8531	8537	8543	8549	8555	8561	8567
72	8573	8579	8585	8591	8597	8603	8609	8615	8621	8627
73	8633	8639	8645	8651	8657	8663	8669	8675	8681	8686
74	8692	8698	8704	8710	8716	8722	8727	8733	8739	8745
75	8751	8756	8762	8768	8774	8779	8785	8791	8797	8802
76	8808	8814	8820	8825	8831	8837	8842	8848	8854	8859
77	8865	8871	8876	8882	8887	8893	8899	8904	8910	8915
78	8921	8927	8932	8938	8943	8949	8954	8960	8965	8971
79	8976	8982	8987	8993	8998	9004	9009	9015	9020	9025
80	9031	9036	9042	9047	9053	9058	9063	9069	9074	9079
81	9085	9090	9096	9101	9106	9112	9117	9122	9128	9133
82	9138	9143	9149	9154	9159	9165	9170	9175	9180	9186
83	9191	9196	9201	9206	9212	9217	9222	9227	9232	9238
84	9243	9248	9253	9258	9263	9269	9274	9279	9284	9289
85	9294	9299	9304	9309	9315	9320	9325	9330	9335	9340
86	9345	9350	9355	9360	9365	9370	9375	9380	9385	9390
87	9395	9400	9405	9410	9415	9420	9425	9430	9435	9440
88	9445	9450	9455	9460	9465	9469	9474	9479	9484	9489
89	9494	9499	9504	9509	9513	9518	9523	9528	9533	9538
90	9542	9547	9552	9557	9562	9566	9571	9576	9581	9586
91	9590	9595	9600	9605	9609	9614	9619	9624	9628	9633
92	9638	9643	9647	9652	9657	9661	9666	9671	9675	9680
93	9685	9689	9694	9699	9703	9708	9713	9717	9722	9727
94	9731	9736	9741	9745	9750	9754	9759	9763	9768	9773
95	9777	9782	9786	9791	9795	9800	9805	9809	9814	9818
96	9823	9827	9832	9836	9841	9845	9850	9854	9859	9863
97	9868	9872	9877	9881	9886	9890	9894	9899	9903	9908
98	9912	9917	9921	9926	9930	9934	9939	9943	9948	9952
99	9956	9961	9965	9969	9974	9978	9983	9987	9991	9996

Natural Logarithms of Numbers

Use ln 10 = 2.3026 to find logarithms of numbers greater than 10 or less than 1.

n	0	1	2	3	4	5	6	7	8	9
1.0	0.0000	0.0100	0.0198	0.0296	0.0392	0.0488	0.0583	0.0677	0.0770	0.0862
1.1	0.0953	0.1044	0.1133	0.1222	0.1310	0.1398	0.1484	0.1570	0.1655	0.1740
1.2	0.1823	0.1906	0.1989	0.2070	0.2151	0.2231	0.2311	0.2390	0.2469	0.2546
1.3	0.2624	0.2700	0.2776	0.2852	0.2927	0.3001	0.3075	0.3148	0.3221	0.3293
1.4	0.3365	0.3436	0.3507	0.3577	0.3646	0.3716	0.3784	0.3853	0.3920	0.3988
1.5	0.4055	0.4121	0.4187	0.4253	0.4318	0.4383	0.4447	0.4511	0.4574	0.4637
1.6	0.4700	0.4762	0.4824	0.4886	0.4947	0.5008	0.5068	0.5128	0.5188	0.5247
1.7	0.5306	0.5365	0.5423	0.5481	0.5539	0.5596	0.5653	0.5710	0.5766	0.5822
1.8	0.5878	0.5933	0.5988	0.6043	0.6098	0.6152	0.6206	0.6259	0.6313	0.6366
1.9	0.6419	0.6471	0.6523	0.6575	0.6627	0.6678	0.6729	0.6780	0.6831	0.6881
2.0	0.6932	0.6981	0.7031	0.7080	0.7130	0.7178	0.7227	0.7276	0.7324	0.7372
2.1	0.7419	0.7467	0.7514	0.7561	0.7608	0.7655	0.7701	0.7747	0.7793	0.7839
2.2	0.7885	0.7930	0.7975	0.8020	0.8065	0.8109	0.8154	0.8198	0.8242	0.8286
2.3	0.8329	0.8373	0.8416	0.8459	0.8502	0.8544	0.8587	0.8629	0.8671	0.8713
2.4	0.8755	0.8796	0.8838	0.8879	0.8920	0.8961	0.9002	0.9042	0.9083	0.9123
2.5	0.9163	0.9203	0.9243	0.9282	0.9322	0.9361	0.9400	0.9439	0.9478	0.9517
2.6	0.9555	0.9594	0.9632	0.9670	0.9708	0.9746	0.9783	0.9821	0.9858	0.9895
2.7	0.9933	0.9970	1.0006	1.0043	1.0080	1.0116	1.0152	1.0189	1.0225	1.0260
2.8	1.0296	1.0332	1.0367	1.0403	1.0438	1.0473	1.0508	1.0543	1.0578	1.0613
2.9	1.0647	1.0682	1.0716	1.0750	1.0784	1.0818	1.0852	1.0886	1.0919	1.0953
3.0	1.0986	1.1019	1.1053	1.1086	1.1119	1.1151	1.1184	1.1217	1.1249	1.1282
3.1	1.1314	1.1346	1.1378	1.1410	1.1442	1.1474	1.1506	1.1537	1.1569	1.1600
3.2	1.1632	1.1663	1.1694	1.1725	1.1756	1.1787	1.1817	1.1848	1.1878	1.1909
3.3	1.1939	1.1970	1.2000	1.2030	1.2060	1.2090	1.2119	1.2149	1.2179	1.2208
3.4	1.2238	1.2267	1.2296	1.2326	1.2355	1.2384	1.2413	1.2442	1.2470	1.2499
3.5	1.2528	1.2556	1.2585	1.2613	1.2641	1.2670	1.2698	1.2726	1.2754	1.2782
3.6	1.2809	1.2837	1.2865	1.2892	1.2920	1.2947	1.2975	1.3002	1.3029	1.3056
3.7	1.3083	1.3110	1.3137	1.3164	1.3191	1.3218	1.3244	1.3271	1.3297	1.3324
3.8	1.3350	1.3376	1.3403	1.3429	1.3455	1.3481	1.3507	1.3533	1.3558	1.3584
3.9	1.3610	1.3635	1.3661	1.3686	1.3712	1.3737	1.3762	1.3788	1.3813	1.3838
4.0	1.3863	1.3883	1.3913	1.3938	1.3962	1.3987	1.4012	1.4036	1.4061	1.4085
4.1	1.4110	1.4134	1.4159	1.4183	1.4207	1.4231	1.4255	1.4279	1.4303	1.4327
4.2	1.4351	1.4375	1.4398	1.4422	1.4446	1.4469	1.4493	1.4516	1.4540	1.4563
4.3	1.4586	1.4609	1.4633	1.4656	1.4679	1.4702	1.4725	1.4748	1.4771	1.4793
4.4	1.4816	1.4839	1.4861	1.4884	1.4907	1.4929	1.4952	1.4974	1.4996	1.5019
4.5	1.5041	1.5063	1.5085	1.5107	1.5129	1.5151	1.5173	1.5195	1.5217	1.5239
4.6	1.5261	1.5282	1.5304	1.5326	1.5347	1.5369	1.5390	1.5412	1.5433	1.5454
4.7	1.5476	1.5497	1.5518	1.5539	1.5560	1.5581	1.5603	1.5624	1.5644	1.5665
4.8	1.5686	1.5707	1.5728	1.5749	1.5769	1.5790	1.5810	1.5831	1.5852	1.5872
4.9	1.5892	1.5913	1.5933	1.5953	1.5974	1.5994	1.6014	1.6034	1.6054	1.6074
5.0	1.6094	1.6114	1.6134	1.6154	1.6174	1.6194	1.6214	1.6233	1.6253	1.6273
5.1	1.6292	1.6312	1.6332	1.6351	1.6371	1.6390	1.6409	1.6429	1.6448	1.6467
5.2	1.6487	1.6506	1.6525	1.6544	1.6563	1.6582	1.6601	1.6620	1.6639	1.6658
5.3	1.6677	1.6696	1.6715	1.6734	1.6752	1.6771	1.6790	1.6808	1.6827	1.6846
5.4	1.6864	1.6883	1.6901	1.6919	1.6938	1.6956	1.6975	1.6993	1.7011	1.7029

Natural Logarithms of Numbers

n	0	1	2	3	4	5	6	7	8	9
5.5	1.7048	1.7066	1.7084	1.7102	1.7120	1.7138	1.7156	1.7174	1.7192	1.7210
5.6	1.7228	1.7246	1.7263	1.7281	1.7299	1.7317	1.7334	1.7352	1.7370	1.7387
5.7	1.7405	1.7422	1.7440	1.7457	1.7475	1.7492	1.7509	1.7527	1.7544	1.7561
5.8	1.7579	1.7596	1.7613	1.7630	1.7647	1.7664	1.7682	1.7699	1.7716	1.7733
5.9	1.7750	1.7767	1.7783	1.7800	1.7817	1.7834	1.7851	1.7868	1.7884	1.7901
6.0	1.7918	1.7934	1.7951	1.7968	1.7984	1.8001	1.8017	1.8034	1.8050	1.8067
6.1	1.8083	1.8099	1.8116	1.8132	1.8148	1.8165	1.8181	1.8197	1.8213	1.8229
6.2	1.8246	1.8262	1.8278	1.8294	1.8310	1.8326	1.8342	1.8358	1.8374	1.8390
6.3	1.8406	1.8421	1.8437	1.8453	1.8469	1.8485	1.8500	1.8516	1.8532	1.8547
6.4	1.8563	1.8579	1.8594	1.8610	1.8625	1.8641	1.8656	1.8672	1.8687	1.8703
6.5	1.8718	1.8733	1.8749	1.8764	1.8779	1.8795	1.8810	1.8825	1.8840	1.8856
6.6	1.8871	1.8886	1.8901	1.8916	1.8931	1.8946	1.8961	1.8976	1.8991	1.9006
6.7	1.9021	1.9036	1.9051	1.9066	1.9081	1.9095	1.9110	1.9125	1.9140	1.9155
6.8	1.9169	1.9184	1.9199	1.9213	1.9228	1.9243	1.9257	1.9272	1.9286	1.9301
6.9	1.9315	1.9330	1.9344	1.9359	1.9373	1.9387	1.9402	1.9416	1.9431	1.9445
7.0	1.9459	1.9473	1.9488	1.9502	1.9516	1.9530	1.9545	1.9559	1.9573	1.9587
7.1	1.9601	1.9615	1.9629	1.9643	1.9657	1.9671	1.9685	1.9699	1.9713	1.9727
7.2	1.9741	1.9755	1.9769	1.9782	1.9796	1.9810	1.9824	1.9838	1.9851	1.9865
7.3	1.9879	1.9892	1.9906	1.9920	1.9933	1.9947	1.9961	1.9974	1.9988	2.0001
7.4	2.0015	2.0028	2.0042	2.0055	2.0069	2.0082	2.0096	2.0109	2.0122	2.0136
7.5	2.0149	2.0162	2.0176	2.0189	2.0202	2.0216	2.0229	2.0242	2.0255	2.0268
7.6	2.0282	2.0295	2.0308	2.0321	2.0334	2.0347	2.0360	2.0373	2.0386	2.0399
7.7	2.0412	2.0425	2.0438	2.0451	2.0464	2.0477	2.0490	2.0503	2.0516	2.0528
7.8	2.0541	2.0554	2.0567	2.0580	2.0592	2.0605	2.0618	2.0631	2.0643	2.0656
7.9	2.0669	2.0681	2.0694	2.0707	2.0719	2.0732	2.0744	2.0757	2.0769	2.0782
8.0	2.0794	2.0807	2.0819	2.0832	2.0844	2.0857	2.0869	2.0882	2.0894	2.0906
8.1	2.0919	2.0931	2.0943	2.0956	2.0968	2.0980	2.0992	2.1005	2.1017	2.1029
8.2	2.1041	2.1054	2.1066	2.1078	2.1090	2.1102	2.1114	2.1126	2.1138	2.1151
8.3	2.1163	2.1175	2.1187	2.1199	2.1211	2.1223	2.1235	2.1247	2.1259	2.1270
8.4	2.1282	2.1294	2.1306	2.1318	2.1330	2.1342	2.1354	2.1365	2.1377	2.1389
8.5	2.1401	2.1412	2.1424	2.1436	2.1448	2.1459	2.1471	2.1483	2.1494	2.1506
8.6	2.1518	2.1529	2.1541	2.1552	2.1564	2.1576	2.1587	2.1599	2.1610	2.1622
8.7	2.1633	2.1645	2.1656	2.1668	2.1679	2.1691	2.1702	2.1713	2.1725	2.1736
8.8	2.1748	2.1759	2.1770	2.1782	2.1793	2.1804	2.1816	2.1827	2.1838	2.1849
8.9	2.1861	2.1872	2.1883	2.1894	2.1905	2.1917	2.1928	2.1939	2.1950	2.1961
9.0	2.1972	2.1983	2.1994	2.2006	2.2017	2.2028	2.2039	2.2050	2.2061	2.2072
9.1	2.2083	2.2094	2.2105	2.2116	2.2127	2.2138	2.2149	2.2159	2.2170	2.2181
9.2	2.2192	2.2203	2.2214	2.2225	2.2235	2.2246	2.2257	2.2268	2.2279	2.2289
9.3	2.2300	2.2311	2.2322	2.2332	2.2343	2.2354	2.2365	2.2375	2.2386	2.2397
9.4	2.2407	2.2418	2.2428	2.2439	2.2450	2.2460	2.2471	2.2481	2.2492	2.2502
9.5	2.2513	2.2523	2.2534	2.2544	2.2555	2.2565	2.2576	2.2586	2.2597	2.2607
9.6	2.2618	2.2628	2.2638	2.2649	2.2659	2.2670	2.2680	2.2690	2.2701	2.2711
9.7	2.2721	2.2732	2.2742	2.2752	2.2762	2.2773	2.2783	2.2793	2.2803	2.2814
9.8	2.2824	2.2834	2.2844	2.2854	2.2865	2.2875	2.2885	2.2895	2.2905	2.2915
9.9	2.2925	2.2935	2.2946	2.2956	2.2966	2.2976	2.2986	2.2996	2.3006	2.3016

Exponential Functions

x	e^x	e^{-x}		x	e^x	e^{-x}
0.00	1.0000	1.0000		1.5	4.4817	0.2231
0.01	1.0101	0.9901		1.6	4.9530	0.2019
0.02	1.0202	0.9802		1.7	5.4739	0.1827
0.03	1.0305	0.9705		1.8	6.0496	0.1653
0.04	1.0408	0.9608		1.9	6.6859	0.1496
0.05	1.0513	0.9512		2.0	7.3891	0.1353
0.06	1.0618	0.9418		2.1	8.1662	0.1225
0.07	1.0725	0.9324		2.2	9.0250	0.1108
0.08	1.0833	0.9331		2.3	9.9742	0.1003
0.09	1.0942	0.9139		2.4	11.023	0.0907
0.10	1.1052	0.9048		2.5	12.182	0.0821
0.11	1.1163	0.8958		2.6	13.464	0.0743
0.12	1.1275	0.8869		2.7	14.880	0.0672
0.13	1.1388	0.8781		2.8	16.445	0.0608
0.14	1.1503	0.8694		2.9	18.174	0.0550
0.15	1.1618	0.8607		3.0	20.086	0.0498
0.16	1.1735	0.8521		3.1	22.198	0.0450
0.17	1.1853	0.8437		3.2	24.533	0.0408
0.18	1.1972	0.8353		3.3	27.113	0.0369
0.19	1.2092	0.8270		3.4	29.964	0.0334
0.20	1.2214	0.8187		3.5	33.115	0.0302
0.21	1.2337	0.8106		3.6	36.598	0.0273
0.22	1.2461	0.8025		3.7	40.447	0.0247
0.23	1.2586	0.7945		3.8	44.701	0.0224
0.24	1.2712	0.7866		3.9	49.402	0.0202
0.25	1.2840	0.7788		4.0	54.598	0.0183
0.30	1.3499	0.7408		4.1	60.340	0.0166
0.35	1.4191	0.7047		4.2	66.686	0.0150
0.40	1.4918	0.6703		4.3	73.700	0.0136
0.45	1.5683	0.6376		4.4	81.451	0.0123
0.50	1.6487	0.6065		4.5	90.017	0.0111
0.55	1.7333	0.5769		4.6	99.484	0.0101
0.60	1.8221	0.5488		4.7	109.95	0.0091
0.65	1.9155	0.5220		4.8	121.51	0.0082
0.70	2.0138	0.4966		4.9	134.29	0.0074
0.75	2.1170	0.4724		5.0	148.41	0.0067
0.80	2.2255	0.4493		5.5	244.69	0.0041
0.85	2.3396	0.4274		6.0	403.43	0.0025
0.90	2.4596	0.4066		6.5	665.14	0.0015
0.95	2.5857	0.3867		7.0	1096.6	0.0009
1.0	2.7183	0.3679		7.5	1808.0	0.0006
1.1	3.0042	0.3329		8.0	2981.0	0.0003
1.2	3.3201	0.3012		8.5	4914.8	0.0002
1.3	3.6693	0.2725		9.0	8103.1	0.0001
1.4	4.0552	0.2466		10.0	22026	0.00005

Glossary

absolute maximum or minimum values
Absolute maximum or minimum values
are the greatest or least values, respectively, assumed by a function throughout
its domain of definition. (478)

absolute value If x is a nonzero real num-
ber, the absolute value of x, $|x|$, is x or $-x$,
whichever is positive. $|0| = 0$. (5)

addition of matrices The sum of two $m \times n$
matrices is an $m \times n$ matrix in which the
elements are the sum of the corresponding elements of the given matrices. (69)

amplitude **1.** The amplitude of a sine or a
cosine function of the form $y = A \sin k\theta$ or
$y = A \cos k\theta$ is the absolute value of A,
$|A|$. (163) **2.** The amplitude of a vector
is the directed angle between the positive
x-axis and the vector. (79)

angle An angle is the union of two rays that
have a common endpoint. (125)

angle of depression An angle of depression is the angle between a horizontal
line and the line of sight to an object at a
lower level. (192)

angle of elevation An angle of elevation is
the angle between a horizontal line and
the line of sight to an object at a higher
level. (192)

antiderivative The antiderivative of $f(x)$ is
$F(x)$ if and only if $F'(x) = f(x)$. (485)

antilogarithm If $\log x = a$, then x is called
the antilogarithm of a, abbreviated antilog a. If $\ln x = a$, then $x =$ antiln a. (304)

Arccosine function The Arccosine function is the inverse of the cosine function.
(173)

Arcsine function The Arcsine function is
the inverse of the sine function. (173)

Arctangent function The Arctangent function is the inverse of the tangent
function. (173)

arithmetic mean (average) The arithme-
tic mean of a set of data, $\overline{X}$, is the sum of
the values in the set divided by the num-
ber of values in the set.
$$\overline{X} = \frac{1}{n} \sum_{i=1}^{n} X_i \quad (421)$$

arithmetic means Arithmetic means are
the terms between any two nonconsecutive terms of an arithmetic sequence.
(220)

arithmetic sequence An arithmetic sequence is a sequence in which each term
after the first is equal to the sum of the
preceding term and the common
difference. (219)

array An array is formed by arranging
statistical data into an ordered sequence.
(422)

ARRAY variables ARRAY variables are used
in Pascal to store and process ordered
collections of data. The value of an ARRAY
variable is the ordered set of elements
that are its components. (500)

asymptotes **1.** Asymptotes are lines that a
curve approaches. (362) **2.** The equations of the asymptotes of a hyperbola
with a horizontal transverse axis are
$y - k = \pm \frac{b}{a} (x - h)$. If the transverse
axis is vertical, the equations are
$y - k = \pm \frac{a}{b} (x - h)$. (364)

augmented matrix An augmented matrix
is an array of the coefficients and constants of a system of equations. (76)

axis of symmetry An axis of symmetry is a
line around which a figure is symmetric.
(348)

bar graph A bar graph consists of parallel bars, either vertical or horizontal, which represent the frequency, f, of the values in a class. (435)

BEGIN In Pascal, BEGIN is the statement that identifies the actual starting point of a program. (497)

binomial experiment A binomial experiment is a problem that can be solved using a binomial expansion. (414)

bisector of an angle The bisector of an angle is the set of points equidistant from the sides of the angle. (333)

BOOLEAN variable In Pascal, a BOOLEAN variable is a type of variable that can be either true or false. (513)

broken line graph The broken line graph, sometimes called a frequency polygon, is a statistical graph that shows changing conditions over a period of time. (435)

characteristic The characteristic of a logarithm is the numeral which precedes the decimal point. In 2.314, 2 is the characteristic. (303)

CHAR variables In a Pascal program, if single letters are to be input, they are identified as CHAR variables. (497)

circle A circle is a set of points in a plane at a given distance from a fixed point. The given point is the center of the circle and the given distance is the radius of the circle. The standard form of the equation of a circle with radius r and center (h, k) is $(x - h)^2 + (y - k)^2 = r^2$. (345)

circle graph A circle graph is a statistical graph that shows the relationship between the parts and the whole. A circle is separated into proportional parts called sectors. (436)

circular permutations Suppose n objects are arranged in a circle. Then there are $\frac{n!}{n}$ or $(n - 1)!$ permutations of the n objects around the circle. (394)

class A class is a set of values grouped together in a frequency distribution. (431)

classical curves Classical curves are special graphs formed by graphing polar equations. Roses, lemniscates, limaçons, cardioids, and spirals of Archimedes are examples of classical curves. (259)

class interval The class interval is the width of each class in a frequency distribution. (432)

class limits Class limits are the boundaries of each class in a frequency distribution. (431)

class marks Class marks are the averages of the class limits in a frequency distribution. (432)

combination A combination is the arrangement of objects where the order is not a consideration. (397)

common difference The common difference of an arithmetic sequence is the constant that is the difference between successive terms. (219)

common logarithms Common logarithms are logarithms that use 10 as the base. (302)

common ratio The common ratio is the constant that is the ratio of successive terms in a geometric sequence. (222)

complement Two events are complements when the sum of their probabilities is one. (400)

complex number A complex number is any number that can be written in the form $a + bi$, where a and b are real numbers and i is the imaginary unit. (35)

composite of functions The composite of functions f and g is symbolized $f \circ g$, and maps x into $f(g(x))$. (296)

compound functions Compound functions consist of sums or products of trigonometric functions and/or other functions. (170)

conditional probability The conditional probability of event A, given event B, is found as follows.

$$P(A/B) = \frac{P(A \text{ and } B)}{P(B)}, \text{ where } P(B) \neq 0.$$
(410)

conic section 1. A conic section is a curve formed by the intersection of a plane with a conical surface. (369) 2. A conic section is a set of points in the plane such that for any point of the set the ratio of its distance from a fixed point to its distance from a fixed line is constant. The fixed point is called a focus. The fixed line is called a directrix. (369)

conjugate of a complex number The conjugate of the complex number $a + bi$ is $a - bi$. (35)

conjugate axis The conjugate axis of a hyperbola is the segment perpendicular to the transverse axis at its center. (362)

conjugate hyperbolas Conjugate hyperbolas are two hyperbolas such that the transverse axis of one is the conjugate axis of the other and conversely. Conjugate hyperbolas share the same asymptotes. (367)

constant function A constant function is a function of the form $f(x) = b$. The graph is a horizontal line. (8)

constraints Constraints are conditions given to variables. Constraints are often expressed as linear inequalities. (19)

continuous function A function f is continuous if it is continuous at each point of its domain. (464)

continuous on an interval A function f is continuous on an interval if it is continuous at each point of the interval. (464)

continuous at a point A function f is continuous at $x = a$ if $f(a)$ exists and if $\lim\limits_{x \to a} f(x) = f(a)$. (463)

convergent An infinite series is convergent if it has a sum or limit. (232)

cosecant function 1. For any real number s, the cosecant function is defined as follows.
$$\csc s = \frac{1}{\sin s} \quad (\sin s \neq 0) \quad (103)$$
2. For any angle with measure α, point $P(x, y)$ on its terminal side, and $r = \sqrt{x^2 + y^2}$, the cosecant of α is as follows.
$$\csc \alpha = \frac{r}{y} \quad (y \neq 0) \quad (125)$$

cosine function 1. For any real number s, where $C(s) = (x, y)$ such that $x^2 + y^2 = 1$, the cosine of $s = x$ or $\cos s = x$. (102) 2. For any angle with measure α, point $P(x, y)$ on its terminal side, and $r = \sqrt{x^2 + y^2}$, the cosine of α is as follows.
$$\cos \alpha = \frac{x}{r} \quad (r \neq 0) \quad (125)$$

cotangent function 1. Let s represent any real number. The cotangent function is defined as follows.
$$\cot s = \frac{\cos s}{\sin s} \quad (\sin s \neq 0) \quad (103)$$
2. For any angle with measure α, point $P(x, y)$ on its terminal side, and $r = \sqrt{x^2 + y^2}$, the cotangent of α is as follows.
$$\cot \alpha = \frac{x}{y} \quad (y \neq 0) \quad (125)$$

Cramer's rule Cramer's rule states that the solution to $a_1x + b_1y = c_1$ and $a_2x + b_2y = c_2$ is (x, y) where
$$x = \frac{\begin{vmatrix} c_1 & b_1 \\ c_2 & b_2 \end{vmatrix}}{\begin{vmatrix} a_1 & b_1 \\ a_2 & b_2 \end{vmatrix}} \text{ and } y = \frac{\begin{vmatrix} a_1 & c_1 \\ a_2 & c_2 \end{vmatrix}}{\begin{vmatrix} a_1 & b_1 \\ a_2 & b_2 \end{vmatrix}} \text{ and } \begin{vmatrix} a_1 & b_1 \\ a_2 & b_2 \end{vmatrix} \neq 0$$
(66)

critical points Critical points are points for which the derivative of a function is zero. (55)

cross product The cross product of $\vec{a}$ and $\vec{b}$ if $\vec{a} = (a_1, a_2, a_3)$ and $\vec{b} = (b_1, b_2, b_3)$ is defined as follows. (89)
$$\vec{a} \times \vec{b} = \begin{vmatrix} a_2 & a_3 \\ b_2 & b_3 \end{vmatrix} \vec{i} - \begin{vmatrix} a_1 & a_3 \\ b_1 & b_3 \end{vmatrix} \vec{j} + \begin{vmatrix} a_1 & a_2 \\ b_1 & b_2 \end{vmatrix} \vec{k}$$

cubic polynomial A cubic polynomial is a polynomial of the third degree such as $7x^3 + 4x^2 + 2x - 1$. (31)

decreasing function   If $f'(x) < 0$ for all values of x in the interval $a < x < b$ of function f, then the function is decreasing in that interval.   (476)

definite integral   A definite integral is an integral that has lower and upper limits defined.   (488)

degree of a polynomial   The degree of a polynomial in one variable is the greatest exponent of its variable.   (31)

dependent events   Two events, A and B, are dependent if the outcome of event A affects the outcome of event B. The probability of two dependent events occurring is found as follows.   (405)

$$P(A \text{ and } B) = P(A) \cdot P(B \text{ following } A).$$

derivative   The derivative of $f(x)$ is the function $f'(x)$, which is defined as follows.

$$f'(x) = \lim_{h \to 0} \frac{f(x + h) - f(x)}{h} \quad (53)$$

derivative notation   Derivative notation is $\dfrac{dy}{dx}$ and is read "the derivative of y with respect to x."   (471)

Descartes' Rule of Signs   Suppose $P(x)$ is a polynomial whose terms are arranged in descending powers of the variable. The number of positive real zeros of $y = P(x)$ is the same as the number of changes in sign of the coefficients of the terms, or is less than this by an even number. The number of negative real zeros is the same as the number of changes in sign of $P(-x)$, or is less than this by an even number.   (47)

determinant   The determinant is defined as follows for a 2×2 matrix.   (65)

$$\det \begin{bmatrix} a_1 & b_1 \\ a_2 & b_2 \end{bmatrix} = \begin{vmatrix} a_1 & b_1 \\ a_2 & b_2 \end{vmatrix} = a_1 b_2 - a_2 b_1$$

difference quotient   The difference quotient is the slope of the secant line intersecting the graph of function f at $(a, f(a))$ and $(a + h, f(a + h))$. It is given by the following ratio. $\dfrac{f(a + h) - f(a)}{h}$ (469)

differentiable   A function is differentiable at a if the derivative of the function exists at a and is finite.   (469)

differentiation   Differentiation is the process of finding derivatives.   (469)

dimensions of a matrix   The dimensions of a matrix are the number of rows and number of columns.   (65)

directrix   See conic section.

discontinuous   A function is discontinuous if there is a "break" in the graph of the function.   (464)

distance formula   The distance, d, between two points (x_1, y_1) and (x_2, y_2) is given by the following formula.

$$d = \sqrt{(x_2 - x_1)^2 + (y_2 - y_1)^2} \quad (11)$$

distance from a point to a line   The distance from a point (x_1, y_1) to a line $Ax + By + C = 0$ can be found by the following formula.

$$d = \frac{Ax_1 + By_1 + C}{\pm\sqrt{A^2 + B^2}} \quad (331)$$

divergent   An infinite series is divergent if it has no sum or limit.   (232)

domain   **1.** The domain of a relation is the set of all abscissas of the ordered pairs of the relation.   (3)   **2.** The domain of a function is the set for which the function is defined.   (5)

dot product   See inner product.

double angle identities   The double angle identities are as follows.

$$\sin 2\theta = 2 \sin \theta \cos \theta$$
$$\cos 2\theta = \cos^2 \theta - \sin^2 \theta$$
$$= 1 - 2 \sin^2 \theta$$
$$= 2 \cos^2 \theta - 1$$
$$\tan 2\theta = \frac{2 \tan \theta}{1 - \tan^2 \theta} \quad (150)$$

e   The following limit defines the number e.

$$e = \lim_{k \to \infty} \left(1 + \frac{1}{k}\right)^k = 1 + 1 + \frac{1}{2!} + \frac{1}{3!} + \cdots$$

Thus, $e \approx 2.718$.   (290)

eccentricity **1.** The eccentricity, e, of an ellipse is defined as $e = \frac{c}{a}$. For an ellipse, $e < 1$. (366) **2.** The eccentricity of a hyperbola is defined as $e = \frac{c}{a}$. For a hyperbola, $e > 1$. (366) **3.** The eccentricity of a parabola is 1. (369)

ellipse An ellipse is the set of all points in the plane such that the sum of the distances from two given points in the plane, called the foci, is constant. The standard form of the equation of an ellipse that has center (h, k) and major axis of length $2a$ units is as follows. The equation is $\frac{(x - h)^2}{a^2} + \frac{(y - k)^2}{b^2} = 1$ when the major axis is parallel to the x-axis. The equation is $\frac{(y - k)^2}{a^2} + \frac{(x - h)^2}{b^2} = 1$ when the major axis is parallel to the y-axis. For an ellipse, $b^2 = a^2 - c^2$. (354, 356)

END END is the final statement in a Pascal computer program. (498)

equilateral hyperbola An equilateral hyperbola has perpendicular asymptotes. In the standard form of an equilateral hyperbola, $a = b$. (367)

Euler's formula Euler's formula is $e^{i\alpha} = \cos \alpha + i \sin \alpha$. (312)

even function An even function is a function f such that $f(-x) = f(x)$. The cosine function is an even function. (143)

exponential function **1.** An exponential function has the form $y = a^x$, where a is a positive real number. (289) **2.** The function $y = e^x$ is often called the exponential function. (291)

exponential series The following series is called the exponential series.

$$e^x = 1 + x + \frac{x^2}{2} + \frac{x^3}{3} + \cdots \quad (291)$$

factorial The expression $n!$ (n factorial) is defined as follows if n is an integer greater than zero.

$$n! = n(n - 1)(n - 2) \cdots (1)$$

Also, $0! = 1$. (241)

failure A failure is when the desired outcome of an event does not occur. (400)

focus See conic section.

FOR-DO loop In Pascal, statements that can be used to repeat a sequence of steps a specified number of times are FOR-DO loops. (502)

frequency The frequency, f, is the number of values in a class of a frequency distribution. (432)

frequency distribution A frequency distribution is a system of organizing data by determining classes and the frequency of values in each class. (431)

function A function is a relation in which each element of the domain is paired with exactly one element of the range. (3)

function C Function C is defined such that for each real number s, there corresponds exactly one ordered pair of real numbers, $C(s) = (x, y)$, that are coordinates of a point on the unit circle. (97)

Fundamental Theorem of Calculus If the function $f(x)$ is continuous and F is such that $F'(x) = f(x)$, then $\int_a^b f(x)dx = F(b) - F(a)$ where $F(x)$ is the antiderivative of $f(x)$. (488)

general equation for conic sections The general equation for conic sections can be written in the form $Ax^2 + Bxy + Cy^2 + Dx + Ey + F = 0$ where A, B, and C are not all zeros. (370)

geometric means Geometric means are the terms between any two nonconsecutive terms of a geometric sequence. (223)

geometric sequence A geometric sequence is a sequence in which each term after the first is the product of the preceding term and the common ratio. (222)

half angle identities The half angle identities are as follows.

$$\sin \frac{\alpha}{2} = \pm \sqrt{\frac{1 - \cos \alpha}{2}}$$

$$\cos \frac{\alpha}{2} = \pm \sqrt{\frac{1 + \cos \alpha}{2}}$$

$$\tan \frac{\alpha}{2} = \pm \sqrt{\frac{1 - \cos \alpha}{1 + \cos \alpha}} \quad (151)$$

harmonic mean The harmonic mean, H, of a set of values is a measure of central tendency. It is found by the following formula.

$$H = \frac{n}{\dfrac{1}{X_1} + \dfrac{1}{X_2} + \cdots + \dfrac{1}{X_n}} = \frac{n}{\sum\limits_{i=1}^{n} \dfrac{1}{X_i}} \quad (425)$$

Hero's formula Hero's formula for the area, K, of triangle ABC is

$$K = \sqrt{s(s - a)(s - b)(s - c)}$$

where $s = \dfrac{a + b + c}{2}$. (205)

histogram A histogram is a vertical bar graph whose bars are next to each other. (435)

horizontal line test The horizontal line test can be used to determine if a function will have an inverse function. If any horizontal line drawn on the graph of a function passes through no more than one point of the graph, then the function has an inverse that is also a function. (298)

hyperbola A hyperbola is the set of all points in the plane such that the absolute value of the difference of the distance from two given points, called the foci, is constant. The standard form of the equation of a hyperbola that has center (h, k) and transverse axis of length $2a$ is as follows. The equation is $\dfrac{(x - h)^2}{a^2} - \dfrac{(y - k)^2}{b^2} = 1$ when the transverse axis is parallel to the x-axis. The equation is $\dfrac{(y - k)^2}{a^2} - \dfrac{(x - h)^2}{b^2} = 1$ when the transverse axis is parallel to the y-axis. For the hyperbola, $b^2 = c^2 - a^2$. (361, 363)

identity An identity is any equation that is true for all values of the variables. (131)

identity matrix under addition The identity matrix under addition for any $m \times n$ matrix is an $m \times n$ zero matrix. (69)

identity matrix under multiplication The identity matrix of nth order, I_n, is the square matrix whose elements in the main diagonal, from upper left to lower right, are 1's, while all other elements are 0's. (73)

IF-THEN-ELSE statement The IF-THEN-ELSE statement is a Pascal statement that makes a comparison of two numbers and then tells the computer what to do based on the comparison. (509)

imaginary number An imaginary number is a complex number of the form $a + b\mathbf{i}$ where $b \neq 0$. (35)

imaginary unit The imaginary unit $\mathbf{i}$ is defined by $\mathbf{i}^2 = -1$. (35)

inclusive events Two events, A and B, are inclusive if the outcomes of A and B may be the same. The probability of two inclusive events, A and B, occurring is found as follows. (408)

$$P(A \text{ or } B) = P(A) + P(B) - P(A \text{ and } B)$$

increasing function If $f'(x) > 0$ for all values of x in the interval $a < x < b$ of function f, then the function is increasing in the interval. (476)

independent events Two events, A and B, are independent if the outcome of one event does not affect the outcome of the other event. The probability of two independent events, A and B, occurring is found as follows.

$$P(A \text{ and } B) = P(A) \cdot P(B) \quad (405)$$

index of summation The index of summation is the variable used with the summation symbol Σ. (238)

infinite sequence An infinite sequence has an unlimited number of terms. (227)

infinite series An infinite series is the indicated sum of the terms of an infinite sequence. (229)

initial side The initial side of an angle is the starting position of a ray used to generate an angle by rotation. (125)

inner product of vectors If $\vec{a}$ and $\vec{b}$ are two vectors, (a_1, a_2) and (b_1, b_2), then the inner product (or dot product) of $\vec{a}$ and $\vec{b}$ is defined as follows.
$$\vec{a} \cdot \vec{b} = a_1 b_1 + a_2 b_2 \quad (88)$$

INPUT, OUTPUT In Pascal, (INPUT, OUTPUT) tells the computer that there will be data input and output from the program. (497)

integral The function $F(x)$ is an integral of $f(x)$ with respect to x if and only if $F(x)$ is an antiderivative of $f(x)$. That is, $F(x) = \int f(x)dx$ if and only if $F'(x) = f(x)$. (485)

inverse functions Two functions f and g are inverse functions if and only if both their compositions are the identity function. That is, $f(g(x)) = g(f(x)) = x$. (297)

irrational exponents If x is an irrational number and $a > 0$, then a^x is the real number between a^{x_1} and a^{x_2} for all possible choices of rational numbers x_1 and x_2 and $x_1 < x < x_2$. (288)

irrational number An irrational number is a number that cannot be expressed as $\frac{a}{b}$ where a and b are integers and $b \neq 0$. The value of an irrational number is an infinite, nonrepeating decimal. (226)

inverse of a function The inverse of a function may be found by interchanging the elements of the ordered pairs of the function. The domain becomes the range and the range becomes the domain. (172)

latus rectum A latus rectum of a conic is a line segment through a focus perpendicular to the axis with endpoints on the conic. For a parabola, the length of this segment is $4p$ units, where p is the distance from the vertex to the focus. The length of the latus rectum of an ellipse or hyperbola is $\frac{2b^2}{a}$. (350, 359)

limit of a function The limit of a function $f(x)$ as x approaches a is L, written $\lim\limits_{x \to a} f(x) = L$, if, for every real number $\epsilon > 0$, there exists a real number $\delta > 0$ such that $|f(x) - L| < \epsilon$ and $0 < |x - a| < \delta$. (460)

limit of a polynomial function The limit of a polynomial function, $P(x)$, as x approaches r, is $P(r)$.
$$\lim\limits_{x \to r} P(x) = P(r) \quad (456)$$

limit of a sequence The limit of a sequence, if it exists, is the value which the terms of the sequence approach as n approaches infinity. (227)

linear function A linear function has the form $f(x) = mx + b$ where m and b are real numbers. (8)

linear programming Linear programming is a procedure for finding the maximum or the minimum value of a function in two variables subject to given conditions, called constraints, on the variables. (19)

logarithmic function The logarithmic function $y = \log_a x$, $a > 0$ and $a \neq 1$, is the inverse of the exponential function $y = a^x$. Thus, $y = \log_a x$ if and only if $x = a^y$. (300)

magnitude The magnitude, $|\vec{v}|$, of $\vec{v}$ is the absolute value of the length of the directed line segment that represents $\vec{v}$. (79)

major axis The major axis of an ellipse is the segment with endpoints at the vertices of the ellipse. (354)

mantissa The mantissa of a common logarithm is a positive decimal less than 1. The mantissa of 3.6990, is 0.6990. The mantissa always represents the common logarithm of a number between 1 and 10. (303)

matrix A matrix is any rectangular array of terms called elements. An $m \times n$ matrix is a matrix with m rows and n columns. (65)

mean deviation The mean deviation, $M.D.$, is a measure of variability, which can be found by the following formula.

$$M.D. = \frac{1}{n} \sum_{i=1}^{n} |X_i - \overline{X}| \quad (428)$$

measure of central tendency A measure of central tendency is a number that represents a set of data. (421)

median The median, M_d, is the mid-value of a set of data. (422)

midpoint The midpoint of the segment with endpoints (x_1, y_1) and (x_2, y_2) is

$$\left(\frac{x_1 + x_2}{2}, \frac{y_1 + y_2}{2} \right) \quad (322)$$

minor axis The minor axis of an ellipse is the segment perpendicular to the major axis at the center, with endpoints on the ellipse. (354)

mode The mode of a set of data is the value that appears more frequently than any other in the set. (422)

modulus The modulus of a complex number $y + yi$ is the distance from the origin to the point (x, y) in the complex plane. That is, $r = \sqrt{x^2 + y^2}$. (268)

multiplication of matrices The product of an $m \times n$ matrix, A, and an $n \times r$ matrix, B, is an $m \times r$ matrix, AB. The ijth element of AB is the product of the ith row of A and the jth column of B. (72)

mutually exclusive events Two events, A and B, are mutually exclusive if the outcomes of A and B can never be the same. The probability of two mutually exclusive events, A and B, occurring is found as follows. $P(A$ or $B) = P(A) + P(B)$ (408)

natural logarithms Natural logarithms, symbolized ln x, are logarithms to base e. (308)

normal 1. The normal to a curve at any point on the curve is the line perpendicular to the tangent at the point. (377) 2. The normal of a line is the line segment from the origin to the line, perpendicular to the line. (327)

normal distribution A normal distribution has a bell-shaped, symmetrical graph centered about the mean of the data. About 68% of the items are within one standard deviation of the mean. About 95% of the items are within two standard deviations. About 99% of the items are within three standard deviations. (444)

normal form Normal form of a linear equation is $x \cos \phi + y \sin \phi - p = 0$, where ϕ is the angle from the positive x-axis to the normal and p is the length of the normal. (327)

nth order matrix A matrix of the nth order is a square matrix with n rows and n columns. (65)

odd function An odd function is a function f such that $f(-x) = -f(x)$. The sine function is an odd function. (143)

odds The odds of the successful outcomes of an event is the ratio of the probability of its success to the probability of its failure. (401)

parabola A parabola is the set of all points that are the same distance from a given point, the focus, and a given line, the directrix. In the standard form of the equation of a parabola, the center is (h, k) and the distance from the vertex to the focus is p. The equation is $(y - k)^2 = 4p(x - h)$ when the directrix is parallel to the y-axis. The equation is $(x - h)^2 = 4p(y - k)$ when the directrix is parallel to the x-axis. (348)

parallel lines Two lines are parallel if and only if the slopes of the lines are equal. (319)

Pascal Pascal is a high level computer programming language. (497)

Pascal's triangle Pascal's triangle is a triangular array of numbers. The numbers in the array are the coefficients of the terms in the expansion of $(x + y)^n$ for $n = 0, 1, 2$, etc. (242)

period of a function The period of a function is the least positive value of α for which $f(x) = f(x + \alpha)$. (98)

periodic function A function is periodic if, for some real number α, $f(x + \alpha) = f(x)$ for each x in the domain of f. (98)

permutation A permutation is the arrangement of objects in a certain order. (390)

permutations with repetitions The number of permutations of n objects of which p are alike and q are alike is found by evaluating the expression $\frac{n!}{p!q!}$. (393)

perpendicular lines Two lines are perpendicular if and only if the slope of one is the negative reciprocal of the slope of the other. (320)

perpendicular vectors Perpendicular vectors are two vectors whose inner product is zero. (88)

phase shift The phase shift of a function of the form $y = A \sin (k\theta + C)$, is $-\frac{c}{k}$. If $c > 0$, the shift is to the left and if $c < 0$ the shift is to the right. This definition applies to all trigonometric functions. (165)

point-slope form If the point (x_1, y_1) lies on a line having slope m, the point-slope form of the equation of the line can be written as follows.
$$y - y_1 = m(x - x_1) \quad (14)$$

polar axis The polar axis is a ray whose initial point is the pole. (253)

polar coordinates The polar coordinates of a point P are written in the form (r, θ), where r is the distance from the pole to the point P and θ is the measure of an angle that has the polar axis as its initial side and $\overrightarrow{OP}$ as its terminal side. (253)

polar equation A polar equation is an equation that uses polar coordinates. (255)

polar equation of a conic section The polar equation of any conic section where the pole is at a focus and the polar axis is perpendicular to the directrix can be written as follows, where e is the eccentricity and $2p$ is the distance from the focus to the directrix.
$$r = \frac{2ep}{1 + e \cos \theta} \quad (382)$$

polar graph A polar graph represents the set of all points (r, θ) that satisfy a given polar equation. (255)

pole The pole is a fixed point O in a plane. It is also called an origin. (253)

polygonal convex set A polygonal convex set is the region formed when a system of linear inequalities is graphed so that the intersection set is a convex polygon and its interior. (17)

polynomial A polynomial, in one variable, x, is an expression of the form $a_0x^n + a_1x^{n-1} + \cdots + a_{n-1}x + a_n$. The coefficients are real numbers and n is a nonnegative integer. (31)

polynomial equation A polynomial equation is a polynomial that is set equal to zero. (31)

principal values Principal values of trigonometric functions are the values in the domain of the functions sine, cosine, and tangent. (176)

procedures Procedures are subprograms in a Pascal computer program. Some common procedures are: DISPOSE, READ, and WRITELN. (519)

PROGRAM statement In Pascal, the PROGRAM statement is the statement that alerts the computer to expect a Pascal program. (497)

quadrantal angle A quadrantal angle is an angle in standard position whose terminal side coincides with one of the coordinate axes. (145)

quadratic expression A quadratic expression is a second degree polynomial such as $5x^2 + 6x - 3 = 0$. (31)

quadratic formula The roots of a quadratic expression of the form $ax^2 + bx + c = 0$ are given by the following formula.
$$x = \frac{-b \pm \sqrt{b^2 - 4ac}}{2a} \quad (34)$$

quadratic mean The quadratic mean, Q, is a measure of central tendency that can be found as follows.
$$Q = \sqrt{\frac{X_1^2 + X_2^2 + X_3^2 + \cdots + X_n^2}{n}}$$
$$= \sqrt{\frac{\sum_{i=1}^{n} X_i^2}{n}} \quad (426)$$

quartic polynomial A quartic polynomial is a polynomial of the fourth degree. (31)

quartile A quartile is one of four parts of data formed when an array of a set of data is separated into four parts having an equal number of data. (428)

quintic polynomial A quintic polynomial is a polynomial of the fifth degree. (31)

radian A radian is the measure of a central angle whose sides intercept an arc that is the same length as the radius of the circle. (137)

range **1.** The range is the set of all ordinates of a relation. (3) **2.** The range is the difference of the largest and smallest values in the array of a set of data. (422)

rational exponents For any nonzero number b, and any integers m and n, with $n > 1$, $b^{\frac{m}{n}} = \sqrt[n]{b^m} = (\sqrt[n]{b})^m$ except when $\sqrt[n]{b}$ is not a real number. (285)   that

rational number A rational number is a number that can be expressed as $\frac{a}{b}$, where a and b are integers and $b \neq 0$. (226)

READ statement The Pascal statement that indicates the values for the variables to be input during the running of the program is the READ statement. (498)

reference angle A reference angle is an acute angle in the first quadrant with vertex at the origin that is used to find the trigonometric functions of angles in other quadrants. (141)

relation A relation is a set of ordered pairs. A relation can also be represented as a graph, a table of values, or by any rule in words or symbols that determines pairs of values. (3)

relative maximum or minimum A relative maximum or minimum is a point that   represents the maximum or minimum respectively, for a certain interval. (56)

REPEAT-UNTIL loop The REPEAT-UNTIL loop is used in a Pascal program when it is required that a set of statements repeat until some condition is satisfied. (521)

resultant vector A resultant vector is the sum of two or more vectors. (80)

root A root of a polynomial equation $P(x) = 0$ is a value of x for which the value of the polynomial $P(x)$ is zero. (31)

scalar A scalar is a real-number constant. The term scalar is used to distinguish a vector or matrix from a real number. (71)

scalar product **1.** The product of an $m \times n$ matrix, A, and a scalar, k, is an $m \times n$ matrix, kA. Each element of kA is equal to k times the corresponding element of A. (71) **2.** The product of a vector, (a_1, a_2), and a scalar, k, is a vector, (ka_1, ka_2). (83)

secant function **1.** For any real number s, the secant function is defined as follows.
$$\sec s = \frac{1}{\cos s} \quad (\cos s \neq 0) \quad (103)$$
2. For any angle with measure α, point $P(x, y)$ on its terminal side, and $r = \sqrt{x^2 + y^2}$, the secant of α is as follows.
$$\sec \alpha = \frac{r}{x} \quad (x \neq 0) \quad (125)$$

secant line   A secant line to a curve is a line that intersects the curve at two or more points.   (52)

second derivative   The second derivative of function f, $f''(x)$, is the derivative of $f'(x)$.   (478)

sector   A sector of a circle is the region bounded by an arc of a circle and the radii drawn to its endpoints.   (210)

segment   A segment of a circle is the region bounded by an arc and its chord.   (211)

semi-interquartile range   The semi-interquartile range, Q_R is a measure of variability of a set of data. It is half of the difference between the first quartile point and the third quartile point.

$$Q_R = \frac{Q_3 - Q_1}{2} \quad (428)$$

sequence   A sequence is a set of numbers in a specific order.   (219)

series   A series is the indicated sum of the terms of a sequence.   (220, 224)

sine function   **1.** For any real number s, where $C(s) = (x, y)$ such that $x^2 + y^2 = 1$, the sine of $s = y$ or $\sin s = y$.   (102)
2. For any angle with measure α, point $P(x, y)$ on its terminal side, and $r = \sqrt{x^2 + y^2}$, the sine of α is as follows.

$$\sin \alpha = \frac{y}{r} \quad (r \neq 0) \quad (125)$$

slope   **1.** The slope of a line through (x_1, y_1) and (x_2, y_2) is given by the following equation, if $x_2 \neq x_1$.

$$\text{slope} = \frac{y_2 - y_1}{x_2 - x_1} \quad (11)$$

2. The slope of a line is equal to the tangent of the angle that the line makes with the positive x-axis.   (325)

slope-intercept form   The slope-intercept form of the equation of a line is $y = mx + b$. The slope is m and the y-intercept is b.   (12)

slope of the tangent   The slope of the tangent to the graph of $y = f(x)$ at the point (x, y) is $f'(x)$, defined as follows.

$$f'(x) = \lim_{h \to 0} \frac{f(x + h) - f(x)}{h} \quad (52)$$

square matrix   A square matrix has the same number of rows as columns.   (65)

standard deviation   Standard deviation, σ, of a set of data is the quadratic mean of the individual deviations from the arithmetic mean. It can be found as follows.

$$\sigma = \sqrt{\frac{1}{n} \sum_{i=1}^{n} (X_i - \overline{X})^2} \quad (429)$$

standard error of the mean   The standard error of the mean is used to give a level of confidence about the sample mean. It can be found as follows.

$$\sigma_x = \frac{\sigma}{\sqrt{n}} \quad (448)$$

standard form   The standard form of a linear equation is $Ax + By + C = 0$, where A, B, and C are real numbers and A and B are not both 0.   (7)

standard position   An angle with its vertex at the origin and its initial side along the positive x-axis is in standard position.   (125)

stationary values   Stationary values are points at which the function is neither increasing nor decreasing.   (477)

STRING variables   In a Pascal program, if words or phrases are to be input, they are identified as STRING variables.   (497)

success   A success is when the desired outcome of an event occurs.   (400)

sum of an infinite geometric series   The sum, S, of an infinite geometric series for which $|r| < 1$ is given by the following formula.

$$S = \frac{a}{1 - r} \quad (231)$$

sum of an infinite series   If S_n is the sum of n terms of a series, and S is a number such that $S > S_n$ for all n, and $S - S_n$ approaches zero as n increases without limit, then the sum of the infinite series is S.

$$\lim_{n \to \infty} S_n = S \quad (230)$$

tangent line   A tangent line, or tangent, is a straight line that touches a curve at a point. If A is a fixed point on the curve and B is a variable point, then the tangent line is the limiting position of $\overleftrightarrow{AB}$ as B approaches A.   (51)

tangent function   **1.** Let s represent any real number. The tangent function is defined as follows.

$$\tan s = \frac{\sin s}{\cos s} \quad (\cos s \neq 0) \quad (103)$$

2. For any angle with measure α, point $P(x, y)$ on its terminal side, and $r = \sqrt{x^2 + y^2}$, the tangent of α is as follows.

$$\tan \alpha = \frac{y}{x} \quad (x \neq 0) \quad (125)$$

terminal side   The terminal side of an angle is the final position of a ray used to generate the angle by rotation.   (125)

translation formulas   The translation formulas are $x = x' + h$ and $y = y' + k$ where (h, k) represents the origin of the coordinate system (x', y').   (352)

transverse axis   The transverse axis of a hyperbola is the line segment of length $2a$ that has its endpoints at the vertices.   (362)

trigonometric equation   A trigonometric equation is an equation involving a trigonometric function that is true for some, but not all, values of the variable.   (187)

trigonometric functions   **1.** For any angle with measure α, point $P(x, y)$ on its terminal side, and $r = \sqrt{x^2 + y^2}$, the trigonometric functions of α are as follows.

$$\sin \alpha = \frac{y}{r} \quad \cos \alpha = \frac{x}{r} \quad \tan \alpha = \frac{y}{x}$$

$$\csc \alpha = \frac{r}{y} \quad \sec \alpha = \frac{r}{x} \quad \cot \alpha = \frac{x}{y} \quad (125)$$

2. For an acute angle A in right triangle ABC, the trigonometric functions are as follows. (126)

$$\sin A = \frac{\text{side opposite}}{\text{hypotenuse}} \quad \cos A = \frac{\text{side adjacent}}{\text{hypotenuse}}$$

$$\tan A = \frac{\text{side opposite}}{\text{side adjacent}} \quad \cot A = \frac{\text{side adjacent}}{\text{side opposite}}$$

$$\sec A = \frac{\text{hypotenuse}}{\text{side adjacent}} \quad \csc A = \frac{\text{hypotenuse}}{\text{side opposite}}$$

trigonometric series   The trigonometric series for $\cos x$ and $\sin x$ are given as follows.

$$\cos x = 1 - \frac{x^2}{2!} + \frac{x^4}{4!} - \frac{x^6}{6!} + \cdots$$

$$\sin x = 1 - \frac{x^3}{3!} + \frac{x^5}{5!} - \frac{x^7}{7!} + \cdots (312)$$

two-point form   The two-point form of the equation of a line is as follows.

$$y - y_1 = \frac{y_2 - y_1}{x_2 - x_1}(x - x_1) \quad (320)$$

unit circle   A unit circle is a circle on the coordinate plane with its center at the origin and radius 1 unit.   (97)

unit vectors   Unit vectors are vectors of length one unit in the directions of the x, y, and z axes. They are denoted $\vec{\mathbf{i}}, \vec{\mathbf{j}},$ and $\mathbf{k}$, respectively.   (84, 87)

vector   A vector is a quantity that possesses both magnitude and direction.   (79)

WHILE-DO loop   A WHILE-DO loop is a means of repeating a sequence of steps until a condition is satisfied in a Pascal program.   (506)

WRITE statement   A WRITE statement is the Pascal statement that calls for output when a continuation of the same line is desired.   (498)

WRITELN statement   The Pascal statement that calls for output on the current line followed by an advance to the next line is the WRITELN statement.   (498)

x-intercept   The x-intercept is the x-coordinate of the point at which the graph of a function crosses the x-axis. (8)

y-intercept   The y-intercept is the y-coordinate of the point at which the graph of a function crosses the y-axis. (8)

zero of a function   A zero of a function is a value of x for which $f(x) = 0$.   (47)

Selected Answers

CHAPTER 1   RELATIONS AND FUNCTIONS

Page 5   Exploratory Exercises   1. D-{0}, R-{0}
3. D-{5, 6}, R-{5, 6} **5.** D-{−3, 0, 1, 2}, R-{0, 2, 4, −6}
7. D-{−2}, R-{7, 8, 9} **9.** D-{4, 9}, R-{−3, −2, 2, 3}
11. yes **13.** yes **15.** yes **17.** no **19.** no

Pages 6–7   Written Exercises   1. {(1, 0), (2, 3),
(3, 6), (4, 9), (5, 12)} **3.** {(−3, 9), (−2, 4)} **5.** {(4, 2),
(4, −2)} **7.** D-{1, 2, 3, 4, 5}, R-{0, 3, 6, 9, 12}
9. D-{−3, −2}, R-{9, 4} **11.** D-{4}, R-{2, −2} **13.** yes
15. yes **17.** no **19.** yes **21.** yes **23.** no **25.** 7
27. −2 **29.** $6\frac{3}{4}$ **31.** $7 - 4a^2$ **33.** 4 **35.** −5
37. −671 **39.** $8 - 6a - 6a^2 - a^3$ **41.** 0 **43.** −3
45. 2 **47.** [t] **49.** 13 **51.** 0 **53.** 10.04
55. $|n^2 + 8n + 3|$ **57.** 1 **59.** 0 **61.** $\pm 4\frac{1}{2}$

Page 9   Exploratory Exercises   1. $3x - y + 2 = 0$
3. $x - 3 = 0$ **5.** $y + 4 = 0$ **7.** 2 **9.** none **11.** yes
13. no **15.** no **17.** yes

Pages 9–10   Written Exercises

1.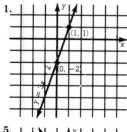

3.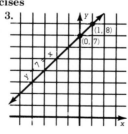

5.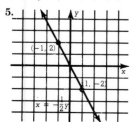

7.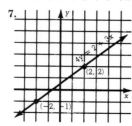

9. −12 **11.** $-\frac{5}{9}$ **13.** none **15.** (0, 1) **17.** (0, 3)
19. (2, −4)

Page 12   Exploratory Exercises   1. 3 **3.** 6
5. 13 **7.** 0 **9.** undefined **11.** $\frac{12}{5}$

Page 12   Written Exercises   1. $3\sqrt{5}$ **3.** $\sqrt{74}$
5. 5 **7.** 5t **9.** $\sqrt{1 + 9n^2}$ **11.** −1 **13.** −2
15. undefined **17.** $-\frac{1}{2}$ **19.** 30 **21.** 12 **23.** yes
25. yes

Page 12   Challenge Exercises   27. 4 **29.** 2 **31.** 4

Page 14   Exploratory Exercises   1. $m = \frac{3}{2}$,
y-intercept is $-\frac{7}{2}$, $y = \frac{3}{2}x - \frac{7}{2}$ **3.** $m = -\frac{5}{11}$,
y-intercept is $\frac{2}{11}$, $y = -\frac{5}{11}x + \frac{2}{11}$ **5.** $m = \frac{1}{2}$,
y-intercept is −2, $y = \frac{1}{2}x - 2$ **7.** $m = 4$, y-intercept is
$\frac{1}{2}$, $y = 4x + \frac{1}{2}$ **9.** $m = -\frac{4}{3}$, y-intercept is 0, $y = -\frac{4}{3}x$

Page 15   Written Exercises   1. $y = 4x - 10$
3. $y = -6x - 22$ **5.** $y = -5x - 37$ **7.** $y = \frac{3}{4}x + 11\frac{1}{2}$
9. $y = \frac{2}{3}x + 5$ **11.** $y = -x - 2$ **13.** $x = -1$
15. $y = \frac{7}{2}x - \frac{31}{2}$ **17.** $y = -\frac{3}{5}x + \frac{14}{5}$ **19.** $y = 7x - 18$
21. $y = -\frac{1}{3}x + 3$ **23.** $\overleftrightarrow{AB} = 8x - 3y - 37 = 0$,
$\overleftrightarrow{AC} = 9x + 5y + 17 = 0$, $\overleftrightarrow{BC} = x + 8y - 13 = 0$

Page 18   Exploratory Exercises   1. $x > 2$
3. $y \le x + 2$ **5.** $1 < y < 4$ **7.** (3, 2) **9.** (0, 0), (3, 2)
11. (0, 0), (3, 2), (−4, 2), (−2, 4)

Pages 18-19 Written Exercises

1.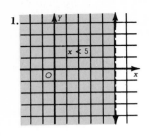

3.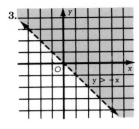

5.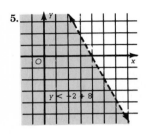

7.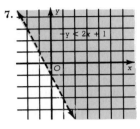

9.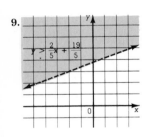

11.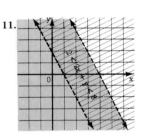

13.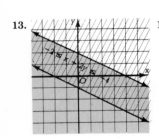

15.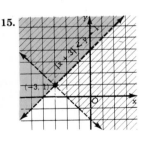

17.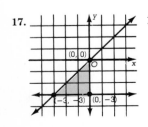

19.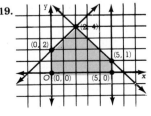

21.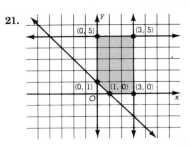

Pages 20-21 Exploratory Exercises   1. 14   **3.** 15
5. 1   **7.** 9   **9.** 1   **11.** -4 **13.** 17   **15.** -32
17. max 8, min 0   **19.** max 20, min -12
21. max 13, min 0

Page 21   Written Exercises

1.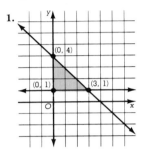

3.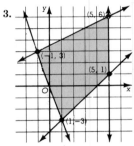

5. max 27, min -1 **7.** max 4, min -2 **9.** max 6, min
-2 **11.** max 17, min 3   **13.** max 42, min 18   **15.** max
68, min -12

Page 23   Exploratory Exercises   1. $x + y \leq 800$
3. $y \geq 300$

5.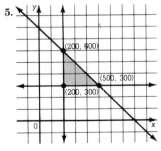

7. 200 units of lumber,
600 units of plywood

Pages 23-24 Written Exercises   1. 900 widgets,
1400 gadgets; $1060   **3.** 1200 widgets, 1100 gadgets;
$748   **5.** 50 bicycles, 75 tricycles; $600   **7.** 30% beef,
20% pork; $76   **9.** 1960 gallons #1, 1840 gallons #2;
$4964

Page 25 Using Mathematics 1. 250 units/week

Pages 27–28 Chapter Review 1. D-{3, 4, 5}, R-{5}
3. D-{8, 10}, R-{−5, −4, 4, 5} **5.** D-{7, 8, 9}, R-{49,
64, 81} **7.** {(0, −7), (1, −2), (2, 3), (3, 8)} **9.** {(5, 1),
(6, 2), (5, −1), (6, −2)} **11.** yes **13.** no **15.** yes
17. yes **19.** no **21.** 6 **23.** 126 **25.** 0 **27.** −3
29. $x - 3y + 5 = 0$ **31.** $2x - 2y = 0$ or $x - y = 0$
33. $y + 8 = 0$

35.
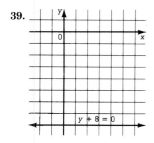

37.
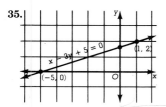

39.
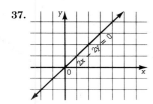

41. $\dfrac{8}{3}$ **43.** 20

45.
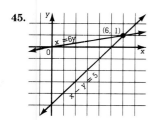

47. 13 **49.** 5 **51.** $\dfrac{12}{5}$ **53.** $\dfrac{4}{3}$ **55.** $y = 2x - 5$

57. $y = \dfrac{3}{5}x$ **59.** $y = x + 4$ **61.** $y = \dfrac{1}{4}x + \dfrac{15}{4}$
63. $y = \dfrac{7}{2}x - 10$

65.
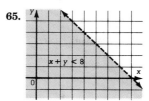

67.
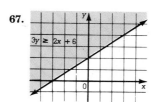

69.
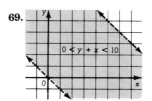

71.
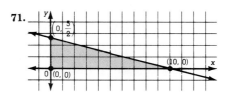

73.
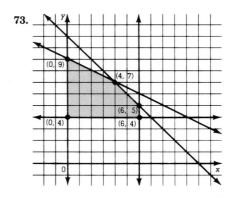

75. 49 **77.** −27 **79.** 31.1 **81.** 14 **83.** max 70, min
10 **85.** max 13, min −8 **87.** 2 large, 6 small; $220

CHAPTER 2 THEORY OF EQUATIONS

Page 32 Exploratory Exercises **1.** no **3.** no
5. yes **7.** yes **9.** no **11.** yes **13.** yes **15.** no

Pages 32–33 Written Exercises **1.** $x = 2$
3. $x = \pm 2$ **5.** $z = 2, -1$ **7.** $u = \pm 2$ **9.** $x = 1, 2, 3, 4$

11. $r = 9$ **13.** $y = \pm 3$ **15.** $y = \frac{1}{7}, -\frac{3}{2}$ **17.** $x = \frac{9}{4}, \frac{7}{5}$

19. $x = \frac{1}{6}, -\frac{1}{3}$ **21.** $x = \frac{5}{6}, -\frac{3}{2}$ **23.** $b = \pm \frac{11}{4}$

25. $x = -a, -b$

Page 36 Exploratory Exercises **1.** $-i$ **3.** $5 + 2i$

5. $-\frac{1}{2} - \frac{1}{2}i$ **7.** $5 + i\sqrt{2}$ **9.** 4 **11.** $\frac{1}{4}$ **13.** $\frac{4}{9}$

15. 225 **17.** $\frac{1}{64}$ **19.** $\frac{4}{49}$

Page 36 Written Exercises **1.** $y = -8, 11$

3. $x = 2, -10$ **5.** $x = \frac{1}{2}, \frac{1}{4}$ **7.** $y = \frac{3}{2}, -7$

9. $x = \frac{3 \pm \sqrt{37}}{2}$ **11.** $x = 2 \pm \frac{2\sqrt{6}}{3}$ **13.** $x = 4, -\frac{5}{3}$

15. $x = \frac{5}{4}, 1$ **17.** $n = \frac{8}{7}, -4$ **19.** $y = \frac{3}{2}, -\frac{2}{3}$

21. $x = \frac{-3 \pm i\sqrt{15}}{4}$ **23.** $y = \frac{-4 \pm i\sqrt{14}}{6}$

25. $x = -1, -\frac{4}{3}$ **27.** $b = \frac{-1 \pm \sqrt{97}}{8}$

29. $x = \frac{1 \pm i\sqrt{39}}{5}$ **31.** $x = \frac{-b \pm \sqrt{b^2 - 4ac}}{2a}$

Page 39 Exploratory Exercises **1.** Divisor, $x - 2$;
Dividend, $3x^3 - 5x + 10$; Quotient, $3x^2 + 6x + 7$;
Remainder, 24 **3.** Divisor, $x + 3$; Dividend,
$x^3 - 11x + 10$; Quotient, $x^2 - 3x + 2$; Remainder, 16
5. Divisor, $x + 1$; Dividend, $2x^3 - 5x + 1$; Quotient,

$2x^2 - 2x - 3$; Remainder, 4 **7.** Divisor, $x - \frac{1}{2}$;

Dividend, $x^3 + \frac{3}{2}x^2 + 3x - 2$; Quotient, $x^2 + 2x + 4$;

Remainder, 0 **9.** Divisor, $x + \frac{1}{3}$; Dividend,

$3x^3 + x^2 - 6x + 3$; Quotient, $3x^2 - 6$; Remainder, 5

Page 39 Written Exercises **1.** $x + 6$
3. $x^2 + 2x + 6, R = 15$ **5.** $x^3 - 2x^2 - 4x + 8$
7. $x^2 - 2x + 2$ **9.** $x^2 + 4x + 4, R = 4$
11. $2x^2 + 2x, R = -3$ **13.** $8x - 44, R = 231$
15. 4; no **17.** 55; no **19.** 0; yes **21.** 0; yes
23. -3; no

Page 39 Challenge Exercises
25. $2y^3 + 3y^2 + 2y - 1$ **27.** $b^2 - 2b - 3, R = 7$

29. $x^2 - \frac{5}{2}x - \frac{1}{2}$

Page 41 Exploratory Exercises **1.** $P(3) = 0$
3. $P(3) = 0$ **5.** yes **7.** yes

Page 41 Written Exercises **1.** $R = -1$ **3.** $R = 11$
5. $R = 0$ **7.** $R = 12$ **9.** $R = 92$ **11.** no **13.** no
15. yes **17.** no **19.** no **21.** $k = -20$
23. $k = -4$

Page 41 Challenge Exercises **25.** $x^2 - 6x + 25$

Page 44 Exploratory Exercises **1.** 2 **3.** 2 **5.** 2
7. 3 **9.** 3 **11.** 3 **13.** 3

Page 44 Written Exercises **1.** $0, \frac{1}{2}$ **3.** $\frac{5}{2}, -4$

5. $-\frac{3}{2}, \frac{1}{3}$ **7.** $-2, \frac{1}{2}, 3$ **9.** $-\frac{3}{2}, -5, \frac{1}{3}$ **11.** $2, -2, -1$

13. $3, 3, -\frac{1}{2}$ **15.** once **17.** twice **19.** -1, twice;

-3, twice **21.** -1, twice; 3, once
23. $x^3 - 4x^2 + 6x - 4 = 0$ **25.** $x^3 - 1 = 0$
27. $x^4 - 6x^3 + 13x^2 - 24x + 36 = 0$

Page 47 Exploratory Exercises **1.** $\pm 2, \pm 1$ **3.** ± 6,
$\pm 1, \pm 3, \pm 2$ **5.** $\pm 18, \pm 1, \pm 2, \pm 9, \pm 3, \pm 6$ **7.** $\pm 3, \pm 1$,

$\pm \frac{3}{2}, \pm \frac{1}{2}$ **9.** $\pm 6, \pm 1, \pm 2, \pm 3, \pm \frac{3}{2}, \pm \frac{1}{4}, \pm \frac{1}{2}, \pm \frac{3}{4}$

11. $\pm 12, \pm 1, \pm 4, \pm 3, \pm 2, \pm 6$

Page 47 Written Exercises **1.** 1 **3.** $\pm 1, -2, -3$

5. none **7.** $1, -3, \frac{1}{2}$ **9.** $\frac{3}{4}$ **11.** -6 **13.** ± 1

15. none **17.** $\frac{1}{2}$ **19.** $\frac{1}{2}, -\frac{1}{3}$

Page 50 Exploratory Exercises **1.** 2 or 0 **3.** 1
5. 1 **7.** 0 **9.** 4, 2, or 0 **11.** 1 **13.** 3 or 1 **15.** 2 or
0 **17.** 3 or 1 **19.** 0

Page 51 Written Exercises **1.** between -3 and -2,
between -1 and 0 **3.** between -1 and 0, between 4
and 5 **5.** between 1 and 2 **7.** $-1, 2$ **9.** $2.8, -1.8$
11. $-1, -2$ **13.** -2.5 **15.** $1, -1$ **17.** 2 **19.** 1
21. -5 **23.** 0

Page 54 Exploratory Exercises **1.** $2x + h$
3. $4x + 2h$ **5.** $-4x - 2h + 3$ **7.** $2x$ **9.** $4x$
11. $-4x + 3$

Pages 54–55 Written Exercises **1.** 2 **3.** 4 **5.** 8

7. 2 **9.** 3 **11.** 0.6 **13.** $1\frac{1}{6}$ **15.** -11 **17.** $y = 4x - 4$

19. $y = -7x - 2$ **21.** $y = -\frac{1}{4}$ **23.** $y = 12x + 17$

Page 58 Exploratory Exercises 1. $(1, -4)$

3. $\left(-\frac{3}{2}, -\frac{19}{2}\right)$ **5.** $(3, -19), (-3, 17)$

Page 58 Written Exercises 1. $\left(\frac{1}{2}, -6\frac{1}{4}\right)$, min.

3. $(-1, -16)$, min. **5.** $(0, 3)$, max; $\left(\frac{2}{3}, \frac{77}{27}\right)$, min.

7. $(0, 0)$, point of inflection

9.

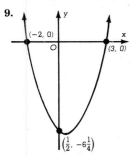

11.

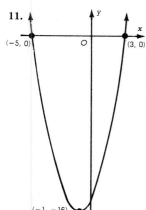

13.

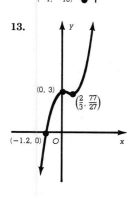

15.

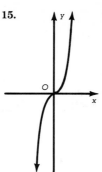

17.

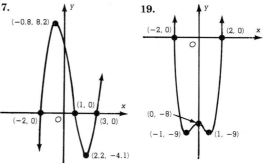

19.

23. $w = 7$ feet, $l = 7$ feet **25.** $w = 100$ feet,

$l = 66\frac{2}{3}$ feet **27.** \$58.80

Page 59 Using Mathematics
1. $x^3 - x^2 - 4x - 4 = 0$
3. $x^4 - 9x^3 + 30x^2 + 44x + 24 = 0$
5. $x^4 + 13x^3 + 29x^2 - 13x - 30 = 0$

Pages 61–62 Chapter Review 1. $x = 4, 6, \frac{2}{3}$

3. $x = \frac{1}{2}, -4$ **5.** $x = \frac{-5 \pm \sqrt{61}}{6}$

7. $5x^2 + 6x + 4, R = 10$ **9.** $R = -4$ **11.** $-3, -3, 2$

13. $\frac{1}{2}, \frac{1}{4}$ **15.** 2 or 0 **17.** 0 **19.** 2 **21.** -2

23. ± 1.3 **25.** 10 **27.** $y = 10x - 5$ **29.** $\left(\frac{1}{2}, \frac{17}{4}\right)$ max.

31. $-1.6, 2.6$

CHAPTER 3 MATRICES AND VECTORS
Page 67 Exploratory Exercises 1. 62 **3.** -8

5. 0

7. $x = \dfrac{\begin{vmatrix} 5 & 2 \\ 1 & -3 \end{vmatrix}}{\begin{vmatrix} 3 & 2 \\ 4 & -3 \end{vmatrix}}, \; y = \dfrac{\begin{vmatrix} 3 & 5 \\ 4 & 1 \end{vmatrix}}{\begin{vmatrix} 3 & 2 \\ 4 & -3 \end{vmatrix}}$

9. $x = \dfrac{\begin{vmatrix} 6 & 1 \\ 2 & -1 \end{vmatrix}}{\begin{vmatrix} 2 & 1 \\ 6 & -1 \end{vmatrix}}, \; y = \dfrac{\begin{vmatrix} 2 & 6 \\ 6 & 2 \end{vmatrix}}{\begin{vmatrix} 2 & 1 \\ 6 & -1 \end{vmatrix}}$

11. $x = \dfrac{\begin{vmatrix} 6 & 1 \\ -12 & -2 \end{vmatrix}}{\begin{vmatrix} 4 & 1 \\ 1 & -2 \end{vmatrix}}, \; y = \dfrac{\begin{vmatrix} 4 & 6 \\ 1 & -12 \end{vmatrix}}{\begin{vmatrix} 4 & 1 \\ 1 & -2 \end{vmatrix}}$

Page 67 Written Exercises 1. -50 **3.** 1 **5.** -93
7. $x = 1, y = 1$ **9.** $x = 1, y = 4$ **11.** $x = 0, y = 6$
13. $x = 3, y = -1$ **15.** $x = 4, y = 3$ **17.** $x = 4, y = -4$
19. $x = 3, y = \dfrac{1}{2}$ **21.** $x = -\dfrac{3}{5}, y = 3$

Pages 67–68 Challenge Exercises 23. -890
25. $x = -3, y = \dfrac{1}{3}, z = 1$

Page 70 Exploratory Exercises 1. $\begin{bmatrix} a_{11} & a_{12} & a_{13} \\ a_{21} & a_{22} & a_{23} \\ a_{31} & a_{32} & a_{33} \end{bmatrix}$

3. $\begin{bmatrix} a_{11} & a_{12} & a_{13} & a_{14} \\ a_{21} & a_{22} & a_{23} & a_{24} \\ a_{31} & a_{32} & a_{33} & a_{34} \\ a_{41} & a_{42} & a_{43} & a_{44} \\ a_{51} & a_{52} & a_{53} & a_{54} \\ a_{61} & a_{62} & a_{63} & a_{64} \end{bmatrix}$ **5.** $\begin{bmatrix} -6 & -5 \\ -8 & -4 \end{bmatrix}$ **7.** $\begin{bmatrix} 2 & -1 \\ 0 & 3 \end{bmatrix}$

Pages 70–71 Written Exercises 1. $\begin{bmatrix} -2 & 11 & -2 \\ 9 & -1 & -6 \\ 11 & -2 & 1 \end{bmatrix}$

3. $\begin{bmatrix} 3 & 15 & -13 \\ -7 & 10 & -8 \\ 28 & 2 & 1 \end{bmatrix}$ **5.** $\begin{bmatrix} -4 & 1 & -16 \\ -1 & -5 & 6 \\ 5 & -2 & 5 \end{bmatrix}$

7. $\begin{bmatrix} -9 & -3 & -5 \\ 15 & -16 & 8 \\ -12 & -6 & 5 \end{bmatrix}$ **9.** $x = 7, y = 2$

11. $x = 4, y = 0$

Page 72 Exploratory Exercises 1. $[18 \quad 30]$
3. $[6\sqrt{5} \quad -6 \quad 24]$ **5.** $\begin{bmatrix} \dfrac{9}{2} & -\dfrac{3}{2} \\ -3 & 3 \end{bmatrix}$ **7.** 2×6
9. 4×3 **11.** 3×1

Page 73 Written Exercises 1. $\begin{bmatrix} 21 & 0 \\ 15 & 9 \end{bmatrix}$

3. $\begin{bmatrix} 6 & -6 & 12 \\ 10 & 8 & -4 \end{bmatrix}$ **5.** $\begin{bmatrix} 34 & 12 \\ 36 & -12 \\ 16 & 18 \end{bmatrix}$ **7.** $\begin{bmatrix} -30 & 60 \\ 46 & -8 \end{bmatrix}$

9. $\begin{bmatrix} 49 & 0 \\ 50 & 9 \end{bmatrix}$ **11.** $\begin{bmatrix} 162 & -54 & 180 \\ 48 & -156 & 240 \\ 138 & 24 & 60 \end{bmatrix}$ **13.** $\begin{bmatrix} 14 & -29 \\ 3 & 7 \end{bmatrix}$

15. $a_{11}x + a_{12}y + b_1 = 0$
$a_{12}x + a_{22}y + b_2 = 0$

Page 75 Exploratory Exercises 1. -1 **3.** 0
5. 26 **7.** 14 **9.** 164 **11.** yes **13.** no **15.** yes
17. yes **19.** yes

Page 76 Written Exercises 1. $\begin{bmatrix} -5 & 3 \\ 2 & -1 \end{bmatrix}$

3. none **5.** $\begin{bmatrix} \dfrac{1}{26} & -\dfrac{2}{13} \\ \dfrac{2}{13} & \dfrac{5}{13} \end{bmatrix}$ **7.** $\begin{bmatrix} \dfrac{1}{7} & -\dfrac{1}{14} \\ \dfrac{3}{7} & \dfrac{2}{7} \end{bmatrix}$

9. $\begin{bmatrix} -\dfrac{3}{41} & \dfrac{8}{41} \\ -\dfrac{4}{41} & \dfrac{29}{164} \end{bmatrix}$ **11.** $x = \begin{bmatrix} \dfrac{21}{13} & 1 \\ -\dfrac{10}{13} & -1 \end{bmatrix}$

13. $x = \begin{bmatrix} 0 & 0 \\ 0 & 0 \end{bmatrix}$ **15.** $x = \begin{bmatrix} \dfrac{60}{29} & -\dfrac{12}{29} \\ -\dfrac{5}{29} & \dfrac{59}{29} \end{bmatrix}$

Page 78 Exploratory Exercises Answers may
vary. One possible answer is given. **1.** Multiply row 2
by 5 and add to row 1. **3.** Multiply row 2 by -3 and
add to row 1. **5.** Multiply row 1 by 3 and row 2 by 2.
Then add row 2 to row 1. **7.** Multiply row 1 by -2
and add to row 2. **9.** Add row 2 to row 1. Multiply row
1 by 2 and add it to row 2. **11.** Multiply row 1 by 2
and row 2 by 3. Then add row 1 to row 2.

Pages 78–79 Written Exercises 1. $x = -1, y = 2$

3. $x = \dfrac{1}{3}, y = -\dfrac{10}{3}$ **5.** $x = -1, y = 2, z = -3$

7. $x = -\dfrac{97}{19}, y = \dfrac{155}{19}$ **9.** $x = 7, y = 1, z = -2$

11. $w = -2, x = 1, y = -1, z = 2$ **13.** $y = 2x^2 - 3x + 5$

Page 79 For the Scholar $A = 11$

Page 82 Exploratory Exercises 7. yes

Page 82 Written Exercises

1.

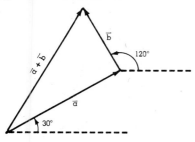

3.

5.

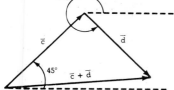

13. 4.0 cm; 60° **15.** 3.9 cm; 5° **17.** 4.8 cm; −2°
19. 7.0 cm; 53° **21.** 10.3 cm; 16° **23.** 3.1 cm; 187°
25. 1.8 cm; 3.0 cm **27.** 2.1 cm; 2.1 cm

Page 84–85 Exploratory Exercises 1. 5 **3.** $\sqrt{89}$
5. $\sqrt{106}$ **7.** $\sqrt{377}$ **9.** $4\vec{i} + 3\vec{j}$ **11.** $5\vec{i} + 8\vec{j}$
13. $5\vec{i} + -9\vec{j}$ **15.** $-16\vec{i} + 11\vec{j}$ **17.** (2, 7) **19.** (−9, 1)
21. (1, 1) **23.** (3, 4) **25.** (−7, 5) **27.** no
Page 85 Written Exercises 1. (−3, 2) **3.** (2, 6)
5. (1, 1) **7.** $\sqrt{13}$ **9.** $2\sqrt{10}$ **11.** $\sqrt{2}$ **13.** (−1, −3)
15. (−20, 10) **17.** (−10, 12) **19.** (0, −14) **21.** (−30, 22) **23.** (0, 0)

Page 87 Exploratory Exercises
1.

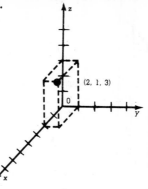

3.

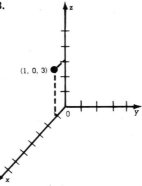

5. **7.**

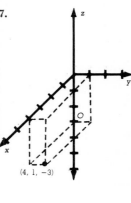

9.

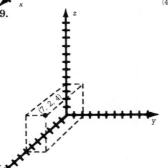

11. $\sqrt{14}$ 13. $\sqrt{10}$ 15. $\sqrt{17}$ 17. $\sqrt{26}$ 19. $\sqrt{69}$
21. $2\vec{i} + \vec{j} + 3\vec{k}$ 23. $\vec{i} + 3\vec{k}$ 25. $-\vec{i} + 4\vec{k}$
27. $4\vec{i} + \vec{j} + -3\vec{k}$ 29. $7\vec{i} + 2\vec{j} + 4\vec{k}$

Pages 87–88 Written Exercises 1. (2, 0, 3)
3. (5, 4, −11) **5.** (−12, 5, 1) **7.** $\sqrt{13}$ **9.** $\sqrt{162}$
11. $\sqrt{170}$ **13.** $2\vec{i} + 3\vec{k}$ **15.** $5\vec{i} + 4\vec{j} + -11\vec{k}$
17. $-12\vec{i} + 5\vec{j} + \vec{k}$ **19.** (−1, −1, −10) **21.** (9, −19, −2)
23. (19, −37, 6) **25.** $-\vec{i} + -\vec{j} + -10\vec{k}$
27. $9\vec{i} + -19\vec{j} + -2\vec{k}$ **29.** $19\vec{i} + -37\vec{j} + 6\vec{k}$

Page 90 Exploratory Exercises 1. 2, no **3.** 32,
no **5.** 7, no **7.** 1, no **9.** 8, no

11. $\begin{vmatrix} \vec{i} & \vec{j} & \vec{k} \\ 2 & 3 & -4 \\ -2 & -3 & 1 \end{vmatrix} = \begin{vmatrix} 3 & -4 \\ -3 & 1 \end{vmatrix}\vec{i} - \begin{vmatrix} 2 & -4 \\ -2 & 1 \end{vmatrix}\vec{j} +$

$\begin{vmatrix} 2 & 3 \\ -2 & -3 \end{vmatrix}\vec{k}$

15. $\begin{vmatrix} \vec{i} & \vec{j} & \vec{k} \\ 1 & -3 & 2 \\ 5 & 1 & -2 \end{vmatrix} = \begin{vmatrix} -3 & 2 \\ 1 & -2 \end{vmatrix}\vec{i} - \begin{vmatrix} 1 & 2 \\ 5 & -2 \end{vmatrix}\vec{j} + \begin{vmatrix} 1 & -3 \\ 5 & 1 \end{vmatrix}\vec{k}$

17. $\begin{vmatrix} \vec{i} & \vec{j} & \vec{k} \\ -6 & 2 & 10 \\ 4 & 1 & 9 \end{vmatrix} = \begin{vmatrix} 2 & 10 \\ 1 & 9 \end{vmatrix}\vec{i} - \begin{vmatrix} -6 & 10 \\ 4 & 9 \end{vmatrix}\vec{j} + \begin{vmatrix} -6 & 2 \\ 4 & 1 \end{vmatrix}\vec{k}$

Page 90 Written Exercises 1. −17 **3.** 27 **5.** −2
7. 68 **9.** 11 **11.** yes **13.** no **15.** no **17.** no
19. (−9, 6, 0); (−9, 6, 0) · (2, 3, −4) = −18 + 18 + 0 =
0; (−9, 6, 0) · (−2, −3, 1) = 18 + −18 + 0 = 0
21. (1, −19, 31); (1, −19, 31) · (7, 2, 1) = 7 − 38 + 31 =
0; (1, −19, 31) · (2, 5, 3) = 2 − 95 + 93 = 0
23. (4, 12, 16); (4, 12, 16) · (1, −3, 2) = 4 − 36 + 32 =
0; (4, 12, 16) · (5, 1, −2) = 20 + 12 − 32 = 0
25. (8, 94, −14); (8, 94, −14) (−6, 2, 10) = −48 + 188 +
−140 = 0; (8, 94, −14) (4, 1, 9) = 32 + 94 + −126 = 0
27. (16, 4, −10); (16, 4, −10) · (3, −2, 4) = 48 − 8 − 40
= 0; (16, 4, −10) · (1, −4, 0) = 16 − 16 + 0 = 0

Page 91 Using Mathematics 1. 250 km/h, 16°
south of west **3.** 86 newtons, 55° west of north

Pages 93–94 Chapter Review 1. −1 **3.** 0

5. $x = \frac{2}{3}, y = -2$ 7. $\begin{bmatrix} 9 & -1 & 9 \\ 3 & 3 & 0 \\ -2 & -8 & 4 \end{bmatrix}$

9. $\begin{bmatrix} 3 & -1 & 6 \\ 6 & -4 & 1 \\ -13 & 0 & 2 \end{bmatrix}$ 11. $\begin{bmatrix} 6 & 3 \\ -9 & 12 \end{bmatrix}$

13. [31   −23]

15. $\begin{bmatrix} \frac{5}{17} & \frac{2}{17} \\ \frac{1}{17} & -\frac{3}{17} \end{bmatrix}$ 17. $\begin{bmatrix} -3 & -4 \\ -4 & -5 \end{bmatrix}$

19. $x = \begin{bmatrix} 6 & 11 \\ 7 & 12 \end{bmatrix}$

21. $x = -10, y = -6, z = 0$
27. 1.8 cm; 135° **29.** 11.4 cm; 35° **31.** 1.4 cm;
1.4 cm **33.** 0.9 cm; 0.5 cm **35.** (5, 12) **37.** 13
39. (5, −6) **41.** (12, −17) **43.** (4, −1, −3) **45.** $\sqrt{26}$
47. (1, 5, 2) **49.** (−2, 9, 6) **51.** $\vec{i} + 5\vec{j} + 2\vec{k}$
53. $-2\vec{i} + 9\vec{j} + 6\vec{k}$ **55.** −16 **57.** 0 **59.** (7, 22, 2)

CHAPTER 4 THE CIRCULAR FUNCTIONS
Pages 99–100 Exploratory Exercises 1. III
3. II **5.** I **7.** II **9.** I **11.** Answers may vary.
13. $4 - 2\pi n$ where n is a positive integer.

Page 100 Written Exercises 1. (−1, 0) **3.** (1, 0)

5. $\left(-\frac{\sqrt{2}}{2}, \frac{\sqrt{2}}{2}\right)$ 7. (0, −1) 9. $\frac{\pi}{3}$ 11. π

13. $\frac{5\pi}{3}$ 15. $\left(\frac{1}{2}, \frac{\sqrt{3}}{2}\right)$ 17. (−1, 0) 19. $\left(\frac{1}{2}, -\frac{\sqrt{3}}{2}\right)$

21. $\left(\frac{1}{2}, -\frac{\sqrt{3}}{2}\right)$ 23. $\left(\frac{1}{2}, \frac{\sqrt{3}}{2}\right)$ 25. $\left(\frac{5}{13}, -\frac{12}{13}\right)$

27. $\left(-\frac{5}{13}, -\frac{12}{13}\right)$ **29.** 1.57 **31.** 0.25 **33.** −4.71

35. −6.03 **37.** $7.85 + 2\pi n$ where n is any positive
integer. **39.** $6.53 + 2\pi n$ where n is any positive
integer.

Pages 103–104 Exploratory Exercises
1. positive **3.** negative **5.** positive **7.** positive
9. I **11.** III **13.** 0.6 **15.** 0.8 **17.** 1 **19.** 1

Pages 104–105 Written Exercises

1.

s	$\cos s$	$\sin s$	$\tan s$	$\sec s$	$\csc s$	$\cot s$
0	1	0	0	1	—	—
$\dfrac{\pi}{6}$	$\dfrac{\sqrt{3}}{2}$	$\dfrac{1}{2}$	$\dfrac{\sqrt{3}}{3}$	$\dfrac{2\sqrt{3}}{3}$	2	$\sqrt{3}$
$\dfrac{\pi}{4}$	$\dfrac{\sqrt{2}}{2}$	$\dfrac{\sqrt{2}}{2}$	1	$\sqrt{2}$	$\sqrt{2}$	1
$\dfrac{\pi}{3}$	$\dfrac{1}{2}$	$\dfrac{\sqrt{3}}{2}$	$\sqrt{3}$	2	$\dfrac{2\sqrt{3}}{3}$	$\dfrac{\sqrt{3}}{3}$
$\dfrac{\pi}{2}$	0	1	—	—	1	0

3. 1 **5.** $-\dfrac{\sqrt{2}}{2}$ **7.** -1 **9.** $-\dfrac{\sqrt{3}}{3}$ **11.** -1 **13.** $\dfrac{\sqrt{3}}{2}$

15. $\dfrac{\sqrt{7}}{3}$ **17.** $\dfrac{4\sqrt{7}}{7}$ **19.** $-\dfrac{\sqrt{3}}{3}$ **21.** $-\dfrac{2\sqrt{3}}{3}$

23. $\dfrac{17}{8}$ **25.** $-\dfrac{17}{15}$ **27.** any multiple of 2π **29.** 2π

Page 109 Exploratory Exercises 1. IV **3.** IV
5. II **7.** III **9.** II

Page 109 Written Exercises 1. 0.1736 **3.** 1.560
5. -0.3249 **7.** 1.211 **9.** -0.6361 **11.** undefined
13. -0.4173 **15.** -0.4617 **17.** 0.1454 **19.** 0.7330
21. 0.1367 **23.** 0.5061 **25.** 1.3235 **27.** 1.4108

Page 110 Challenge Exercises

29.

x	0	0.2	0.4	0.6	0.8	1.0	1.2	1.4	1.6
$\sin x$	0	0.20	0.39	0.56	0.72	0.84	0.93	0.99	1.0

1.8	2.0	2.2	2.4	2.6	2.8	3.0	3.2	3.4	3.6
0.97	0.91	0.81	0.68	0.52	0.34	0.14	-0.06	-0.26	-0.44

3.8	4.0	4.2	4.4	4.6	4.8	5.0	5.2
-0.61	-0.76	-0.87	-0.95	-0.99	-1.0	-0.96	-0.88

5.4	5.6	5.8	6.0	6.2	6.4
-0.77	-0.63	-0.46	-0.28	-0.08	0.12

31.

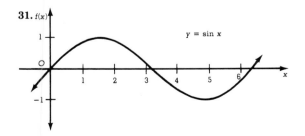

$y = \sin x$

Page 113 Exploratory Exercises 1. decreasing
3. increasing **5.** increasing **7.** decreasing
9. increasing **11.** decreasing

Page 113–114 Written Exercises 1. none
3. $\dfrac{\pi}{2}, \dfrac{3\pi}{2}$ **5.** $\dfrac{\pi}{2}, \dfrac{3\pi}{2}$ **7–9.** Answers may vary.

11.–13.

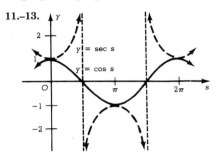

15. Graph on page 111 of text. **17.** $-\dfrac{\pi}{2}$ **19.** $-\dfrac{3\pi}{2}$

21. III **23.** IV **25.** $\dfrac{\pi}{4}, \dfrac{5\pi}{4}$ **27.** none **29.** $0, \dfrac{3\pi}{2}, 2\pi$

Page 117 Exploratory Exercises 1. $\dfrac{\pi}{2} + \dfrac{\pi}{3}$

3. $\dfrac{\pi}{4} - \dfrac{7\pi}{6}$ **5.** $\dfrac{\pi}{4} + \dfrac{\pi}{6}$ **7.** $\dfrac{5\pi}{4} + \dfrac{\pi}{3}$

Page 117 Written Exercises

1. $\cos\left(\dfrac{\pi}{2} + \dfrac{\pi}{2}\right) = \cos\dfrac{\pi}{2}\cos\dfrac{\pi}{2} - \sin\dfrac{\pi}{2}\sin\dfrac{\pi}{2}$

$\qquad \cos\pi = (0 \cdot 0) - (1 \cdot 1)$

$\qquad\quad -1 = -1$

3. $\sin\left(\dfrac{\pi}{2} + \dfrac{\pi}{2}\right) = \sin\dfrac{\pi}{2}\cos\dfrac{\pi}{2} + \cos\dfrac{\pi}{2}\sin\dfrac{\pi}{2}$

$\qquad \sin\pi = (1 \cdot 0) + (0 \cdot 1)$

$\qquad\quad 0 = 0$

5. $\cos\left(0 - \dfrac{\pi}{3}\right) = \cos 0 \cos\dfrac{\pi}{3} + \sin 0 \sin\dfrac{\pi}{3}$

$\qquad \cos\left(-\dfrac{\pi}{3}\right) = \left(1 \cdot \dfrac{1}{2}\right) + \left(0 \cdot \dfrac{\sqrt{3}}{2}\right)$

$\qquad\qquad \dfrac{1}{2} = \dfrac{1}{2}$

7. $\dfrac{\sqrt{6} + \sqrt{2}}{4}$ **9.** $\dfrac{\sqrt{2} + \sqrt{6}}{4}$ **11.** $\dfrac{-\sqrt{2} - \sqrt{6}}{4}$

13. $\dfrac{\sqrt{2} + \sqrt{6}}{4}$ **15.** $\dfrac{-\sqrt{2} - \sqrt{6}}{4}$ **17.** $\sin s$ **19.** $-\cos s$

21. $-\sin s$ **23.** $\cos s$ **25.** $\dfrac{\tan s_1 - \tan s_2}{1 + \tan s_1 \tan s_2}$

27. $\dfrac{\cot s_1 \cot s_2 + 1}{\cot s_2 - \cot s_1}$

43. $\dfrac{\sqrt{6} - \sqrt{2}}{4}$ **45.** $\dfrac{\sqrt{2} + \sqrt{6}}{4}$ **47.** $\dfrac{7}{8}$

Page 120   **Exploratory Exercises**   **1.** $\dfrac{\sqrt{2 - \sqrt{3}}}{2}$

3. $\dfrac{\sqrt{2 - \sqrt{2 - \sqrt{2}}}}{2}$ **5.** $\dfrac{\sqrt{2 - \sqrt{2}}}{2}$

7. $\dfrac{\sqrt{2 + \sqrt{2 - \sqrt{2}}}}{2}$

Page 120   **Written Exercises**   **1.** $\dfrac{\sqrt{3}}{2}$ **3.** $\dfrac{4\sqrt{5}}{9}$

5. $-\dfrac{120}{169}$ **7.** $-\dfrac{3\sqrt{7}}{8}$ **9.** $\dfrac{\sqrt{2 + \sqrt{3}}}{2}$ **11.** $-\dfrac{\sqrt{6}}{6}$

13. $\dfrac{\sqrt{26}}{26}$ **15.** $-\dfrac{\sqrt{8 + 2\sqrt{7}}}{4}$ **17.** $\dfrac{\sqrt{2 - \sqrt{3}}}{2}$

19. $\dfrac{\sqrt{30}}{6}$ **21.** $\dfrac{5\sqrt{26}}{26}$ **23.** $\dfrac{1}{4}\sqrt{8 - 2\sqrt{7}}$ **25.** $\dfrac{1}{2}$

27. $-\dfrac{1}{9}$ **29.** $\dfrac{119}{169}$ **31.** $-\dfrac{1}{8}$ **33.** $\dfrac{2 \tan s}{1 - \tan^2 s}$

35. $3 \sin s - 4 \sin^3 s$

Page 122   **Chapter Review**   **1.** $\left(-\dfrac{\sqrt{2}}{2}, -\dfrac{\sqrt{2}}{2}\right)$

3. $(-1, 0)$ **5.** $(1, 0)$ **7.** $\left(\dfrac{1}{2}, -\dfrac{\sqrt{3}}{2}\right)$ **9.** $\dfrac{4}{5}$ **11.** $\dfrac{4}{3}$ **13.** 1

15. $\sqrt{3}$ **17.** $\dfrac{2\sqrt{3}}{3}$ **19.** -1 **21.** $\dfrac{\sqrt{3}}{2}$ **23.** 0

25. 0.3283 **27.** 0.9613 **29.** 1.022 **31.** -4.876
33. 1.4603 **35.** 1.2537 **37.** 0.7941

39.

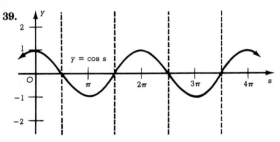

41.

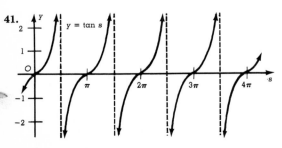

CHAPTER 5   THE TRIGONOMETRIC FUNCTIONS

Pages 127–128   **Exploratory Exercises**   **1.** $\dfrac{y}{a}$ **3.** $\dfrac{h}{b}$

5. $\dfrac{h}{a}$ **7.** $\dfrac{h}{x}$ **9.** $\dfrac{x}{b}$ **11.** 0 **13.** $\dfrac{1}{2}$ **15.** $\dfrac{2\sqrt{3}}{3}$ **17.** $\sqrt{3}$

19. 1

Page 128   **Written Exercises**   **1.** $\sin \alpha = \dfrac{12}{13}$,

$\csc \alpha = \dfrac{13}{12}$, $\tan \alpha = \dfrac{12}{5}$, $\cot \alpha = \dfrac{5}{12}$, $\cos \alpha = \dfrac{5}{13}$,

$\sec \alpha = \dfrac{13}{5}$ **3.** $\sin \alpha = \dfrac{4}{5}$, $\csc \alpha = \dfrac{5}{4}$, $\tan \alpha = \dfrac{4}{3}$,

$\cot \alpha = \dfrac{3}{4}$, $\cos \alpha = \dfrac{3}{5}$, $\sec \alpha = \dfrac{5}{3}$ **5.** $\sin \alpha = 0$, $\csc \alpha$

undefined, $\tan \alpha = 0$, $\cot \alpha$ undefined, $\cos \alpha = -1$,

$\sec \alpha = -1$ **7.** $\sin \alpha = -\dfrac{3}{\sqrt{34}}$, $\csc \alpha = -\dfrac{\sqrt{34}}{3}$,

$\tan \alpha = -\dfrac{3}{5}$, $\cot \alpha = -\dfrac{5}{3}$, $\cos \alpha = \dfrac{5}{\sqrt{34}}$,

$\sec \alpha = \dfrac{\sqrt{34}}{5}$ **9.** $\dfrac{1 + \sqrt{3}}{2}$ **11.** $\dfrac{\sqrt{2} + 1}{2}$ **13.** $\dfrac{\sqrt{2} - 2}{2}$

15. $\sqrt{3} - 1$ **17.** $\sqrt{3}$ **19.** $\dfrac{\sqrt{3}}{2}$ **21.** $2 + \sqrt{3}$ **23.** 0.6000

25. 0.7500 **27.** 0.8824 **29.** 0.3492 **31.** 0.9370
33. 1.3333 **35.** 2.8636 **37.** 2.1250

39. $1 \stackrel{?}{=} 0^2 + 1^2$ **41.** $1 - \left(\dfrac{\sqrt{2}}{2}\right)^2 \stackrel{?}{=} \left(\dfrac{\sqrt{2}}{2}\right)^2$
    $1 = 1$

$$1 - \dfrac{1}{2} \stackrel{?}{=} \dfrac{1}{2}$$

$$\dfrac{1}{2} = \dfrac{1}{2}$$

43. $\left(\dfrac{1}{2}\right)^2 + \left(\dfrac{\sqrt{3}}{2}\right)^2 \stackrel{?}{=} 1$

$$\dfrac{1}{4} + \dfrac{3}{4} \stackrel{?}{=} 1$$

$$1 = 1$$

45. $\frac{1}{2} \overset{?}{=} \left(\frac{\sqrt{3}}{2}\right)^2 - \left(\frac{1}{2}\right)^2$

$\frac{1}{2} \overset{?}{=} \frac{3}{4} - \frac{1}{4}$

$\frac{1}{2} = \frac{1}{2}$

47. 5 m

Page 129 Using Mathematics 1. 0.2784 **3.** 2.282
5. 1.150 **7.** 0.1074 **9.** 42°40' **11.** 32°30' **13.** 8°10'

Page 131 Exploratory Exercises 1. 0.2784
3. 2.282 **5.** 1.150 **7.** 0.1074 **9.** 42°40' **11.** 32°30'
13. 8°10'

Page 131 Written Exercises 1. 0.4384 **3.** 1.471
5. 0.9981 **7.** 0.8098 **9.** 0.2717 **11.** 4.554
13. 0.8331 **15.** 0.0701 **17.** 5°00' **19.** 17°30'
21. 30°40' **23.** 23°30' **25.** 67°12' **27.** 86°47'
29. 38°33' **31.** 46°15'

Page 134 Exploratory Exercises 1. $\frac{\sqrt{3}}{3}$ **3.** 0.109
5. $\frac{\sqrt{3}}{3}$ **7.** 0.9976 **9.** 9.514 **11.** 0.5831

Page 134–135 Written Exercises 1. $\frac{4\sqrt{7}}{7}$ **3.** $\frac{1}{3}$
5. $\frac{\sqrt{7}}{3}$ **7.** $\frac{3\sqrt{5}}{5}$ **9.** 0.7692 **11.** $\frac{3}{5}$ **13.** $\frac{4}{3}$ **15.** 0.5882
17. $\frac{4\sqrt{17}}{17}$ **19.** 1 **21.** $\frac{\sqrt{3}}{2}$ **23.** $\frac{3}{4}$ **25.** $\sin \theta$
27. $2 \sin x$ **29.** 2 **31.** $\frac{\sin \theta}{\sin (90 - \theta)}$
33. $\pm \frac{\sqrt{\sec^2 \theta - 1}}{\sec \theta}$ **35.** $\pm \sqrt{\csc^2 \theta - 1}$

Page 136 Exploratory Exercises 1. Pythagorean
Identity **3.** Reciprocal Identity, Quotient Identity
5. Quotient Identity **7.** Quotient Identity ,
Reciprocal Identity **9.** Pythagorean Identity

11. $\csc^2 \alpha - \cot^2 \alpha \overset{?}{=} 1$
$(1 + \cot^2 \alpha) - \cot^2 \alpha \overset{?}{=}$
$1 = 1$

13. $\tan x \csc x \overset{?}{=} \sec x$
$\frac{\sin x}{\cos x} \cdot \frac{1}{\sin x} \overset{?}{=}$
$\frac{1}{\cos x} \overset{?}{=}$
$\sec x = \sec x$

15. $\sin \theta \cot \theta \overset{?}{=} \cos \theta$
$\sin \theta \cdot \frac{\cos \theta}{\sin \theta} \overset{?}{=}$
$\cos \theta = \cos \theta$

17. $\frac{\tan x}{\sin x} \overset{?}{=} \sec x$
$\frac{\frac{\sin x}{\cos x}}{\sin x} \overset{?}{=}$
$\frac{1}{\cos x} \overset{?}{=}$
$\sec x = \sec x$

19. $\sec^2 \theta - 1 \overset{?}{=} \tan^2 \theta$
$(\tan^2 \theta + 1) - 1 \overset{?}{=}$
$\tan^2 \theta = \tan^2 \theta$

Page 137 Written Exercises
1. $\sin^2 A \cot^2 A \overset{?}{=} (1 - \sin A)(1 + \sin A)$
$\overset{?}{=} 1 - \sin^2 A$
$\overset{?}{=} \cos^2 A$
$\overset{?}{=} (\sin A \cot A)^2$
$\sin^2 A \cot^2 A = \sin^2 A \cot^2 A$

3. $\tan B \overset{?}{=} \dfrac{\cos B}{\sin B \cot^2 B}$
$\overset{?}{=} \dfrac{\cos B}{\sin B} \cdot \dfrac{1}{\cot^2 B}$
$\overset{?}{=} \cot B \cdot \dfrac{1}{\cot^2 B}$
$\overset{?}{=} \dfrac{1}{\cot B}$
$\tan B = \tan B$

5. $\dfrac{1}{\sec^2 x} + \dfrac{1}{\csc^2 x} - 1 \overset{?}{=} 0$
$\cos^2 x + \sin^2 x - 1 \overset{?}{=}$
$1 - 1 \overset{?}{=} 0$

7. $\csc \theta \overset{?}{=} \sin \theta (1 + \cot^2 \theta)$
$\overset{?}{=} \sin \theta (\csc^2 \theta)$
$\overset{?}{=} \dfrac{1}{\csc \theta}(\csc^2 \theta)$
$\csc \theta = \csc \theta$

9. $\dfrac{\sin (90° - w)}{\cos (90° - w)} \overset{?}{=} \cot w$
$\dfrac{\cos w}{\sin w} \overset{?}{=}$
$\cot w = \cot w$

11. $1 + \tan^2 (90° - x) \overset{?}{=} \dfrac{1}{\cos^2 (90° - x)}$
$1 + \cot^2 x \overset{?}{=} \csc^2 x$
$\csc^2 x = \csc^2 x$

13.
$$\frac{\sec B}{\cos B} - \frac{\tan B}{\cot B} \stackrel{?}{=} 1$$

$$\left(\sec B \cdot \frac{1}{\cos B}\right) - \left(\tan B \cdot \frac{1}{\cot B}\right) \stackrel{?}{=}$$

$$\sec^2 B - \tan^2 B \stackrel{?}{=}$$

$$(\tan^2 B + 1) - \tan^2 B \stackrel{?}{=}$$

$$1 = 1$$

15.
$$\sec^4 \alpha - \sec^2 \alpha \stackrel{?}{=} \frac{1}{\cot^4 \alpha} + \frac{1}{\cot^2 \alpha}$$

$$\sec^2 \alpha \,(\sec^2 \alpha - 1) \stackrel{?}{=} \tan^4 \alpha + \tan^2 \alpha$$

$$\sec^2 \alpha \cdot \tan^2 \alpha \stackrel{?}{=} \tan^2 \alpha \,(\tan^2 \alpha + 1)$$

$$\sec^2 \alpha \cdot \tan^2 \alpha = \tan^2 \alpha \cdot \sec^2 \alpha$$

17.
$$\frac{1 + \tan^2 A}{\csc^2 A} \stackrel{?}{=} \tan^2 A$$

$$\frac{\sec^2 A}{\csc^2 A} \stackrel{?}{=}$$

$$\frac{\dfrac{1}{\cos^2 A}}{\dfrac{1}{\sin^2 A}} \stackrel{?}{=}$$

$$\frac{\sin^2 A}{\cos^2 A} = \tan^2 A$$

19. $\tan x = 1$

21. $\tan x = 2$

23. $\tan x = \pm \dfrac{\sqrt{6}}{2}$ **25.** $\sec x = \sqrt{2}$ **27.** $\dfrac{1}{9}$

Page 139 Exploratory Exercises 1. 0.314
3. 4.19 **5.** 180° **7.** 135°

Page 140 Written Exercises 1. 4.71 **3.** 3.66
5. 1.31 **7.** 3.93 **9.** 225° **11.** 330° **13.** 720° **15.** 43°
17. 7.85 **19.** 26.2 **21.** 7.85 **23.** 20.2 **25.** 35.8°
27. 172° **29.** 8.28 cm

Page 143 Exploratory Exercises 1. 26° **3.** 16°
5. 53° **7.** 2° **9.** sin 45° **11.** −tan 40° **13.** −sin 20°
15. tan 24°

Page 143 Written Exercises 1. −sin 30° **3.** −cot 80°
5. −cos 30° **7.** −sec 45° **9.** −tan 40° **11.** tan 30°
13. −cos 35° **15.** −cot 8° **17.** −sec 33° **19.** −sec 17°
21. 0.7071 **23.** −0.8391 **25.** −0.3420
27. 0.4452 **29.** −0.5 **31.** −0.1763 **33.** −0.866
35. −1.414 **37.** −0.8391 **39.** 0.5774 **41.** −0.8192
43. −7.115 **45.** −1.192 **47.** −1.046 **49.** odd
51. odd

Page 144 Using Mathematics 1. 47° **3.** 48°
5. 57° **7.** 58° **9.** 43° **11.** 44° **13.** 68° **15.** 69°

17. June 21

Page 146 Exploratory Exercises
1.

	radians	0	$\dfrac{\pi}{2}$	π	$\dfrac{3\pi}{2}$	2π	$-\dfrac{\pi}{2}$	$-\pi$	$-\dfrac{3\pi}{2}$	-2π
x	degrees	0°	90°	180°	270°	360°	−90°	−180°	−270°	−360°
sin x		0	1	0	−1	0	−1	0	1	0
cos x		1	0	−1	0	1	0	−1	0	1

3. $\dfrac{\pi}{2}$ or 90°, $-\dfrac{3\pi}{2}$ or −270° **5.** π or 180°, $-\pi$ or −180°,

0 or 0°, 2π or 360°, -2π or −360°

7. $\dfrac{3\pi}{2}$ or 270°, $-\dfrac{\pi}{2}$ or −90°

Page 146 Written Exercises 1. −1 **3.** 0 **5.** −1
7. undefined **9.** undefined **11.** undefined **13.** k is an
even integer **15.** $k = 4n - 3$ for some integer n
17. $k = 2n - 1$ for some integer n.

Page 146 Challenge Exercises 19. Let $k = 2n$,
where n is any integer. Then $\sin (k \cdot 90°) =$
$\sin (2n \cdot 90°) = \sin (180° \cdot n)$. But $\sin (180° \cdot n) =$
$\sin 0°$ for all integers n.
Since $\sin 0° = 0$, $\sin (k \cdot 90°) = 0$.

Page 148 Exploratory Exercises 1. $\dfrac{\sqrt{6} + \sqrt{2}}{4}$

3. $2 + \sqrt{3}$ **5.** $\dfrac{\sqrt{6} + \sqrt{2}}{4}$ **7.** $2 - \sqrt{3}$ **9.** $-\dfrac{\sqrt{3}}{2}$

11. $\cos x$ **13.** $-\tan x$ **15.** 1

Page 149 Written Exercises 1. $\dfrac{\sqrt{6} + \sqrt{2}}{4}$

3. $\dfrac{\sqrt{2} - \sqrt{6}}{4}$ **5.** $-\left(\dfrac{\sqrt{6} + \sqrt{2}}{4}\right)$ **7.** $\sqrt{3} - 2$

9. $-\left(\dfrac{\sqrt{6} + \sqrt{2}}{4}\right)$ **11.** $\dfrac{1}{2}$ **13.** $\dfrac{33}{65}$ **15.** $\dfrac{31}{481}$

17. $-\dfrac{16}{65}$ **19.** $\dfrac{360}{481}$ **21.** $\dfrac{56}{33}$ **23.** $\dfrac{480}{31}$

25. $\sin \theta \stackrel{?}{=} \sin (180° - \theta)$
$$\stackrel{?}{=} \sin 180° \cos \theta - \cos 180° \sin \theta$$
$$\stackrel{?}{=} 0 \cdot \cos \theta - (-1) \sin \theta$$
$$\sin \theta = \sin \theta$$

27.
$$\cos \left(\frac{3\pi}{2} + \theta\right) \stackrel{?}{=} \sin \theta$$

$$\cos \frac{3\pi}{2} \cos \theta - \sin \frac{3\pi}{2} \sin \theta \stackrel{?}{=}$$

$(0 \cdot \cos \theta) - (-1 \cdot \sin \theta) \overset{?}{=}$

$0 + \sin \theta \overset{?}{=}$

$\sin \theta = \sin \theta$

29. $-\cot \theta \overset{?}{=} \tan (90° + \theta)$

$\overset{?}{=} \dfrac{\sin (90° + \theta)}{\cos (90° + \theta)}$

$\overset{?}{=} \dfrac{\sin 90° \cos \theta + \cos 90° \sin \theta}{\cos 90° \cos \theta - \sin 90° \sin \theta}$

$\overset{?}{=} \dfrac{1 \cdot \cos \theta + 0 \cdot \sin \theta}{0 \cdot \cos \theta - 1 \cdot \sin \theta}$

$\overset{?}{=} \dfrac{\cos \theta}{-\sin \theta}$

$-\cot \theta = -\cot \theta$

31. $\tan (\pi - \theta) \overset{?}{=} -\tan \theta$

$\dfrac{\tan \pi - \tan \theta}{1 + \tan \pi \tan \theta} \overset{?}{=}$

$\dfrac{0 - \tan \theta}{1 + 0} \overset{?}{=}$

$-\tan \theta = -\tan \theta$

33. $-\sin \theta \overset{?}{=} \cos \left(\dfrac{\pi}{2} + \theta \right)$

$\overset{?}{=} \cos \dfrac{\pi}{2} \cos \theta - \sin \dfrac{\pi}{2} \sin \theta$

$\overset{?}{=} 0 \cdot \cos \theta - 1 \cdot \sin \theta$

$-\sin \theta = -\sin \theta$

35. $\cos (\pi + \theta) \overset{?}{=} -\cos \theta$

$\cos \pi \cos \theta - \sin \pi \sin \theta \overset{?}{=}$

$-\cos \theta - 0 \cdot \sin \theta \overset{?}{=}$

$-\cos \theta = -\cos \theta$

39. $\cos (\alpha + B) + \cos (\alpha - B) \overset{?}{=} 2 \cos \alpha \cos B$

$\cos \alpha \cos B - \sin \alpha \sin B + \cos \alpha \cos B + \sin \alpha \sin B \overset{?}{=}$

$2 \cos \alpha \cos B = 2 \cos \alpha \cos B$

Page 149　Challenge Exercises　41. $\dfrac{\cot \alpha \cot B - 1}{\cot B + \cot \alpha}$

Page 152　Exploratory Exercises　1. I or II　**3.** II
5. I or II　**7.** II　**9.** I, II, III, or IV　**11.** $\cos 20°$
13. $\sin 70°$　**15.** $\tan 100°$　**17.** $\cos 31°$　**19.** $\cos 6x$

Page 153　Written Exercises　1. $\dfrac{24}{25}$　**3.** $\dfrac{24}{7}$

5. $\dfrac{3\sqrt{10}}{10}$　**7.** $\dfrac{120}{169}$　**9.** $\dfrac{120}{119}$　**11.** $-\dfrac{\sqrt{26}}{26}$

13. $\dfrac{\sqrt{2 - \sqrt{2}}}{2}$　**15.** $\sqrt{2} - 1$　**17.** $\dfrac{\sqrt{2 + \sqrt{2 + \sqrt{3}}}}{2}$

19. $-\dfrac{4}{5}$　**21.** $\dfrac{4}{3}$　**23.** $-\dfrac{7}{25}$　**25.** $\dfrac{2\sqrt{5}}{5}$　**27.** -2

29. $1 + \cos 2A \overset{?}{=} \dfrac{2}{1 + \tan^2 A}$

$\overset{?}{=} \dfrac{2}{\sec^2 A}$

$2 \cos^2 A = 2 \cos^2 A$

33. $\csc A \sec A \overset{?}{=} 2 \csc 2A$

$\dfrac{1}{\sin A} \cdot \dfrac{1}{\cos A} \overset{?}{=}$

$\dfrac{1}{\sin A \cos A} \overset{?}{=}$

$\dfrac{1}{\dfrac{\sin 2A}{2}} \overset{?}{=}$

$2 \cdot \dfrac{1}{\sin 2A} \overset{?}{=}$

$2 \csc 2A = 2 \csc 2A$

37. $\cos^4 A \overset{?}{=} \dfrac{2 \cos 2A + \cos^2 2A + 1}{4}$

$\overset{?}{=} \dfrac{(\cos 2A + 1)^2}{4}$

$\overset{?}{=} \dfrac{2(\cos^2 A - 1 + 1)^2}{4}$

$\overset{?}{=} \dfrac{4 \cos^4 A}{4}$

$\cos^4 A = \cos^4 A$

41. $\tan \dfrac{x}{2} \overset{?}{=} \dfrac{1 - \cos x}{\sin x}$

$\pm\sqrt{\dfrac{1 - \cos x}{1 + \cos x}} \overset{?}{=} \dfrac{1 - \cos x}{\sin x}$

$\dfrac{1 - \cos x}{1 + \cos x} \overset{?}{=} \dfrac{(1 - \cos x)^2}{\sin^2 x}$

$\dfrac{1}{1 + \cos x} \overset{?}{=} \dfrac{1 - \cos x}{1 - \cos^2 x}$

$\dfrac{1}{1 + \cos x} \overset{?}{=} \dfrac{1 - \cos x}{(1 - \cos x)(1 + \cos x)}$

$\dfrac{1}{1 + \cos x} = \dfrac{1}{1 + \cos x}$

Page 156　Chapter Review　1. $\sin \alpha = \dfrac{3\sqrt{34}}{34}$,

$\csc \alpha = \dfrac{\sqrt{34}}{3}$, $\cos \alpha = \dfrac{5\sqrt{34}}{34}$, $\sec \alpha = \dfrac{\sqrt{34}}{5}$, $\tan \alpha = \dfrac{3}{5}$,

$\cot \alpha = \dfrac{5}{3}$　**3.** $\sin \alpha = \dfrac{4}{5}$, $\csc \alpha = \dfrac{5}{4}$, $\cos \alpha = -\dfrac{3}{5}$,

$\sec \alpha = -\dfrac{5}{3}$, $\tan \alpha = -\dfrac{4}{3}$, $\cot \alpha = -\dfrac{3}{4}$　**5.** 0　**7.** $\dfrac{3}{4}$

9. 1.8714

11. 0.9276 **13.** 6°24′ **15.** $\dfrac{\sqrt{5}}{3}$ **17.** $\sqrt{17}$

19. $\dfrac{\sin\theta}{\sec\theta} \overset{?}{=} \dfrac{1}{\tan\theta + \cot\theta}$

$\overset{?}{=} \dfrac{1}{\dfrac{\sin\theta}{\cos\theta} + \dfrac{\cos\theta}{\sin\theta}}$

$\overset{?}{=} \dfrac{1}{\dfrac{\sin^2\theta + \cos^2\theta}{\cos\theta\sin\theta}}$

$\overset{?}{=} \cos\theta\sin\theta$

$\dfrac{\sin\theta}{\sec\theta} = \dfrac{\sin\theta}{\sec\theta}$

23. $\dfrac{1-\cos\theta}{1+\cos\theta} \overset{?}{=} (\csc\theta - \cot\theta)^2$

$\overset{?}{=} \csc^2\theta - 2\cot\theta\csc\theta + \cot^2\theta$

$\overset{?}{=} \dfrac{1}{\sin^2\theta} - 2\left(\dfrac{\cos\theta}{\sin\theta}\cdot\dfrac{1}{\sin\theta}\right) + \dfrac{\cos^2\theta}{\sin^2\theta}$

$\overset{?}{=} \dfrac{1}{\sin^2\theta} - \dfrac{2\cos\theta}{\sin^2\theta} + \dfrac{\cos^2\theta}{\sin^2\theta}$

$\overset{?}{=} \dfrac{(1-\cos\theta)^2}{\sin^2\theta}$

$\overset{?}{=} \dfrac{(1-\cos\theta)^2}{1-\cos^2\theta}$

$\overset{?}{=} \dfrac{(1-\cos\theta)^2}{(1-\cos\theta)(1+\cos\theta)}$

$\dfrac{1-\cos\theta}{1+\cos\theta} = \dfrac{1-\cos\theta}{1+\cos\theta}$

25. 60° **27.** 240° **29.** 16.7 cm **31.** 3.9 cm **33.** −cos 30° **35.** −csc 38° **37.** −0.8660 **39.** −1.624

41. 1 **43.** 0 **45.** $\dfrac{\sqrt{2}+\sqrt{6}}{4}$ **47.** $\dfrac{\sqrt{6}+\sqrt{2}}{4}$

49. $\dfrac{\sqrt{10}}{10}$ **51.** $\dfrac{3\sqrt{10}}{10}$

CHAPTER 6   GRAPHS AND INVERSES OF THE TRIGONOMETRIC FUNCTIONS

Page 162 Exploratory Exercises 1. 1 **3.** 0 **5.** 0
7. 0 **9.** positive **11.** negative **13.** negative

15. negative **17.** cos 20° **19.** sin 50°

Page 162 Written Exercises 1. $n\cdot 360°$ where n is any integer **3.** $45° + n\cdot 180°$ where n is any integer **5.** $n\cdot 180°$ where n is any integer **7.** real numbers **9.** real numbers except $\theta = n\cdot 180°$ where n is any integer **11.** real numbers except $\theta = 90° + n\cdot 180°$ where n is any integer **13.** $-1 \le y \le 1$ **15.** real numbers **17.** real numbers

19.

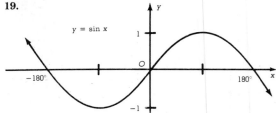

25. $x = 135°$ and $x = 315°$ **27.** none
29. $x = 0°$, 90°, and 360°

Page 166 Exploratory Exercises 1. 2, 72°, none **3.** 3, 360°, 90° **5.** none, 90°, 90° **7.** 110, 18°, none **9.** 2, 360°, none **11.** 7, 60°, none **13.** $\dfrac{1}{4}$, 720°, none

15. 10, 1080°, 900°

Pages 166–167 Written Exercises

1. $y = 3\sin\left(\dfrac{1}{2}x - 30°\right)$ or $y = -3\sin\left(\dfrac{1}{2}x - 30°\right)$

3. $y = \dfrac{2}{3}\sin(2x - 90°)$ or $y = -\dfrac{2}{3}\sin(2x - 90°)$

5. $y = \dfrac{1}{2}\sin\left(\dfrac{4}{3}x + \dfrac{\pi}{3}\right)$ or $y = -\dfrac{1}{2}\sin\left(\dfrac{4}{3}x + \dfrac{\pi}{3}\right)$

7. $y = \dfrac{1}{3}\cos 2x$ or $y = -\dfrac{1}{3}\cos 2x$

9. $y = 4\cos\left(\dfrac{1}{2}x - 45°\right)$ or $y = -4\cos\left(\dfrac{1}{2}x - 45°\right)$

11. $y = \dfrac{7}{3}\cos(2.4x - 648°)$ or $y = -\dfrac{7}{3}\cos(2.4x - 648°)$

13. 3, 360°, none **15.** 2, 360°, 180° **17.** 4, 720°, none

19.

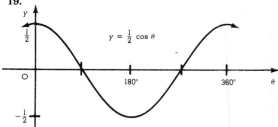

23.

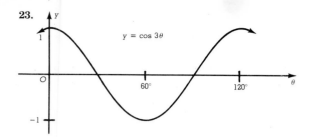

$y = \cos 3\theta$

27.

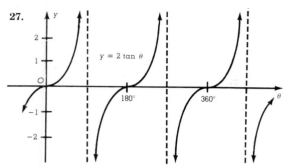

$y = 2 \tan \theta$

31.

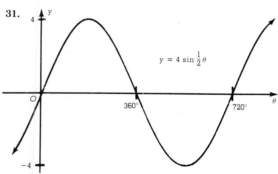

$y = 4 \sin \frac{1}{2}\theta$

35. $A = 2$, period $= 80°$

Page 169 Exploratory Exercises 1. $1, 360°, -90°$

3. $3, 360°, 90°$ **5.** $3, 60°, 30°$ **7.** $\frac{1}{2}, 720°, 360°$ **9.** $\frac{1}{10},$

$3\pi, \frac{\pi}{2}$ **11.** $2, 120°, -60°$

Page 169–170 Written Exercises

1.

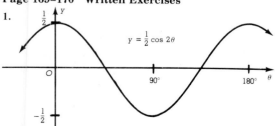

$y = \frac{1}{2} \cos 2\theta$

5.

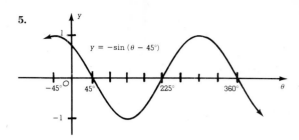

$y = -\sin(\theta - 45°)$

9.

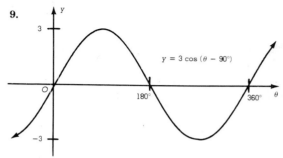

$y = 3 \cos(\theta - 90°)$

13.

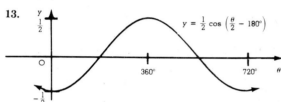

$y = \frac{1}{2} \cos\left(\frac{\theta}{2} - 180°\right)$

17.

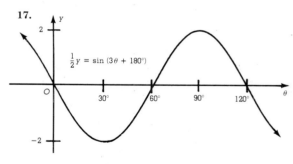

$\frac{1}{2} y = \sin(3\theta + 180°)$

21.

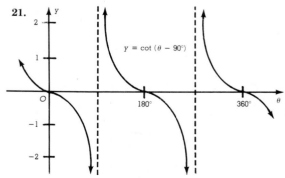

$y = \cot(\theta - 90°)$

Page 172 Exploratory Exercises 1. 1 **3.** $\dfrac{\pi}{2}$ **5.** 3

7. $\dfrac{\pi}{2}$ **9.** 0 **11.** 0 **13.** $\dfrac{\pi + 2\sqrt{2}}{4}$ **15.** $\dfrac{\sqrt{2}}{2} + 1$

17. $\dfrac{\pi\sqrt{2}}{8}$

Page 172 Written Exercises

3.

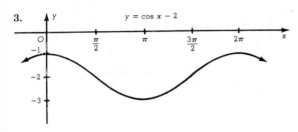

$$y = \cos x - 2$$

7.

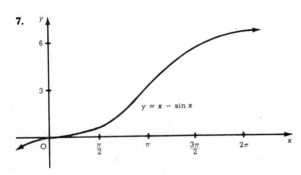

$$y = x - \sin x$$

11.

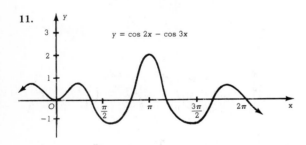

$$y = \cos 2x - \cos 3x$$

15.

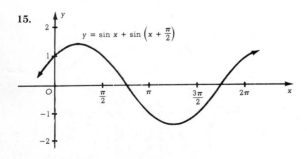

$$y = \sin x + \sin \left(x + \dfrac{\pi}{2}\right)$$

Page 174 Exploratory Exercises 1. $\{(1, 3), (4, 2),$
$(5, 1)\}$ **3.** $\{(2, 3), (2, 4)\}$ **5.** $\{(-2, -1), (-2, -3),$
$(-4, -1), (6, 0)\}$ **7.** $\theta = \arcsin x$ **9.** $y = \arctan(-3)$

11. $\theta = \arctan \dfrac{4}{3}$ **13.** $\theta = \arcsin n$ **15.** $\theta = \arccos y$

Page 174 Written Exercises 1. $x = 0°, 180°, 360°$
3. $x = 45°, 225°$ **5.** $x = 30°, 210°$ **7.** $x = 60°, 300°$

9. $x = 210°, 330°$ **11.** $\dfrac{5}{4}$ **13.** $\dfrac{5}{12}$ **15.** $\dfrac{4}{5}$ **17.** 1

19. $\dfrac{\sqrt{3}}{3}$

21. $\arccos \dfrac{\sqrt{3}}{2} + \arcsin \dfrac{\sqrt{3}}{2} \overset{?}{=} \dfrac{\pi}{2}$

$$\dfrac{\pi}{6} + \dfrac{\pi}{3} \overset{?}{=}$$

$$\dfrac{\pi}{2} = \dfrac{\pi}{2}$$

23. $\tan^{-1} 1 + \cos^{-1} \dfrac{\sqrt{3}}{2} \overset{?}{=} \sin^{-1} \dfrac{1}{2} + \sec^{-1} \sqrt{2}$

$$45° + 30° \overset{?}{=} 30° + 45°$$

$$75° = 75°$$

Page 175 Using Mathematics 1. 67 min
3. 39.5 min

Page 178 Exploratory Exercises 1. 60° **3.** 45°
5. 41° **7.** 0° **9.** 150° **11.** $-45°$ **13.** 60° **15.** 90°
17. $-19°$ **19.** 90°

Page 178–179 Written Exercises 1. $-45°$
3. $60° + n \cdot 360°$ and $120° + n \cdot 360°$ where n is any
integer **5.** $135° + n \cdot 180°$ where n is any integer
7. $45° + n \cdot 360°$ and $315° + n \cdot 360°$ where n is
any integer **9.** 0° **11.** $48°35' + n \cdot 360°$ and
$131°25' + n \cdot 360°$ where n is any integer **13.** $\dfrac{4}{5}$

15. $78°41' + n \cdot 180°$ where n is any integer **17.** $-\dfrac{4}{3}$

19. $120° + n \cdot 360°$ and $240° + n \cdot 360°$ where n is any

integer **21.** $\dfrac{1}{2}$ **23.** $26°34' + n \cdot 180°$ where n is any

integer **25.** $\dfrac{\sqrt{2}}{2}$ **27.** $270° + n \cdot 360°$ where n is any

integer **29.** $\sqrt{\dfrac{1}{2}\left(1 - \dfrac{5}{\sqrt{34}}\right)} \approx 0.2669$ **31.** $\dfrac{1}{2}$

33. $\dfrac{\sqrt{3}}{2}$ **35.** $-\dfrac{\sqrt{2}}{2}$ **37.** $\dfrac{\sqrt{2}}{2}$ **39.** $\dfrac{33}{56}$

Page 179   Challenge Exercises

1. $uv - \sqrt{(1 - u^2)(1 - v^2)}$

Page 181   Exploratory Exercises   1. real numbers
3. real numbers except $90° + n \cdot 180°$ where n is any
integer   **5.** $0° \leq x \leq 180°$ **7.** $-1 \leq x \leq 1$ **9.** real
numbers   **11.** $-1 \leq x \leq 1$ **13.** $-1 \leq y \leq 1$ **15.** real
numbers   **17.** $-1 \leq y \leq 1$ **19.** real numbers   **21.** real
numbers except $90° + n \cdot 180°$ where n is any integer
23. $0° \leq y \leq 180°$

Pages 181–182 Written Exercises   1. $y = x - 2$
3. $x = 3$ **5.** $y = \text{Sin } x$ **7.** $y = x$ **9.** $y = \dfrac{x + 1}{3}$

11. Arcsin x

17.

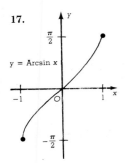
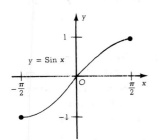

y = Arcsin x

y = Sin x

21.

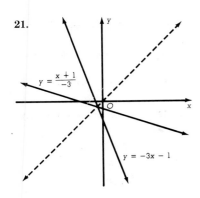

$y = \dfrac{x + 1}{-3}$

$y = -3x - 1$

25. no   **27.** no   **29.** yes   **31.** true   **33.** false
35. true   **37.** False. There is no value for $\cos^{-1} \pi$ while

$\dfrac{1}{\cos \pi} = -1$.

Page 184   Chapter Review   1. sin 50°   **3.** cos 28°

5.

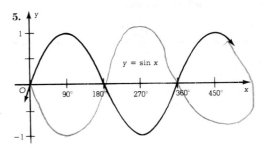

y = sin x

9. 4, 180°, none   **11.** none, 360°, 90°   **13.** none, 36°,
none   **15.** $y = 3 \sin (x - 45°)$ or $y = -3 \sin (x - 45°)$

17. $y = \dfrac{1}{3} \sin (2x - 180°)$ or $y = -\dfrac{1}{3} \sin (2x - 180°)$

19.

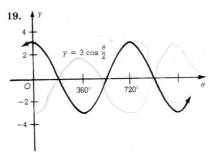

$y = 3 \cos \dfrac{\theta}{2}$

23.

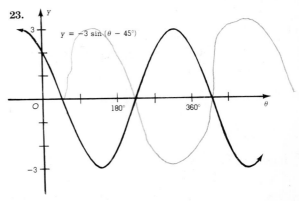

$y = -3 \sin (\theta - 45°)$

27. $y = \arctan x$ **29.** $\dfrac{1}{2}$ **31.** $\dfrac{3}{4}$ **33.** undefined
35. $\dfrac{\sqrt{2}}{2}$ **37.** $\dfrac{\sqrt{2}}{2}$ **39.** 0   **41.** 0   **43.** $y = \pm\sqrt{x - 1}$

45.

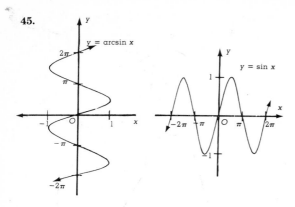

49. no

CHAPTER 7 APPLICATIONS OF TRIGONOMETRY

Page 189 Exploratory Exercises 1. 60° **3.** 45° **5.** 120° **7.** 45° **9.** 30° **11.** 2 **13.** 2 **15.** 0 **17.** 4

Pages 189–190 Written Exercises 1. $90° + n \cdot 360°$, $210° + n \cdot 360°$, $-30° + n \cdot 360°$ where n is any integer **3.** $45° + n \cdot 90°$ where n is any integer **5.** $45° + n \cdot 90°$ where n is any integer **7.** $x = \pm 60° + n \cdot 180°$ where n is any integer **9.** $\pm 60° + n \cdot 360°$ where n is any integer **11.** 0°, −30° **13.** 60°, −60° **15.** 30°, −90° **17.** 90° **19.** 90°, 30° **21.** 45° **23.** 0°, 90° **25.** −90° **27.** 90°, 150° **29.** 0° **31.** 0°, ≈ 71°34′ **33.** ±30° **35.** 0° **37.** 18°, 90° **39.** 0°

Page 193 Exploratory Exercises

1. $\sin 20° = \dfrac{a}{35}$ **3.** $\cos B = \dfrac{1}{2}$ **5.** $\cos 16° = \dfrac{a}{13}$

7. $7^2 - b^2 = 16^2$ **9.** $5^2 + 6^2 = c^2$ **11.** equal sides 7.0 cm; altitude 5.9 cm

Pages 193–194 Written Exercises 1. $B = 49°$, $c = 9.9$, $a = 6.5$ **3.** $B = 67°38'$, $c = 23.8$, $a = 9.1$ **5.** $B = 45°$, $a = 7$, $b = 7$ **7.** $B = 52°45'$, $a = 8.4$, $c = 13.8$ **9.** $B = 34°5'$, $a = 13.25$ $b = 9.1$ **11.** $a = 52.1$ **13.** $A = 67°$ **15.** $b = 8.6$ **17.** $A = 30°15'$ **19.** $c = 19.9$ **21.** 3.26 cm **23.** 29°12′ **25.** 131.7 ft **27.** 10.57 cm **29.** 31.7 cm² **31.** 1167 ft

33. 42.1 meters

Page 199 Exploratory Exercises 1. none **3.** none **5.** none **7.** 1 **9.** 1 **11.** none

13. $\dfrac{20}{\sin 40°} = \dfrac{b}{\sin 60°}$ **15.** $\dfrac{14}{\sin 50°} = \dfrac{10}{\sin B}$

Pages 199–200 Written Exercises 1. 1; $C = 74°$, $b = 8.9$, $c = 10.2$ **3.** 1; $C = 91°10'$, $a = 75.8$, $b = 97.8$ **5.** 1; $C = 80°$, $a = 13.1$, $b = 17.6$ **7.** none **9.** none **11.** 2; $B = 30°28'$, $C = 124°32'$, $c = 243.7$; $B = 149°32'$, $C = 5°28'$, $c = 28.2$ **13.** $C = 80°$; $b = 26.9$; $c = 30.6$ **15.** $B = 33°10'$; $C = 96°50'$, $c = 18.1$ **17.** 114°37′, 20°23′; 13.79 ft **19.** 54.87 ft

23.
$$\frac{\sin B}{b} = \frac{\sin A}{a}$$
$$\frac{a}{b} = \frac{\sin A}{\sin B}$$
$$\frac{a}{b} + 1 = \frac{\sin A}{\sin B} + 1$$
$$\frac{a + b}{b} = \frac{\sin A + \sin B}{\sin B}$$
$$\frac{b}{a + b} = \frac{\sin B}{\sin A + \sin B}$$

Page 202 Exploratory Exercises 1. Law of Cosines **3.** Law of Sines **5.** Law of Cosines **7.** Law of Cosines **9.** Law of Sines

Pages 202–203 Written Exercises 1. $a = 6.4$, $B = 47°46'$, $C = 80°4'$ **3.** $a = 7.8$, $B = 44°13'$, $C = 84°47'$ **5.** $A = 44°25'$, $B = 57°7'$, $C = 78°28'$ **7.** $a = 202.6$, $B = 55°53'$, $C = 62°42'$ **9.** $C = 14.1$, $A = 104°55'$, $B = 35°45'$ **11.** $C = 81°$, $a = 9.1$, $b = 12.1$ **13.** $A = 53°34'$, $B = 59°33'$, $C = 66°53'$ **15.** $C = 30°56'$, $B = 109°4'$, $b = 14.7$ **17.** $b = 18.5$, $A = 40°57'$, $C = 79°3'$ **19.** $A = 99°25'$, $B = 51°40'$, $C = 28°55'$ **21.** $A = 30°12'$, $C = 104°20'$, $c = 23.1$ **23.** 35°41′ **25.** 228.4 miles **27.** 61.9 ft

Page 205 Exploratory Exercises

1. $K = \dfrac{1}{2} \cdot 3 \cdot 4 \cdot \sin 120°$

3. $K = \sqrt{9(9 - 4)(9 - 6)(9 - 8)}$

5. $K = \dfrac{1}{2} \cdot 18.6^2 \cdot \dfrac{\sin 63°50' \sin 96°50'}{\sin 19°20'}$

7. $K = \dfrac{1}{2} \cdot 6 \cdot 4 \cdot \sin 52°$

Page 206 **Written Exercises** **1.** 33.2 **3.** 6.4
5. 1.6 **7.** 97.9 **9.** 37.9 **11.** $K = 5.2$ **13.** $K = 11.6$
15. $K = 465.6$ **17.** $K = 9.5$ **19.** perimeter = 1434 ft,
area = 86,804 sq ft **21.** 24 sq cm **23.** 70.7 sq cm

Page 209 **Exploratory Exercises**

1. 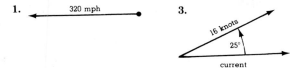 320 mph   **3.**

5. 60.2 kg, 48°22′ **7.** 39.8 N, 90°

Pages 209–210 Written Exercises **1.** 19.3 lb
3. 10 lb **5.** 111.8 N, 26°34′ or 63°26′ **7.** 260.5 mph,
3°32′ west of north **9.** 171.5 N, 28°7′ **11.** 19°28′
13. 3.7 N, 10°7′, east of south **15.** 8 seconds **17.** 19 m

Page 212 **Exploratory Exercises** **1.** 3.93 **3.** 1.57
5. 1.08 **7.** 2.98 **9.** 3.14 **11.** 12.6

Page 212–213 **Written Exercises** **1.** 9.6 sq units
3. 202.7 sq units **5.** 1.9 sq units **7.** 37.3 sq units
9. 4.7 sq units **11.** 474.9 sq units **13.** 54.4 sq units
15. 1.1 sq units **17.** 140.1 sq units
19. radius = 5 cm, area = 78.5 sq cm
21. radius = 10 cm, area = 314.2 sq cm
23. 530.1 sq cm **25.** 1680.7 ft **27.** 837 sq cm

Page 215–216 **Chapter Review** **1.** $45° + n \cdot 90°$
where n is any integer **3.** $0° + n \cdot 360°$ and
$90° + n \cdot 180°$ where n is any integer **5.** $-45°$, 71°34′
7. 0°, 30° **9.** $B = 27°$, $c = 10.9$, $b = 4.9$ **11.** $A = 7°$,
$c = 5.6$, $a = 0.7$ **13.** 24.35 ft **15.** 7.4 ft **17.** 2;
$C = 47°33′$, $B = 93°45′$, $b = 274.5$; $C = 132°27′$,
$B = 8°51′$, $b = 42.3$ **19.** 2; $B = 37°18′$, $C = 113°42′$,
$c = 22.7$; $B = 142°42′$, $C = 8°18′$, $c = 3.6$ **21.** 28.8 cm
23. $a = 36.9$, $B = 57°24′$, $C = 71°36′$ **25.** $b = 21.0$,
$A = 52°15′$, $C = 108°45′$ **27.** $A = 30°30′$, $B = 36°51′$,
$C = 112°39′$ **29.** $A = 36°1′$ **31.** 9.7 sq units
33. 17.4 sq units **35.** 2.8 sq units **37.** 1039 sq cm
39. 215.1 km/h at 8°1′ west of south **41.** 78°48′
43. 159.3 sq units **45.** 25.1 sq units
47. 118.5 sq units **49.** 7.8 sq units

CHAPTER 8 SEQUENCES AND SERIES
Page 221 **Exploratory Exercises** **1.** 17, 21, 25, 29,
33 **3.** 37, 43, 49, 55, 61 **5.** 12, 19, 26, 33, 40 **7.** 6, 7.5,
9, 10.5, 12 **9.** $a + 9$, $a + 12$, $a + 15$, $a + 18$, $a + 21$
11. $4x, 5x, 6x, 7x, 8x$ **13.** $-5b, -7b, -9b, -11b, -13b$
15. $r + 1, r - 6, r - 13, r - 20, r - 27$

Pages 221–222 **Written Exercises** **1.** -25 **3.** 11
5. 15 **7.** 6 **9.** $3 - 4\sqrt{3}$ **11.** 149 **13.** 12, 16.5, 21
15. $-4, -1, 2, 5$ **17.** $1, 1\frac{3}{4}, 2\frac{1}{2}, 3\frac{1}{4}, 4$ **19.** 181.3
21. 77 **23.** 8 **25.** 231

Page 225 **Exploratory Exercises** **1.** $\frac{1}{2}, \frac{1}{4}, \frac{1}{8}, \frac{1}{16}$
3. $\frac{4}{3}, \frac{8}{3}, \frac{16}{3}, \frac{32}{3}$ **5.** 1.75, 0.875, 0.4375, 0.21875
7. 12.5, 31.25, 78.125, 195.3125 **9.** yes **11.** yes
13. yes

Page 225 **Written Exercises** **1.** $-2, -1\frac{1}{3}, -\frac{8}{9}, -\frac{16}{27}$
3. $\frac{128}{6561}$ **5.** $16\sqrt{2}$ **7.** $8\sqrt{2}, -16, 16\sqrt{2}, -32$
9. $\frac{1}{4}, 1, 4$, or $\frac{1}{4}, -1, 4$ **11.** $-2, 6, -18, 54$ **13.** $\frac{127}{128}$
15. $201\frac{2}{3}$ **17.** 255.5

Page 226 **Using Mathematics** **1.** 3.1214452
3. 3.002176 **5.** 3.3396825
Page 229 **Exploratory Exercises** **1.** 2^{n-1}
3. $2n + 3$ **5.** $3 \cdot \left(\frac{2}{3}\right)^{n-1}$ **7.** $\frac{5n - 1}{2n}$

Page 229 **Written Exercises** **1.** 1 **3.** 3 **5.** 0
7. No limit exists. **9.** $\frac{2}{5}$ **11.** 2 **13.** 3 **15.** 0 **17.** 0
19. No limit exists. **21.** No limit exists. **23.** 0 **25.** $\frac{5}{2}$

Page 232 **Exploratory Exercises** **1.** $\dfrac{4 - 4\left(\frac{1}{4}\right)^{10}}{1 - \frac{1}{4}}$
3. $\dfrac{20 - 20(0.1)^{10}}{1 - 0.1}$ **5.** $\dfrac{25 - 25(0.2)^{10}}{1 - 0.2}$ **7.** $5\frac{1}{3}$ **9.** $22\frac{2}{9}$
11. $31\frac{1}{4}$

Page 232 **Written Exercises** **1.** $\frac{4}{3}$ **3.** $\frac{3}{2}(\sqrt{3} + 1)$
5. $\frac{1}{10}$ **7.** $\frac{2}{9}$ **9.** No sum exists since $r = 1.5$. **11.** $\frac{5}{9}$

13. $\dfrac{3}{11}$ 15. $\dfrac{41}{333}$ 17. $2\dfrac{205}{999}$ 19. $\dfrac{7}{22}$ 21. 68 ft

Page 236 Exploratory Exercises 1. divergent
3. convergent **5.** convergent

Page 236 Written Exercises 1. convergent
3. convergent **5.** convergent **7.** The ratio test fails.
9. convergent **11.** divergent

Page 237 Using Mathematics 1. 1, 1, 2, 3, 5, 8, 13,
21, 34, 55, 89, 144, 233, 377, 610, 987, 1597, 2584, 4181,
6765 **3.** 3, 4, 7, 11, 18, 29, 47, 76, 123, 199

Page 239 Exploratory Exercises 1. $3 + 4 + 5 + 6$;
18 **3.** $8 + 10 + 12 + 14$; 44
5. $-1 + 1 + 3 + 5 + 7 + 9$; 24 **7.** $17 + 20 + 23$; 60

Page 239 Written Exercises
1. $5 + 7 + 9 + 11 + 13$; 45 **3.** $5 + 6 + 7 + 8$; 26
5. $10 + 11 + 12 + 13 + 14$; 60 **7.** $4 + 16 + 64 + 256$;
340 **9.** $6 + 12 + 20 + 30$; 68
11. $1.5 + 2.5 + 4.5 + 8.5 + 16.5$; 33.5

13. $2 + 1 + \dfrac{1}{2} + \cdots$; 4 **15.** $6 + 4 + \dfrac{8}{3} + \cdots$; 18

17. $\dfrac{81}{100} + \dfrac{729}{1000} + \dfrac{6561}{10,000} + \cdots$; $8\dfrac{1}{10}$ **19.** $\displaystyle\sum_{k=1}^{4} 3k$

21. $\displaystyle\sum_{k=1}^{6} 2^k$ **23.** $\displaystyle\sum_{k=2}^{10} \dfrac{1}{k}$ **25.** $\displaystyle\sum_{k=1}^{4} (3 \cdot 10^k)$

27. $\displaystyle\sum_{k=0}^{3} (11 - 2k)$ **29.** $\displaystyle\sum_{k=0}^{3} (-2)^{3-k}$ **31.** $\displaystyle\sum_{k=1}^{\infty} 2k$

33. $\displaystyle\sum_{k=2}^{\infty} \dfrac{k}{5}$ **35.** $\displaystyle\sum_{k=1}^{\infty} 3^k$

Pages 239–240 Challenge Exercises 37. true
39. false **41.** true **43.** true

Page 243 Exploratory Exercises 1. 6! **3.** 8!
5. $\dfrac{8!}{4!}$ **7.** $\dfrac{17!}{14!}$

Page 243 Written Exercises 1. 120 **3.** 5040
5. 2160 **7.** 144 **9.** 5 **11.** 90 **13.** $(n + 2)^7 = n^7 +$
$14n^6 + 84n^5 + 280n^4 + 560n^3 + 672n^2 + 448n + 128$
15. $(2 + d)^4 = 16 + 32d + 24d^2 + 8d^3 + d^4$
17. $(2x - 3y)^3 = 8x^3 - 36x^2y + 54xy^2 - 27y^3$
19. $(2x + y)^6 = 64x^6 + 192x^5y + 240x^4y^2 + 160x^3y^3 +$
$60x^2y^4 + 12xy^5 + y^6$
21. $(2x + \sqrt{3})^4 = 16x^4 + 32\sqrt{3}x^3 + 72x^2 + 24\sqrt{3}x + 9$

23. $\left(3v - \dfrac{1}{2}w\right)^5 = 243v^5 - \dfrac{405}{2}v^4w + \dfrac{135}{2}v^3w^2 -$
$\dfrac{45}{4}v^2w^3 + \dfrac{15}{16}vw^4 - \dfrac{1}{32}w^5$ **25.** $35a^4b^3$ **27.** $90x^3y^2$

29. $-112\sqrt{2}a^5$ **31.** $(x + y)^5 = x^5 + 5x^4y + 10x^3y^2 +$
$10x^2y^3 + 5xy^4 + y^5$ **33.** $(r - s)^6 = r^6 - 6r^5s +$
$15r^4s^2 - 20r^3s^3 + 15r^2s^4 - 6rs^5 + s^6$ **35.** $x^2 - x$
37. $x^2 + x$ **39.** $x - y$

Page 244 Challenge Exercise 2.45

Page 244 For the Scholar 600 Angus

Pages 247–248 Written Exercises 11. 600
13. 330 **15.** 3025 **17.** 2016

Page 248 For the Scholar $\dfrac{4}{7}$

Pages 249–250 Chapter Review 1. 6.9, 8.2, 9.5,
10.8, 12.1, 13.4 **3.** 6, 3.5, 1, -1.5, -4 **5.** 1, $\dfrac{1}{7}$, $\dfrac{1}{49}$, $\dfrac{1}{343}$

7. 0.2, 1, 5, 25, 125 or 0.2, -1, 5, -25, 125
9. $\dfrac{2}{5}$ **11.** No limit exists. **13.** No

limit exists. **15.** $\dfrac{9}{2}$ **17.** $\dfrac{8}{11}$ **19.** convergent
21. divergent **23.** $6 + 8 + 10 + 12 + 14 + 16 + 18$; 84

25. $\displaystyle\sum_{k=0}^{\infty} (2k - 1)$ **27.** 720 **29.** 210 **31.** $a^6 - 6a^5x +$
$15a^4x^2 - 20a^3x^3 + 15a^2x^4 - 6ax^5 + x^6$ **33.** $128x^7 -$
$448x^6y + 672x^5y^2 - 560x^4y^3 + 280x^3y^4 - 84x^2y^5 +$
$14xy^6 - y^7$ **35.** $5005x^6$

CHAPTER 9 POLAR COORDINATES AND COMPLEX NUMBERS

Page 256 Exploratory Exercises 1. 180° **3.** $-45°$
5. $-480°$ **7.** 330° **9.** 115° **11.** $-172°$

13. $\left(3, -\dfrac{11\pi}{6}\right), \left(-3, \dfrac{7\pi}{6}\right), \left(-3, -\dfrac{5\pi}{6}\right)$

15. $(-2.4, -305°), (2.4, -125°), (2.4, 235°)$

Pages 256–257 Written Exercises

5.   7.

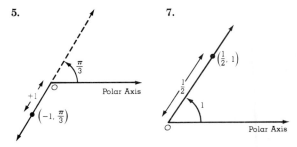

13. $(100, 50°)$, $(-100, 230°)$, $(-100, -130°)$, $(100, -310°)$

15. $(120, 70°)$, $(-120, 250°)$, $(-120, -110°)$, $(120, -290°)$

17. $(100, 340°)$, $(-100, 160°)$, $(-100, -200°)$, $(100, -20°)$

19.

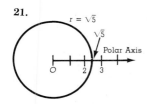

$r = 2$

Polar Axis

21.

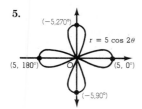

$r = \sqrt{5}$

Polar Axis

Page 261 Exploratory Exercises 1. 1; 6; $(6, 0°)$
3. 0.5; 4.5; $(4.5, 60°)$ **5.** -0.5; 1.5; $(1.5, 120°)$
7. -1; 0; $(0, 180°)$ **9.** -0.5; 1.5; $(1.5, 240°)$
11. 0.5; 4.5; $(4.5, 300°)$

Page 261 Written Exercises

5.

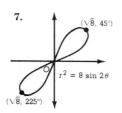

$(-5, 270°)$

$r = 5 \cos 2\theta$

$(5, 180°)$ $(5, 0°)$

$(-5, 90°)$

7.

$(\sqrt{8}, 45°)$

$r^2 = 8 \sin 2\theta$

$(\sqrt{8}, 225°)$

13. $(6, 0°)$ **15.** $(1.7, 60°)$ or $(-1.7, 240°)$

Page 264 Exploratory Exercises 1. $\dfrac{\pi}{3}$ or 1.05
3. 1.29

Page 264 Written Exercises 1. $(5, 0.93)$ or $(5, 53°)$

3. $\left(\sqrt{2}, \dfrac{\pi}{4}\right)$ or $(\sqrt{2}, 45°)$ **5.** $(\sqrt{29}, -1.19)$ or $(\sqrt{29},$

$-68°)$ **7.** $(\sqrt{13}, -0.59)$ or $(\sqrt{13}, -34°)$ **9.** $\left(\dfrac{\sqrt{3}}{2}, \dfrac{1}{2}\right)$ or

$(0.87, 0.5)$ **11.** $(0, 3)$ **13.** $(2, 0)$ **15.** $(-1.04, 2.27)$

17. $r \cos \theta = 5$ **19.** $\theta = \dfrac{\pi}{4} + n \cdot 180°$ **21.** $r = \pm 5$

23. $x^2 + y^2 = 49$ **25.** $x = y$ **27.** $y = 2$ **29.** $x = -2$

Page 266 Exploratory Exercises 1. $-i$ **3.** $-6 +$
$4i$ **5.** $4 + 5i$ **7.** $2 + i$ **9.** $-10 + 10i$ **11.** $24 - 10i$
13. 13 **15.** 49

Page 266 Written Exercises 1. 1 **3.** $-2 - 7i$

5. $-2 - i$ **7.** $2 + 2i\sqrt{2}$ **9.** $1 + i$ **11.** $7 + 5i\sqrt{2}$

13. 3 **15.** $20 + 15i$ **17.** $-9 - 46i$ **19.** $\dfrac{7 - 3i}{2}$

21. $\dfrac{-29 + 17i}{10}$ **23.** $\dfrac{1 + 4i\sqrt{3}}{7}$ **25.** $\dfrac{7\sqrt{2} + 21i}{11}$

27. $\dfrac{-44 + 117i}{50}$

Page 267 Using Mathematics 1. $(6, 65°)$
3. $(14, 155°)$

Page 269 Exploratory Exercises

1. $\sqrt{2}\left(\cos\left(-\dfrac{\pi}{4}\right) + i \sin\left(-\dfrac{\pi}{4}\right)\right)$

3. $7\left(\cos\dfrac{\pi}{2} + i \sin\dfrac{\pi}{2}\right)$ **5.** $5(\cos \pi + i \sin \pi)$

7. $2\sqrt{3}\left(\cos\left(-\dfrac{\pi}{6}\right) + i \sin\left(-\dfrac{\pi}{6}\right)\right)$ **9.** 2 **11.** i

13. $-\dfrac{\sqrt{3}}{4} + \dfrac{1}{4}i$

Page 270 Written Exercises 1. $\sqrt{2}\left(\cos\dfrac{\pi}{4} + i \sin\dfrac{\pi}{4}\right)$

3. $3\left(\cos\dfrac{\pi}{2} + i \sin\dfrac{\pi}{2}\right)$ **5.** $\sqrt{26}(\cos 3.34 + i \sin 3.34)$

7. $\sqrt{29}(\cos 1.95 + i \sin 1.95)$ **9.** $2\left(\cos\dfrac{\pi}{3} + i \sin\dfrac{\pi}{3}\right)$

11. $\cos\dfrac{3\pi}{2} + i \sin\dfrac{3\pi}{2}$ **13.** $-1 - i$ **15.** $6 - 6i\sqrt{3}$

17. $-1.98 + 0.28i$ **19.** $4\sqrt{3} + 4i$ **21.** $\dfrac{5\sqrt{3}}{2} - \dfrac{5}{2}i$

Page 272 Exploratory Exercises

1. $10(\sin 3\pi + i \sin 3\pi)$ **3.** $2\left(\cos\left(-\dfrac{\pi}{6}\right) + i \sin\left(-\dfrac{\pi}{6}\right)\right)$

5. -10 **7.** $\sqrt{3} - i$

Page 272 Written Exercises

1. $16(\cos 2\pi + i \sin 2\pi)$ **3.** $3\left(\cos\dfrac{\pi}{12} + i \sin\dfrac{\pi}{12}\right)$

5. $6.4(\cos 2.3 + i \sin 2.3)$ **7.** $10\left(\cos\dfrac{17\pi}{12} + i \sin\dfrac{17\pi}{12}\right)$

9. $6\left(\cos\dfrac{13\pi}{12} + i \sin\dfrac{13\pi}{12}\right)$ **11.** $-2i$ **13.** $-2\sqrt{3} + 2i$

15. $-4i$ **17.** 16 **19.** $2.90 + 0.78i$ **21.** $-4.26 + 4.77i$
23. $-2.59 - 9.66i$ **25.** $-5.80 - 1.55i$

Page 277 Exploratory Exercises 1. -27

3. $-\dfrac{1}{2} + \dfrac{\sqrt{3}}{2}i$ **5.** $-16\sqrt{2} - 16i\sqrt{2}$ **7.** $\sqrt{2} + i\sqrt{2}$

9. $-\frac{1}{2} - \frac{\sqrt{3}}{2}i$

Page 277   Written Exercises   1. $-4 + 4i$ **3.** $54 + 54i$
5. $-527 - 336i$ **7.** $1.08 + 0.29i$ **9.** $0.72 + 1.08i$

11. $0.81 + 0.59i$ **13.** $\frac{1}{2} + \frac{\sqrt{3}}{2}i, -1, \frac{1}{2} - \frac{\sqrt{3}}{2}i$

15. $0.31 + 0.95i, -0.81 + 0.59i, -0.81 - 0.59i, 1,$

$0.31 - 0.95i$ **17.** $\frac{\sqrt{3}}{2} + \frac{1}{2}i, i, -\frac{\sqrt{3}}{2} + \frac{1}{2}i, -\frac{\sqrt{3}}{2} - \frac{1}{2}i,$

$-i, \frac{\sqrt{3}}{2} - \frac{1}{2}i$

19.

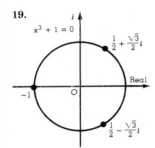

21.

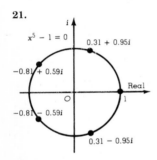

Pages 279–280   Chapter Review

5. $(-3, -310°), (3, 230°), (3, -130°)$ **7.** $\left(2, -\frac{7\pi}{4}\right),$

$\left(-2, -\frac{3\pi}{4}\right), \left(-2, \frac{5\pi}{4}\right)$

11.

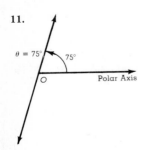

17.

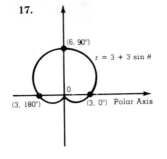

19. $\left(2\sqrt{3}, \frac{4\pi}{3}\right)$ **21.** $(\sqrt{13}, -0.59)$ **23.** $(3\sqrt{2}, 3\sqrt{2})$

25. $(1.33, -1.49)$ **27.** $-i$ **29.** $6 - i$ **31.** $-3 - 4i$

33. $29 + 3i$ **35.** $\frac{18 + 13i}{29}$ **37.** $\frac{12 + 35i}{37}$

39. $6\left(\cos\frac{3\pi}{2} + i\sin\frac{3\pi}{2}\right)$ **41.** $4\left(\cos\frac{2\pi}{3} + i\sin\frac{2\pi}{3}\right)$

43. $\sqrt{34}(\cos(-0.54) + i\sin(-0.54))$ **45.** $-2\sqrt{3} + 2i$

47. $-i\sqrt{3}$ **49.** $1.62 + 2.52i$ **51.** $-4 + 4i\sqrt{3}$

53. $-5.53 + 1.36i$ **55.** $\frac{3}{4} + \frac{3\sqrt{3}}{4}i$ **57.** $-12 - 4i\sqrt{3}$

59. $\frac{5\sqrt{3}}{4} + \frac{5}{4}i$ **61.** 4096 **63.** -4 **65.** $0.92 + 0.38i$

67. $2, 0.62 + 1.90i, -1.62 + 1.18i, -1.62 - 1.18i,$
$0.62 - 1.90i$

**CHAPTER 10   EXPONENTIAL AND
                      LOGARITHMIC FUNCTIONS**

Page 286   Exploratory Exercises   1. 49 **3.** $\frac{1}{9}$

5. 4 **7.** 81 **9.** 2 **11.** $\frac{1}{8}$ **13.** $8\frac{8}{9}$ **15.** $\frac{9}{4}$ **17.** $\frac{1}{25}$

19. 4

Page 286   Written Exercises   1. $r^3s^{\frac{3}{2}}$ **3.** $a^{\frac{1}{4}}$
5. x^4y^2 **7.** $5a^{\frac{2}{3}}b$ **9.** $4x^3y^5$ **11.** $2xy^{\frac{8}{5}}$ **13.** $24^{\frac{1}{4}}a^3b^4$
15. $4y^4c^{\frac{1}{2}}$ **17.** $y^{\frac{3}{5}}$ **19.** $20^{\frac{1}{2}}x^2y^6$ **21.** $12^{\frac{2}{6}}a^{\frac{2}{3}}b^{\frac{1}{3}}c^2$
23. $25^{\frac{1}{5}}a^{-1}b^{-2}$ **25.** $\sqrt[6]{64}$ **27.** $\sqrt[5]{15}$ **29.** $\sqrt[4]{a^3y}$
31. $\sqrt[7]{x^4y^3}$ **33.** $r^2\sqrt[4]{r^2q^3}$ **35.** $\sqrt[10]{a^2b}$ **37.** $3x^2\sqrt[3]{9x}$
39. $2a\sqrt[3]{4ay}$ **41.** $\sqrt[5]{4m^2n^3}$ **43.** $\sqrt{17}$ **45.** x^5
47. $125x$ **49.** 1 **51.** $x^{-2}y^8a^{-5}$ **53.** $5^{\frac{1}{3}}ac^{\frac{4}{3}}$

Page 290 Exploratory Exercises **1.** 1.4 **3.** 0.4
5. 1.7 **7.** 0.9

Page 290 Written Exercises **1.** 22.6 **3.** 0.2
5. 2.0 **7.** 3.6 **9.** 5.6

11.

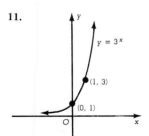

15.

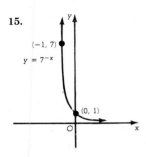

Page 290 Challenge Exercises **17.** 8 **19.** 1024

Page 290 For the Scholar 6

Page 293 Exploratory Exercises **1.** 3.0 **3.** 1.6
5. 1.9 **7.** 1.7

Page 293 Written Exercises **1.** 81.5 **3.** 49.4
5. 3.3 **7.** 1.8 **9.** 2.0 **11.** 601.8 **13.** 3.5 **15.** 64
17. 2.8 **19.** 0.0000248, 0.0000028

Page 293 Challenge Exercises **21.** 1.57 **23.** 9.14
25. 6.39

Page 295 Using Mathematics **1.** $1574.24
3. $2027.37 **5.** $492,836.70 **7.** $3.48 **9.** 14.2%

Page 299 Exploratory Exercises **1.** 3; 3 **3.** 24; 16
5. 4^{10} or 1,048,576; 4^{10} or 1,048,576 **7.** 1319; 221

9. 14; $13\frac{1}{2}$ **11.** yes

Page 299 Written Exercises **1.** $f \circ g(x) = 2x + 8$,
$g \circ f(x) = 2x + 11$ **3.** $\frac{1}{2}x - 4, \frac{1}{2}x - 1$
5. $3x^2 - 24x + 48, 3x^2 - 4$ **7.** $16x - 4, 16x - 10$
9. $5x^4 - 10x^2 + 5, 25x^4 - 1$
11. $x^2 + 7x + 12, x^2 + 5x + 7$ **13.** yes **15.** no
17. no

21.

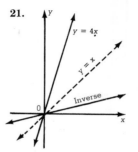

23.

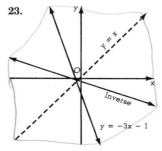

Page 301 Exploratory Exercises **1.** $\log_2 8 = 3$
3. $\log_{10} 10,000 = 4$ **5.** $\log_3 \frac{1}{27} = -3$ **7.** $2^4 = 16$

9. $2^5 = 32$ **11.** $16^{\frac{1}{2}} = 4$ **13.** 3 **15.** -3 **17.** -4
19. 5 **21.** 3

Page 302 Written Exercises **1.** 5 **3.** -2 **5.** 15
7. 81 **9.** $\frac{1}{2}$ **11.** $\frac{1}{3}$ **13.** 24 **15.** 4 **17.** 5184 **19.** $\frac{1}{2}$
21. 2

Page 302 For the Scholar 4

Page 305 Exploratory Exercises **1.** 2 **3.** 3.5740
5. 0.375 **7.** 37,500 **9.** 0.00375

Page 305 Written Exercises **1.** 1.8116 **3.** 0.9499
5. 0.5527 − 3 **7.** 0.0899 − 2 **9.** 7760 **11.** 0.0543
13. 0.0822 **15.** 8.443 **17.** 236 **19.** 597 **21.** 10.8
23. 6.9 **25.** 0.0085

Page 307 Exploratory Exercises **1.** $x = \dfrac{\log 46}{\log 2}$
3. $x = \dfrac{\log 63}{2 \log 6}$ **5.** $x = \dfrac{\log 121}{\log 5}$ **7.** $x = \dfrac{\log 16}{\log 3}$
9. $x = -\dfrac{1}{\log 2}$ **11.** $x = \dfrac{\log 14}{\log 2}$ **13.** $\dfrac{\log 7}{\log 4}$
15. $\dfrac{\log_8 5}{\log_8 10}$ **17.** $\dfrac{\log t}{\log a}$

Pages 307–308 Written Exercises **1.** 5.524
3. 1.156 **5.** 2.980 **7.** 2.524 **9.** -3.322 **11.** 3.808
13. 3.092 **15.** 3.965 **17.** 4.894 **19.** 3.609 **21.** 145

23. 1.756   **25.** −7.743   **27.** $\dfrac{1}{8}$ **29.** $-\dfrac{1}{3}$

31. $t = 11.6$ days   **33.** $T = 7.48$ years

35. $T = 1.85$ hours

Page 310   Exploratory Exercises   1. 0.9478

3. 1.4540   **5.** 1.53   **7.** 4.81   **9.** 5.48

Pages 310–311   Written Exercises   1. 4.0413

3. 6.4770   **5.** 0   **7.** 35.4   **9.** 183   **11.** 2.33   **13.** $t =$
133.1   **15.** $t = 48.52$ **17.** $t = 51.02$ **19.** $t = 4.28$ hours
or about 4 hours, 17 min   **21.** $k = -0.0462$

23. $t = 4.45$ days   **25.** \$2187.12   **27.** \$2383.60

29. 4.4%   **31.** $k = -0.2299$

Page 311   Challenge Exercises   33. 0   **35.** 274 min

Page 314   Exploratory Exercises   1. $i\pi + 1.3863$

3. $i\pi + 2.1972$ **5.** $i\pi + 2.0605$ **7.** $i\pi + 0.6981$

9. $2e^{\frac{i\pi}{3}}$ **11.** $\sqrt{2}e^{\frac{5i\pi}{4}}$ **13.** $e^{\frac{i\pi}{4}}$

Page 314   Written Exercises   1. $i\pi + 3.8754$

3. $i\pi + 6.2916$ **5.** $i\pi + 4.2298$ **7.** $i\pi + 8.371$

9. $\sqrt{2}e^{\frac{3i\pi}{4}}$ **11.** $6e^{\frac{i\pi}{2}}$ **13.** $2e^{\frac{2i\pi}{3}}$ **15.** $4e^{\frac{7i\pi}{6}}$

Page 314   Challenge Exercises   17. 0.006925; actual
value, 0

Page 316   Chapter Review   1. $a^{\frac{3}{5}}$ **3.** $2ab^{\frac{3}{4}}c^2$

5. $\sqrt[5]{15}$ **7.** $4x\sqrt[5]{4x}$ **9.** $\dfrac{1}{3}$ **11.** $\dfrac{1}{8}x^{12}$

13.   **15.**

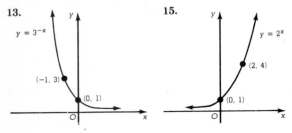

17. 2.25   **19.** $3x + 1, 3x - 3$ **21.** $x^2 + 4x + 6,$
$x^2 + 2x + 4$ **23.** $x = 15$ **25.** $0.6618 - 2$ **27.** 1.6314
29. $x = 1.990$ **31.** 2.1552   **33.** 40.5   **35.** 7.7 years

37. $i\pi + 3.8330$ **39.** $3e^{\frac{5i\pi}{4}}$

CHAPTER 11   THE STRAIGHT LINE

Page 321   Exploratory Exercises   1. neither

3. perpendicular   **5.** parallel   **7.** $2x - y - 6 = 0$
9. $2x - y - 18 = 0$ **11.** $x + 2y - 8 = 0$
13. $x + 2y - 4 = 0$

Page 321   Written Exercises   1. $3x - y + 6 = 0$
3. $6x - y - 3 = 0$ **5.** $2x + 3y - 16 = 0$
7. $x - 2y - 6 = 0$ **9.** $5x + 4y + 43 = 0$
11. $2x + 3y - 40 = 0$

Page 324   Exploratory Exercises   1. $(1, 0)$

3. $(8, 9)$ **5.** $\left(\dfrac{a}{2}, \dfrac{b}{2}\right)$

Page 324   Written Exercises   1. 16 square units
3. 13, 7.8   **5.** Draw a figure and label the vertices

$A(-3, 1)$, $B(0, 5)$, $C(12, 0)$ and $D(9, -4)$. The slope of $\overline{AB}$

is $\dfrac{1-5}{-3}$ or $\dfrac{4}{3}$. The slope of $\overline{BC}$ is $-\dfrac{5}{12}$. The slope of $\overline{DC}$

is $\dfrac{-4}{9-12}$ or $\dfrac{4}{3}$. The slope of $\overline{AD}$ is $\dfrac{1+4}{-3-9}$ or $-\dfrac{5}{12}$.

Thus $\overline{AB}$ is parallel to $\overline{DC}$, $\overline{BC}$ is parallel to $\overline{AD}$, and
$ABCD$ is a parallelogram.

7. $AC = \sqrt{(c-0)^2 + (0-a)^2} = \sqrt{a^2 + c^2}$;
$BD = \sqrt{(c-0)^2 + (a-0)^2} = \sqrt{a^2 + c^2}$;
Therefore $\overline{AC} \cong \overline{BD}$.

11. Draw a figure and label the vertices $A(a, 0)$, $B(0, b)$,
and $C(0, 0)$. The square of side $\overline{CA}$ is a^2. The square of
side $\overline{CB}$ is b^2. The square of the hypotenuse $\overline{AB}$ is
$(\sqrt{(a-0)^2 + (0-b)^2})^2$ or $a^2 + b^2$. Therefore, the
square of the hypotenuse is equal to the sum of the
squares of the other sides.

Page 326   Exploratory Exercises   1. $71°34'$
3. $116°34'$ **5.** $-75°58'$ or $104°2'$ **7.** $68°12'$ **9.** $33°41'$
11. $5°54'$ **13.** $17°6'$ **15.** $-17°1'$

Page 326   Written Exercises   1. $26°34'$ **3.** $21°10'$
5. $-18°26'$ **7.** $-78°41'$ **9.** $-25°21'$ **11.** $4°24'$
15. $82°52'$ **17.** $25°21'$ **19.** -15.5 **21.** $3x + y = 0$ or
$x - 3y = 0$

Pages 329–330   Exploratory Exercises

1. 2; 3; 4; $\sqrt{13}$ **3.** 5; 1; -7; $\sqrt{26}$ **5.** 4; -1; 9; $\sqrt{17}$

7. $\dfrac{-2x}{\sqrt{13}} - \dfrac{3y}{\sqrt{13}} - \dfrac{4}{\sqrt{13}} = 0$, $p = \dfrac{4}{\sqrt{13}}$, Quadrant III

9. $\dfrac{5x}{\sqrt{26}} + \dfrac{y}{\sqrt{26}} - \dfrac{\sqrt{7}}{\sqrt{26}} = 0$, $p = \dfrac{7}{\sqrt{26}}$, Quadrant I

11. $\dfrac{-4x}{\sqrt{17}} + \dfrac{y}{\sqrt{17}} - \dfrac{9}{\sqrt{17}} = 0$; $p = \dfrac{9}{\sqrt{17}}$, Quadrant II

13. $x + \sqrt{3}y - 14 = 0$ **15.** $\sqrt{2}x + \sqrt{2}y + 12 = 0$

Page 330   Written Exercises   1. $x + \sqrt{3}y - 6 = 0$

3. $x + y + 25\sqrt{2} = 0$ **5.** $\sqrt{3}x - y + 4 = 0$

7. $\dfrac{x}{\sqrt{2}} + \dfrac{y}{\sqrt{2}} - \dfrac{8}{\sqrt{2}} = 0$ **9.** $\dfrac{2x}{\sqrt{13}} - \dfrac{3y}{\sqrt{13}} - \dfrac{1}{\sqrt{13}} = 0$

11. $\dfrac{3}{5}x + \dfrac{4}{5}y - \dfrac{1}{5} = 0$ **13.** $p = \dfrac{1}{\sqrt{13}}$ or 0.28, $\phi = -56°19'$

15. $p = \dfrac{1}{5}$, $\phi = 53°8'$ **17.** $x + y - 6 = 0$

19. $x + \sqrt{3}y - 2 = 0$ or $x + \sqrt{3}y + 2 = 0$

Page 332   Exploratory Exercises   **1.** positive

3. negative   **5.** positive   **7.** $|d| = \dfrac{3\sqrt{5}}{2}$ or 3.35

9. $|d| = \dfrac{18}{\sqrt{53}}$ or 2.47

Pages 332–333   Written Exercises   **1.** $|d| = \dfrac{1}{\sqrt{29}}$ or

0.19   **3.** $|d| = \dfrac{1}{\sqrt{10}}$ or 0.32   **5.** $|d| = 2.4$ **7.** $|d| = \dfrac{8}{\sqrt{34}}$

or 1.37   **9.** $x - 5y + 10 + 3\sqrt{26} = 0$,

$x - 5y + 10 - 3\sqrt{26} = 0$ **11.** $|h_1| = \dfrac{11}{\sqrt{2}}$ or 7.78,

$|h_2| = \dfrac{55}{\sqrt{65}}$ or 6.82, $|h_3| = \dfrac{55}{\sqrt{85}}$ or 5.97

Page 335   Exploratory Exercises   **1.** $d_1 = d_2$
3. $d_1 = d_2$

Page 335   Written Exercises
3. $(\sqrt{5} + 2\sqrt{2})x + (\sqrt{2} - \sqrt{5})y + 3\sqrt{5} - \sqrt{2} = 0$
5. $x + y = 0$ **7.** $(1 - \sqrt{2})x + y - 5 + 5\sqrt{2} = 0$
9. $(2\sqrt{10} - 3\sqrt{29})x + (5\sqrt{10} - \sqrt{29})y + 3\sqrt{10} - 7\sqrt{29} = 0$
11. $(\sqrt{10} - 3\sqrt{2})x + (\sqrt{10} + \sqrt{2})y + 2\sqrt{10} + \sqrt{2} = 0$
13. $x - 1 = 0, y - 4 = 0$
15. $x - 3y + 2 = 0, 3x + y + 6 = 0$

Page 336   Using Mathematics   **1.** $(x, y) = (-1, 4) +$
$t(1, -7)$ **3.** $(x, y) = (-3, -2) + t(4, 6)$ **5.** $x = 4 + 2t$;
$y = 9 - 7t$ **7.** $y = -x + 5$ **9.** $y = -\dfrac{1}{2}x + \dfrac{13}{2}$

Page 339   Exploratory Exercises

1. $-\dfrac{x}{\sqrt{2}} + \dfrac{y}{\sqrt{2}} - \dfrac{4}{\sqrt{2}} = 0$ **3.** $-\dfrac{2x}{\sqrt{5}} + \dfrac{y}{\sqrt{5}} - \dfrac{6}{\sqrt{5}} = 0$

5. $22°37'$ **7.** $p = \dfrac{4}{\sqrt{13}}$, $\phi = 146°19'$ **9.** $p = \dfrac{3}{\sqrt{82}}$,

$\phi = 186°20'$ **11.** $2.31, 2.83, 4, -11.5$ **13.** $3.46, 4.24,$
$6, 17.3$

Page 340   Written Exercises   **7.** $r \cos \theta = 10$

9. $\dfrac{4}{\sqrt{10}} = r \cos (\theta - 161°34')$

11. $\dfrac{1}{\sqrt{13}} = r \cos (\theta - 56°19')$ **13.** $y = 0$ **15.** $x = 1$

17. $x + \sqrt{3}y - 8 = 0$ **19.** $0 = r \cos (\theta - 116°34')$ or

$0 = r \cos (\theta - 296°34')$ **21.** $\dfrac{20}{\sqrt{34}} = r \cos (\theta - 120°58')$

Pages 341–342   Chapter Review
1. $4x - y + 11 = 0$ **3.** $x + 3y - 12 = 0$ **7.** $-8°8'$

9. $45°$ **11.** $87°16'$ **13.** $\dfrac{3x}{\sqrt{13}} + \dfrac{2y}{\sqrt{13}} - \dfrac{6}{\sqrt{13}} = 0$;

$p = \dfrac{6}{\sqrt{13}}$ or 1.66; $\phi = 33°41'$

15. $-\dfrac{3x}{\sqrt{13}} + \dfrac{2y}{\sqrt{13}} - \dfrac{5}{2\sqrt{13}} = 0$, $p = \dfrac{5}{2\sqrt{13}}$ or 0.69,

$\phi = 146°19'$ **17.** $\dfrac{2x}{\sqrt{85}} + \dfrac{9y}{\sqrt{85}} - \dfrac{10}{\sqrt{85}} = 0$, $p = \dfrac{10}{\sqrt{85}}$

or 1.08, $\phi = 77°28'$ **19.** $|d| = 1.66$ **21.** $|d| = 6.38$
23. $(\sqrt{10} + 3\sqrt{5})x + (2\sqrt{10} + \sqrt{5})y - 3\sqrt{10} - 2\sqrt{5} =$
0 **25.** $x + \sqrt{3}y - 6 = 0$ **27.** $\dfrac{3}{\sqrt{5}} = r \cos (\theta - 206°34')$

CHAPTER 12   CONICS
Page 347   Exploratory Exercises   **1.** $x^2 + y^2 = 64$
3. $(x - 2)^2 + (y + 7)^2 = 81$ **5.** $(x + 3)^2 + (y + 5)^2 = 1$

7. $(2, 3), \sqrt{7}$ **9.** $(2, 6), \sqrt{10}$ **11.** $(-3, -2), \dfrac{\sqrt{7}}{2}$

Page 347   Written Exercises   **1.** $x^2 + y^2 = 18$
3. $(x - 3)^2 + (y + 2)^2 = 16$ **5.** $(x + 4)^2 + (y + 1)^2 = 25$

7. $\left(x + \dfrac{1}{4}\right)^2 + (y - 1)^2 = 9$ **9.** $(x - 1)^2 + (y + 3)^2 = 16$

11. $\left(x - \dfrac{3}{2}\right)^2 + \left(y - \dfrac{7}{2}\right)^2 = \dfrac{29}{2}$

13. $(x - 3)^2 + (y - 4)^2 = 5$
15. $(x - 2)^2 + (y + 1)^2 = 25$
17. $(y - 4)^2 + (y - 2)^2 = 18$
19. $(x - 4)^2 + (y + 3)^2 = 25$
21. $(x - 5)^2 + (y + 5)^2 = 25$
23. $(x - 1)^2 + (y - 1)^2 = 25$

Pages 347–348   Challenge Exercises
25. $x^2 + y^2 = 1$ or $(x - \sqrt{2})^2 + y^2 = 1$
27. $(x - k)^2 + (y - k)^2 = 49$ Each circle has its center
on the line $x - y = 0$.   **29.** $3x - 4y - 4 = 0$

Page 351 Exploratory Exercises 1. $y^2 = 8x$
3. $(x - 2)^2 = 8(y - 4)$ **5.** $(y - 4)^2 = 24(x + 1)$
7. vertex $(0, 0)$, focus $\left(-\dfrac{1}{2}, 0\right)$, directrix $x = \dfrac{1}{2}$
9. vertex $(0, 3)$, focus $(1, 3)$, directrix $x = -1$
11. vertex $(2, -1)$, focus $(2, 1)$, directrix $y = -3$
13. $x^2 = 11y$ **15.** $(x - 3)^2 = 10(y + 1)$
17. $(y + 1)^2 = 4(x - 1)$

Page 351 Written Exercises 1. vertex $(0, 0)$, focus $(0, 2.75)$, directrix $y = -2.75$ axis $x = 0$, latus rectum 11
3. vertex $(3, -1)$, focus $\left(3, 1\dfrac{1}{2}\right)$, directrix $y = -3\dfrac{1}{2}$, axis $x = 3$, latus rectum 10 **5.** vertex $(1, -1)$, focus $(2, -1)$, directrix $x = 0$, axis $y = -1$, latus rectum 4
7. $x^2 = -12y$ **9.** $(x - 3)^2 = 4(y - 4)$
11. $(y - 1)^2 = 4(x + 2)$ **13.** $(x - 4)^2 = -1(y - 3)$
15. $(x - 2)^2 = -8(y + 4)$ **17.** $y^2 = -6\left(x - 1\dfrac{1}{2}\right)$

Pages 351–352 Challenge Exercises
19. $y^2 - 4x - 4y = 0$ **21.** $(x - 4)^2 + (y - 3)^2 = 16$
25. It represents the maximum height the object reaches under given conditions.

Page 354 Exploratory Exercises 1. $(3, 1)$,
$x = x' + 3$, $y = y' + 1$ **3.** $(-1, 0)$, $x = x' - 1$, $y = y'$
5. $(3, 4)$, $x = x' + 3$, $y = y' + 4$ **7.** $(-2, 5)$, $x = x' - 2$, $y = y' + 5$

Page 354 Written Exercises 1. $(x')^2 + (y')^2 = 4$
3. $(x')^2 + (y')^2 = 1$ **5.** $(y')^2 = 2x'$ **7.** $(x')^2 = 6y'$
9. $(x')^2 + (y')^2 = 25$ **11.** $(x' + a)^2 + (y' - a)^2 = c^2$
13. $(x')^2 = 4y'$ **15.** $(x')^2 = 4p(y' + 4)$

Page 358 Exploratory Exercises 1. $\dfrac{x^2}{36} + \dfrac{y^2}{16} = 1$
3. $\dfrac{(y - 5)^2}{16} + \dfrac{(x - 3)^2}{4} = 1$ **5.** $\dfrac{x^2}{49} + \dfrac{y^2}{45} = 1$

Page 358 Written Exercises 1. center $(5, 0)$, foci $(5 + \sqrt{21}, 0)$ and $(5 - \sqrt{21}, 0)$, vertices $(10, 0)$ and $(0, 0)$
3. center $(3, 4)$, foci $(6, 4)$ and $(0, 4)$, vertices $(8, 4)$ and $(-2, 4)$ **5.** center $(-3, 1)$, foci $(-3 + \sqrt{3}, 1)$ and $(-3 - \sqrt{3}, 1)$, vertices $(-1, 1)$ and $(-5, 1)$ **7.** center $(0, -5)$, foci $(\sqrt{21}, -5)$ and $(-\sqrt{21}, -5)$, vertices $(5, -5)$ $(-5, -5)$ **9.** center $(-5, 4)$, foci $(-5, 6)$ and $(-5, 2)$, vertices $(-5, 4 + \sqrt{6})$ and $(-5, 4 - \sqrt{6})$
11. center $\left(-\dfrac{1}{2}, \dfrac{1}{2}\right)$, foci $\left(-\dfrac{1}{2}, \dfrac{1}{2} + \sqrt{3}\right)$ and $\left(-\dfrac{1}{2}, \dfrac{1}{2} - \sqrt{3}\right)$, vertices $\left(-\dfrac{1}{2}, 2\dfrac{1}{2}\right)$ and $\left(-\dfrac{1}{2}, -1\dfrac{1}{2}\right)$

Page 360 Exploratory Exercises 1. $(2\sqrt{5}, 0)$, $(-2\sqrt{5}, 0)$ **3.** $(3 + \sqrt{15}, 5), (3 - \sqrt{15}, 5)$ **5.** $\dfrac{\sqrt{5}}{3}$
7. $\dfrac{\sqrt{15}}{4}$ **9.** $\dfrac{16}{3}$ **11.** $\dfrac{1}{2}$

Page 361 Written Exercises 1. center $(0, 0)$, foci $(\sqrt{5}, 0)$ and $(-\sqrt{5}, 0)$, $e = \dfrac{\sqrt{5}}{3}$, latus rectum $= \dfrac{8}{3}$
3. center $(3, 1)$, foci $(3, 1 + \sqrt{5})$ and $(3, 1 - \sqrt{5})$, $e = \dfrac{\sqrt{5}}{3}$, latus rectum $= \dfrac{8}{3}$ **5.** center $(2, -3)$, foci $(2, -3 + 2\sqrt{6})$ and $(2, -3 - 2\sqrt{6})$, $e = \dfrac{2\sqrt{6}}{5}$, latus rectum $= \dfrac{2}{5}$ **7.** $\dfrac{y^2}{4} + \dfrac{x^2}{1.75} = 1$
9. $\dfrac{(x - 2)^2}{81} + \dfrac{(y + 2)^2}{45} = 1$ **11.** $\dfrac{(x - 2)^2}{16} + \dfrac{(y - 5)^2}{15} = 1$
13. $\dfrac{(y - 2)^2}{18} + \dfrac{(x - 1)^2}{9} = 1$

Page 361 Challenge Exercises
15. $49x^2 + 9y^2 + 294x - 126y + 441 = 0$
17. $x^2 + y^2 = 19.24$ **19.** greatest, 2095.2 mi; least, 424.8 mi

Page 365 Exploratory Exercises 1. $\dfrac{x^2}{64} - \dfrac{y^2}{25} = 1$
3. $\dfrac{(y + 2)^2}{16} - \dfrac{(x - 6)^2}{25} = 1$ **5.** $\dfrac{x^2}{64} - \dfrac{y^2}{36} = 1$
7. $\dfrac{y^2}{4} - \dfrac{(x - 1)^2}{4} = 1$

Pages 365–366 Written Exercises 1. center $(0, 0)$, foci $(0, 10)$ and $(0, -10)$, vertices $(0, 8)$ and $(0, -8)$, asymptotes $y = \pm\dfrac{4}{3}x$ **3.** center $(0, 0)$, foci $(\sqrt{117}, 0)$ and $(-\sqrt{117}, 0)$, vertices $(6, 0)$ and $(-6, 0)$, asymptotes $y = \pm\dfrac{3}{2}x$ **5.** center $(-6, -3)$, foci $(-6 + 3\sqrt{5}, -3)$ and $(-6 - 3\sqrt{5}, -3)$, vertices $(0, -3)$ and $(-12, -3)$, asymptotes $y + 3 = \pm\dfrac{1}{2}(x + 6)$
7. $\dfrac{(x - 4)^2}{4} - \dfrac{(y + 2)^2}{5} = 1$ **9.** $\dfrac{(x - 3)^2}{9} - \dfrac{(y + 1)^2}{4} = 1$

Page 368 Exploratory Exercises 1. $\dfrac{x^2}{9} - \dfrac{y^2}{5} = 1$
3. $y^2 - \dfrac{(x - 2)^2}{4} = 1$ **5.** $e = \dfrac{\sqrt{14}}{3}$ **7.** $e = \sqrt{5}$ **9.** $\dfrac{10}{3}$
11. 8 **13.** $\dfrac{y^2}{5} - \dfrac{x^2}{9} = 1$ **15.** $\dfrac{(x - 2)^2}{4} - y^2 = 1$

17.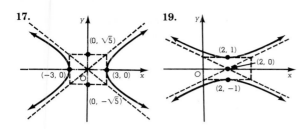

19.

Pages 368–369 Written Exercises

3. 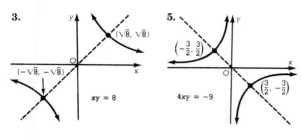 $xy = 8$

5. $4xy = -9$

7. center $(2, 0)$, foci $(2, 6)$ and $(2, -6)$, vertices $(2, \sqrt{30})$ and $(2, -\sqrt{30})$, asymptotes $y = \pm\sqrt{5}(x - 2)$ **9.** center $(5, -3)$, foci $(5 + \sqrt{13}, -3)$ and $(5 - \sqrt{13}, -3)$, vertices $(7, -3)$ and $(3, -3)$, asymptotes $y + 3 = \pm\dfrac{3}{2}(x - 5)$

11. $\dfrac{(y + 1)^2}{4} - \dfrac{(x - 3)^2}{5} = 1$ **13.** $\dfrac{x^2}{9} - \dfrac{y^2}{16} = 1$

15. $\dfrac{17(x - 1)^2}{9} - \dfrac{17y^2}{144} = 1$ **17.** $\dfrac{(x + 3)^2}{16} - \dfrac{(y - 1)^2}{16} = 1$

19. $\dfrac{(y - 3)^2}{16} - \dfrac{(x - 5)^2}{48} = 1$ **21.** $\dfrac{2y^2}{25} - \dfrac{2x^2}{25} = 1$

Page 369 Challenge Exercises **23.** $\dfrac{x^2}{4} - y^2 = 1$

25. $\dfrac{5}{3}$

Page 371 Exploratory Exercises

1. $(x - 4)^2 + y^2 = 5$ **3.** $\dfrac{(x - 3)^2}{25} + \dfrac{(y - 1)^2}{9} = 1$

5. $\left(y + \dfrac{1}{2}\right)^2 = -2(x - 2)$ **7.** $\dfrac{(y + 4)^2}{2} - \dfrac{(x + 1)^2}{6} = 1$

13.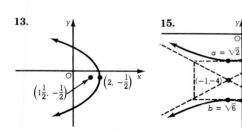

15.

Page 371 Written Exercises

5.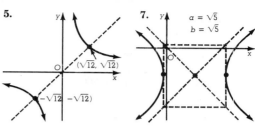

7. $a = \sqrt{5}$ $b = \sqrt{5}$

11.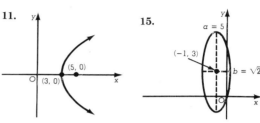

15. $a = 5$ $b = \sqrt{2}$ $(-1, 3)$

Page 372 Using Mathematics **1.** 11.5 sq meters **3.** 3.9 sq meters

Page 374 Written Exercises

5. 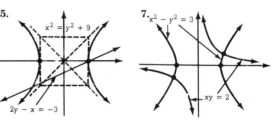 $x^2 = y^2 + 9$ $2y - x = -3$

7. $x^2 - y^2 = 3$ $xy = 2$

9. 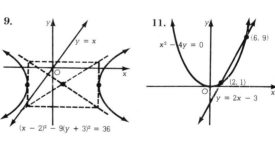 $y = x$ $(x - 2)^2 - 9(y + 3)^2 = 36$

11. $x^2 - 4y = 0$ $(6, 9)$ $(2, 1)$ $y = 2x - 3$

17. 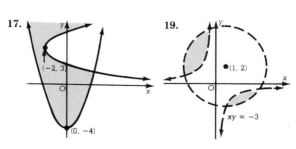 $(-2, 3)$ $(0, -4)$

19. $(1, 2)$ $xy = -3$

Page 378 Exploratory Exercises 1. $-\dfrac{8}{3\sqrt{5}}$ **3.** $\dfrac{16}{25}$
5. $2x + \sqrt{21}y - 25 = 0$ **7.** $9x - 8y - 145 = 0$ **9.** -3
11. 0 **13.** 1

Pages 378–379 Written Exercises
1. $-2x + \sqrt{15}y = 19,\ 2y = -\sqrt{15}x$ **3.** $x = 8,\ y = 3$
5. $y = 4x + 1,\ 4y = -x + 4$ **7.** $5y = 11x + 13,$
$11y = -5x - \dfrac{3}{5}$ **9.** $7y = -8\sqrt{3}x + 112,$
$16\sqrt{3}y = 14x + 15\sqrt{3}$ **11.** $y = -x + 8,\ y = x - 6$

13. $6y = 5x - 16,\ 5y = -6x + 37\dfrac{1}{2}$

15. $x = -4,\ y = -3$ **17.** $\sqrt{55}$ or 7.42
19. $\sqrt{3}$ or 1.73 **21.** $\sqrt{46}$ or 6.78 **23.** $y = 5$ and
$y = -5$ **25.** $y = -8$ and $y = 8$

Page 379 Challenge Exercises 27. $\left(4,\ -\dfrac{7}{2}\right)$
29. The tangents are perpendicular.

Page 382 Exploratory Exercises 1. ellipse
3. circle **5.** parabola **7.** hyperbola

13. 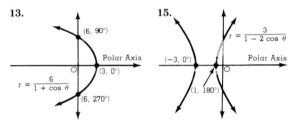 **15.**

17. $r = 5$ or -5

Page 383 Written Exercises 1. $p = \dfrac{9}{4},\ e = 1$

3. $p = \dfrac{9\sqrt{7}}{14},\ e = \dfrac{\sqrt{7}}{4}$ **5.** $p = \dfrac{2\sqrt{5}}{5},\ e = \sqrt{5}$

7. $p = \dfrac{4}{\sqrt{5}},\ e = \dfrac{\sqrt{5}}{3}$ **9.** $p = \dfrac{9\sqrt{34}}{68},\ e = \dfrac{\sqrt{34}}{5}$

11. $r = \dfrac{4.5}{1 \pm \cos\theta}$ **13.** $r = \dfrac{2.25}{1 \pm 0.25\sqrt{7}\cos\theta}$

15. $r = \dfrac{4}{1 \pm \sqrt{5}\cos\theta}$ **17.** $r = \dfrac{8}{3 \pm \sqrt{5}\cos\theta}$

19. $r = \dfrac{9}{5 \pm \sqrt{34}\cos\theta}$

Pages 385–386 Chapter Review
1. $(x - 3)^2 + (y + 7)^2 = 9$ **3.** focus $(7, 5)$, vertex $(7, 3)$,
directrix $y = 1$, axis $x = 7$ **5.** $(x')^2 + (y')^2 = 4$
7. center $(4, 6)$, foci $(4 + 3\sqrt{3}, 6)$ and $(4 - 3\sqrt{3}, 6)$,
vertices $(-2, 6)$ and $(10, 6)$ **9.** $\dfrac{(x - 2)^2}{25} + \dfrac{(y + 1)^2}{16} = 1$
11. center $(2, 3)$, foci $(2, 8)$ and $(2, -2)$, vertices $(2, 6)$

and $(2, 0)$, asymptotes $(y - 3) = \pm\dfrac{3}{4}(x - 2)$
13. $\dfrac{2y^2}{49} - \dfrac{2x^2}{49} = 1$ **15.** $\dfrac{(y - 1)^2}{4} - \dfrac{(x - 1)^2}{5} = 1$

17. **21.**
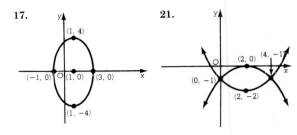

23. 8 **25.** $r = 3$

CHAPTER 13 PROBABILITY

Page 391 Exploratory Exercises 1. independent
3. not independent **5.** independent **7.** false **9.** false
11. true

Pages 391–392 Written Exercises 1. 24 **3.** 7
5. 39,916,800 **7.** 120 **9.** 72 **11.** 6 **13.** 60
15. 518,400 **17.** 480 **19.** 239,500,800 **21.** 24
23. 72 **25.** 17,576,000 **27.** 15,625,000 **29.** 14 **31.** 4

Page 396 Exploratory Exercises 1. not reflective
3. reflective **5.** not reflective **7.** not reflective
9. circular **11.** circular **13.** circular **15.** not
circular

Pages 396–397 Written Exercises 1. 720 **3.** 3360
5. 420 **7.** 181,440 **9.** 907,200 **11.** 180 **13.** 1440
15. 120 **17.** 144 **19.** 120 **21.** 969 **23.** 144

Page 399 Exploratory Exercises 1. permutation
3. combination **5.** combination **7.** combination
Pages 399–400 Written Exercises 1. 6 **3.** 1
5. 30 **7.** 12 **9.** 2002 **11.** 715 **13.** 56 **15.** 3570
17. 28,561 **19.** 126 **21.** 2808 **23.** 2520 **25.** 252
27. 64 **29.** 165 **31.** 80

Page 402 Exploratory Exercises 1. $\dfrac{1}{1}$ **3.** $\dfrac{7}{8}$ **5.** $\dfrac{3}{7}$

7. $\dfrac{4}{13}$ **9.** $\dfrac{1}{7}$ **11.** $\dfrac{1}{4}$ **13.** $\dfrac{1}{52}$

Pages 402–403 Written Exercises 1. $\dfrac{1}{6}$ **3.** $\dfrac{1}{51}$ **5.** $\dfrac{1}{6}$

7. $\dfrac{9}{11}$ **9.** $\dfrac{1}{2}$ **11.** $\dfrac{7}{50}$ **13.** $\dfrac{3}{38}$ **15.** $\dfrac{9}{38}$ **17.** $\dfrac{2}{7}$ **19.** $\dfrac{1}{7}$

21. $\dfrac{11}{25}$ **23.** $\dfrac{1}{15}$ **25.** $\dfrac{8}{15}$ **27.** $\dfrac{11}{100}$ **29.** $\dfrac{11}{50}$ **31.** $\dfrac{9}{92}$

Page 404 Using Mathematics 1. F, 216; G, 343; H, 512 **3.** Vacation begins Friday at three **5.** Prepare

Page 406 Exploratory Exercises 1. dependent **3.** independent **5.** dependent **7.** $\frac{1}{15}$ **9.** $\frac{1}{36}$ **11.** $\frac{8}{195}$

Pages 406–407 Written Exercises 1. $\frac{1}{36}$ **3.** $\frac{1}{24}$ **5.** $\frac{1}{16}$ **7.** $\frac{1}{117,600}$ **9.** $\frac{25}{36}$ **11.** $\frac{5}{6}$ **13.** $\frac{27}{1000}$ **15.** $\frac{121}{204}$ **17.** $\frac{1}{635,013,559,600}$ **19.** $\frac{19}{1,160,054}$ **21.** more than 7 people

Page 409 Exploratory Exercises 1. mutually exclusive **3.** mutually exclusive **5.** inclusive **7.** $\frac{4}{15}$ **9.** $\frac{34}{39}$ **11.** $\frac{2}{3}$

Pages 409–410 Written Exercises 1. $\frac{2}{3}$ **3.** $\frac{13}{55}$ **5.** $\frac{26}{33}$ **7.** $\frac{12}{221}$ **9.** $\frac{188}{663}$ **11.** $\frac{35}{64}$ **13.** $\frac{21}{64}$ **15.** $\frac{2}{429}$ **17.** $\frac{175}{429}$ **19.** $\frac{3}{5}$ **21.** $\frac{16}{25}$

Page 412 Exploratory Exercises 1. A is 4 shows on third throw; B is 6 shows on first two throws **3.** A is one coin shows tails; B is at least one coin shows heads **5.** A is the marble came from the first bag; B is a blue marble drawn **7.** $\frac{1}{6}$ **9.** $\frac{2}{3}$ **11.** $\frac{2}{5}$

Pages 412–413 Written Exercises 1. $\frac{1}{6}$ **3.** $\frac{3}{3}$ **5.** $\frac{3}{11}$ **7.** $\frac{1}{4}$ **9.** $\frac{1}{7}$ **11.** $\frac{2}{15}$ **13.** $\frac{1}{15}$ **15.** $\frac{1}{4}$ **17.** $\frac{2}{5}$ **19.** $\frac{3}{10}$ **21.** $\frac{3}{7}$ **23.** $\frac{19}{51}$ **25.** $\frac{3}{8}$

Page 415 Exploratory Exercises 1. binomial, $\frac{3}{8}$ **3.** binomial, $\frac{1}{28,561}$ **5.** binomial, $\frac{1}{9}$

Pages 415–416 Written Exercises 1. $\frac{1}{8}$ **3.** $\frac{1}{2}$ **5.** $\frac{3125}{7776}$ **7.** $\frac{625}{648}$ **9.** $\frac{1}{81}$ **11.** $\frac{16}{27}$ **13.** $\frac{193}{512}$ **15.** $\frac{319}{512}$ **17.** $\frac{32}{625}$ **19.** $\frac{64}{15,625}$ **21.** $\frac{576}{15,625}$ **23.** $\frac{59,049}{100,000}$ **25.** $\frac{1}{100,000}$ **27.** $\frac{1,959,552}{9,765,625}$ **29.** $\frac{236,196}{1,953,125}$

Page 418 Chapter Review 1. 120 **3.** $-\frac{9}{5}$ **5.** 240 **7.** 50,400 **9.** 12 **11.** 165 **13.** 2860 **15.** $\frac{4}{5}$ **17.** $\frac{1}{11}$ **19.** $\frac{125}{4096}$ **21.** $\frac{5}{36}$ **23.** $\frac{9}{14}$ **25.** $\frac{1}{2}$ **27.** $\frac{1}{4}$ **29.** $\frac{3}{8}$

CHAPTER 14 DESCRIPTIVE STATISTICS

Page 423 Exploratory Exercises 1. 15.5 **3.** 27.5 **5.** no mode **7.** 10 **9.** 15.5 **11.** 30.75 **13–15.** Answers will vary.

Pages 423–424 Written Exercises 1. 78.8 **3.** 1 lb **5.** 17.5 **7.** Answers will vary. **9.** {10, 700; 10, 700; 10, 700; 10, 700; 11, 600; 11, 600; 14, 700; 14, 700; 50,000; 50,000} **11.** $11,600 **13.** company - mean; union - mode **15.** higher **17.** More American families own cars than do not. More American women wear size 7 shoes than any other size. **19.** 2.9 **21.** 204

Page 424 Challenge Exercises 23. 59 cm

Page 426 Exploratory Exercises 1. harmonic mean **3.** arithmetic mean

Page 427 Written Exercises 1. 4.21 **3.** 8.9 **5.** $\overline{X} = 4.8$, $M_d = 5$, $H = 3.8$, $Q = 5.3$ **7.** 48.6 mph **9.** $3.10/lb. **11.** 43.5 mph

Page 430 Exploratory Exercises 1. 11.09 **3.** 0.084 **5.** 0.16 **7.** 0.0948 **9.** 0.75 **11.** 0.6

Pages 430–431 Written Exercises 1. 7.73 **3.** 3.05 **5.** 85 **7.** 403.5 **9.** 20.25 **11.** 16.75 **13.** 25.31 **15.** 23 **17.** 10.25 **19.** $M.D. = 8.53$, $\sigma = 10.45$, The standard deviation is greater.

Page 433 Exploratory Exercises 1. $6000 **3.** $3000, $9000, $15,000, $21,000, $27,000 **5.** 39% **7.** class interval, 0.2; class limits, 2.0, 2.2, 2.4, 2.6, 2.8, 3.0, 3.2, 3.4, 3.6; class marks, 2.1, 2.3, 2.5, 2.7, 2.9, 3.1, 3.3, 3.5 **9.** class interval, 10; class limits, 5, 15, 25, 35, 45, 55 **11.** class interval, 2.5; class limits, 1.25, 3.75, 6.25, 8.75, 11.25, 13.75

Pages 433–434 Written Exercises

1.

Class Limits	Class Marks	Tally	Frequency (f)
0–10	5	|||	3
10–20	15	|||	3
20–30	25	⊮ ||	7
30–40	35	⊮ ||||	9
40–50	45	⊮ ⊮		11
50–60	55	⊮ |||	8
60–70	65	⊮ |||	8
70–80	75	⊮ ||	7
80–90	85	|||	3
90–100	95			1

5.

Class Limits	Class Marks (X)	Tally	Frequency (f)
55–60	57.5	卌	5
60–65	62.5	卌 卌	10
65–70	67.5	卌 卌	10
70–75	72.5	卌 IIII	9
75–80	77.5	卌 I	6
80–85	82.5	I	1
85–90	87.5	I	1
90–95	92.5	III	3

11. A measurement reported as 2112.7 m would usually be discarded. One could not rely on the error being in the second digit.

Page 437 Exploratory Exercises 1. 950, 1000, 1050, 1100, 1150, 1200, 1250, 1300 **3.** 50 **5.** 360

7. 28%

9.

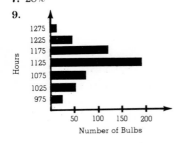

Page 438 Written Exercises

1.

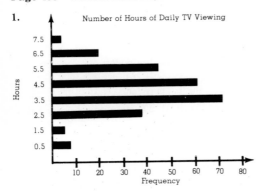

7.

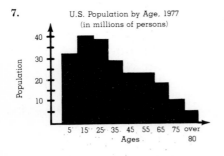

11.

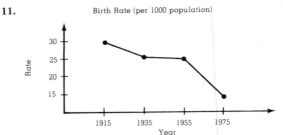

15. Civilian Labor Force in 1979 (in millions of persons)

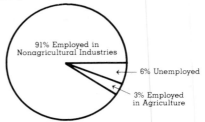

Page 439 Using Mathematics 1. $y = 125$, $y = 42.5$
3. $s = 310$, $s = 730$

Page 442 Exploratory Exercises 1. $1485
3. $4650 **5.** $2275 **7.** $780 **9.** 100 **11.** cumulative frequency 11, 35, 65, 75, 88, 96, 100 **13.** $155

Page 443 Written Exercises 1. 19.3 **3.** 20.1
5. No. There is no limit in the class "$50,000 and over."
7. $30,000 - $40,000

9.

Class Limits	Class Marks (X)	Tally	Frequency
0–$8.00	$4.00	III	3
$8.00–$16.00	$12.00	卌 卌 II	12
$16.00–$24.00	$20.00	卌 III	8
$24.00–$32.00	$28.00	卌	5
$32.00–$40.00	$36.00	卌 IIII	9
$40.00–$48.00	$44.00	卌 I	6
$48.00–$56.00	$52.00	IIII	4
$56.00–$64.00	$60.00	I	1

11. Cumulative frequency 3, 15, 23, 28, 37, 43, 47, 48
13. $25.60

Page 443 Challenge Exercises 25. $36.98

Page 443 For the Scholar 571,428

Page 446 Exploratory Exercises 1. 136.6 **3.** 68.3
5. 3415 **7.** 1707.5 **9.** 68,300 **11.** 34,150 **13.** 6.7%
15. 38.3% **17.** 6.7%

Page 447 Written Exercises 1. 68.3% **3.** 20.1 to 27.9 **5.** 68.3% **7.** 0.866 **9.** 0.1585 **11.** 107 to 173
13. 45.82 to 55.18 **15.** 0.325 **17.** 0.500 **19.** 25.5%

Pages 449–450 Exploratory Exercises 1. 0.955

3. 5 **5.** 0.24 **7.** 187.1 to 212.9 **9.** 23.38 to 24.62
11. 190.2 to 209.8 **13.** 23.53 to 24.47

Page 450 Written Exercises 1. 0.14 **3.** 4.506 to
4.694 **5.** 0.198 **7.** 15.684 to 16.716 **9.** 3.4
11. 11.567 to 13.233 **13.** 0.454

Page 450 For the Scholar 32 sq units

Page 452 Chapter Review 1. 5 **3.** 3.5 **5.** 2.3
7. 1.6 **9.** 1.74 **11.** 1.0

13.

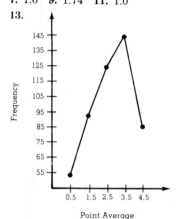

Point Average

15. 2.84
17. 1.12 to 4.34
19. 0.06

CHAPTER 15 LIMITS, DERIVATIVES, AND INTEGRALS

Page 457 Exploratory Exercises

1.

x	1.9	1.99	2.01	2.1
$5x$	9.5	9.95	10.05	10.5

; $\lim\limits_{x \to 2} 5x = 10$

5.

x	-2.1	-2.01	-1.99	-1.9
$x^2 - 4$	0.41	0.04	-0.04	-0.39

;
$\lim\limits_{x \to -2} (x^2 - 4) = 0$

9.

x	-3.1	-3.01	-2.99	-2.9
$2x - 5$	-11.2	-11.02	-10.98	-10.8

;
$\lim\limits_{x \to -3} (2x - 5) = -11$

Page 458 Written Exercises 1. 4 **3.** $\frac{2}{3}$ **5.** 7 **7.** 6
9. $\frac{1}{3}$ **11.** 8 **13.** 3 **15.** $\frac{3}{4}$ **17.** 2 **19.** 2 **21.** 1

Page 462 Exploratory Exercises 1. $|x - 2| < 0.1$
3. $|x - 8| < \delta$ **5.** $|x - 8| < 0.001$
7. $-0.001 < x - 4 < 0.001$ **9.** $-\delta < x - 7 < \delta$
11. $-0.00003 < x - 8 < 0.00003$ **13.** $0.6 < x < 1.2$,
$0.3 < f(x) < 0.6$ **15.** $-3.5 < x < -2.5$, $5.9 < f(x) < 6.1$
17. $|x - 2.5| < 0.3$; $|f(x) - 7.05| < 0.95$

Pages 462–463 Written Exercises
1. $1.995 < x < 2.005$ **3.** $4.9 < x < 5.1$
5. $1.997 < x < 2.003$ **7.** $5.6 < x < 6.4$ **9.** $1 < f(x) < 7$
11. $42.25 < f(x) < 56.25$ **13.** $-0.85 < f(x) < -0.65$
15. $4 - a < f(x) < 4 + a$ **17.** $|f(x) - L|$ or
$|(2x - 6) - 2| < \epsilon$ when $0 < |x - 4| < \delta$
$$2|x - 4| < \epsilon$$
$$|x - 4| < \frac{\epsilon}{2}$$
Choose $\delta \leq \frac{\epsilon}{2}$ and the conditions of the definition are
satisfied. **19.** $\delta \leq 0.01$ **21.** $\delta \leq 0.01$ **23.** $\delta \leq 0.01$
25. $\delta \leq 0.01$

Page 465 Exploratory Exercises 1. $x = 0$
3. $x = 3$ **5.** at every integer x **7.** $f(1) = 2$
9. $f(-\sqrt{5}) = -2\sqrt{5}$

Page 465 Written Exercises 1. continuous
3. infinite discontinuity at $x = 0$ **5.** continuous
7. point discontinuity at $x = 1$ **9.** continuous
11. continuous **13.** Answers will vary. A typical
answer is $f(x) = x$. **15.** Answers will vary. A typical
answer is $f(x) = \frac{x^2 - 4}{x - 2}$ **17.** $f(1) = 6$,
$\lim\limits_{x \to 1} (x + 5) = f(1)$; continuous **19.** $f(4) = 0$,
$\lim\limits_{x \to 4} \frac{x^2 - 16}{x + 4} = f(4)$; continuous

Page 468 Exploratory Exercises 1. -6 **3.** -5
5. 0 **7.** 3 **9.** 3

Pages 468–469 Written Exercises
1. $\lim\limits_{x \to 2} (x^2 - 5x + 6) = \lim\limits_{x \to 2} (x - 3)(x - 2)$
$= \left[\lim\limits_{x \to 2} (x - 3)\right]\left[\lim\limits_{x \to 2} (x - 2)\right] = (-1)(0)$ or 0
3. $\lim\limits_{x \to a} \left(\sqrt{p} \cdot x + \frac{q - \sqrt{q^2 - 4pr}}{2\sqrt{p}}\right) \cdot \lim\limits_{x \to a} \left(\sqrt{p} \cdot x + \frac{q + \sqrt{q^2 - 4pr}}{2\sqrt{p}}\right)$ **5.** $\frac{4}{27}$ **7.** 1 **9.** 0 **11.** 4 **13.** $\frac{1}{3}$
15. 17 **17.** 0 **19.** $\frac{1}{2}$

Page 471 Exploratory Exercises 1. 1 **3.** -2
5. $4x + 2h$ **7.** $3x^2 + 3xh + h^2$ **9.** 5 **11.** $2x + h$

Page 472 Written Exercises 1. 1 **3.** -2 **5.** $4x$
7. $3x^2$ **9.** 5 **11.** $2x$ **13.** $0, y = 0$

15. $-2, y = -2x - 3$ **17.** $6, y = 6x + 2$ **19.** $-\frac{1}{9}$,
$y = \frac{-x + 6}{9}$ **21.** $-1, y = -x + 4$ **23.** (1, 1) **25.** (0, 1)
27. $\left(\frac{1}{3}, 5\frac{1}{3}\right)$ **29.** none **31.** none

Page 475   Exploratory Exercises   1. Theorem 11, Power Formula   **3.** Power formula   **5.** Theorem 13, Theorem 11, Power Formula   **7.** Theorems 11 and 14, Power Formula   **9.** Theorem 14, Power Formula   **11.** Theorems 14 and 15   **13.** Theorem 11, Power Formula

Pages 475–476   Written Exercises   1. $32x^3 - 30x^2$

3. $\dfrac{1}{3\sqrt[3]{x^2}}$ **5.** $15x^4 - 18x^2$ **7.** $4(x^3 - 2x + 1)^3(3x^2 - 2)$

9. $-\dfrac{x}{\sqrt{(x^2 - 4)^3}}$ **11.** $\dfrac{-4(x + 1)}{(x - 1)^3}$ **13.** $5x^4 + 9x^2 - 8x$

15. 2   **17.** 6   **19.** -4 **21.** $\dfrac{x^2 + 2x}{(x + 1)^2}$ **23.** $\dfrac{-2(2x - 1)}{(x^2 - x)^3}$

25. $\dfrac{-3x^3}{2\sqrt{1 - x^3}} + \sqrt{1 - x^3}$ **27.** $10x^3(x - 5)^5(x - 2)$

29. $\dfrac{2}{(x + 1)^2}$

Page 479   Exploratory Exercises   1. $f'(x) = 2x + 6$
3. $f'(x) = 2x - 2$ **5.** $f'(x) = 3x^2 - 3$
7. $f'(x) = 4x^2(3 - x)$ **9.** $4x(2x^2 - 1)$ **11.** 2   **13.** 2
15. $6x$ **17.** $24x - 12x^2$ **19.** $24x^2 - 4$

Page 479   Written Exercises   1. $x > 0$ **3.** $x > -3$
5. $x > 2$ or $x < 1$ **7.** $x > 3$ or $-3 < x < 0$ **9.** $x < -1$
or $x > 1$ **11.** $x < 1$ **13.** $-1 < x < 1$ **15.** $\dfrac{2}{3} < x < 2$

17. $x > 3$ **19.** $x = \dfrac{1}{2}$, maximum
21. $x = 2$, minimum; $x = 1$, maximum
23. $(0, 0)$, point of inflection; $x = 3$, maximum

Page 479   For the Scholar   5000

Page 480   Using Mathematics
1. $f(125) = 31,\ 250\ \text{m}^2$ **3.** 324, maximum product;

18, 18, integers   **5.** $3\dfrac{1}{3}'' \times 3\dfrac{1}{3}''$

Page 484   Exploratory Exercises

1. $\displaystyle\lim_{n\to\infty}\sum_{i=1}^{n}\left(\dfrac{i}{n}\right)^2\left(\dfrac{1}{n}\right)$ **3.** $\displaystyle\lim_{n\to\infty}\sum_{i=1}^{n}\left(\dfrac{i}{n}\right)^5\left(\dfrac{1}{n}\right)$ **5.** $\displaystyle\lim_{n\to\infty}\sum_{i=1}^{n}\left(\dfrac{ai}{n}\right)^3\left(\dfrac{a}{n}\right)$

7. $\displaystyle\lim_{n\to\infty}\sum_{i=1}^{n}\left(\dfrac{5i}{n}\right)\left(\dfrac{5}{n}\right) - \lim_{n\to\infty}\sum_{i=1}^{n}\left(\dfrac{2i}{n}\right)\left(\dfrac{2}{n}\right)$

9.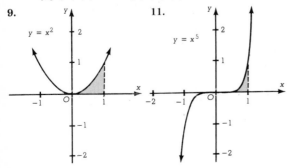

11.

Page 484   Written Exercises   1. $\dfrac{1}{3}$ **3.** $\dfrac{1}{6}$ **5.** $\dfrac{a^4}{4}$

7. $10\dfrac{1}{2}$ **9.** $11\dfrac{2}{3}$ **11.** $\dfrac{1}{6}$ **13.** $\dfrac{b^2 - a^2}{2}$

Page 487   Exploratory Exercises   1. $x^2 + C$ where C is any constant   **3.** $x^2 + x + C$ where C is any constant   **5.** $x^4 + C$ where C is any constant

Page 487   Written Exercises   1. $x^2 + C$
3. $x^8 + x^2 + C$ **5.** $\dfrac{1}{21}(x + 5)^{21} + C$ **7.** $-x^2 + 3x + C$

9. $\dfrac{3}{4}\sqrt[3]{(x^2 + 2x + 2)^2} + C$ **11.** $3\sqrt[3]{x^4} + C$

13. $-\dfrac{1}{x^2} + C$ **15.** $4\sqrt{x} + C$

Page 490   Exploratory Exercises   1. 12 sq units
3. $12\dfrac{1}{2}$ sq units   **5.** 9 sq units

Page 491   Written Exercises
1. $\dfrac{8}{3}$ sq units   **3.** 18 sq units   **5.** $\dfrac{4}{3}$ sq units

7.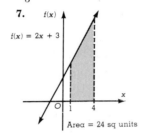

9.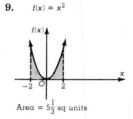

11.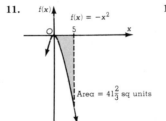

15.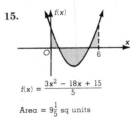

17. 4   **19.** $2\dfrac{2}{3}$ **21.** $22\dfrac{1}{2}$ **23.** $-8\dfrac{2}{3}$ **25.** $\dfrac{2}{3}$ **27.** $13\dfrac{1}{6}$

Page 494   Chapter Review   1. $a^2 + 3a + 2$ **3.** 0
5. $4.98 < x < 5.02$ **7.** $\delta \le 0.01$
9. point discontinuity at $x = -3$ and $x = 2$

11. 0   **13.** $\dfrac{1}{2}$ **15.** $-8,\ y = -8x - 6$ **17.** $12x^2$

19. $x > 1$ **21.** $x = +\sqrt{\dfrac{2}{3}}$, minimum; $x = -\sqrt{\dfrac{2}{3}}$,

maximum   **23.** 4 sq units   **25.** $-\dfrac{4}{x} + C$

27. $x - \dfrac{x^2}{2} + C$ **29.** 36   **31.** 36

Index

B

Bar graphs, 435, 451
Basic Counting Principle, 389, 417
Bimodal, 422
Binomial experiments, 414-417
Binomial Theorem, 240-243, 249
  probability, 414-415
  proof of, 246-247
Bisectors, 333-334, 341
Boundaries, 15
Break-even point, 25
Broken line graphs, 435-436, 451

C

Calculators
  changing to degrees, 138
  changing to polar form, 338
  changing to radians, 138
  e, 292
  exponents, 289
  finding circular functions, 101, 108, 116
  finding trigonometric functions, 101, 129, 142, 177
  logarithms, 304
  solving right triangles, 191, 192
  solving triangles, 191, 192, 201, 208
Calculus, 454-493
  antiderivatives, 485, 488, 493
  continuity, 463-465, 492
  derivatives, 469-480, 488, 493
  fundamental theorem of, 488, 493
  integration, 485-490, 493
  limits, 455-462, 466-472, 492-493
  power formula, 472, 493
  second derivatives, 478, 480
  second derivative test, 478-479, 493
Cardioids, 259, 277
Carrier waves, 195
Catenary curves, 293
Centers
  of an ellipse, 354
  of circles, 345-346, 353, 383
  of hyperbolas, 362-363, 366
Central tendencies, 421-427
  arithmetic means, 421-429, 440, 451
  harmonic means, 425-426, 451
  medians, 422-423, 427-429, 451
  modes, 422-423, 451
  quadratic means, 426, 451
Chapter reviews, 27-28, 61-62, 93-94, 122, 156, 184, 215-216, 249-250, 279-280, 316, 341-342, 385-386, 418, 452, 494

Chapter summaries, 26, 60-61, 92-93, 121, 154-155, 183, 214-215, 248-249, 277-278, 314-315, 340-341, 383-385, 417, 451-452, 492-493
Chapter tests, 29, 63, 95, 123, 157, 185, 217, 251, 281, 317, 343, 387, 419, 453, 495
Characteristics, 303-304, 315
  negative, 304
Circle graphs, 436-437, 451
Circles, 345-346, 370-371
  center of, 345-346, 383
  equations of, 345, 370-371, 375, 380, 383
  graphs of, 257-258, 260
  polar equations, 380
  radius of, 345-346, 383
  sectors of, 210-212, 215
  segments of, 211-212, 215
  tangents, 375-377, 385
  translation of axis, 353
  unit, 97
Circular functions, 96-121, 137
  addition formulas, 114-118, 121, 147-150, 155
  C, 97-98, 102, 121
  cosecant (csc), 102-108, 112-113, 121
  cosine (cos), 102-108, 111-121
  cotangent (cot), 102-109, 113, 121
  double number formulas, 118, 121, 150, 152, 155
  finding values, 105-109, 121
  graphs of, 110-113
  half number formulas, 119, 121, 151, 155
  periodic, 98, 121
  radians, 107-109
  secant (sec), 102-108, 112, 121
  sine, 102-112, 115-121
  tangent (tan), 102-108, 111-113, 121
  trigonometric tables, 108, 531
  wrapping function, 97-99
Circular permutations, 394-396, 417
Circular sectors, 210-212, 215
Circular segments, 211-212, 215
Classes, 431-432, 451
  limits, 431-432
  marks, 432, 440
  medians, 441, 451
Cofunctions, 131-132
  identities, 132, 154
Combinations, 397-398, 417
Common differences, 219, 248
Common logarithms, 302-307, 315
  antilogarithms, 304-305
  characteristic, 303-304, 315
  in solving exponential equations, 306-307
  mantissa, 303-304, 315
  tables of, 303, 536-537
Common ratios, 222, 248
Comparison test, 235, 249
Complements, 400-401

in graphing, 476–479, 493
notation, 471
of constant functions, 472
of products, 473–474, 493
of roots, 474
of sums, 473, 493
power formula, 472–473, 493
second, 478–480
techniques, 472–475, 493
theorems of, 473–475, 493
Descartes, René, 47
Descartes' Rule of Signs, 47–48, 61
Determinants, 65–67, 89–90, 92
Cramer's rule, 66–67, 92
expansion of a third order, 66, 92
minor, 65
of the system, 67
value of second order, 65, 92
Difference identities
cosine (cos), 115, 121, 147, 155
sine (sin), 115, 121, 147, 155
tangent (tan), 148, 155
Difference quotient, 469
Differentiable functions, 469
Differentiation, 469
Dimensions of matrices, 65
Diminished roots, 59
Directrices
of an ellipse, 370
of hyperbolas, 370
of parabolas, 348–350, 370, 383
Discontinuity, 463–465
everywhere, 464
infinite, 464
jump, 464–465
point, 464
Discriminants, 35
Distance
between parallel lines, 332
formula, 10–11, 26, 322
from a point to a line, 330–334, 341
Divergent series, 232–235, 249
comparison test, 235, 249
ratio test, 233, 249
Division
of complex numbers, 271, 278
of limits, 466–467, 492
of polynomials, 36–38
Remainder Theorem, 40–41, 60
synthetic, 36–38
Domain, 3, 5, 26
Dot products, 88
Double angle identities
cosine (cos), 118, 121, 150, 152, 155
sine (sin), 118, 121, 150, 152, 155
tangent (tan), 150, 155

Double number formulas, 118, 121, 150, 152, 155

E

e, 290–292, 315
definition of, 291, 315
Euler's formula, 312–315
graph of, 292
natural logarithms, 308–310, 313–315
table of powers, 292, 512
Eccentricity
of an ellipse, 358–360, 381–382, 384
of conics, 369–370, 381–385
of hyperbolas, 366–367, 382, 384
Elements, 65
Elevation, 192
Ellipse, 354–360, 370, 381–384
axes of symmetry, 354
center of, 354
directrices, 370
eccentricity, 358–360, 381–384
equations of, 356–359, 370, 375, 381–384
foci of, 354–359, 383
latus rectum, 359–360, 384
major axis, 354, 356, 384
minor axis, 354
polar equations, 381–382, 385
semi-major axis, 354–355, 358–359, 383
semi-minor axis, 354–355, 383
tangents to, 375
vertices, 354, 357
Equal matrices, 68
Equations
changing to polar equations, 263
completing the square, 33–34
exponential, 306–307
Fundamental Theorem of Algebra, 42, 60
identity, 187
Integral Root Theorem, 46–47, 60
linear, 7–9, 12–14, 26, 319, 327–329, 336–341
normal form, 327–329, 337, 341
of an ellipse, 356–359, 370, 375, 381–384
of asymptotes, 364, 384
of circles, 345, 370–371, 375, 380, 383
of conic sections, 344, 370, 375, 380–385
of hyperbolas, 362–363, 366, 370–371, 375, 382, 384
of parabolas, 348–350, 370, 380, 382–383
of tangents, 375–376, 378
parametric, 336
point-slope form, 14, 26, 319
polar, 255–260, 263, 337–341, 380–382, 385
polynomial, 31–35, 42–47, 60
quadratic, 33–35, 60
quadratic formula, 34–35, 60
Rational Root Theorem, 45–47, 60
roots of, 31–35, 42–47, 60

Gauss-Jordan method, 76-78
non-singular, 67
$m \times n$, 65
multiplicative identity, 73-74, 92
multiplicative inverse, 74-75, 92
multiplying, 71-75, 92
nth order, 65
row operations, 76, 92
scalar product, 71, 92
square, 65
subtracting, 70, 92
zero, 69
Maximum values, 55-57, 61, 477-480, 493
absolute, 478
relative, 56, 478-480, 493
Means
arithmetic, 220, 421-429, 440, 451
deviation, 428, 451
geometric, 223-224
harmonic, 425-426, 451
quadratic, 426, 451
standard error of, 448-449, 452
Measures of central tendency, 421-427
arithmetic means, 421-429, 440, 451
harmonic means, 425-426, 451
medians, 422-423, 427-429, 451
modes, 422-423, 451
quadratic means, 426, 451
Measures of variability, 428-429
mean deviations, 428, 451
semi-interquartile ranges, 428-429, 451
standard deviations, 429, 441-451
Median class, 441, 451
Medians, 422-423, 427-429, 451
arrays, 422
Midpoint formula, 322, 340
Minimum values, 55-57, 61, 477-480, 493
absolute, 478
relative, 56, 478-479, 493
Minor axis, 354
semi, 354-355, 383
Minors, 65
Minutes, 130
Modes, 422-423, 451
bimodal, 422
Modulus, 268, 270
Multiple roots, 43
Multiplication
identity, 73-74, 92
FOIL method, 265
of complex numbers, 265-266, 270-273, 278
of limits, 466, 492
of matrices, 71-75, 92
scalars times vectors, 81, 83-84, 86-87, 93
Multiplicative identity
for matrices, 73-74, 92
for real numbers, 73

Multiplicative inverses
for matrices, 74-75, 92
for non-zero real numbers, 74
Mutually exclusive events, 408-409, 417

N

Nappes, 369
Natural logarithms, 308-310, 313-315
antilogarithms, 309
table of, 308-309, 538-539
Neighborhoods, 51
Nested loops, 520
n factorial ($n!$), 241-242, 249
Non-singular matrix, 67
Normal distributions, 444-448, 452
Normal form, 327-329, 337, 341
from standard form, 328-329, 341
Normals, 327, 377-378, 385
nth order, 65
nth term, 219-220, 223, 238, 248
Numbers
complex, 35, 264-267, 268-278
e, 290-292, 308-315
Euler, 290
Fibonacci, 237
imaginary, 35, 264
pi (π), 226, 313
pure imaginary, 264

O

Odd functions, 143
Odds, 401, 417
Operations
addition, 69-70, 80, 83-84, 86-87, 93, 265-266, 278
division, 36-38, 271, 278
multiplication, 71-75, 81, 83-84, 86-87, 93, 265-266, 270-273, 278
row, 76, 92
subtraction, 70, 81, 83-84, 86-87, 93, 265-266, 278
using polar form, 270-276, 278
using rectangular form, 265-266, 278
with complex numbers, 265-266, 270-271, 278
with matrices, 69-75, 92
with polynomials, 36-38
with vectors, 80-81, 83-84, 86-87, 93
Ordered pairs, 3
representing vectors, 82-84, 93
Ordered triples, 85-86
representing vectors, 86-87, 93
Ordinates, 3

P

Parabolas, 348-353, 372
 axis of, 348
 directrix, 348-350, 370, 383
 equations of, 348-350, 370, 375, 380, 382-383
 focus, 348-350, 383
 latus rectum of, 350, 383
 polar equations, 380, 382
 tangents to, 375-376
 translation of axis, 353
 vertex, 348-350, 383
Parabolic cylinders, 372
Parallel lines, 319
 distance between, 332
Parallelogram method, 80
Parameters, 336
Parametric equations, 336
Pascal, 496-522
 ABS function, 511
 ARCTAN function, 511
 arrays, 500
 assignment statements, 500-501
 ATAN function, 511
 BEGIN statements, 497
 BOOLEAN variables, 513-515
 branching, 509
 CONST statements, 500
 COS function, 511
 DIV function, 498, 511
 EXP function, 511
 FOR statements, 502-503
 functions, 511-512, 516-518
 GLOBAL variables, 517
 IF-THEN-ELSE statements, 509
 LN function, 511
 LOCAL variables, 517
 loops, 502-507
 matrices, 500
 MOD function, 511
 order of operations, 498
 powers, 511, 516-517
 procedures, 519-520
 punctuation, 498
 READ statements, 498
 relational operators, 509
 remarks, 498
 REPEAT-UNTIL statements, 505-507
 ROUND function, 511
 RUN statements, 498
 SIN function, 511
 SQR function, 511
 SQRT function, 504, 511
 square roots, 502-503, 509, 511
 squares, 502-503, 511
 subprograms, 502, 506, 516-517, 519-520

 symbols for operations, 498
 title, 497
 TRUNC function, 511
 variables, 497
 vectors, 500
 WHILE-DO statements, 506-507
 WRITELN statements, 498, 503
 WRITE statements, 498, 501, 503
Pascal's triangle, 242-243
Periodic functions, 98, 121
Periods, 98, 121, 161, 164, 166-169, 183
Permutations, 390-396, 398, 417
 circular, 394-396, 417
 linear, 390-391, 395, 417
 with repetitions, 393, 417
Perpendicular lines, 320, 340
Perpendicular vectors, 88-90
Phase shift, 165-169, 183
Pi (π), 226
 Euler's formula, 313
Point discontinuity, 464
Point of inflection, 55-56, 61
Points
 break-even, 25
 critical, 55-57, 61, 477
 distance to lines, 330-334, 341
 of inflection, 55-56, 61, 477-478
Point-slope form, 14, 26, 319
Polar axis, 253, 277
Polar coordinates, 253-263, 277-278
 from rectangular coordinates, 262-263, 278
 to rectangular coordinates, 262, 278
 transformations, 267
Polar equations, 255-260, 263
Polar form, 337-341, 268-278
 dividing, 271, 278
 from standard form, 337-338
 graphing, 338
 multiplying, 270-273, 278
 of conic sections, 380-382, 385
 powers of, 272-273, 278
 roots of, 274-276, 278
 to standard form, 339
Polar graphs, 255-260, 277
 cardioids, 259, 277
 circles, 255-258, 260
 lemniscates, 259, 277
 limacons, 258-259, 277
 lines, 255
 roses, 259-260, 277
 spirals, 259, 277
Polar transformations, 267
Pole, 253, 277
Polygonal convex sets, 17-20, 26
Polynomial equations, 31-35, 42-47, 60
 completing the square, 33-34
 Fundamental Theorem of Algebra, 42, 60

diminished, 59
Fundamental Theorem of Algebra, 42, 60
graphs of, 276
imaginary, 35
Integral Root Theorem, 46–47, 60
multiple, 43
of complex numbers, 274–278
of limits, 466–467, 492
of polar form, 274–276, 278
of quadratic equations, 33–35
principal, 274
quadratic formula, 34–35, 60
Rational Root Theorem, 45–47, 60
simple, 43
Roses, 259–260, 277

S

Sample sets, 447–449
Scalar, 71, 79
Secant (sec)
circular function, 102–108, 121
graph of, 112, 160
trigonometric function, 125–133, 141, 145–146, 154
Secant lines, 52
Second derivatives, 478–480
Second derivative test, 478–479, 493
Sectors, 210–212, 215
Segments, 211–212, 215
Semi-interquartile ranges, 428–429, 451
Semi-major axis, 354–355, 358–359, 383
Semi-minor axis, 354–355, 383
Sequences, 218–224, 227–228
arithmetic, 219–220, 248
arithmetic means, 220
common difference, 219, 248
common ratio, 222, 248
Fibonacci, 237
geometric, 222–224, 248
geometric means, 223–224
infinite, 227–228
nth term, 219–220, 223, 248
terms of, 219, 248
Series
arithmetic, 220–221, 230, 233
comparison test, 235, 249
convergent, 232–236, 249, 312
divergent, 232–235, 249
exponential, 291, 312
geometric, 224, 230–233, 238, 248–249
in expressing π, 226
infinite, 226, 229–236, 238, 249, 290–291
nth term, 238
ratio test, 233, 249
sigma notation, 238, 242
trigonometric, 312

Sigma notation, 238
binomial theorem, 242
index of summation, 238
Simple roots, 43
Simplest form, 46
Sine (sin)
amplitude, 163, 166, 168, 183
circular functions, 102–112, 115–121
difference identity, 115, 121, 147, 155
double angle identity, 118, 121, 150, 152, 155
graph of, 110–112, 159–171
half angle identity, 119, 121, 151, 155
inverse of, 172–173, 176–183
law of, 196–202, 204, 207, 214
period, 161, 164, 166, 168, 183
phase shift, 165–168, 183
sum identity, 115–118, 121, 147, 155
trigonometric function, 125–133, 141–155
Slope-intercept form, 12–14, 26, 319
Slopes, 11–12, 26, 319–320
angles of inclination, 320, 325, 340
of parallel lines, 319, 340
of perpendicular lines, 320, 340
of tangents, 52–56
undefined, 11
Spiral of Archimedes, 259, 277
Square matrix, 65
Standard errors, 448–449, 452
Standard deviations, 429
in frequency distributions, 441–451
in normal distributions, 444–448
Standard form, 7, 26, 319
from polar form, 339
to normal form, 328–329, 341
to polar form, 337–338
Standard position, 125
Stationary values, 477–479
Statistics, 420–452
arithmetic means, 421–429, 440, 451
arrays, 422–423
bar graphs, 435, 451
bimodal, 422
broken line graphs, 435–436, 451
circle graphs, 436–437, 451
classes, 431–432, 441, 451
class limits, 431–432
class marks, 432–440
cumulative frequency, 441
frequency distributions, 431–452
frequency polygons, 435
graphs, 435–437, 451
harmonic means, 425–426, 451
histograms, 435–436, 451
measures of central tendency, 421–427
measures of variability, 428–429
median class, 441, 451
medians, 422–423, 427–429, 451

2 3 4 5 6 7 8 9 10 11 12 13 14 15—95 94 93 92 91 90 89 88 87 86